The Biological Basis of Medicine

VOLUME 5

THE BIOLOGICAL BASIS OF MEDICINE

Edited by
E. EDWARD BITTAR

Department of Physiology, The University of Wisconsin, Madison, Wisconsin, U.S.A.

Assisted by
NEVILLE BITTAR

Department of Medicine, The University of Wisconsin, Madison, Wisconsin, U.S.A.

VOLUME 5

1969
ACADEMIC PRESS
LONDON AND NEW YORK

ACADEMIC PRESS INC. (LONDON) LTD
Berkeley Square House
Berkeley Square
London, W1X 6BA

U.S. Edition published by
ACADEMIC PRESS INC.
111 Fifth Avenue
New York, New York 10003

Library of Congress Catalog Card Number: 68–17681
SBN: 12–102705–8

PRINTED IN GREAT BRITAIN BY
T. & A. CONSTABLE LTD
EDINBURGH

Contributors to Volume 5

B. BORGSTRÖM, *Division of Physiological Chemistry, Chemical Centre, University of Lund, Lund, Sweden.*

A. DAHLQVIST, *Research Department, University Hospital, Lund, Sweden.*

H. DANIELSSON, *Department of Chemistry, Karolinska Institutet, Stockholm, Sweden.*

K. EINARSSON, *Department of Chemistry, Karolinska Institutet, Stockholm, Sweden.*

J. L. E. ERICSSON, *Department of Pathology, Sabbatsberg Hospital, Karolinska Institutet Medical School, Stockholm, Sweden.*

F. HAGUENAU, *Laboratoire de Médecine Expérimentale du Collège de France, Paris, France.*

L. HERTZ, *Department of Biochemistry A, University of Copenhagen, Copenhagen, Denmark.*

R. LESTER, *Department of Medicine, Boston University School of Medicine, Boston, Massachusetts, U.S.A.*

T. LINDBERG, *Department of Pediatrics, Malmö General Hospital, Malmö, Sweden.*

C. S. LIEBER, *Section of Liver Disease and Nutrition, Bronx Veterans Administration Hospital and Department of Medicine, Mt. Sinai School of Medicine, New York, N.Y., U.S.A.*

F. LUNDQUIST, *Department of Biochemistry, University of Copenhagen, Copenhagen, Denmark.*

R. M. MARCHBANKS, *Department of Biochemistry, University of Cambridge, Cambridge, England.*

H. NEWEY, *Department of Physiology, The University of Sheffield, Sheffield, England.*

D. RICHTER, *Neuropsychiatric Research Unit, Medical Research Council Laboratories, Carshalton, Surrey, England.*

F. J. C. ROE, *Chester Beatty Research Institute, London, England.*

D. H. SMYTH, *Department of Physiology, The University of Sheffield, Sheffield, England.*

G. P. TALWAR, *Department of Biochemistry, All India Institute of Medical Sciences, New Delhi, India.*

E. H. THAYSEN, *Gastroenterological Unit, Municipal Hospital, Aalborg, Denmark.*

R. F. TROXLER, *Department of Medicine, Boston University School of Medicine, Boston, Massachusetts, U.S.A.*

V. P. WHITTAKER, *Department of Biochemistry, University of Cambridge, Cambridge, England.*

Preface

This work in six volumes aims at providing a balanced treatment between contemporary medical science and the applications of cellular biology in medicine. Contributions by more than 100 investigators, including zoologists, biochemists, physiologists, pharmacologists, geneticists, cytologists, pathologists and clinical investigators, serve to illustrate the increasing importance of the interdisciplinary approach. Volume I contains sections on the dynamic state of the cell, growth, cell injury and ageing. Volume 2 covers material on hormones, the control of intracellular processes and the effects of both biological and physical agents. The remaining 4 volumes deal with major biological phenomena such as atherosclerosis and hypertension, cancer and immunology of tissue transplantation, as well as with the ultrastructure, chemistry and pathophysiology of individual organ cells and subcellular organelles.

It is now generally appreciated that cell biology occupies not only a key position among the biological sciences, but also serves as the meeting-ground for the physiologist, biochemist, cytologist, pathologist and others. One of the underlying intentions of the present work is to demonstrate afresh that cell biology offers the basis upon which life in health and disease can be properly understood. However daring it may seem, our belief is that ultimately cellular biology will be the discipline unifying the basic medical sciences. One hopes both students and teachers of medicine and human biology at all levels will find these volumes stimulating and of unique value.

Our indebtedness to those who have written the six volumes goes without saying. We should also like to thank the staff of Academic Press for their unfailing efficiency and courtesy.

E. Edward Bittar
Neville Bittar

vii

CONTENTS

I. The Nervous System

II. The Liver and Gall Bladder

CONTENTS

III.   The Alimentary Tract

IV.   The Cancer Cell

Contents of Volume 1

Contents of Volume 2

Contents of Volume 3

Contents of Volume 4

CONTENTS OF VOLUME 6

I.   Hair and Skin

II.   The Cardiovascular System

III.   The Lung

IV.   The Kidney

PART I
The Nervous System

CHAPTER 1

The Biochemistry of Brain Tissue

LEIF HERTZ

Department of Biochemistry A,
University of Copenhagen, Copenhagen, Denmark

I. Complexity of Brain

A. *Cellular elements*

1. *Histological heterogeneity*

The brain is a heterogeneous tissue both anatomically and histologically. This heterogeneity is of great importance in the evaluation and interpretation of biochemical findings and will therefore be briefly discussed here.

Macroscopically, different structures (e.g. cerebral and cerebellar cortex, central white matter, and basal ganglia) may with relative ease and certainty be separated from each other, but even so tissue from a single, well-defined structure, e.g. the cerebral cortex, shows histologically great complexity, as can be seen from Fig. 1. Two main elements, viz. nerve cells and neuroglial cells, constitute the bulk of the tissue, but each of these may on morphological grounds be divided into several subgroups, and characteristic cells or part of cells which constitute only a minor fraction of the total volume of the tissue.

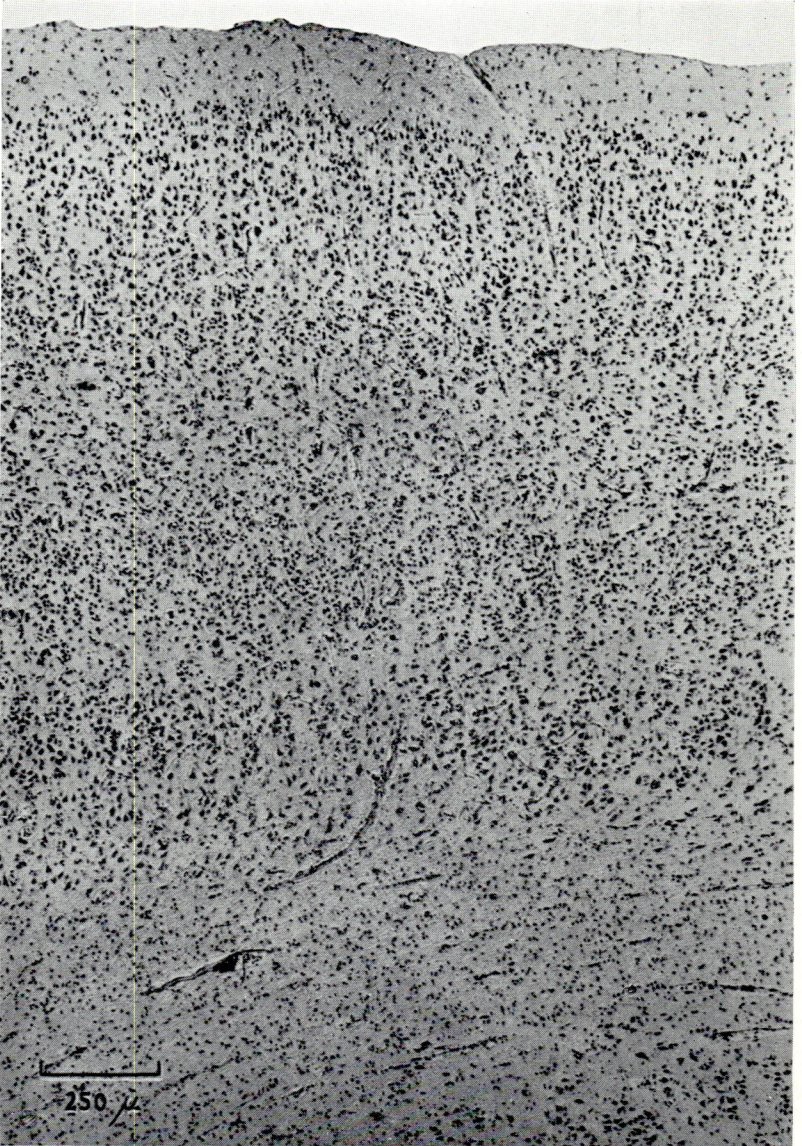

FIG. 1. Section from the human visual cortex. The preparation includes grey matter (upper part) containing both nerve cells and glia cells and white matter (lower part) with its abundant neuroglia. It shows stained perikarya of neurons and stained glia cells together with unstained elements which mainly represent neuropil (in grey matter) and myelin (in white matter) (From Sholl, 1956).

2. *Nerve cells*

The nerve cells may be classified according to the size and shape of their cell bodies (perikarya), or according to the number, length and mode of branching of their processes. Virtually nothing is known about possible biochemical differences between the different types of neurons.

The nerve cell perikarya account for only about 5% of the volume in mammalian brain cortex (Economo, 1926; Rebhan, 1956; Haug, 1956; see also Fig. 1). The volume occupied by their processes is, however, probably several times greater, and it has been estimated that the proximal and distal dendrites account for about one-fourth of the total volume of the grey matter (Schadé and Baxter, 1960; Schadé *et al.*, 1964). The white matter which owes its colour to myelin (see I. A, 5) contains few or no nerve cell bodies and the axons constitute a relatively small part of its volume.

3. *Glia cells*

The glia cells are traditionally divided into fibrous and protoplasmatic astrocytes, oligodendrocytes and microglia. In grey matter the characteristic neuroglial cells are the protoplasmatic astrocyte and the oligodendrocyte, whereas the fibrous astrocyte is found mainly in white matter.

The volume occupied by easily recognizable glia cell bodies is relatively small though the glia cells in grey matter may outnumber the nerve cells by a factor of about ten (Nurnberger and Gordon, 1957; Pope, 1958).

4. *Neuropil*

Thus a considerable fraction of the tissue volume remains to be accounted for, and in the grey matter the main part of this fraction is made up by the so-called "neuropil" (see for example Ham, 1965). This term refers to a rather badly defined, intricately interwoven network of minute neuronal and neuroglial processes which become obvious in electron micrographs (see Fig. 2), but in ordinary light microscopy appear almost structureless (cf. Fig. 1). It corresponds roughly to the "intercellular grey substance" (Nissl, 1898; Bauer, 1951), and the possible importance of this part of the brain is indicated by the observation that its relative amount increases during phylogenetic (Nissl, 1898; Economo, 1926; Tower and Elliott, 1952; Tower, 1954; Friede, 1954; cf. however Hawkins and Olszewski, 1957) and ontogenetic (Brizee and Jacobs, 1959; Tower and Bourke, 1966) development.

The ratio between glia cells and nerve cells in the "neuropil" is uncertain and probably varies in the different parts of the nervous system. In the hippocampal cortex – from which Fig. 2 was drawn – astroglia cells thus seem to constitute only 5–6% (Blackstad, 1967), whereas Hydén (1967) estimated that about nine-tenths of the Deiters' cell surroundings are made up by glia cells. The previously mentioned observation by Schadé *et al.*

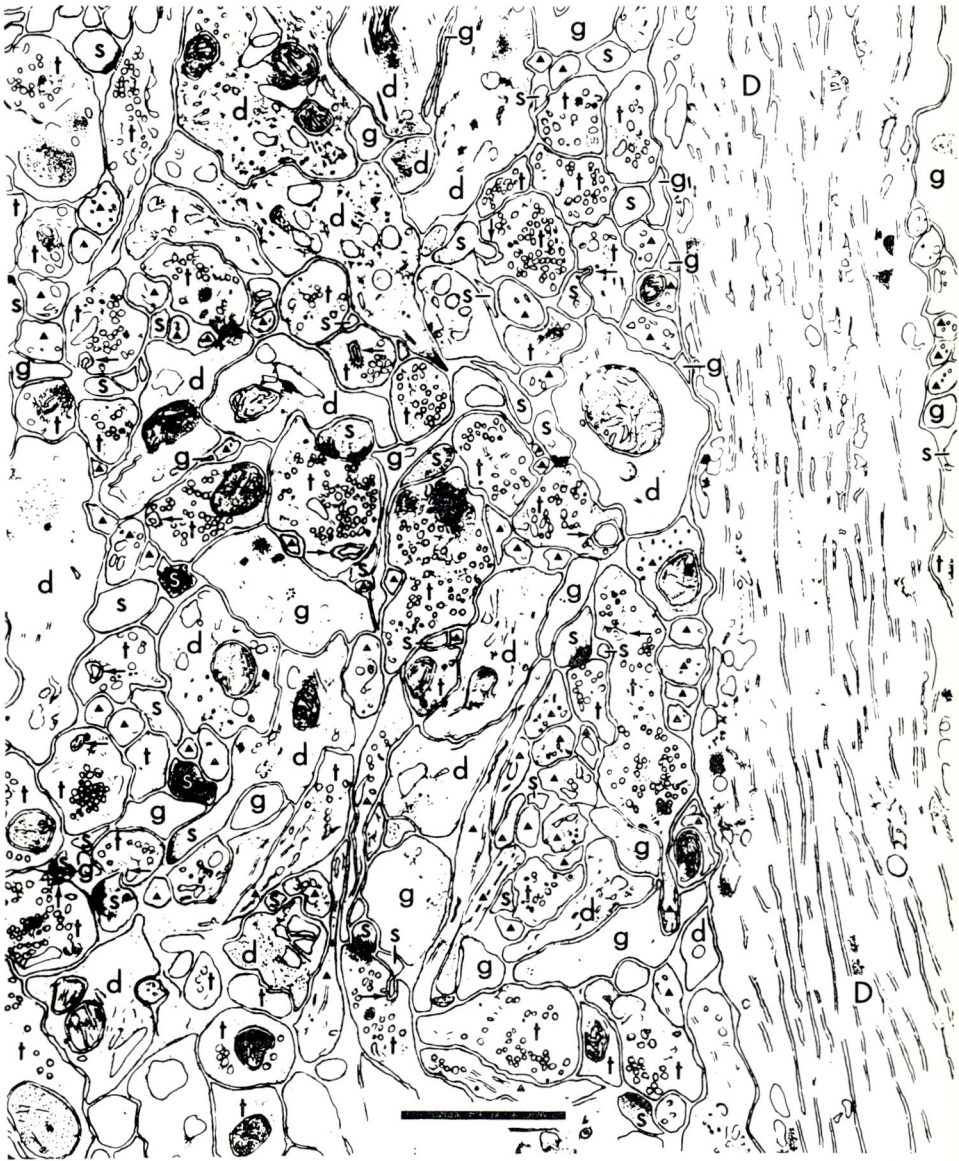

FIG. 2. Line drawing of an electron micrograph of stratum radiatum of regio superior of the rat hippocampal cortex. The micrograph was one of a series, and identification of most structures was therefore possible. The bar indicates 1 μ. D, Dendritic shaft or larger branch; d, finer dendritic branch; s, spine; t, axon swelling with synaptic vesicles; g, astroglial process; ▲, axon. (From Westrum and Blackstad, 1962.)

(1960, 1964) that the dendrites altogether occupy about one-fourth of the brain cortex supports the concept that well above half of its volume may be occupied by glia cells.

5. *Myelin*

The most characteristic component of white matter is myelin. This is a white, fatty material which covers and thus isolates single nerve fibres both in the central and in the peripheral nervous system. In the latter the formation of myelin has been thoroughly studied (Geren, 1954; Geren and Schmitt, 1955), and it has been found that a segment of myelin is formed from a single Schwann cell which embraces and later encircles and winds around a piece of the nerve fibre. In this way the nerve fibre becomes wrapped into a double-contoured spiral formed by the cell membranes of the Schwann cell.

Less is known about the formation of myelin in the white matter of the central nervous system, but oligodendrocytes probably play a similar role here. The nerve cells and the nerve fibres traversing the "neuropil" possess no myelin sheath (cf. Fig. 2) and are accordingly badly isolated from their surroundings.

6. *Non-nervous elements*

Other tissues are almost invariably included in samples of nervous tissue, e.g. muscle, connective tissue and blood cells in the vessels. These contribute relatively little to the total volume of both grey and white matter.

B. *Extracellular space*

For years, a controversial question has been the magnitude of the extra-cellular space in brain. Basing their conclusions on electron micrographs, most recent investigators (Horstmann and Meves, 1959; Kuffler and Potter, 1964) have arrived at an estimate that only about 5% of the total volume of the brain cortex is occupied by extracellular fluid. This fluid is mainly localized in intercellular clefts of about 150 Å in width. On the other hand, Van Harreveld *et al.* have claimed that the extracellular space is considerably larger *in vivo*, but shrinks during the period between the arrest of the circulation and conventional fixation (Van Harreveld, 1962). This concept is supported by their finding that a special fixation technique yields an extracellular space of about 20% (Van Harreveld *et al.*, 1965). It has however been stated that the fixation method employed is probably no more rapid than the generally employed technique, and that intercellular clefts about 150 Å wide may also be observed in tissue cultures where no shrinking is to be expected (Kuffler and Nicholls, 1966).

C. *Biochemical implications*
1. *Problems*

The anatomical and histological complexity of the brain is of great importance for the biochemist who generally is faced with measurements and analyses either of preparations (e.g. the perfused whole brain, whole-brain homogenates) which contain a multitude of different structures, or of preparations from one structure (e.g. brain-cortex slices) which nevertheless contain several different cell types in unknown proportions. The results obtained can therefore only give an average picture of what is occurring in metabolically different cell types.

The uncertainty concerning the size of the extracellular space may seem of minor biochemical importance, since it makes no greater quantitative difference whether some cellular component is found in cells constituting an unknown fraction of 80% or an unknown fraction of 95% of the total volume. For the interpretation of possible metabolic interconnections between glia cells and neurons it is, however, of crucial importance whether compounds (e.g. ions, metabolic intermediates) which are released from cells are transported through a relatively large extracellular space, in which their concentrations become negligible, or whether they become confined to narrow clefts of such small volume that their concentrations become high enough to exert biochemical effects on adjacent cells (cf. V).

2. *Preparations*

To overcome the difficulties sketched above, methods have been developed which distinguish between metabolism in different cell types and which also allow some conclusions to be drawn about transport routes. Each of the different preparations used has its own advantages and – often serious – limitations, and some of them will be briefly discussed below together with a few of the more complex preparations.

a. *Whole brain*

The metabolism (e.g rate of oxygen uptake, ion exchange) by the whole intact brain *in situ* has been examined both in humans and in higher mammals. Such studies are essential if one is to obtain information, e.g. of the "blood-brain barrier" and of possible biochemical effects evoked by mental activity. Furthermore, they serve to give normal values which may be compared with results obtained with simpler preparations. Their complexity prevents, however, any more detailed analysis.

b. *Slices and homogenates*

By far the larger amount of biochemical information on brain tissue surviving *in vitro* has been obtained by using either brain slices (0·3–0·5 mm thick) or brain homogenates kept in appropriate media. The homogenates have often been made from the whole brain but no difficulties are encountered in preparing homogenates (or slices) from single structures in species with relatively large brains. However, marked metabolic differences may be found between sliced and homogenized tissues (cf. II. B, 1–2; II. C, 1–3).

c. Preparations containing predominantly one cellular component

Microdissection of fresh material (Hydén, 1959) represents a straightforward and relatively easy way of obtaining isolated, single nerve cells or lumps of glia cells. These two groups can be exceedingly well separated as can be seen in Fig. 3 showing glia cell lumps and Deiters' nerve cells, which like the pyramidal cells of the cortex are easy to work with on account of their relatively large size. The only drawback of the method is that the nerve cells of necessity lose part of their dendrites which is then a source of contamination in the glia cell samples (Hydén and Lange, 1961; Hamberger, 1963; Kuffler and Nicholls, 1966). Damage of the membranes has also been observed (Roots and Johnston, 1964; Johnston and Roots, 1965), but this criticism was rejected by Hydén (1967), and metabolically the samples seem surprisingly intact (cf. II. D and IV. C, 2). Also methods which allow isolation of glia and nerve cell samples on a macroscale (e.g. differential centrifugation) have been developed (Roots and Johnston, 1964; Rose, 1967; Bradford and Rose, 1967). In some of these procedures (see for example Rose, 1967) rather heavy contamination with the other cell type may occur, and the only advantage of the macromethods seem to be that greater amounts of cells are harvested.

Specimens containing predominantly one cell type may be obtained from tissues which chiefly contain the cell type in question, e.g. tissue cultures or tumours (Victor and Wolf, 1937). However, risk of having preparations which are metabolically abnormal seems considerable.

White matter contains no nerve cell bodies but many glia cells. This fact has been used for the estimation of average respiratory rates or enzymatic activities per glia cell. On the assumption that all glia cells are metabolically identical, the total metabolic activity of the glia cells present in grey matter has been calculated, and on the basis of the values so obtained, the remaining activity attributed to the nerve cells (Heller and Elliott, 1955; Korey and Orchen, 1959; Tower, 1960; Ridge, 1967a). However, the validity of this assumption has been seriously questioned (Waelsch, 1960; Tower and Bourke, 1966; Hertz, 1966).

d. Preparations from special animal species

Certain preparations, e.g. the central nervous system of the leech, contain large and distinctly separated glia cells, so that penetration with microelectrodes can be performed. Since the distribution of certain ions (mainly potassium) across the cell membrane determines the membrane potential, conclusions about the routes of diffusion may be drawn (Nicholls and Kuffler, 1964). It must, on the other hand, be pointed out that a genuine "neuropil" is found in these preparations (Coggeshall and Fawcett, 1964),

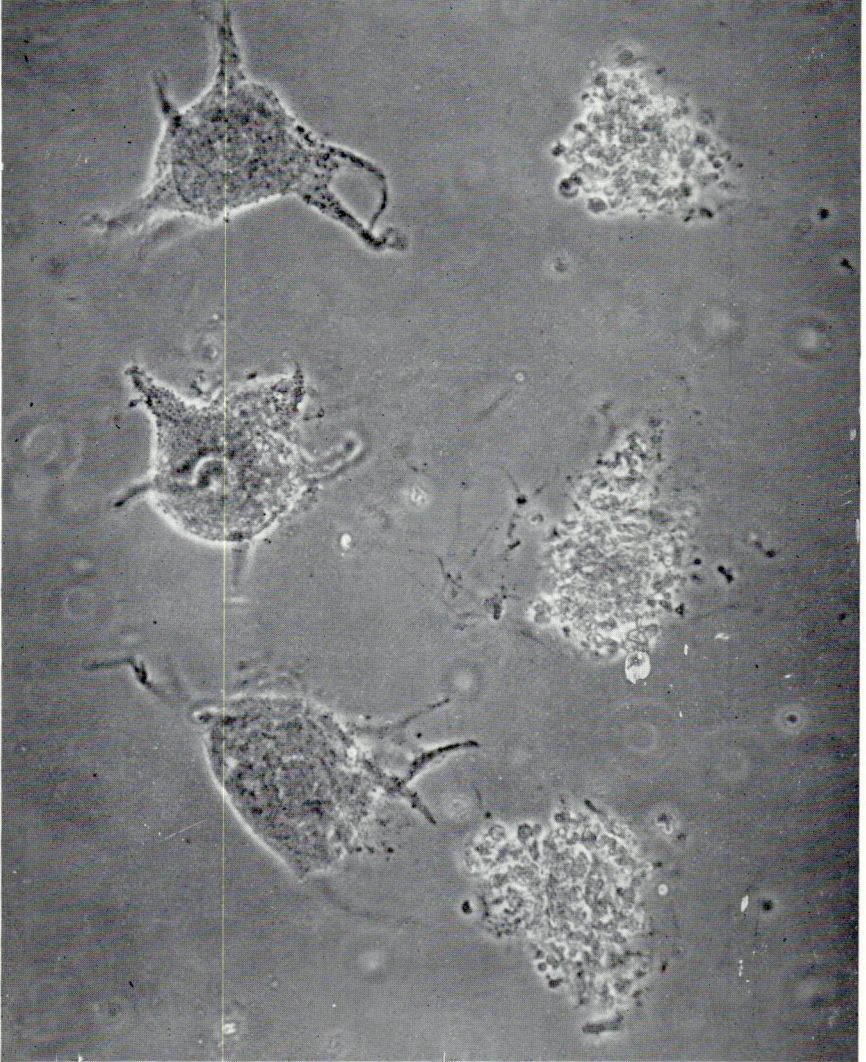

FIG. 3. Upper row. Three Deiters' nerve cells dissected freehand, cleaned from the surrounding glia, and photographed in the phase contrast microscope. Lower row. Three collections of glia cells, each of which originally surrounded the nerve cell situated above. (From Hydén, 1967.)

and that the small glia cells found here, and which cannot be studied in the same way, may differ fundamentally from those studied.

e. Subcellular fractions

Studies of subcellular elements may be performed after free-hand micro-dissection (Cummins and Hydén, 1962; Hydén, 1967). By far the majority of such investigations have, however, been made with preparations obtained by density gradient centrifugation (Whittaker, 1959; Robertis, 1963, 1967; Whittaker and Sheridan, 1965). The intricate network of membranes in the "neuropil" may conceivably represent a source of error since no statements have been made about the fate of these membranes during and after the centrifugation.

3. Interpretation

It seems evident that only the integration of results obtained with preparations representing all levels of complexity will ultimately lead to a biochemical understanding of brain function. The heterogeneous whole-brain preparations are required, because they mimic *in vivo* conditions most closely, and because many important studies have been performed within the last years using such preparations. The relatively simple preparations obtained from one structure (e.g. brain slices and homogenates) are likewise of importance because much useful information has been derived from them, and the histologically more or less pure and metabolically altered samples are essential for decisive information with respect to the localization of the different metabolic events. This had been realized by Ehrenberg (1833) in his paper "Nothwendigkeit einer feineren mechanischen Zerlegung des Gehirns und der Nerven vor der chemischen". The limitations of the methods used have, however, retarded such investigations by more than a century. Indeed, many sources of error still exist, so that it is of the utmost importance to attack the same problems by employing different techniques and by relying only on results obtained with different procedures.

II. Oxygen Uptake

A. Whole brain

1. In situ

Under normal circumstances the rate of oxygen uptake by a tissue provides a good estimate of total energy production. The measurement itself is relatively easily performed, and rather detailed information can be made available. This makes the rate of oxygen uptake the parameter of choice for comparisons between different preparations and cells.

In the normal human brain *in vivo* the average oxygen utilization has been found by several authors to range between 3·3 and 3·9 ml./100 g/min, and from a survey by Kety (1957) the mean oxygen consumption in normal human adults can be calculated to be 3·6 ml./100 g/min, or 95 μmoles/g wet wt/hr. An increased rate of oxygen consumption has been found in monkeys during evoked convulsions (Schmidt et al., 1945). Intellectual activity, in contrast, causes no augmentation of the average metabolism of the brain, but may possibly lead to local increases. Mental disorders and psychomimetic drugs generally do not affect the oxygen consumption, whereas in coma and under the influence of anesthesia there is about a 40% decrease in respiratory rate (Kety, 1957).

2. *Brain perfusion*

Similar results have been obtained with the isolated perfused cat brain by Geiger and Magnes (1947). In a group of apparently conscious cats these workers obtained a mean oxygen consumption of about 130 μmoles/g wet wt/hr. Again a decrease to about 60% was observed when cerebral activity was abolished following the addition of a barbiturate to the perfusing medium. Metrazol or strychnine, on the other hand, caused about a doubling of the respiratory intensity, but only if convulsions occurred.

B. *Oxygen uptake* in vitro

1. *Brain slices*

The rate of oxygen uptake by brain slices is greater the smaller the animal species. In the rat this amounts to 100 μmoles/g wet wt/hr, and in man to about 50 μmoles/g wet wt/hr, as can be seen in Fig. 4. This variation must be taken into consideration whenever preparations from different species are being compared.

Furthermore, respiratory intensity varies with the structural origin of the tissue. Thus slices from the cerebral and cerebellar cortex and from the basal ganglia show the highest rates of oxygen uptake, whereas tissue from the brain stem shows somewhat less activity, and slices from the spinal cord or from the central parts of cerebral white matter show little activity. This is indicated in the first column of Table I, which shows the oxygen uptake values obtained by different authors using slices from different species incubated in "physiological" media. All of these values have been corrected with the help of Fig. 4 so as to show what the respiratory rates would have been in human tissue. The topographical variation makes a comparison between rates of oxygen uptake by the whole brain and by slices difficult. In the rat it has, however, been found that the average respiratory rate by the whole, but sliced brain amounts to approximately 80% (per volume unit) of that obtained with superficial cortical slices (Elliott, 1952; Hertz, 1969).

Provided a suitable substrate (e.g. glucose) is present, the oxygen uptake of brain slices may be maintained at almost the same level during incubation over a period of several hours. This is, however, critically dependent upon the presence of at least 20 mM sodium in the external medium (e.g. Hertz and Schou, 1962), and in the absence of this ion the rate of oxygen uptake declines rapidly (Fig. 5) until a level corresponding to about 10% of the initial oxygen consumption is reached. Potassium (Hertz, 1969), calcium and magnesium in trace amounts are also required for optimum maintenance of respiration (Dickens and Greville, 1935).

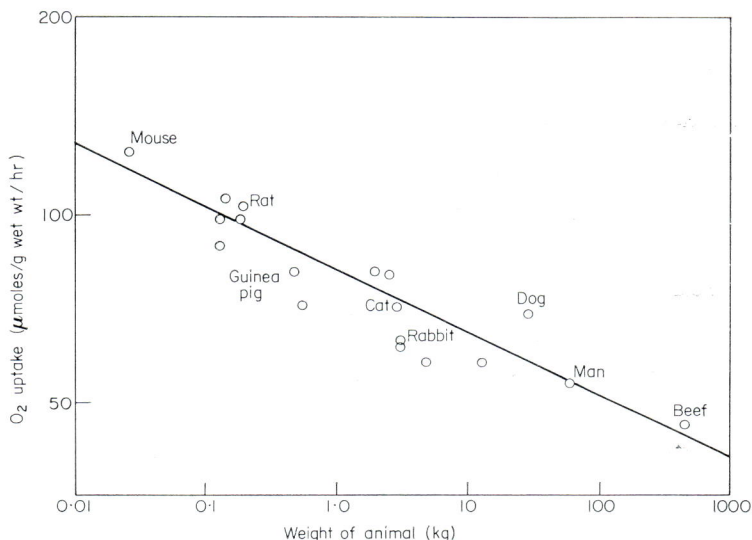

FIG. 4. Correlation between rate of oxygen uptake in brain-cortex slices and body weight in different species. Both axes are drawn on a logarithmic scale, and each point represents an individual animal (except in the case of mice for which pooled slices from several animals were used). (After Elliott and Henderson, 1948.)

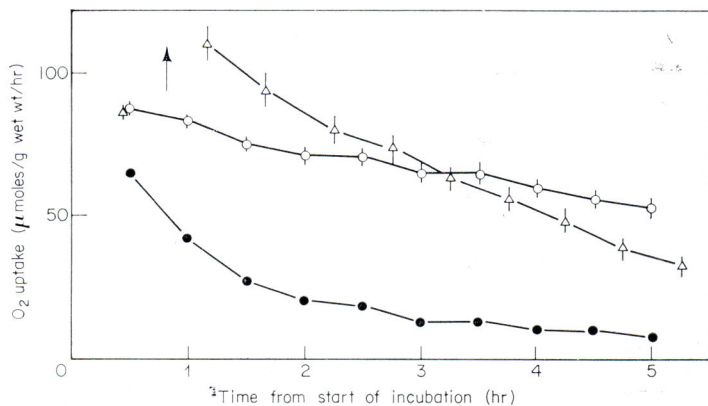

FIG. 5. Rates of oxygen uptake by rat brain-cortex slices at different times during the incubation in media containing potassium chloride (5 mM) and either sodium chloride (120 mM) ($\bigcirc$, $\triangle$) or sucrose (250 mM) ($\bullet$). In one experiment ($\triangle$) potassium chloride equivalent to a final concentration of 48 mM was added during the incubation (at the arrow). SEM are indicated by vertical bars if they extend beyond the symbols. (From Hertz and Clausen, 1963.)

TABLE I

Rates of oxygen uptake in different structures

Structure	Animal species	Resting rate of oxygen uptake (μmoles/g wet wt/hr)	Stimulated rate of oxygen uptake (μmoles/g wet wt/hr)
Cerebral cortex	Man (McIlwain, 1953c)	41–51	81*
	Rat (Hertz and Clausen, 1963)	50	79
	Guinea pig (Bollard and McIlwain, 1957)	40	70*
	Rabbit† (Ridge, 1967b)	47	86
	Ox (Hertz and Clausen, 1963)	54	85
	Average	47	80
Cerebellar cortex	Rabbit† (Ridge, 1967b)	53	93
	Ox (Hertz and Clausen, 1963)	55	100
	Average	54	97
Caudate nucleus	Rabbit† (Ridge, 1967b)	41	69
	Ox (Hertz and Clausen, 1963)	46	97
	Average	44	83
Diencephalon	Guinea pig (Bollard and McIlwain, 1957)	38	
	Rabbit† (Ridge, 1967b)	29	43
	Average	34	
Medulla oblongata	Guinea pig (Bollard and McIlwain, 1957)	22	36*
	Rabbit† (Ridge, 1967b)	17	21
	Ox (Hertz and Clausen, 1963)	14	13
	Average	18	23
Spinal cord (total transversal sections)	Ox (Hertz and Clausen, 1963)	9	9
(grey matter)	Ox (Hertz and Clausen, 1963)	29	26
Cerebral white matter (central parts)	Rabbit† (Ridge, 1967b)	11	10
	Ox (Hertz and Clausen, 1963)	10	10
	Average	11	10
(subcortical)	Man (Bollard and McIlwain, 1957)	25	
	Guinea pig (Bollard and McIlwain, 1957)	20	35*
	Guinea pig (Kurokawa, 1960)	22	38
	Guinea pig (Kurokawa, 1960)	22	40*
	Rabbit (Bollard and McIlwain, 1957)	11	

Rates of oxygen uptake by different brain tissue structures have been measured in various species. All respiratory rates here have therefore been recalculated so as to fit human tissue. This was done by multiplying the observed rates of oxygen uptake in rat, guinea pig, rabbit and ox tissue by 0·55, 0·70, 0·80 and 1·25, respectively (cf. Fig. 4).

The first column shows the "resting" rates of oxygen uptake, whereas the second column shows the respiratory rates following the addition of excess (about 50 mM) potassium or during the application of electrical pulses. The experiments in which pulses were applied are indicated by *.

† All these values (from Ridge, 1967b) have been multiplied by 0·5 since they differ from the rest by a factor of this order of magnitude.

2. Homogenates

Gently homogenized preparations of brain cortex show an initial rate of oxygen uptake which amounts to about two-thirds of that observed in a corresponding brain slice. However, there is no maintenance requirement for sodium ions, and the respiratory intensity declines rapidly both in the presence and absence of sodium (Elliott and Libet, 1942; Hertz, 1969).

3. Single cells

Relatively good agreement is found between the measured rates of oxygen uptake in large micro-dissected cells (I. C, 2 c), and the average respiratory rates per glia cell and nerve cell calculated on the basis of the respiratory rates in white and grey matter and the cell density (I. C, 2 c). The values found are shown in Table II and indicate a respiratory rate of $1-10 \times 10^{-4}$

TABLE II

Respiratory rates in nerve cells and glia cells

Cell type	Basis of estimate		Respiration per cell (μl. O_2/hr)	Respiration per unit weight (μmoles/g initial wet wt/hr)
Nerve cell	measurement	(1)	$10 \cdot 1 \times 10^{-4}$	1080
Nerve cell	measurement	(2)	$10 \quad \times 10^{-4}$	
Nerve cell	measurement	(3)	$5 \cdot 0 \times 10^{-4}$	263
Nerve cell	measurement	(4)		70
Nerve cell	calculation	(5a)	$0 \cdot 6 - 0 \cdot 9 \times 10^{-4}$	
Nerve cell	calculation	(6)	$1 \cdot 4 \times 10^{-4}$	
Glia cell	measurement	(1)	0	
Glia cell	measurement	(2)	$0 - 10 \times 10^{-5}$	
Glia cell	measurement	(3)	$0 \cdot 5 - 1 \times 10^{-5}$	40–80
Glia cell	measurement	(4)		74
Glia cell	calculation	(6)	$1 \cdot 1 \times 10^{-5}$	41
Astrocyte	tumour	(7)		6
Astrocyte	tumour	(5b)	$0 \cdot 1 \times 10^{-5}$	8–19
Oligodendrocyte	tumour	(7)		51
Oligodendrocyte	tumour	(5b)	$0 \cdot 5 \times 10^{-5}$	62

The rates of oxygen uptake shown above were obtained by measurements on cellularly homogeneous samples of neurons and glia cells [refs (1)–(4), (5b) and (7)] or based on measurements of respiratory rates in grey and white matter (refs (5a) and (6); cf. I. C, 2c). Isolation of the cells was accomplished by microdissection [refs (1)–(3)], differential centrifugation [ref. (4)] or involved tumour tissue [ref. (5b)].

Measurements on single microdissected samples are generally performed with large nerve cells, while indirect methods involving calculation yield average respiratory rates. This difference may be reflected in the systematic deviation obtaining between the two methods, as found in the respiratory rates per nerve cell.

Results from (1) Epstein and O'Connor, 1965; (2) Hydén and Lange, 1965; (3) Hertz, 1966; (4) Rose, 1965; (5) Heller and Elliott, 1955; (6) Korey and Orchen, 1959, and (7) Victor and Wolf (1937).

μl./hr/cell in nerve cells and about 1×10^{-5} μl./hr/cell in glia cells. In nerve cells the respiration is well maintained, but it declines rapidly in the glia cell samples. The absence of sodium leads to further enhancement of the rate of the respiratory decline in the glia cells, whereas the maintenance of respiration in the nerve cells is unaffected by the lack of sodium (Hertz, 1966).

When expressed per unit weight there is a lesser consistency and the rate of oxygen consumption lies between 70 (Rose 1965, 1967), 260 (Hertz, 1966) and 1080 (Epstein and O'Connor, 1965) μmoles/g wet wt/hr for nerve cells and 40–70 μmoles/g wet wt/hr for glia cells. At least in tumours, oligodendrocytes respire more intensely than astrocytes (Victor and Wolf, 1937; Heller and Elliott, 1955; Allen, 1957).

4. Subcellular fractions

Nerve-ending particles prepared by differential and density-gradient centrifugation (I. C, 2 e) have been observed to respire at a rate of 90 μmoles/100 mg protein/hr (Bradford, 1967), which probably corresponds to about 50–100 μmoles/g wet wt/hr.

C. Stimulation of oxygen uptake in vitro

1. Ion-induced stimulation

It is well established that brain slices react to an increase in the concentration of K^+ (or of Cs^+, Rb^+, Li^+, NH_4^+ or choline$^+$) with an augmentation of 50–100% in their rate of oxygen uptake (for references, see Hertz and Schou, 1962). This response has long since been known as specific for brain (Dickens and Greville, 1935; Hertz and Clausen, 1963; Hertz, 1969) and muscle (Hegnauer et al., 1934). The metabolic reactions by muscle to changes in ionic concentrations in the media differ, however, so much from those observed with brain slices that different mechanisms seem to be at work (Hertz and Clausen, 1963; Hertz, 1969). From the second column in Table I it can be seen that the stimulation is even specific for slices containing grey matter from the rostral part of the brain, whereas no response is found with grey matter from the spinal cord or with white matter from the central parts of the brain (Hertz and Clausen, 1963; Ridge, 1967b).

At least 20 mM potassium is required to produce an increase in respiration, and a maximum response is obtained with about 50 mM. A certain minimum concentration of sodium is required (Dickens and Greville, 1935; Canzanelli et al., 1942; Tsukada and Takagaki, 1955; Hertz and Schou, 1962). The presence of a substrate is also essential (Dickens and Greville, 1935; Kratzing, 1953). Stimulation is prevented by pharmacological concentrations of several drugs (e.g. barbiturates, phenothiazines and ethanol) which have little or no effect on the unstimulated oxygen uptake (McIlwain, 1953a; Ghosh and Quastel, 1954; Lindan et al., 1957; Beer and Quastel, 1958; Wallgren and Kulonen, 1960; Majchrowicz, 1965).

Respiratory stimulation by high concentrations of potassium is lost after homogenization of the tissue (Elliott and Libet, 1942; Ghosh and Quastel, 1954). It has been suggested that this may be due to a destruction of the neurons, but arguing against this interpretation is the observation that relatively well preserved nerve cell bodies seen microscopically are present in homogenates (Elliott and Libet, 1942).

Experiments with isolated cells have demonstrated more directly that the nerve cells (i.e. nerve cell bodies, cf. I. C, 2 c) do not respond metabolically to raised potassium concentrations (Hertz, 1966; cf. however, also Bradford and Rose, 1967), whereas glia cell samples (cf. I. C, 2 c) show an increase in their rate of oxygen uptake (Hertz, 1966; Bradford and Rose, 1967).

2. Electrical stimulation

During and immediately after the application of electrical pulses the rate of oxygen uptake by brain slices rises (McIlwain, 1951a; McIlwain, 1954). The degree of stimulation depends upon the voltage applied and the frequency of the pulses (McIlwain and Joanny, 1963), the maximum response being identical with that observed after the addition of potassium. The presence of both sodium (Gore and McIlwain, 1952; Bachelard et al., 1962) and potassium ions (Cummins and McIlwain, 1961) is essential.

Electrically-induced stimulation shows great sensitivity to drugs (McIlwain, 1953a; McIlwain and Greengard, 1957; Wallgren and Kulonen, 1960), and is abolished by homogenization (Narayanaswami and McIlwain, 1954).

Several analogies are thus found between the potassium-induced and the electrically-induced stimulation; conceivably the latter may be due to potassium release from the cells (cf. IV). Minor differences including sensitivity to atropine (McIlwain, 1951b) and to anticonvulsant hydantoin derivatives (Greengard and McIlwain, 1955) have also been described.

3. Other stimulatory procedures

a. Glutamate

L-Glutamate at a concentration of 5–10 mM causes an increase in the rate of oxygen consumption in brain slices (Krebs, 1935; Weil-Malherbe, 1936; Lipsett and Crescitelli, 1950; Rossiter, 1955; Tsukada et al., 1958; Takagaki et al., 1959; Gonda and Quastel, 1963).

b. Drugs

Certain drugs (e.g. veratrine) raise the membrane permeability to monovalent cations (Shanes, 1958). The treatment of brain slices with such drugs leads to increased oxygen consumption (Wollenberger, 1955; Yoshida et al., 1963), a response which is dependent upon the presence of potassium in the medium. No such effect is observed with homogenates (Wollenberger, 1955).

Ouabain in certain concentrations (10^{-5}–10^{-4} M) may cause a respiratory increase (Rolleston and Newsholme, 1966). This stimulation is only observed when calcium is present in the medium (Schwartz, 1962; Bourke and Tower, 1966*b*; Swanson and Ullis, 1966).

c. Calcium deficiency

The calcium ion seems on the whole to play a considerable role in the metabolism of brain tissue. A lowering of its concentration in the medium leads to increased oxygen uptake in brain slices (Dickens and Greville, 1935; Kratzing, 1953; Quastel and Quastel, 1961; Bourke and Tower, 1966*b*).

d. Uncouplers

Suitable concentrations of drugs, which cause an uncoupling of oxydative phosphorylation (e.g. 2,4-dinitrophenol) lead to stimulation of oxygen uptake in brain slices (e.g. McIlwain and Gore, 1952; Gonda and Quastel, 1963). The maximum respiratory rate is approximately the same as that seen with raised concentrations of potassium or with electrical pulses.

D. Comparison of oxygen uptake in different preparations

The rate of oxygen uptake by the normal human brain (95 μmoles/g wet wt/hr) agrees fairly well with that obtained in the perfused cat brain (130 μmoles/g wet wt/hr) after due allowance is made for the difference in size of the species (cf. Fig. 4).

If the ratio of 0·80 which is the ratio between the average respiratory activity of whole brain and the respiratory rate in rat cortical slices, applies to man, then the respiratory rates of brain slices observed during incubation in "physiological" and in potassium-rich media can be said to correspond to about 35, and 55–70 μmoles/g wet wt/hr respectively (cf. Table I). The latter value, that of brain slices in potassium-rich media, is comparable to the normal *in vivo* respiratory rate, whilst the former is comparable to the *in vivo* oxygen consumption found during coma. Furthermore, pharmacological concentrations of anaesthetics affect the oxygen uptake *in vivo* and that observed *in vitro* during incubation in potassium-rich media in parallel ways (i.e. causing a decrease of about 40% in either case). For these reasons it has been suggested that the stimulation of respiration is due to a mechanism that is essential for normal brain function (Quastel and Quastel, 1961; McIlwain, 1966; Hertz, 1969).

The rate of oxygen consumption in isolated cells is close to that observed in slices. A sample from the rat consisting of 5% nerve cell bodies (cf. I. A, 2) and 95% "neuropil" (i.e. corresponding to a cortical slice) may be expected to show an oxygen uptake of about 13 (5% of 260 – cf. the nerve cell respiration of about 260 μmoles/g wet wt/hr) plus 67 (95% of 70 – cf. the glia cell respiration of 40–70 μmoles/g wet wt/hr) μmoles/g wet wt/hr, which equals 80 μmoles/g wet wt/hr and thus is almost identical to the rate of oxygen consumption in the slice of about 90 μmoles/g wet wt/hr.

From these values it may be deduced that about 15–20% of the oxygen uptake occurs in the nerve cells (nerve cell bodies) and the remainder in the "neuropil". This estimate is at variance with calculations based upon the respiratory rates found in white and grey matter (Heller and Elliott, 1955; Elliott and Heller, 1957; Korey and Orchen, 1959; Tower, 1960 – cf. I. C, 2 c) according to which by far the major part of the oxygen uptake occurs in the nerve cells and not in the glia cells. It also contradicts the work of Epstein and O'Connor (1965) who described high respiratory rates in nerve cells. That nerve cell respiration during incubation in sodium-deficient media undergoes no change is a finding which supports the concept that the neurons contribute very little to the total oxygen uptake, i.e. that fraction of the oxygen uptake which is unaffected by the sodium-deficient medium (Hertz, 1966; cf. Fig. 5). The observation that the potassium-induced stimulation of oxygen uptake is localized in "neuropil" samples (Hertz, 1966) is in accord with the view that this part of the brain is important.

III. Metabolic Turnover

A. *Degradation and synthesis in brain*

Information about the rate of oxygen uptake leads to an overall estimate of metabolic activity in different brain preparations. A more detailed understanding of the biochemistry of brain function requires, however, also knowledge of the individual processes occurring during the metabolic degradation of the energy-yielding compounds (mainly carbohydrates) and during the synthesis of essential compounds (e.g. lipids, nucleic acids and transmitters). The turnover of certain amino acids [viz. glutamate and γ-amino butyric acid (GABA)] may require special attention since on the one hand these compounds are formed in the course of metabolic degradation (cf. III. B, 1) and, on the other, possess transmitter properties (III. D, 5).

B. *Energy-yielding processes*

1. *In vivo*

There is good evidence that the intact brain predominantly utilizes glucose as its substrate and source of energy (Kety, 1957) and that the quantity of glucose consumed during *in vivo* experiments corresponds to the amount of carbon dioxide and lactate produced (Kety, 1957). This unique position of glucose in the metabolism of the brain may be related to the fact that most other compounds (e.g. glutamate) cross only with difficulty the "blood-brain barrier" (Schwerin *et al.*, 1950; O'Neal and Koeppe, 1966). However, this does not imply that glucose exclusively is metabolized along the glycolytic pathway and the subsequent tricarboxylic acid cycle. Conceivably the pentose phosphate shunt might play a major part in cerebral glucose metabolism. Roberts (1956) has pointed out that the succinyl-coenzyme A step in the tricarboxylic acid cycle might be bypassed by the

"GABA-shunt", as indicated in Fig. 6. The presence of both pathways has been established *in vivo*, but their quantitative role remains unknown (Sacks, 1957; Lajtha *et al.*, 1959; Moss, 1964).

Under ordinary experimental conditions the production of lactate is small (6 μmoles/g wet wt/hr), but it increases to about 400 μmoles/g wet wt/hr when convulsions occur (McIlwain, 1966). The *in vivo* concentration of each of the two main energy-rich phosphate compounds, i.e. phospho-creatine and ATP, is around 3 μmoles/g wet wt (McIlwain, 1966). Hypoxia, hypoglycemia and convulsions cause a decrease of these compounds, whereas administration of barbiturates leads to an increase (McIlwain, 1966).

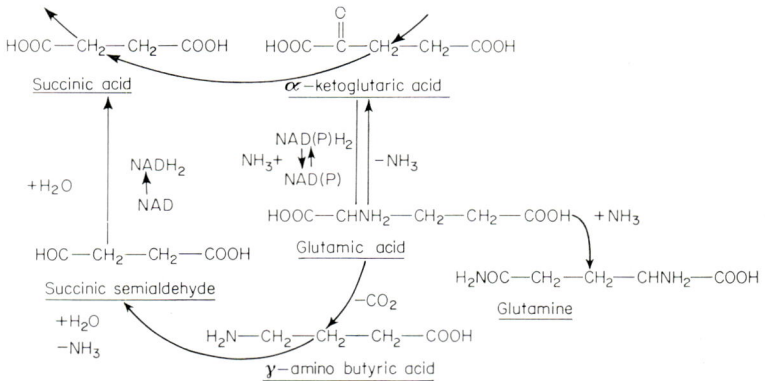

FIG. 6. Part of the tricarboxylic acid cycle and the "GABA shunt". (After Laborit, 1965.)

2. *In vitro*

a. *Glycolysis*

The rate of aerobic lactate production in brain slices is slightly higher *in vitro* (about 25 μmoles/g wet wt/hr) than *in vivo* (e.g. Elliott and Henderson, 1948; McIlwain, 1953b; Thomas and McIlwain, 1956). In the absence of oxygen the glycolytic rate is increased (the "Pasteur-effect") to about 100–200 μmoles/g wet wt/hr (Elliott and Penfield, 1948; Dixon, 1949), but this increase is far too small to substitute for the decrease in production of energy-rich phosphates caused by the abolition of oxidative phosphorylation.

High concentrations of potassium, cesium or rubidium cause an obvious rise in aerobic lactate production (Ashford and Dixon, 1935; Kimura, 1937; Dixon, 1949). As in the case of oxygen uptake, this stimulation requires the presence of sodium (Takagaki and Tsukada, 1957) and is only found in brain slices, and not in homogenates (Kimura, 1937). The application of electrical pulses or glutamate or certain drugs (e.g. veratrine) also leads to increased aerobic glycolysis. All these agents (including excess potassium) cause an unexplained inhibition of anaerobic glycolysis (Ashford and Dixon,

1935; Dickens and Greville, 1935; Weil-Malherbe, 1938; Dixon, 1949; Elliott, 1955; McIlwain, 1956).

b. *Tricarboxylic acid cycle*

The pentose phosphate shunt may be involved in resting metabolism (Hotta, 1962; Piras and Zadunaisky, 1965; Nishimura and Kimura, 1965; cf. however, also Reading, 1964), but the available evidence suggests that excess K^+ and electrical pulses act by stimulating the turnover via the glycolytic pathway and the subsequent turnover of the tricarboxylic acid cycle (Kozava, 1961; Piras and Zadunaisky, 1965; O'Neill *et al.*, 1965). These pathways are thus thought to account for the major fraction of the stimulated respiration (Kimura and Niwa, 1953; cf., however, Nishimura and Kimura, 1965). This concept is in agreement with the finding that pyruvate or lactate is almost as effective a substrate as glucose in the maintenance of not only the resting and the stimulated respiration (Dickens and Greville, 1935; Lipsett and Crescitelli, 1950; Kratzing, 1953; Ghosh and Quastel, 1954), but also of a reasonably high concentration of energy-rich phosphates (Heald, 1960; Woodman and McIlwain, 1961; Abadom and Scholefield, 1962). These substances are also able to sustain several energy-requiring processes, e.g. the synthesis of acetylcholine (Quastel *et al.*, 1936), and the accumulation of potassium (Joanny *et al.*, 1963; Joanny and Hillman, 1963; Joanny *et al.*, 1966). The only tricarboxylic acid intermediate which is able to maintain all these functions is oxalo-acetate (Ito, 1960; Abadom and Scholefield, 1962; Joanny *et al.*, 1963). In several respects (e.g. the maintenance of the concentrations of energy-rich phosphates and of potassium) α-ketoglutarate is almost as effective as oxaloacetate (Abadom and Scholefield, 1962; Joanny *et al.*, 1963), but oddly enough, sensitivity to high concentrations of potassium is abolished when ketoglutarate is used as the substrate (Lipsett and Crescitelli, 1950; Kratzing, 1953). Citrate, succinate, fumarate and malate, on the other hand, are hardly able to replace glucose (for references, see Hertz, 1969).

The failure of these compounds to act satisfactorily as substrates may be due to poor penetration into the tissue. Nevertheless, it seems more difficult to explain why, for example, α-ketoglutarate can maintain only certain metabolic functions. One possibility is that the tricarboxylic acid cycle intermediates are compartmented into at least two pools of which the added substrate has access to only one of these compartments. Such a compartmentation is known to exist in the case of glutamate (Berl *et al.*, 1961; Gaitonde, 1965; Berl *et al.*, 1968), and it has been suggested that two separate tricarboxylic acid cycles may be operating in the brain (Berg *et al.*, 1966; O'Neal and Koeppe, 1966; Berg *et al.*, 1967).

Nothing can as yet be said about the histological localization of the two separate tricarboxylic acid cycles, but both microdissected Deiters' cells and their surrounding glia cells are able to oxidize pyruvate, α-keto-glutarate, succinate and glutamate (Hamberger, 1961). The succinoxydase activity is normally highest in the glia cell samples, but physiological stimulation causes a decrease in the neuroglial activity, and an increase in the neuronal activity (Hydén and Pigon, 1960). Based upon these and other observations, Hydén (1964, 1967) has suggested a "biochemical and functional interplay between neuron and glia" (cf. also Olken, 1963).

c. Oxydative phosphorylation

Cytochrome oxidase is known to be present in both nerve cells and glia cells (Hydén and Pigon, 1960; Hamberger, 1963). Oxydative phosphorylation probably occurs in either cell type during *in vitro* experiments. It is consistent with this concept that brain slices regain about three-quarters of the *in vivo* level of both phosphocreatine and ATP after initial splitting (McIlwain, 1966; Swanson, 1968).

The application of electrical pulses or of high concentrations of potassium leads to reduction in the level of energy-rich phosphates (Heald, 1954, 1960). This is due to an increased rate of breakdown of the energy-rich phosphates which can be as rapid as 1200–1400 μmoles/g wet wt/hr. As pointed out by Heald (1960), this high rate of breakdown strongly suggests that the stimulation of oxygen uptake is the result of an augmentation of energy-requiring processes and not of an uncoupling of oxydative phosphorylation. Were it the latter, one would have then expected a rate of breakdown equivalent to the rate of oxygen uptake before the onset of stimulation, i.e. about 300–400 μmoles/g wet wt/hr. Evidence against uncoupling is also provided by the observation that high concentrations of potassium cause increased incorporation of ^{32}P into the energy-rich phosphates (Brossard and Quastel, 1963), whereas the addition of 2,4-dinitrophenol leads to a decrease (Tsukada *et al.*, 1958; cf. II. C, 3 *d*).

C. Amino acid metabolism

1. Glutamic acid, glutamine and GABA

The role of these amino acids in brain metabolism has been the subject of much discussion. They are found in high concentrations (1–10 mM) in the brain *in vivo*, and one of them, glutamate, has been used therapeutically though with doubtful results (Strecker, 1957).

Tracer experiments have shown that glutamate, GABA and glutamine are rapidly formed from glucose (Quastel, 1959; Vrba *et al.*, 1962). Both this process and the formation of glutamine from glutamate may be enhanced by excess potassium (Quastel, 1959; Kini and Quastel, 1959, 1960; Lahiri and Quastel, 1963; Berl *et al.*, 1968).

All three amino acids are taken up by brain slices from the medium against concentration gradients (Stern *et al.*, 1949; Elliott and Gelder, 1958; Takagaki *et al.*, 1959; Tsukada *et al.*, 1963). Evidence is available which indicates that the uptake of glutamine, and possibly glutamate, may be increased by high concentrations of potassium (Quastel, 1959; Tsukada *et al.*, 1963). The release of both GABA and glutamate, but not of glutamine, from the tissue to the medium is, on the other hand, enhanced by excess potassium, as can be seen in Fig. 7 (Machiyama *et al.*, 1967; Hertz, 1968; T. Arnfred and L. Hertz, unpublished experiments). These findings could indicate that the active transport of one or more of these amino acids is among the energy-requiring processes which are stimulated by high concentrations of potassium.

The addition of 5–10 mM L-glutamate to the medium causes the same metabolic effects as those of potassium (Rossiter, 1955; cf. II. C, 3 *a* and III. B, 2 *a*) and it also leads to a raised potassium content of the slices (cf. IV. C, 1 *b*). GABA and glutamine do not have such effects.

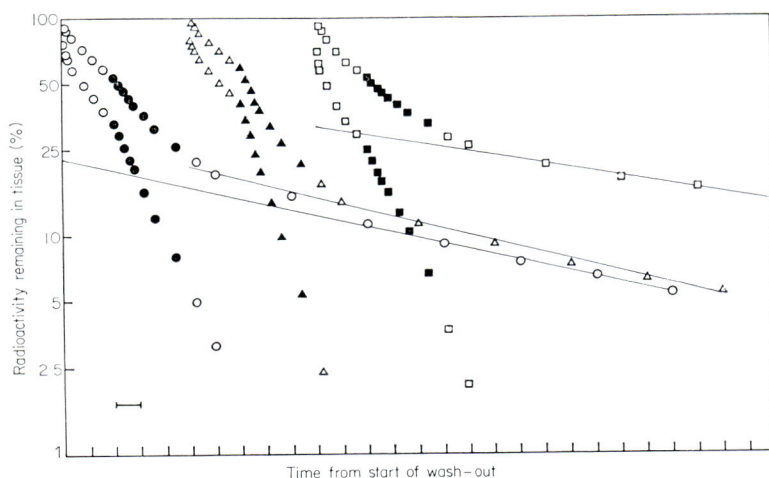

FIG. 7. Wash-out of ^{14}C-labelled glutamate ($\bigcirc$ and $\bullet$), γ-aminobutyrate ($\triangle$ and $\blacktriangle$), and glutamine ($\square$ and $\blacksquare$) from rat brain-cortex slices into a non-radioactive medium containing either 5 mM ($\bigcirc$, $\triangle$ and $\square$) or 55 mM ($\bullet$, $\blacktriangle$ and $\blacksquare$) potassium.

The fully drawn lines indicate the terminal, approximately straight parts of the wash-out curves (fitted by eye) and their extrapolation to zero time. By subtraction of these lines from the observed courses the lower curves were obtained, which show the wash-out from the more rapidly exchanging fractions (cf. IV. C, 3a).

For graphical reasons curves $\triangle$ and $\square$ have been displaced to the right. The abscissa indicates on an equidistant scale the length of the wash-out period, and the bar (—) shows a 10 min period. The ordinate indicates on a logarithmic scale the fraction of the original radioactivity remaining in the tissue. The steepness with which the radioactivity declines is a measure of the efflux rates of the radio-isotope and hence of the corresponding non-radioactive substance. Results are the unpublished experiments of T. Arnfred & L. Hertz.

2. *Other amino acids*

Other amino acids are actively taken up from the medium, or formed from glucose, but high concentrations of potassium seem to inhibit both their uptake and their formation (see Hertz, 1969). Aspartate may, however, replace glutamate in its effect on potassium content (Terner *et al.*, 1950) and its release is enhanced by excess potassium (T. Arnfred and L. Hertz, unpublished experiments).

D. *Synthetic processes*

1. *Carbohydrates*

Carbohydrates are not only metabolized but also synthesized and stored in the brain as glycogen. High concentrations of potassium cause a decrease in this synthesis (Kleinzeller and Rybová, 1957).

2. *Lipids*

Lipid metabolism in the central nervous system is of special interest particularly in connection with the myelinization and demyelinization of white matter. Also grey matter contains lipids of biological interest, e.g. certain phospholipids, the turnover of which may be increased by potassium or by electrical pulses (Heald, 1960).

3. *Nucleic acids*

Much attention has been focused upon the metabolism of the nucleic acids, especially RNA, in the brain in relation to learning processes. Since this is a problem which is to be discussed in detail in Chapter 3, it will suffice here to mention that the RNA content, and the base composition of both glia cells and nerve cells, changes during learning (Hydén, 1967).

4. *Proteins*

The changes in RNA described above may indicate an altered production of protein. It seems noteworthy that the amount of proteins per nerve cell rises during stimulation (Hydén, 1967).

Ultimately protein metabolism in brain will turn out to be of paramount importance to brain function (cf. Richter, 1965). Despite the little information available, it is now known by means of autoradiography that proteins are formed in the Nissl bodies (Droz, 1965) and that they migrate down the axon (Droz and Leblond, 1963; cf. also Waelsch and Lajtha, 1961).

5. *Transmitters*

Synaptic transmission is obviously of fundamental importance in brain function. From an energetics point of view the production of transmitters is, however, of minor importance since, for example, the maximum synthesis of acetylcholine in brain slices probably accounts for only about 1% of the oxygen uptake in the isolated tissue (McIlwain, 1966). This does not imply that the release of a transmitter may not lead to procesess requiring considerably more energy (cf. IV. A, 3).

Both glutamate and GABA (e.g. Krnjević, 1965; Galindo *et al.*, 1967) have several characteristics in common with ordinary transmitters, but occur in the brain cortex in much higher concentrations than the classical transmitter substances (cf. V). Neither GABA nor glutamate seem to be localized preferentially in the presynaptic nerve terminals (Mangan and Whittaker, 1966).

The biochemistry of the synaptosome is dealt with in Chapter 2.

IV. Ionic Turnover

A. *Correlation between ion movements and membrane potentials*

1. *Ion concentration and electric potential*

The relationship between the concentration of an ion inside and outside the cell and the equilibrium membrane potential for that ionic species is given by the Nernst equation. In the case of a monovalent diffusible cation one may thus write that, at 37°C

$$E_m \text{ (in mV)} = 61 \log \frac{I_o}{I_i}$$

where I_o and I_i are the concentrations of the ion outside and inside the cell and 61 is the Nernst coefficient. Should more than one diffusible ion (e.g. K^+, Na^+ and Cl^-) contribute to the membrane potential, a more elaborate equation such as that derived by Goldman (1943), must be used. This is an equation in which E_m is related to both the concentrations and the permeability coefficients of these ions.

This interdependence between the membrane potential and ionic concentrations implies that any change in the electric potential causes a redistribution of the diffusible ions across the cell membrane. It also implies that any change in internal or external concentration of a diffusible ion affects the membrane potential. This is the case regardless whether the change is due to an alteration in external ionic concentration (for example, a membrane potential change brought about by addition of ions or by release of ions from neighbouring cells) or to alterations in the extent of ion transport across the cell membrane. In these circumstances, the redistribution of other ions may occur secondarily.

Much of the work on the relationship between ion transport and membrane potentials in nervous tissue has been done on the giant axon of the squid (Hodgkin, 1957). A few salient points dealing with this subject are discussed below.

2. *Resting conditions*

Like most other cells, resting nerve cells (or nerve fibres) are negatively charged relative to their surroundings. In spite of the negative charge inside the cells the intracellular sodium concentration is much lower than the external sodium concentration. This sodium gradient is in all likelihood maintained actively, i.e. by an outward transport of sodium ions. Sodium- and potassium-stimulated ATPases ($Na^+ - K^+ - ATPases$) seem to be involved in the sodium transfer (Skou, 1957, 1960; Post *et al.*, 1960) and the outward sodium transport is probably coupled to an inward transport of potassium ions. Due to high membrane permeability to this ion (and to anions) the potassium concentration remains nevertheless almost at electrochemical equilibrium.

The high permeability of the membrane to potassium implies that the resting nerve cell (nerve cell fibre) behaves as a potassium-sensitive electrode, i.e. that its membrane potential is largely determined by the ratio between internal and external concentrations of potassium (cf. IV. A, 1), and consequently is sensitive to any alterations in K^+ ion concentration. This is, however, not the case with Na^+, since the membrane potential is only slightly affected by changes in sodium concentration.

3. *Excitation*

During excitation of a nerve cell (nerve fibre) the membrane permeability to sodium increases transiently to become higher than that to potassium. The result is that the negative membrane potential changes to a positive sodium equilibrium potential, and that a net uptake of sodium ions occurs. The sodium uptake is followed by a release of potassium ions since the potential inside the cell no longer supports a high intracellular content of potassium. Within milliseconds membrane permeability to sodium returns, however, to its previous low value, and a negative potassium-equilibrium potential is re-established.

These two potential changes constitute the action potential. Permeability changes are induced by procedures which lead to a relatively slight decrease in the magnitude of the negative potential (e.g. the application of electrical pulses, or increasing the external concentration of potassium) and by applying transmitters.

It is to be emphasized that the ion movements involved during excitation are "down-hill" and hence may be regarded as processes which do not consume energy. Complete restitution, i.e. reaccumulation of potassium ions and extrusion of sodium ions corresponding to the potassium loss and sodium gain during the action potential is, however, dependent upon the supply of energy.

B. *Ion metabolism* in vivo

1. *Ion content and transport*

It is in keeping with the crucial role of potassium and sodium in nervous tissue function that the concentrations of these ions, especially potassium, are kept relatively constant not only in the brain (about 100 μmoles potassium and 50 μmoles sodium/g wet wt of grey matter; cf. Yannet, 1940; Ames and Nesbett, 1958; Bachelard *et al.*, 1962) but also in the cerebrospinal fluid (about 3 mM potassium and 140 mM sodium; cf. Merritt and Fremont-Smith, 1938; Cooper *et al.*, 1955).

There is evidence that the sodium content of mammalian glia cells *in vivo* may be high (Gerschenfeld *et al.*, 1959; Katzman, 1961; Koch *et al.*, 1962). It has also been suggested that the transport of ions in brain occurs through the glia cells. However, this is not true of large glia cells of the leech ganglion (Nicholls and Kuffler, 1964), but it must be kept in mind that these cells may differ from those present in the "neuropil" (I. C, 2 *d*; cf. also Hertz, 1965*b*).

2. *Membrane potentials*

Membrane potentials of 60–90 mV have been recorded *in vivo* (Phillips, 1956). These intracellular potentials can only be recorded from cells which are large enough to allow penetration, and probably originate mainly from nerve cell bodies. Resting potentials from glia cells have, however, been recorded in special preparations, such as the leech ganglion, or the Necturus optic nerve (cf. I. C, 2 *d*). No action potentials have been observed in these glia cells, but low resistance connections between individual glia cells are known to allow the spread of potential changes over more than 1 mm (Kuffler and Potter, 1964; Kuffler *et al.*, 1966).

C. *Ion metabolism* in vitro

1. *Ion content*

a. *Swelling*

Brain slices have a great tendency to swell, i.e. to take up water during incubation. The degree of the swelling varies from 15% under optimum conditions of preparation and incubation (G. Franck and E. Schoffeniels, personal communication; cf. also Bourke and Tower, 1966*a*) to more than 50%. Incubation in potassium-rich media leads to increased swelling (Elliott, 1955; Pappius and Elliott, 1956*a*; Bourke and Tower, 1966*a*) which may be secondary to uptake of potassium, and sodium ions together with accompanying anions.

The swelling itself is a matter of considerable interest (e.g. in relation to the mechanism of brain edema; cf. Pappius, 1965). Because of swelling there are uncertainties about expressing the ionic concentration of brain slices, and several authors have attempted to express this in relation to the initial (unswollen) weight of the tissue. Such corrections as have been made give rise to an apparent increase in the internal potassium concentration and a decrease in the internal sodium concentration (Hertz, 1969).

b. *Potassium*

The maximal potassium concentration of brain slices suspended in a "physiological" medium is 70–80 μmoles/g final wet wt, a value lower than that *in vivo*. This is due to a pronounced loss of K^+ during and immediately after the preparation of the tissue. Subsequently some reaccumulation of K^+ occurs in slices (Krebs *et al.*, 1951; Pappius and Elliott, 1956*b*; Bachelard *et al.*, 1962; Bourke and Tower, 1966*b*) and in isolated glia cells, but not in nerve cells (Hamberger and Röckert, 1964; Bradford and Rose, 1967). The reaccumulation is enhanced by glutamate (Terner *et al.*, 1950; Takagaki *et al.*, 1959; Tsukada *et al.*, 1963).

The potassium content of brain slices rises when the potassium concentration of the medium is increased. As can be seen from Fig. 8, the rise is steep over the K^+ concentration range of 5–20 mM, but negligible over the range of 20–50 mM. This constancy is partly, but not exclusively, due to a concomitant increase in swelling (Bourke and Tower, 1966a; H. Lund-Andersen and L. Hertz, unpublished experiments). Application of electrical pulses or of veratrine, on the other hand, causes a reduction in potassium content (Wollenberger, 1955; Cummins and McIlwain, 1961; Joanny and Hillman, 1964).

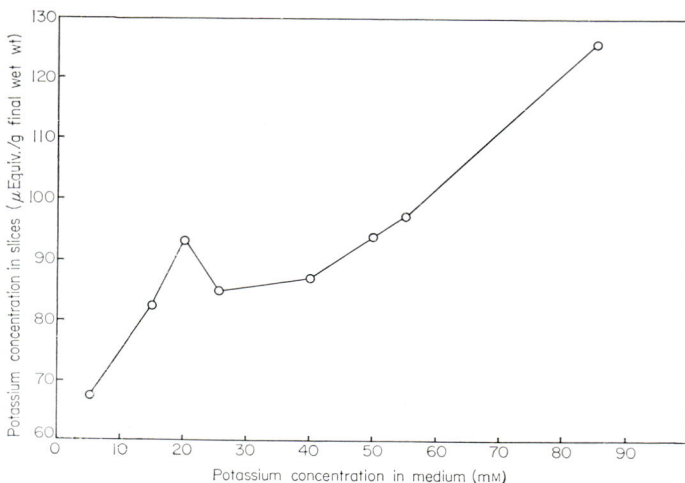

FIG. 8. Potassium concentration in rat brain cortex slices (μequiv./g final wet wt) as a function of the concentration of potassium in the medium (mM). (Results are the unpublished experiments of H. Lund-Andersen and L. Hertz.)

c. Sodium

There is a rise in sodium content and a fall in potassium during and immediately after the preparation of the slices. A subsequent net loss of sodium can be observed when the tissue is carefully prepared (Bachelard et al., 1962; G. Franck and E. Schoffeniels, personal communication).

The sodium concentration rises when electrical pulses are applied (Varon and McIlwain, 1961; Bachelard et al., 1962; Joanny and Hillman, 1963, 1964; Keesey et al., 1965); it also rises, but to a smaller extent, when brain slices are exposed to high concentrations of potassium (H. Lund-Andersen and L. Hertz, unpublished experiments; cf., however, Hertz, 1968).

c. Chloride

The chloride content of brain slices is high, indicating that a considerable amount of it is probably found intracellularly (Bourke and Tower, 1966a). It is unaffected by excess potassium (Bourke and Tower, 1966a; Hertz, 1968) and electrical stimulation (Varon and McIlwain, 1961).

2. Membrane potentials

The ion gradients occurring across brain slices indicate the presence of membrane potentials. However, the magnitude of these potentials cannot be calculated from these gradients since it depends upon the ratio between the ionic concentrations in the cells and in their immediate surroundings (IV. A, 1), i.e. the intercellular fluid of the tissue (I. B).

Direct measurements have shown the presence of potentials of 40–60 mV both in brain slices (Li and McIlwain, 1957; Hillman and McIlwain, 1961; Gibson and McIlwain, 1965) and in isolated neurons (Hillman and Hydén, 1965). An increase in the external potassium concentration (or application of electrical pulses) causes a decrease in their magnitude (Hillman and McIlwain, 1961; Gibson and McIlwain, 1965; Hillman and Hydén, 1965).

3. Ion transport

a. Resting conditions

Whittam (1962) compared the rates of oxygen uptake in brain slices during incubation in "physiological" and in sodium-deficient (or ouabain-containing) media, and concluded that about 40% of the "normal" resting oxygen uptake is due to active transport of sodium and potassium. Though this estimate has been questioned (Wallgren, 1963; Swanson, 1968), it seems beyond doubt that a considerable fraction of the metabolism of brain slices is concerned with the provision of energy for active ion transport (Krebs et al., 1951; Cummins and McIlwain, 1961; Hertz and Clausen, 1963; Keesey and Wallgren, 1965).

Ion transport may be studied in terms of uptake (influx) or washout (efflux) of radio-isotopes (Brinley, 1963). Such studies have demonstrated the existence of different compartments. A small fraction, viz. less than 10% of the radioactivity in the tissue, shows a slow exchange between potassium and sodium ions (Franck and Cornette, 1966; Hertz, 1968); this fraction probably represents the nerve cell bodies (cf. I. A, 2). The larger tissue fraction, on the other hand, represents one or more compartments, marked by rapid turnover of ions (Cummins and McIlwain, 1961; Zadunaisky and Curran, 1963; Keesey and Wallgren, 1965; Franck and Cornette, 1966; Hertz, 1968). These compartments presumably include both the extracellular space and the glia cells.

b. Stimulation

It has been repeatedly suggested that the stimulation of oxygen uptake produced by high concentrations of potassium may be due to increased ion transport (Hertz and Schou, 1962; Minakami et al., 1963). Direct measurements, such as those shown in Fig. 9, demonstrate an increase in potassium transport (Hertz, 1968) which is oxygen-dependent and confined to the rapidly exchanging fraction, probably represented by the glia cells. Moreover, there is increased wash-out of glutamate (cf. III. C, 1), while the transport of sodium, chloride and glutamine is virtually unaffected (Hertz, 1968; T. Arnfred and L. Hertz, unpublished experiments).

Electrical stimulation causes a rise in potassium transport (Cummins and McIlwain, 1961; Franck and Cornette, 1966).

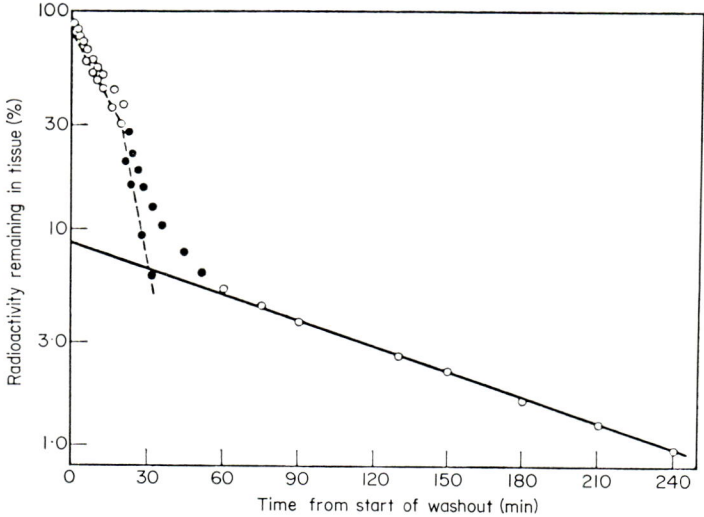

Fig. 9. Fraction of initial radioactivity (^{42}K) which remains in rat brain-cortex slices during wash-out into a non-radioactive medium. The greater part of the wash-out (represented by ○) was performed in a medium containing 5 mM potassium, but during the 20–52 min period the potassium concentration in the medium was increased by 50 mM (represented by ●). The air phase was O_2/CO_2.

The fully drawn line indicates the terminal, approximately straight part of the wash-out curve (fitted by eye) and its extrapolation to zero time. By subtraction of this line from the observed course the dotted line was obtained.

As in Fig. 7 the rate of radioactive decline is a measure of the efflux rate (cf. legend to Fig. 7). (From Hertz, 1968.)

The probable neuroglial localization of both the potassium-induced stimulation of oxygen consumption (II. C, 1) and the rise in ion transport would seem to indicate that glia cells are primarily involved in this response. Active uptake of potassium ions by glia cells has been suggested by various investigators (Horstmann and Meves, 1959; Hertz, 1965a; Wendell-Smith and Blunt, 1965). The constancy of the potassium concentration in brain slices in the presence of a medium concentration increasing from 20 mM to 50 mM (IV. C, 1 b) might be taken to indicate that potassium ions are not only transported inwards, but also *through* glia cells. This concept is supported by the spread of potential changes (i.e. electrical charges) from one glia cell to another (IV. B, 2), but as pointed out earlier the absence of ion transport through the large glia cells in the leech (IV. B, 1) argues against it.

V. Concluding Remarks

The various aspects of brain metabolism dwelt upon in this chapter were selected on the basis of the interests of the author and, consequently, no objective estimate of their importance in brain function can be made on the basis of the attention they have received. For reviews the interested reader is referred to those by Richter (1957), Windle (1958), Heald (1960), Hydén (1960), McIlwain and Rodnight (1962), Elliott *et al.* (1962), Van Harreveld (1966) and McIlwain (1966).

None the less, it can be safely concluded that the turnover of monovalent cations, which plays so crucial a role in the function of peripheral nerve, must also be of primary importance in the brain, and that potassium occupies a unique position as an ion which on the one hand is released during nerve cell activity and on the other affects membrane potentials and hence nerve excitability by changes in its extracellular concentration. In a complicated, closely packed, poorly isolated system like the brain cortex, constant regulation of the extracellular potassium concentration seems essential. Conceivably, this regulation may consist of active K^+ uptake by cells of any type when the extracellular concentration of this ion exceeds a certain limit, and such an uptake seems primarily to occur into glia cells.

Though the evidence for further transport of potassium ions through glia cells is sparse (cf. however, Hertz, 1965a, b), the mechanism seems to be of great interest because it would allow potassium transfer from excited neurons via predetermined neuroglial pathways to other, previously resting, neurons which become excited. Such a neuronal-neuroglial-neuronal impulse transmission system could be of fundamental importance in the integration of nervous activity and the learning process (Hertz, 1965a). Its probable confinement to the highest developed regions of the central nervous system is noteworthy.

The role of glutamate and related amino acids is uncertain. Glutamate on the one hand may be produced in large amounts during metabolic degradation in brain and, on the other, it behaves as an anion which is transported, and formed at increased rates during the incubation of brain slices in potassium-rich media. These observations may indicate that at least part of the "stimulated" potassium transport occurs in the form of coupled movements between potassium and glutamate ions, and that a continuous production of glutamate may be essential for such transport. This may represent a connection between the separate pools of tricarboxylic acid intermediates, and may be of importance in the suggested functional interplay between neuron and glia.

The importance of neuroglia was underlined throughout this chapter. This is in defiance of classical neuroanatomical, neurophysiological and neurochemical thinking but in line with concepts which have emerged during the last decade or so. These concepts are based upon the findings that mental activity affects both the anatomy (Diamond *et al.*, 1966), the physiology (Adey *et al.*, 1963; Svaetichin *et al.*, 1965) and the biochemistry (Hydén and Egyhazi, 1963) of glia cells, and that certain neurological diseases may primarily involve neuroglia (Gomirato and Hydén, 1963). However, the precise functional implications of these processes have not yet been clarified. It has been suggested that the glia cells play mainly a nourishing role by producing, for example, metabolic intermediates and RNA which subsequently are transferred to the nerve cells (Hamberger, 1963; Hydén, 1967). On the other hand, there is evidence that glia cells take a more direct part in impulse transmission, e.g. in the transport of potassium (and glutamate) ions, as suggested above (cf. also Galambos, 1961).

Whatever function the glia cells eventually turn out to serve, the interplay between neurons and glia cells is vital to both life in health and disease. This is already suggested by the intricate anatomical connections found between these two cell types. Thus, although experiments which attempt to distinguish between the roles of either cell are cumbersome and complicated, they are indispensable if new lines of investigation and knowledge are to be sought.

References

Abadom, P. N. and Scholefield, P. G. (1962). *Can. J. Biochem. Physiol.* **40**, 1603-1618.

Adey, W. R., Kado, R. T., Didio, J. and Schindler, W. J. (1963). *Expl Neurol.* **7**, 259-281.

Allen, N. (1957). *J. Neurochem.* **2**, 37-44.

Ames, A. and Nesbett, F. B. (1958). *J. Neurochem.* **3**, 116-126.

Ashford, C. A. and Dixon, K. C. (1935). *Biochem. J.* **29**, 157-168.

Bachelard, H. S., Campbell, W. J. and McIlwain, H. (1962). *Biochem. J.* **89**, 225-232.

Bauer, K. F. (1951). *Z. Anat. EntwGesch.* **115**, 480-489.

Beer, C. T. and Quastel, J. H. (1958). *Can. J. Biochem. Physiol.* **36**, 543-556.

Berg, C. J. van den, Mela, P. and Waelsch, H. (1966). *Biochem. biophys. Res. Commun.* **23**, 479-484.

Berg, C. J. van den, Kržalic, L. T. and Mela, P. (1967). In *Abstracts, First International Meeting of the International Society for Neurochemistry*, p. 21, Strasbourg.

Berl, S., Lajtha, A. and Waelsch, H. (1961). *J. Neurochem.* **7**, 186-197.

Berl, S., Nicklas, W. J. and Clarke, D. D. (1968). *J. Neurochem.* **15**, 131-140.

Blackstad, T. W. (1967). In *The Neuron* (H. Hydén, ed.), pp. 48-118. Elsevier, Amsterdam.

Bollard, B. M. and McIlwain, H. (1957). *Biochem. J.* **66**, 651-655.

Bourke, R. S. and Tower, D. B. (1966a). *J. Neurochem.* **13**, 1071-1097.

Bourke, R. S. and Tower, D. B. (1966b). *J. Neurochem.* **13**, 1099-1117.

Bradford, H. F. (1967). In *Abstracts, First International Meeting of the International Society for Neurochemistry*, p. 30. Strasbourg.

Bradford, H. F. and Rose, S. P. R. (1967). *J. Neurochem.* **14**, 373-375.

Brinley, F. J. jr. (1963). In *Int. Rev. Neurobiol.* (C. C. Pfeiffer and J. R. Smythies, eds), Vol. 5, pp. 183-242. Academic Press, New York.

Brizee, K. R. and Jacobs, L. A. (1959). *Anat. Rec.* **134**, 97-105.

Brossard, M. and Quastel, J. H. (1963). *Can. J. Biochem. Physiol.* **41**, 1243-1256.

Canzanelli, A., Rogers, G. and Rapport, D. (1942). *Am. J. Physiol.* **135**, 309-315.

Coggeshall, R. E. and Fawcett, D. W. (1964). *J. Neurophysiol.* **27**, 229-289.

Cooper, E. S., Lechner, E. and Bellet, S. (1955). *Am. J. Med.* **18**, 613-621.

Cummins, J. and Hydén, H. (1962). *Biochim. biophys. Acta* **60**, 271-283.

Cummins, J. T. and McIlwain, H. (1961). *Biochem. J.* **79**, 330-341.

Diamond, M. C., Law, F., Rhodes, H., Lindner, B., Rosenzweig, M. R., Krech, D. and Bennett, E. L. (1966). *J. comp. Neurol.* **128**, 117-126.

Dickens, F. and Greville, G. D. (1935). *Biochem. J.* **29**, 1468-1483.

Dixon, K. C. (1949). *J. Physiol., Lond.* **110**, 87-97.

Droz, B. (1965). *C. r. hebd. Séanc. Acad. Sci., Paris* **260**, 320-322.

Droz, B. and Leblond, C. P. (1963). *J. comp. Neurol.* **121**, 325-337.

Economo, C. von (1926). *Klin. Wschr.* **5**, 593-595.

Ehrenberg, C. G. (1833). *Annln. Physik.* **28**, 449-465.

Elliott, K. A. C. (1952). In *The Biology of Mental Health and Disease*, pp. 54-70. Hoeber, New York.

Elliott, K. A. C. (1955). *Can. J. Biochem. Physiol.* **33**, 466-480.

Elliott, K. A. C. and Gelder, N. M. van (1958). *J. Neurochem.* **3**, 28-40.

Elliott, K. A. C. and Heller, I. H. (1957). In *Metabolism of the Nervous System*, (D. Richter, ed.), pp. 286-290. Pergamon Press, London.

Elliott, K. A. C. and Henderson, N. (1948). *J. Neurophysiol.* **11**, 471-484.

Elliott, K. A. C. and Libet, B. (1942). *J. Biol. Chem.* **143**, 227-246.

Elliott, K. A. C., Page, I. H. and Quastel, J. H. (eds) (1962). In *Neurochemistry*, 2nd ed., pp. 1-1035. Charles C Thomas, Springfield, Illinois.

Elliott, K. A. C. and Penfield, W. (1948). *J. Neurophysiol.* **11**, 485-490.

Epstein, M. H. and O'Connor, J. S. (1965). *J. Neurochem.* **12**, 389-395.

Franck, G. and Cornette, M. (1966). *Revue Neurol.* **115**, 312-314.

Friede, R. (1954). *Acta anat.* **20**, 290-296.

Gaitonde, M. K. (1965). *Biochem. J.* **95**, 803-810.

Galambos, R. (1961). *Proc. natn. Acad. Sci. U.S.A.* **47**, 129-136.

Galindo, A., Krnjević, K. and Schwartz, S. (1967). *J. Physiol., Lond.* **192**, 359-377.

Geiger, A. and Magnes, J. (1947). *Am. J. Physiol.* **149**, 517-537.

Geren, B. B. (1954). *Expl Cell Res.* **7**, 558-562.

Geren, B. B. and Schmitt, F. O. (1955). In *Fine Structure of Cells*, pp. 251-260. P. Noordhoff Ltd., Groningen.

Gerschenfeld, H. M., Wald, F., Zadunaisky, J. A. and Robertis, E. D. P. de (1959). *Neurology, Minneap.* **9**, 412-425.

Ghosh, J. J. and Quastel, J. H. (1954). *Nature, Lond.* **174**, 28-31.

Gibson, J. M. and McIlwain, H. (1965). *J. Physiol., Lond.* **176**, 261-283.

Goldman, D. E. (1943). *J. gen. Physiol.* **27**, 37-60.

Gomirato, G. and Hydén, H. (1963). *Brain* **86**, 773-780.

Gonda, O. and Quastel, J. H. (1963). *Can. J. Biochem. Physiol.* **41**, 435-453.

Gore, M. B. R. and McIlwain, H. (1952). *J. Physiol., Lond.* **117**, 471-483.

Greengard, O. and McIlwain, H. (1955). *Biochem. J.* **61**, 61-68.

Ham, A. V. (1965). *Histology*, 5th ed., p. 545. Pitman, London.

Hamberger, A. (1961). *J. Neurochem.* **8**, 31-35.

Hamberger, A. (1963). *Acta physiol. scand.* **58**, suppl. 203, 1-52.

Hamberger, A. and Röckert, H. (1964). *J. Neurochem.* **11**, 757-760.

Haug, H. (1956). *J. comp. Neurol.* **104**, 473-492.

Hawkins, A. and Olszewski, J. (1957). *Science, N.Y.* **126**, 76-77.

Heald, P. J. (1954). *Biochem. J.* **57**, 673-679.

Heald, P. J. (1960). In *Phosphorus Metabolism of the Brain*, pp. 1-195. Pergamon Press, London.

Hegnauer, A. H., Fenn, W. O. and Cobb, D. M. (1934). *J. cell. comp. Physiol.* **4**, 505-526.

Heller, I. H. and Elliott, K. A. C. (1955). *Can. J. Biochem. Physiol.* **33**, 395-403.

Hertz, L. (1965a). *Nature, Lond.* **206**, 1091-1094.

Hertz, L. (1965b). *Nature, Lond.* **208**, 601-602.

Hertz, L. (1966). *J. Neurochem.* **13**, 1373-1387.

Hertz, L. (1968). *J. Neurochem.* **15**, 1-16.

Hertz, L. (1969). *Danish Med. Bull.* (In the press.)

Hertz, L. and Clausen, T. (1963). *Biochem. J.* **89**, 526-533.

Hertz, L. and Schou, M. (1962). *Biochem. J.* **85**, 93-104.

Hillman, H. and Hydén, H. (1965). *J. Physiol., Lond.* **177**, 398-410.
Hillman, H. and McIlwain, H. (1961). *J. Physiol., Lond.* **157**, 263-278.
Hodgkin, A. L. (1957). *Proc. R. Soc.* **148**, 1-37.
Horstmann, E. and Meves, H. (1959). *Z. Zellforsch. mikrosk. Anat.* **49**, 569-604.
Hotta, S. S. (1962). *J. Neurochem.* **9**, 43-51.
Hydén, H. (1959). *Nature, Lond.* **184**, 433-435.
Hydén, H. (1960). In *The Cell* (J. Brachet and A. E. Mirsky, eds), Vol. IV, pp. 215-323. Academic Press, New York.
Hydén, H. (1964). In *Recent Advances in Biological Psychiatry* (J. Wortis, ed.), pp. 31-54. Plenum Press, New York.
Hydén, H. (1967). In *The Neuron* (H. Hydén, ed.), pp. 179-219. Elsevier, Amsterdam.
Hydén, H. and Egyhazi, E. (1963). *Proc. natn. Acad. Sci. U.S.A.* **49**, 618-624.
Hydén, H. and Lange, P. W. (1961). In *Regional Neurochemistry* (S. S. Kety and J. Elkes, eds), pp. 190-199. Pergamon Press, London.
Hydén, H. and Lange, P. W. (1965). *Acta physiol. scand.* **64**, 6-14.
Hydén, H. and Pigon, A. (1960). *J. Neurochem.* **6**, 57-72.
Ito, K. (1960). *Jap. J. exp. Med.* **30**, 261-277.
Joanny, P., Corriol, J. and Hillman, H. H. (1963). *J. Physiol., Paris.* **55**, 154-155.
Joanny, P. and Hillman, H. H. (1963). *J. Neurochem.* **10**, 655-664.
Joanny, P. and Hillman, H. H. (1964). *J. Neurochem.* **11**, 413-422.
Joanny, P., Hillman, H. and Corriol. J. (1966). *J. Neurochem.* **13**, 371-374.
Johnston, P. V. and Roots, B. I. (1965). *Nature, Lond.* **205**, 778-780.
Katzman, R. (1961). *Neurology, Minneap.* **11**, 27-36.
Keesey, J. C. and Wallgren, H. (1965). *Biochem. J.* **95**, 301-310.
Keesey, J. C., Wallgren, H. and McIlwain, H. (1965). *Biochem. J.* **95**, 289-300.
Kety, S. S. (1957). In *Metabolism of the Nervous System* (D. Richter, ed.), pp. 221-236. Pergamon Press, London.
Kimura, Y. (1937). *Sci. Pap. Inst. phys. chem. Res., Tokyo* **33**, 231-245.
Kimura, Y. and Niwa, T. (1953). *Nature, Lond.* **171**, 881-882.
Kini, M. M. and Quastel, J. H. (1959). *Nature, Lond.* **184**, 252-256.
Kini, M. M. and Quastel, J. H. (1960). *Science, N.Y.* **131**, 412-414.
Kleinzeller, A. and Rybová, R. R. (1957). *J. Neurochem.* **2**, 45-57.
Koch, A., Ranck, J. B. jr. and Newman, B. L. (1962). *Expl Neurol.* **6**, 186-200.
Korey, S. R. and Orchen, M. (1959). *J. Neurochem.* **3**, 277-285.
Kozava, S. (1961). *Biochem. Pharmac.* **8**, 41.
Kratzing, C. C. (1953). *Biochem. J.* **54**, 312-317.
Krebs, H. A. (1935). *Biochem. J.* **29**, 1620-1644.
Krebs, H. A., Eggleston, L. V. and Terner, C. (1951). *Biochem. J.* **48**, 530-537.
Krnjević, K. (1965). In *Proc. 23rd Internat. Congress of Physiol. Sciences*, pp. 435-443. Tokyo.
Kuffler, S. W. and Nicholls, J. G. (1966). *Ergebn. Physiol.* **57**, 1-90.
Kuffler, S. W., Nicholls, J. G. and Orkand, R. K. (1966). *J. Neurophysiol.* **29**, 768-787.
Kuffler, S. W. and Potter, D. D. (1964). *J. Neurophysiol.* **27**, 290-320.
Kurokawa, M. (1960). *J. Neurochem.* **5**, 283-292.
Laborit, H. (1965). *Les Régulations Métaboliques*, pp. 1-498. Masson et Cie, Paris.
Lahiri, S. and Quastel, J. H. (1963). *Biochem. J.* **89**, 157-163.
Lajtha, A., Berl, S. and Waelsch, H. (1959). *J. Neurochem.* **3**, 322-332.
Li, C. and McIlwain, H. (1957). *J. Physiol., Lond.* **139**, 178-190.
Lindan, O., Quastel, J. H. and Sved, S. (1957). *Can. J. Biochem. Physiol.* **35**, 1135-1144.
Lipsett, M. N. and Crescitelli, F. (1950). *Arch. Biochem.* **28**, 329-337.
Machiyama, Y., Balázs, R. and Richter, D. (1967). *J. Neurochem.* **14**, 591-594.
Majchrowicz, E. (1965). *Can. J. Biochem. Physiol.* **43**, 1041-1051.

Mangan, J. L. and Whittaker, V. P. (1966). *Biochem. J.* **98**, 128-137.

McIlwain, H. (1951*a*). *Biochem. J.* **49**, 382-393.

McIlwain, H. (1951*b*). *Br. J. Pharmac. Chemother.* **6**, 531-539.

McIlwain, H. (1953*a*). *Biochem. J.* **53**, 403-412.

McIlwain, H. (1953*b*). *Biochem. J.* **55**, 618-624.

McIlwain, H. (1953*c*). *J. Neurol. Neurosurg. Psychiat.* **16**, 257-266.

McIlwain, H. (1954). *J. Physiol., Lond.* **124**, 117-129.

McIlwain, H. (1956). *Biochem. J.* **63**, 257-263.

McIlwain, H. (1966). In *Biochemistry and the Central Nervous System*, 3rd ed., pp. 1-412. J. and A. Churchill, London.

McIlwain, H. and Gore, M. B. R. (1952). *Biochem. J.* **50**, 24-28.

McIlwain, H. and Greengard, O. (1957). *J. Neurochem.* **1**, 348-357.

McIlwain, H. and Joanny, P. (1963). *J. Neurochem.* **10**, 313-323.

McIlwain, H. and Rodnight, R. (1962). In *Practical Neurochemistry*, pp. 1-296. J. and A. Churchill, London.

Merritt, H. H. and Fremont-Smith, F. (1938). In *The Cerebrospinal Fluid*, p. 28. Saunders, Philadelphia.

Minakami, S., Kakinuma, K. and Yoshikawa, M. (1963). *Biochim. biophys. Acta* **78**, 808-811.

Moss, G. (1964). *Diabetes* **13**, 585-591.

Narayanaswami, A. and McIlwain, H. (1954). *Biochem. J.* **57**, 663-666.

Nicholls, J. G. and Kuffler, S. W. (1964). *J. Neurophysiol.* **27**, 645-673.

Nishimura, K. and Kimura, Y. (1965). *Jap. J. exp. Med.* **35**, 359-370.

Nissl, F. (1898). *Münch. med. Wschr.* **45**, 1023-1029.

Nurnberger, J. I. and Gordon, M. W. (1957). In *Progress in Neurobiology II. Ultrastructure and Cellular Chemistry of Neural Tissue* (H. Waelsch, ed.), pp. 100-138. Hoeber, New York.

Olken, H. (1963). In *Proceedings of the National Aerospace Electronic Conference*, Dayton, Ohio. pp. 364-369.

O'Neal, R. M. and Koeppe, R. E. (1966). *J. Neurochem.* **13**, 835-847.

O'Neill, J. J., Simon, S. H. and Shreeve, W. W. (1965). *J. Neurochem.* **12**, 797-802.

Pappius, H. (1965). In *Progress in Brain Research* (E. D. P. de Robertis and R. Carrea, eds), Vol. 15, pp. 135-154. Elsevier, Amsterdam.

Pappius, H. M. and Elliott, K. A. C. (1956*a*). *Can. J. Biochem. Physiol.* **34**, 1007-1022.

Pappius, H. M. and Elliott, K. A. C. (1956*b*). *Can. J. Biochem. Physiol.* **34**, 1053-1067.

Phillips, C. G. (1956). *Q. Jl. exp. Physiol.* **41**, 58-84.

Piras, M. M. de, and Zadunaisky, J. A. (1965). *J. Neurochem.* **12**, 657-661.

Pope, A. (1958). In *Biology of Neuroglia* (W. F. Windle, ed.), pp. 211-233. Charles C Thomas, Springfield, Illinois.

Post, R. L., Merritt, C. R., Kinsolving, C. R. and Albright, C. D. (1960). *J. biol. Chem.* **235**, 1796-1802.

Quastel, J. H. (1959). In *Proceedings of the Fourth International Congress of Biochemistry, Vienna*, Vol. 3, pp. 90-114. Pergamon Press, London.

Quastel, J. H. and Quastel, D. M. J. (1961). In *The Chemistry of Brain Metabolism in Health and Disease*, pp. 1-170. Charles C Thomas, Springfield, Illinois.

Quastel, J. H., Tennenbaum, M. and Wheatley, A. H. M. (1936). *Biochem. J.* **30**, 1668-1681.

Reading, H. W. (1964). *Nature, Lond.* **203**, 491-492.

Rebhan, I. (1956). *Acta anat.* **27**, 361-386.

Richter, D. (ed.) (1957). In *Metabolism of the Nervous System*, pp. 1-599. Pergamon Press, London.

Richter, D. (1965). *Br. med. Bull.* **21**, 76-80.

Ridge, J. W. (1967*a*). *Biochem. J.* **102**, 612-617.

Ridge, J. W. (1967*b*). *Biochem. J.* **105**, 831-835.
Robertis, E. D. de (1963). *Science, N.Y.* **140**, 300-301.
Robertis, E. D. de (1967). *Science, N.Y.* **156**, 907-914.
Roberts, E. (1956). In *Progress in Neurobiology* (S. R. Korey and J. J. Nurnberger, eds), Vol. 1, pp. 11-25. Hoeber, New York.
Rolleston, F. S. and Newsholme, E. A. (1966). *Biochem. J.* **101**, 41P.
Roots, B. I. and Johnston, P. V. (1964). *J. Ultrastruct. Res.* **10**, 350-361.
Rose, S. P. R. (1965). *Nature, Lond.* **206**, 621-622.
Rose, S. P. R. (1967). *Biochem. J.* **102**, 33-43.
Rossiter, R. J. (1955). *Can. J. Biochem. Physiol.* **33**, 477-479.
Sacks, W. (1957). *J. appl. Physiol.* **10**, 37-44.
Schadé, J. P., Backer, H. van and Colon, E. (1964). In *Progress in Brain Research* (D. Purpura and J. P. Schadé, eds), Vol. 4, pp. 150-175. Elsevier, Amsterdam.
Schadé, J. P. and Baxter, C. F. (1960). *Expl Neurol.* **2**, 158-178.
Schmidt, C. F., Kety, S. S. and Pennes, H. H. (1945). *Am. J. Physiol.* **143**, 33-52.
Schwartz, A. (1962). *Biochem. Pharmac.* **11**, 389-391.
Schwerin, P., Bessman, S. P. and Waelsch, H. (1950). *J. biol. Chem.* **184**, 37-44.
Shanes, A. M. (1958). *Pharmac. Rev.* **10**, 59-164.
Sholl, D. A. (1956). *The Organization of the Cerebral Cortex*, pp. 1-125. Methuen, New York.
Skou, T. C. (1957). *Biochim. biophys. Acta* **23**, 394-401.
Skou, T. C. (1960). *Biochim. biophys. Acta* **42**, 6-23.
Stern, J. R., Eggleston, L. V., Hems, R. and Krebs, H. A. (1949). *Biochem. J.* **44**, 410-418.
Strecker, H. J. (1957). In *Metabolism of the Nervous System* (R. Richter, ed.), pp. 459-474. Pergamon Press, London.
Svaetichin, G., Negishi, K., Fatehchand, R., Drujan, B. D. and Selvin, A. de Testa (1965). In *Progress in Brain Research* (E. D. P. de Robertis and R. Carrea, eds), Vol. 15, pp. 243-266.
Swanson, P. D. (1968). *J. Neurochem.* **15**, 57-67.
Swanson, P. D. and Ullis, K. (1966). *J. Pharmac. exp. Ther.* **153**, 321-328.
Takagaki, G. and Tsukada, Y. (1957). *J. Neurochem.* **2**, 21-24.
Takagaki, G., Hirano, S. and Nagata, Y. (1959). *J. Neurochem.* **4**, 124-134.
Terner, C., Eggleston, L. V. and Krebs, H. A. (1950). *Biochem. J.* **47**, 139-149.
Thomas, J. and McIlwain, H. (1956). *J. Neurochem.* **1**, 1-7.
Tower, D. B. (1954). *J. comp. Neurol.* **101**, 19-51.
Tower, D. B. (1960). In *Structure and Function of the Cerebral Cortex* (D. B. Tower and J. P. Schadé, eds), pp. 411-424. Elsevier, Amsterdam.
Tower, D. B. and Bourke, R. S. (1966). *J. Neurochem.* **13**, 1119-1137.
Tower, D. B. and Elliott, K. A. C. (1952). *Am. J. Physiol.* **168**, 747-759.
Tsukada, Y. and Takagaki, G. (1955). *Nature, Lond.* **175**, 725-726.
Tsukada, Y., Takagaki, G. and Hirano, S. (1958). *J. Biochem. (Tokyo).* **45**, 489-501.
Tsukada, Y., Nagata, Y., Hirano, S. and Matsutani, T. (1963). *J. Neurochem.* **10**, 241-256.
Van Harreveld, A. (1962). *Fedn Proc. Fedn Am. Socs. exp. Biol.* **21**, 659-664.
Van Harreveld, A. (1966). In *Brain Tissue Electrolytes. Molecular Biology and Medicine Series* (E. E. Bittar, ed.), pp. 1-171. Butterworths, London.
Van Harreveld, A., Crowell, J. and Malhotra, S. K. (1965). *J. biophys. biochem. Cytol.* **25**, 117-137.
Varon, S. and McIlwain, H. (1961). *J. Neurochem.* **8**, 262-275.
Victor, J. and Wolf, A. (1937). *Proc. Ass. Res. nerv. ment. Dis.* **16**, 44-58.
Vrba, R., Gaitonde, M. K. and Richter, D. (1962). *J. Neurochem.* **9**, 465-475.
Waelsch, H. (1960). In *Structure and Function of the Cerebral Cortex* (D. B. Tower and J. P. Schadé, eds), pp. 313-327. Elsevier, Amsterdam.
Waelsch, H. and Lajtha, A. (1961). *Physiol. Rev.* **41**, 709-736.

Wallgren, H. (1963). *Ann. Med. exp. Fenn.* **41**, 166-173.
Wallgren, H. and Kulonen, E. (1960). *Biochem. J.* **75**, 150-158.
Weil-Malherbe, H. (1936). *Biochem. J.* **30**, 665-676.
Weil-Malherbe, H. (1938). *Biochem. J.* **32**, 2257-2282.
Wendell-Smith, C. P. and Blunt, M. J. (1965). *Nature, Lond.* **208**, 600-601.
Westrum, L. E. and Blackstad, T. W. (1962). *J. comp. Neurol.* **119**, 281-292.
Whittaker, V. P. (1959). *Biochem. J.* **72**, 694-706.
Whittaker, V. P. and Sheridan, M. N. (1965). *J. Neurochem.* **12**, 363-372.
Whittam, R. (1962). *Biochem. J.* **82**, 205-212.
Windle, W. F. (ed.) (1958). In *Biology of Neuroglia*, pp. 1-340. Charles C Thomas,
    Springfield, Illinois.
Wollenberger, A. (1955). *Biochem. J.* **61**, 68-77.
Woodman, R. J. and McIlwain, H. (1961). *Biochem. J.* **81**, 83-93.
Yannet, H. (1940). *Am. J. Physiol.* **128**, 683-689.
Yoshida, H., Fujisawa, H. and Kajikawa, K. (1963). *Jap. J. Pharmac.* **13**, 297-304.
Zadunaisky, J. A. and Curran, P. F. (1963). *Am. J. Physiol.* **205**, 949-956.

CHAPTER 2

The Biochemistry of Synaptosomes

R. M. MARCHBANKS and V. P. WHITTAKER

*Department of Biochemistry, University of Cambridge,
Cambridge, England*

I. Introduction

When brain tissue is homogenized under relatively mild conditions, the terminal swellings which constitute the presynaptic portions of central synapses are torn away from their axons and postsynaptic attachments and seal up to form small bags about $0\cdot5\text{–}1$ μ in diameter. These bags retain the morphology, transmitter content and many other chemical features expected of presynaptic nerve terminals. They can be isolated by subcellular fractionation techniques in a relatively pure form and from them can be prepared, by further fractionation, samples of terminal cytoplasm, external membranes and the two characteristic organelles of the presynaptic terminal – small mitochondria and synaptic vesicles. The relationship of the detached endings to the intact presynaptic terminals is somewhat similar to that of microsomes to cisternae of the endoplasmic reticulum and for this reason they have been called synaptosomes (Whittaker *et al.*, 1964).

Synaptosomes came to be discovered as a result of attempts to learn more about the molecular mechanisms involved in the storage and release of transmitter substances. Chemical transmission is now recognized as the main (though not necessarily the only) way by which nerve cells communicate with each other or with the gland or muscle cells which some of them control. Nerve impulses travelling down axons from the cell bodies of excited cells are in general unable, of themselves, to excite (or depress) the next cell; they do so by causing the release, from a store in the presynaptic nerve terminal, of a specific chemical transmitter substance, which, diffusing across the synaptic cleft, lowers (or in some cases raises) the membrane potential of the postsynaptic cell. Depolarization of the latter, if great enough, will cause it to fire; raising the membrane potential (hyperpolarization) depresses its excitability and is the basis of central inhibition.

Current "textbook" concepts of transmitter storage and release are based on two discoveries made about the same time: the discovery that the cytoplasm of the presynaptic nerve terminals contains numerous small vesicles about 500 Å in diameter – the synaptic vesicles already referred to – and the discovery that transmitter is released in small packets or "quanta" rather than molecule by molecule (reviewed by Katz, 1966). It seemed reasonable to put the two findings together and to suggest that the vesicles were the morphological counterparts of the quanta (del Castillo and Katz, 1955; see also de Robertis and Bennett, 1955; Palay, 1956); but questions left unanswered by this hypothesis include, "How does the transmitter get into the vesicle – is it synthesized in the vesicle or is it synthesized in the cytoplasm and taken up by the vesicle?", "How is the transmitter conveyed from the vesicle through the external presynaptic membrane?" and, "How does the arrival of an impulse at the nerve ending induce or facilitate the discharge of the transmitter?"

A critical examination of the various problems involved is beyond the scope of this article. However, it seemed to one of us in 1955-6 (for historical reviews see Whittaker, 1963, 1965a) that the best way of reaching an understanding of the mechanisms of transmitter storage and release might be to use subcellular fractionation techniques to isolate the organelles responsible for transmitter binding and to study the properties of these organelles *in vitro*: the approach was modelled on that of Blaschko *et al.* (1955) in their isolation of catecholamine granules and that of de Duve and colleagues (reviewed by de Duve, 1963-4) in their work on lysosomes.

Possibly the most logical attack would have been to use muscle, since most was known about chemical transmission at the neuromuscular junction, but two factors made this impracticable: the very low concentration of nerve terminals and transmitter in muscle tissue, and the difficulty of homogenizing muscle tissue satisfactorily. More recently, some success has been obtained using the electric organ of *Torpedo*, consisting essentially of stacks of hypertrophied end-plates (Sheridan *et al.*, 1966; Israël *et al.*, 1968). Chemical transmission in brain was at that time less well established than it is now: but the ease of homogenizing brain tissue and a concentration of the transmitter acetylcholine more than ten times greater than in muscle led to the choice of this tissue.

It was already known that acetylcholine existed in homogenates of brain in iso-osmotic media mainly in a particle-bound form in which it was both immune to destruction by cholinesterase and pharmacologically inactive (for review see Feldberg, 1945). Using bound acetylcholine as a marker for the acetylcholine binding sites and succinate dehydrogenase as a mitochondrial marker, it was soon found (Hebb and Whittaker, 1958; Whittaker,

1959) (*a*) that over 70% of the brain acetylcholine remained bound to particulate material after homogenization of brain tissue in 0·32 M sucrose, (*b*) that the acetylcholine-containing particles sedimented with mitochondria on differential centrifugation but could be readily separated from them and from other particulate material by density gradient centrifuging, and (*c*) that the particles concerned were also rich in choline acetyltransferase (E.C. 2.3.1.6), a normally soluble enzyme which existed in the particles in an occluded or latent form. Both acetylcholine and the enzyme were released by procedures known to break down lipoprotein membrane barriers to free diffusion, just as were acid hydrolases from lysosomes.

These findings were greatly clarified by the discovery, using improved electron microscopic techniques, that the fraction rich in bound acetyl-choline consisted largely of detached presynaptic nerve terminals (Whittaker, 1960; Gray and Whittaker, 1960, 1962). The presence of acetylcholine in the fraction was now readily explained: it evidently represented the pre-synaptic store of the transmitter. Since there is no reason to believe that the nerve terminals of cholinergic cells are preferentially preserved during homogenization, one would expect the synaptosome fraction to be rich in other putative transmitters: Whittaker (1959) had indeed found this to be so for 5-hydroxytryptamine and it could be inferred from the work of Chrusćiel (1960) that the preparation was also rich in noradrenalin. Krnjević and Whittaker (1965) further showed that the glutamate and γ-aminobutyrate (GABA) content of the fraction was sufficient to sustain a transmitter role for these aminoacids.

Recent work (described in Section III. B) has confirmed what was apparent from the initial biochemical and morphological observations, namely that synaptosomes are, for the most part, sealed structures with an intact external membrane. They thus provide an interesting model system with which to investigate the properties of neuronal membrane, unencumbered by glial barriers. Since they possess both mitochondria and cell sap, they may be expected to possess metabolic properties similar to those of slices and whole cell preparations, and these too have been the subject of recent investigation (Section III. D. 1).

The phenomenon of bound acetylcholine has, however, been found to be more complex than simply the sequestration of a soluble constituent within a sealed bag of cytoplasm (Section III. C. 2). It was early recognized (Brodkin and Elliott, 1953; Whittaker, 1959) that there was more than one form of bound acetylcholine. A number of mild disruptive treatments such as would be expected to break down lipoprotein membranes (e.g. freezing and thaw-ing, treatment with cobra venom, suspension in hypo-osmotic sucrose) release only part (about half) of the bound acetylcholine of the synaptosome fraction; more vigorous treatments (e.g. with ether and other surface-active substances) release all of it. In considering the partial release of a potentially soluble constituent one has to distinguish between those processes that affect only part of the population of particles in which the compound is presumed to be sequestrated and those that disrupt one compartment in all the particles but not another. The problem was tackled by Johnson and Whittaker (1963) by following, simultaneously with the release of acetylcholine, the liberation of a soluble cytoplasmic marker, lactate dehydrogenase (E.C. 1.1.1.27). They found that on resuspension in hypo-osmotic media, most (80%) of the lactate dehydrogenase was released while 50% of the acetylcholine remained bound. They noted the presence of few intact synaptosomes but many intact synaptic vesicles and concluded that the bound acetylcholine resistant to osmotic disruption (the "stable bound fraction") was associated with the synaptic vesicles in accordance with the earlier morphological speculations already mentioned. This conclusion was confirmed by Whittaker et al. (1964), who succeeded in obtaining a pure fraction of synaptic vesicles containing bound acetylcholine by centrifugal density gradient separation of osmotically disrupted synaptosome preparations. The osmotically labile fraction of acetylcholine (if conserved by the prior addition of an anticholinesterase to the preparation) and lactate dehydrogenase were recovered in another fraction, containing most of the soluble cytoplasm released from the disrupted synaptosomes.

By contrast, after freezing and thawing many times, only about 50% of both lactate dehydrogenase and acetylcholine was released; many morphologically intact synaptosomes but no free vesicles were present in the preparation. It appeared that the 50% release phenomenon in this case was not explained by the selective opening of one compartment – the cytoplasmic – in virtually all the synaptosomes, but rather by the survival of about half the population in an intact form and the destruction of *both* compartments in the other half. This was confirmed by the finding (Whittaker et al., 1964) that frozen and thawed material, when subjected to density gradient separation, did not yield a vesicle fraction but only fractions of soluble cytoplasm, membrane fragments and intact synaptosomes. Labelling experiments (Section III. C. 2b) have confirmed that two pools of acetylcholine exist in synaptosome preparations, a readily exchangeable cytoplasmic and a hardly exchangeable vesicular.

The localization of choline acetyltransferase within the synaptosome has also proved unexpectedly difficult to establish. Initial studies (Whittaker et al., 1964), with guinea pig preparations showed clearly that the enzyme, in this species, was a soluble constituent of the terminal cytoplasm like lactate dehydrogenase. As discussed more fully in Section III. C. 2c, it is now clear (Fonnum, 1967) that in several other species, the enzyme, though fully soluble at the presumed ionic strength of cytoplasm, is nonspecifically adsorbed on to membranes at the low ionic strengths necessary for the disruption and subfractionation of synaptosomes. It would thus seem that in all species studied acetylcholine is synthesized in the cytoplasm, but no clear indication has yet emerged of either how it is transferred to vesicles or how it is released.

Presynaptic nerve terminals are almost certainly involved in functions other than chemical transmission; through them are exerted trophic effects on postsynaptic structures; they may well, at least during development, contain the chemical sensing mechanisms by which specific neuronal contacts are thought to be made. They are the receiving areas for the material continuously elaborated by the cell bodies of neurones and passed to them by the process of axonal flow; and by modifications of their area of contact with postsynaptic membranes, whether induced by local metabolism or by signals from the soma, they may well be involved in processes of learning and memory. Attempts are being made in several laboratories to utilize synaptosome preparations in studies relevant to these functions: thus they have been used to provide samples of terminal cytoplasm in studies of axonal flow (Barondes, 1966, 1968) and of protein synthesis at nerve endings (Morgan and Austin, 1968) (Section III. D. 2).

A certain proportion of synaptosomes are seen to retain a length of postsynaptic membrane still adhering to their periphery (Section II. A. 3). Thus the preparation may be used, after suitable treatment to reduce the content of presynaptic membranes, as a preparation – though presumably a very impure one – of postsynaptic membrane. This has been utilized in recent studies of the binding of cholinergic blocking agents (de Robertis, 1967). This work is discussed further in Section III. B. 2c.

The presence of synaptosomes in brain fractions was early confirmed by de Robertis and co-workers (de Robertis, 1960; de Robertis et al., 1960, 1961, 1962) who have been among the most active of other groups in this field, and by numerous other laboratories. Subjects of disagreement with these workers will be discussed in the appropriate places. Synaptosomes are formed from nerve-endings of a wide variety of species, including invertebrates (Octopus, Jones, 1967; Florey and Winesdorfer, 1968) bird (pigeon) and mammals. The subject has been several times extensively reviewed from different points of view (Whittaker, 1963, 1964, 1965a, b, 1966a, b, 1967, 1969a, b; Michaelson, 1967; de Robertis, 1967).

II. Preparation and Morphology of Fractions

A. Synaptosomes

1. Homogenization conditions

Methods for the isolation of synaptosomes in good yield and purity have recently been critically reviewed (Whittaker, 1969b). In the initial homogenization, conditions must be adequate to disrupt the total cell mass without causing extensive destruction of nerve-endings. Those selected by Gray and Whittaker (1962) (suspension medium 0·32 M sucrose; tissue concentration 10% w/v; use of a smooth-walled Perspex and glass homogenizer with pestle mechanically driven at 840 rev/min; clearance between pestle and mortar of 0·25 mm at 30 mm diameter) appear to be close to optimum for mammalian brain (Whittaker and Dowe, 1965). Judging by the distribution of markers, cells are at least 85% destroyed and nerve terminals are converted to synaptosomes with not less than 70% and possibly close to 90% efficiency.

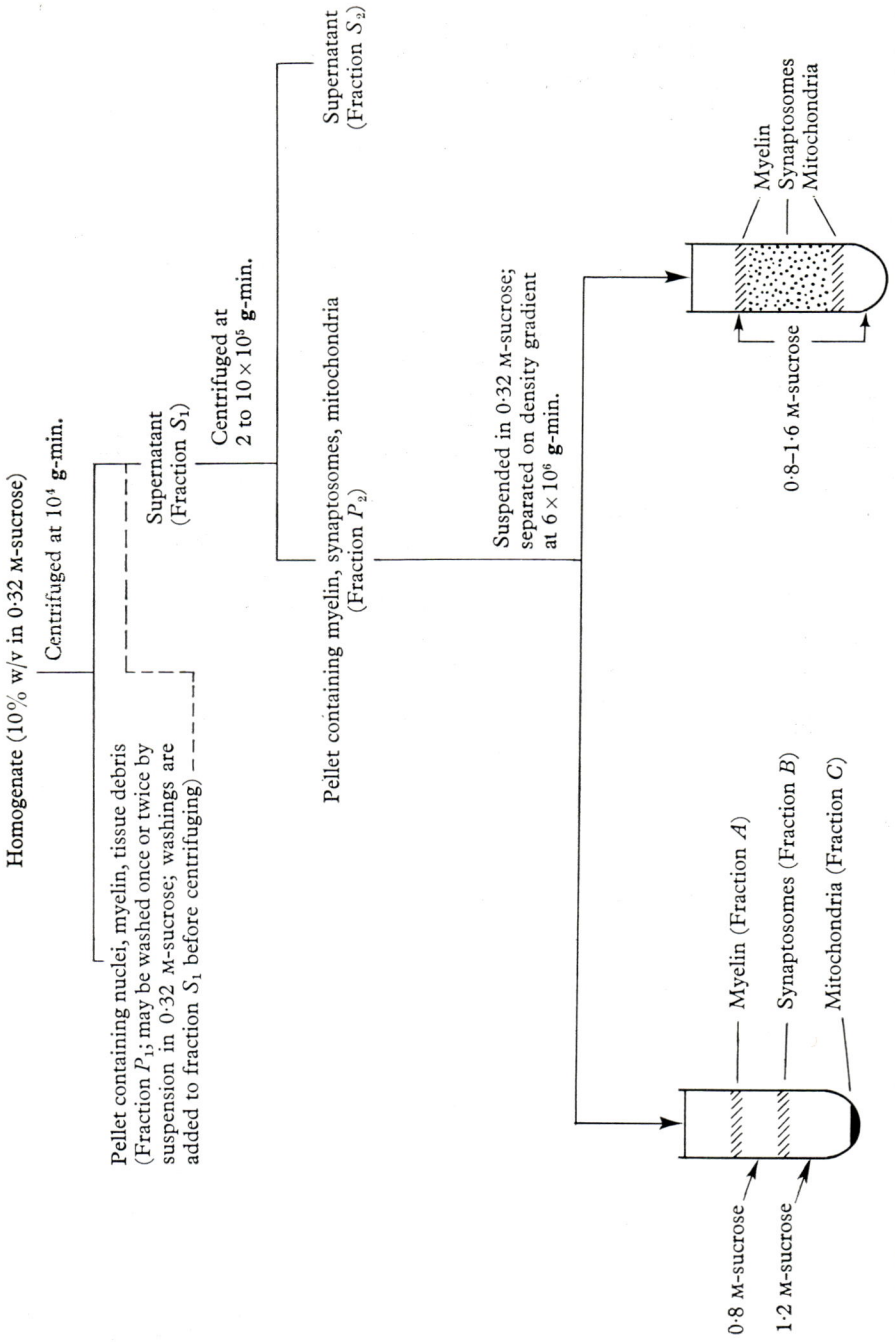

FIG. 1. Methods of preparing fractions enriched in synaptosomes, myelin and mitochondria (After Gray and Whittaker, 1962; Fonnum, 1968).

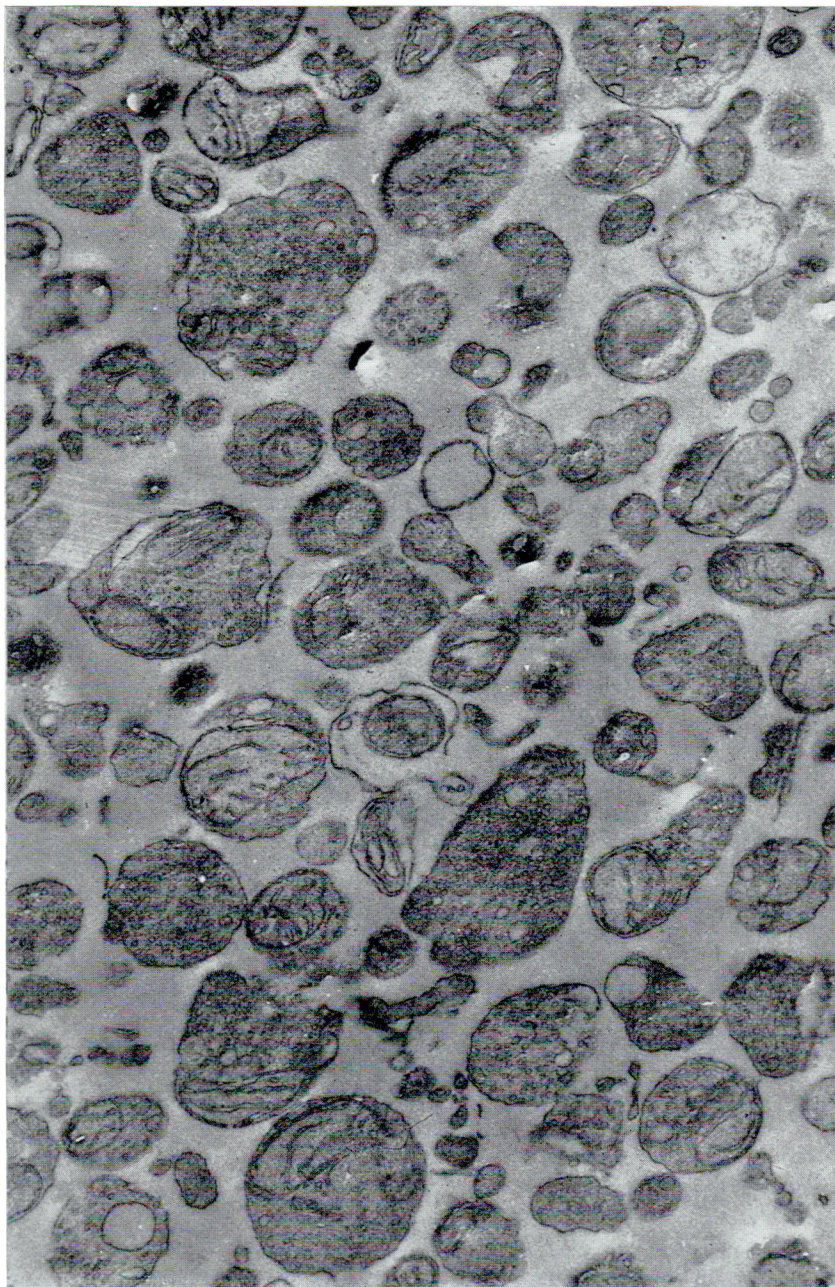

FIG. 2. Preparation of synaptosomes obtained by separation of a crude mitochondrial fraction of rat forebrain on a continuous density gradient (from Whittaker, 1968). × 30 000.

2. Subcellular fractionation

Figure 1 summarizes the fractionation schemes commonly employed in this laboratory. For many purposes, the operationally defined "mitochondrial" fraction (P_2) is an adequate preparation of synaptosomes, especially if it is made from tissue dissected free of most of the white matter, sedimented at low speed and washed to reduce microsomal contamination. Synaptosomes may be further purified (a) by centrifuging fraction P_2 into a simple discontinuous density gradient consisting of equal layers of 0·8 and 1·2 M sucrose that have been allowed to diffuse into each other for at least 1 hr before use (Gray and Whittaker, 1962) or (b) by separating fraction P_2 on a continuous density gradient (Fonnum, 1968). The synaptosome fractions corresponding to 1·15 to 1·25 M sucrose are particularly homogeneous (Whittaker, 1968) (Fig. 2). A fraction lighter than synaptosomes contains most of the myelin originally present in fraction P_2; the mitochondria sediment to regions denser than 1·25 M sucrose.

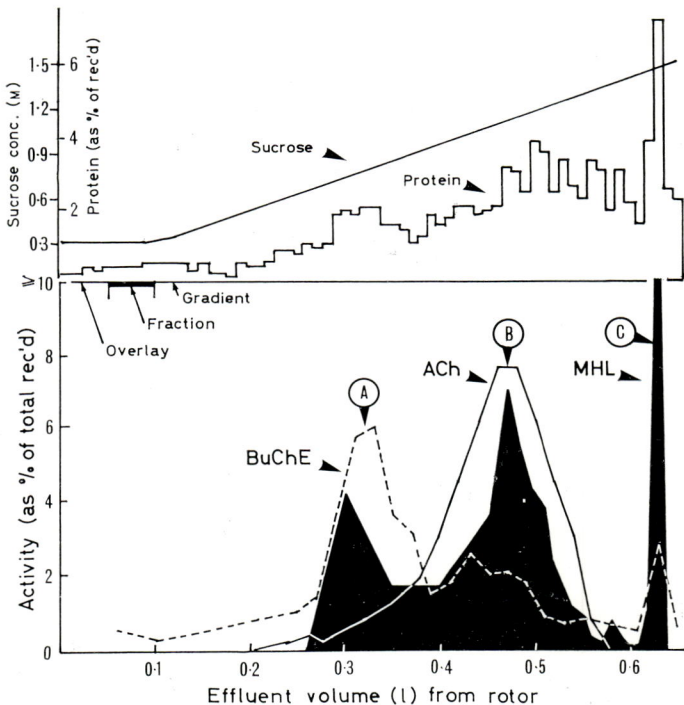

FIG. 3. Separation of synaptosomes (peak B) from mitochondria (peak C), myelin (peak A) and glial elements (peak A and shoulder) by zonal centrifuging. Malate hydro-lyase (E.C. 4.2.1.2) (MHL, black), acetylcholine (ACh, continuous line), and butyrylcholinesterase (BuChE, broken line) were used as mitochondrial, synaptosomal and glial markers respectively (E. K. Miller and V. P. Whittaker, unpublished). 50 ml. of fraction P_2 (Fig. 1) equivalent to 21 g of tissue and an overlay of 50 ml. of 0·32 M-sucrose were loaded on to a continuous sucrose density gradient in a BXIV rotor and centrifuged at 30 000 rev/min for 13 hr. Part of the mitochondrial (C) fraction was allowed to sediment on to the walls of the rotor and the MHL associated with it is not included in the graph.

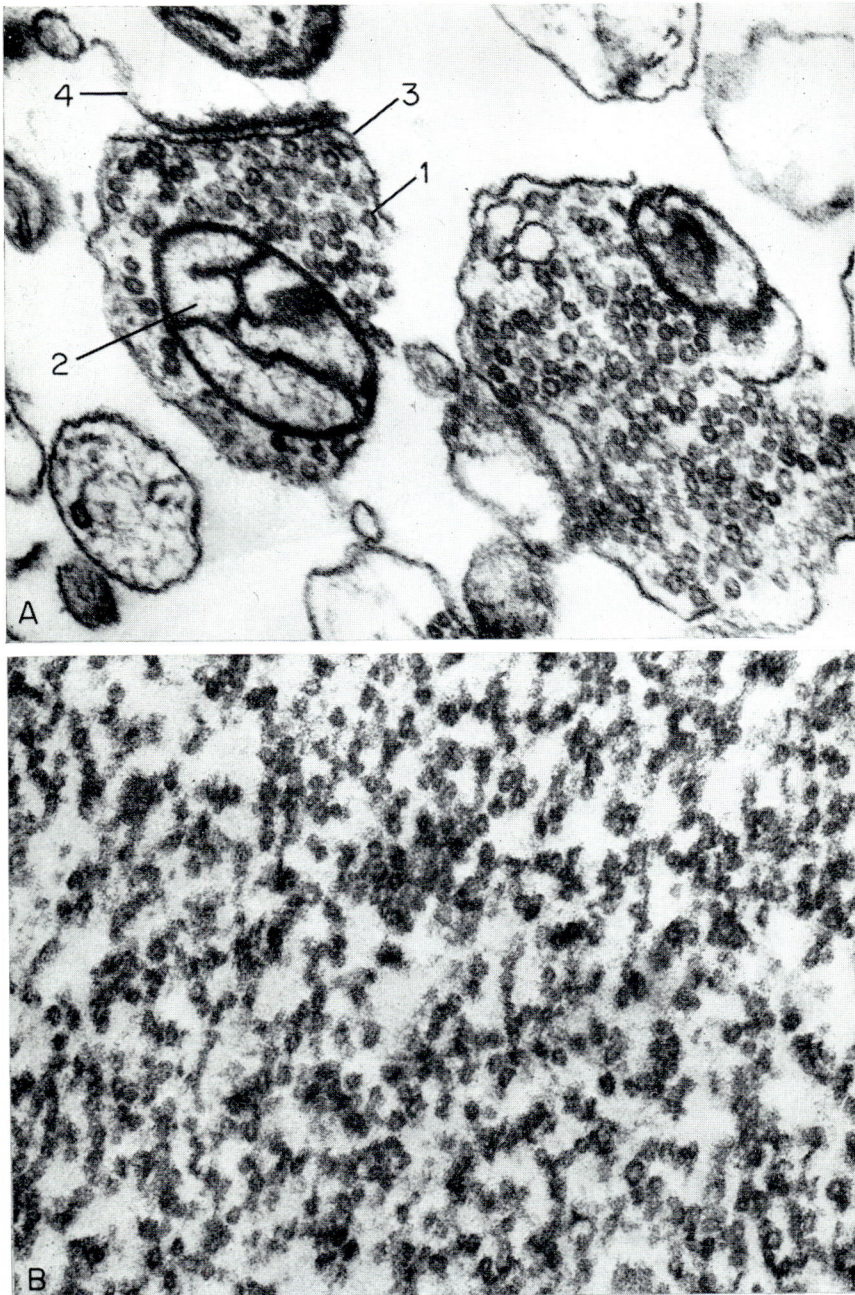

FIG. 4. A, Synaptosome showing (1) synaptic vesicles, (2) intraterminal mitochondrion, (3) external membrane, (4) postsynaptic adhesion. B, Isolated synaptic vesicles (fraction D). For details see Whittaker and Sheridan (1965). × 70 000.

Recently, synaptosomes have been successfully separated on a large scale using a zonal rotor (Fig. 3).

3. Morphology

Synaptosomes appear in thin sections (Fig. 4A) as membrane-bound sacs of cytoplasm containing numerous synaptic vesicles and one or more small mitochondria.

The yield of synaptosomes from guinea pig cortex is about $4 \times 10^{11}/g$ of cortex (Clementi et al., 1966) which is in good agreement with the estimated number of nerve endings in the tissue. The contribution by volume of the component organelles in synaptosomes is shown in Table I.

TABLE I

The contribution by volume of the components of synaptosomes

Component	Mean proportion by volume (%)
External membrane	8
Clear cytoplasm	64
Mitochondria	24
Synaptic vesicles	4

B. Subfractions of synaptosomes

1. Disruption

The best method so far found for releasing the component organelles from synaptosomes is suspension in water or very dilute buffer solution. Studies of the deocclusion of lactate dehydrogenase (R. M. Marchbanks, unpublished) show that when synaptosomes are rendered hypo-osmotic without the mechanical disturbance attendant on suspension in water, the external membrane becomes temporarily permeable to substrates but this normally soluble enzyme does not diffuse out. When equilibrium is reached, the external membrane reseals and the enzyme becomes re-occluded. It is therefore thought that the mechanical agitation of the synaptosomes accompanying suspension in water is partly responsible for the irreversible disruption of the external membrane in its stretched or weakened state.

Care must be taken not to allow the pH or ionic strength to fall too much during disruption otherwise considerable nonspecific adsorption of basic proteins from the cytoplasm into membranes may occur (Fonnum, 1967). The conditions shown in Fig. 5 (2 ml water/amount of pellet derived from 1 g of brain tissue) appear to be optimal for guinea pig preparations, but for rat synaptosomes, Potter (1968) recommends suspension in 1 mM K/PO$_4$ buffer, pH 7·2, to reduce nonspecific adsorption of choline acetyltransferase.

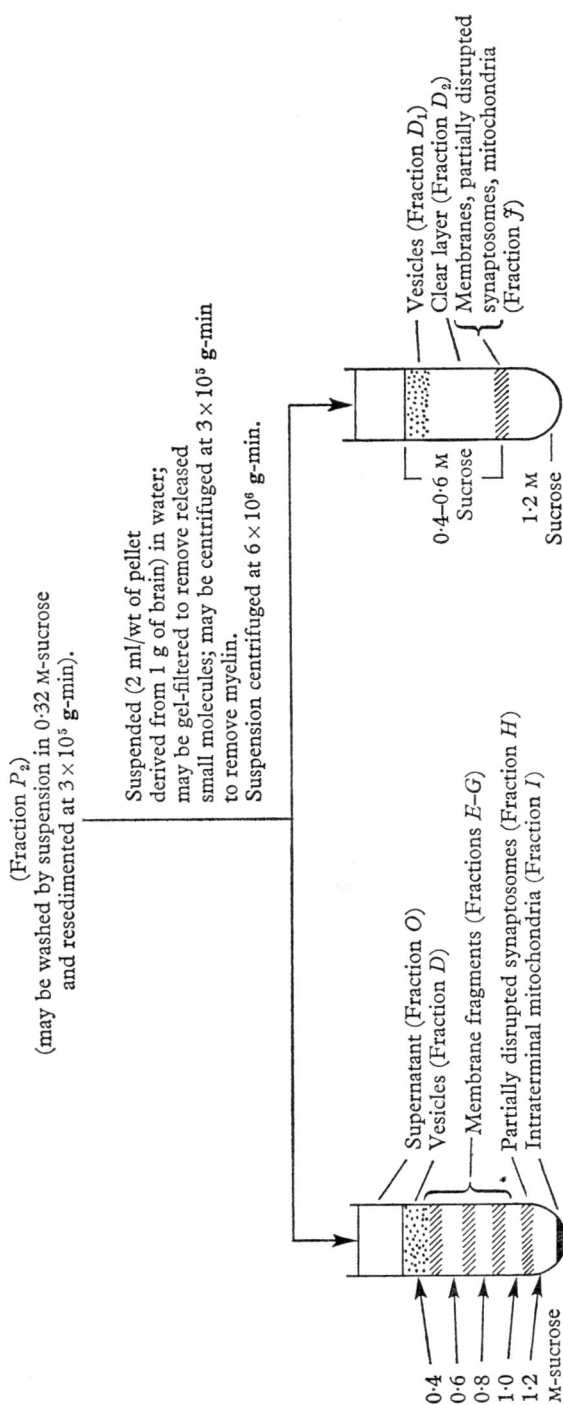

FIG. 5. Separation of synaptosomes into component organelles (Whittaker *et al.*, 1964; Whittaker and Sheridan, 1965). A purified synaptosome preparation may be substituted for fraction P_2 (Hosie, 1965). The presence of much myelin reduces the effectiveness of the separation.

C

2. Fractionation

The disrupted synaptosomes are readily separated into a number of sub-fractions by density gradient centrifuging (Fig. 5) using either discontinuous or continuous gradients. On a discontinuous gradient consisting of layers of sucrose differing in concentration by 0·2 M and ranging from 0·4 to 1·2 M, four white to tan-coloured layers (fractions E–H, Fig. 5) and a pellet (fraction I) of particulate material are obtained, surmounted by a hazy blue layer D and a clear top zone (O). On a continuous gradient ranging from 0·4–0·5 M superimposed on 1·6 M sucrose, the layer corresponding to D is more spread out and can be separated into a faintly hazy layer (D_1), and an almost clear layer (D_2). The material corresponding to fractions E–I collects in a single band (J).

3. Morphology

Fractions D and D_1 consist of rather pure fractions of synaptic vesicles (Fig. 4B). Fractions E–G contain smooth membrane fragments of increasing sizes, fraction H, partially disrupted synaptosomes with intact vesicles and intraterminal mitochondria, fraction I, small mitochondria. Fraction O is devoid of organized lipoprotein membrane structures and in negative staining shows a staining pattern typical of soluble protein.

The identification of these fractions has been aided by chemical characterization. Fractions E–G contain components which would be expected to be present in the external synaptosome membrane (Section III. B. 2); these are highest in specific concentration in fraction G which is morphologically the most homogeneous and whose membranes most resemble synaptosome "ghosts". Fraction E probably contains most of the microsomal contaminations originally present in fraction P_2. Fraction F contains many non-vesicular fragments which may be short lengths of terminal axon, detached post-synaptic membranes or strands of mucoid material.

Fraction O contains about 75% of the soluble constituents of terminal cytoplasm (such as lactate dehydrogenase): the remaining 25% is distributed in decreasing amounts down the gradient; evidently diffusion equilibrium is not attained during the separation. There is little evidence of a second peak of any of these components in fraction H even when care is taken to further disrupt the fractions with detergent, showing that few if any synaptosomes escape with an intact external membrane though many of them are clearly far from being totally disrupted. This tendency of the contents of synaptosomes to "hang together" even after disruption suggests that the cytoplasm must have a gel-like consistency, or there may be some kind of reticulum holding the vesicles together.

The "O–I" gradient thus provides fractions containing all four of the component parts of synaptosomes, cell sap (fraction O) vesicles (fraction D), external membranes (fraction G) and intraterminal mitochondria (fraction I). Fraction H contains elements also present in fractions D, G and I but not O. The distribution of substances in the gradient can thus give much information as to their compartmentation within the synaptosome.

de Robertis and co-workers have used a differential centrifugation procedure to isolate vesicles from hypo-osmotically treated synaptosomes (de Robertis et al., 1963). In our hands this procedure yields an impure vesicle preparation (cf. discussion by Whittaker, 1964, 1965a; Whittaker et al., 1964; Whittaker and Sheridan, 1965, and by Germain and Proulx, 1965; Wiegandt, 1967). It is interesting that de Robertis and his co-workers now concede the necessity for a density gradient step in the production of homogeneous vesicle preparations (Lapetina et al., 1967, 1968). Presumably earlier work from this group on the composition of "vesicles" will have to be re-evaluated.

III. Biochemical Properties of Synaptosomes*

A. General considerations

The presence of cytoplasm occluded within synaptosomes has consequences for the interpretation of their biochemical analysis. Unless the intraterminal cytoplasm is markedly different from the rest of the cytoplasm of the nerve cell, and there is no evidence at present to suggest that it is not, then synaptosomes will always be found to contain typically cytoplasmic constituents.

Since in the density gradient synaptosomes are separated from myelin and mitochondria, the cytoplasmic constituents will appear to be concentrated in synaptosomes relative to the crude mitochondrial fraction. The term "concentrated" is perhaps unfortunate since it implies that the synaptosome and, hence, preterminal region is richer in such constituents than other regions of the nerve cell cytoplasm. There is no convincing evidence that this is so for any constituent under review; however, the usage is very common in publications relating to synaptosomes, and no attempt will be made here to impose a more informative terminology.

B. Properties of synaptosomal membranes

1. Functional properties of the synaptosomal limiting membrane

The integrity of the external synaptosome membrane is such as to retain the K^+ and Na^+ of synaptosomes when the latter are submitted to gel-filtration through a Sephadex column provided the column is equilibrated and eluted with a solution iso-osmotic to the synaptosome suspension. When the Sephadex columns are eluted hypo-osmotically the synaptosomes rupture and lose their internal Na^+ and K^+ which is then retained on the column (Marchbanks, 1967a).

This procedure has been found to be very useful in separating synaptosomes from their suspension medium and thus allowing analysis of their

---

* Abbreviations used: adenosine triphosphate, ATP; coenzyme A, CoA; γ-aminobutyrate, GABA; glutamate decarboxylase, GAD.

contents. By using these techniques it can be shown that K^+ and Na^+ and other small molecules will diffuse across the limiting membrane into the cytoplasmic space at rates comparable to their permeation of other biological membranes. This suggests that the limiting membrane is substantially intact otherwise faster rates of diffusion would be observed. The space inside the synaptosome occupied by these substances can be calculated. Purified mitochondria did not contain K^+ or Na^+ which could be released by hypo-osmotic column treatment so the intraterminal mitochondria are not thought to contribute to the synaptosomal space measured in this way. When allowance is made for the volume occupied by the intraterminal mitochondria the space inside the synaptosome approximates to the volume of the intra-synaptosomal cytoplasm calculated from the size distribution of synaptosomes (Marchbanks, 1966a, 1967a).

Recent results in this laboratory suggest that the synaptosome limiting membrane is not only intact, but also functionally competent with regard to choline transport. Synaptosomes incubated at 25° with glucose and succinate will take up choline and maintain concentrations of it greater than three times that in the external medium (Marchbanks, 1968b). The uptake mechanism is carrier mediated with a half-saturation concentration of choline approximately equal to that found in cerebral cortex slices (Schuberth et al., 1966). Choline uptake is dependent on the presence of external Na^+, and inhibited by hemicholinium and high K^+ concentrations. Similar results regarding choline uptake into synaptosomes have been reported by Potter (1968). The qualitative and quantitative similarities of the choline uptake process in synaptosomes to that found in more organized tissues such as cortex slices and erythrocytes imply that in this respect the limiting membrane of a substantial fraction of the synaptosomes is fully functional. However, it has not yet been established that active transport of Na^+ and K^+ occurs in isolated synaptosomes.

2. Constitution of synaptosome membranes

a. Enzymic

The composition of the limiting membrane and other membranes of synaptosomes has been investigated by hypo-osmotic disruption followed by density gradient centrifugation to separate the limiting membrane from synaptic vesicles, membranes and other fragments as described in Section II. B. There is agreement that synaptosomes are rich in Na^+–K^+ stimulated ATPase (E.C. 3.6.1.3) (Hosie, 1965; Albers et al., 1965; Kurokawa et al., 1965; Bradford et al., 1966). On disruption, the Na^+–K^+ stimulated ATPase is recovered in the fractions thought to be composed mainly of separated external membranes (especially fraction G) (Hosie, 1965; Albers et al., 1965). The synaptic vesicle fraction contains an ATPase but this is not stimulated by Na^+ and K^+ (Hosie, 1965; Germain and Proulx, 1965). A 2:4-dinitrophenol-stimulated ATPase is found in the fraction containing the intraterminal mitochondria. The presence of Na^+–K^+ stimulated ATPase in fractions derived from the external membrane is consistent with the role of this enzyme in the active transport of sodium and potassium, and indicates the existence of these processes at the pre-synaptic terminal.

The enzyme acetylcholinesterase (E.C. 3.1.1.7) is also associated with the synaptosome limiting membrane and is recovered in the external membrane fractions after hypo-osmotic disruption and density gradient separation (Whittaker et al., 1964; Arnaiz et al., 1967). It does not seem to be associated with synaptic vesicles (see also Section III. C. 2d).

K^+-stimulated-p-nitrophenyl phosphatase appears to be bound to the synaptosome limiting membrane (Arnaiz et al., 1967). Salganicoff and de Robertis (1965) find that glutamine synthetase (E.C. 6.3.1.2) is principally concentrated in the microsome fraction, but in a later paper (Arnaiz et al., 1967) these workers claim that there is some of this enzyme bound to synaptic membranes. After hypo-osmotic disruption glutamine synthetase equilibrates in the density gradient at sucrose molarities slightly higher than acetylcholinesterase. However, Sellinger and Verster (1962) noted that the enzyme is only very weakly bonded to membranous elements.

b. *Lipids and proteins*

Lipids are important components of biological membranes and the lipid composition of synaptosomal membranes has been investigated in a number of laboratories. Synaptosomes themselves contain all the usual phospholipids, and are to be distinguished from myelin by their low cerebroside content, and from mitochondria by the relatively low amounts of cardiolipin present (Eichberg et al., 1964). Gangliosides are present in the synaptosome fraction in about the same amounts as the microsome fraction (Wolfe, 1961; Eichberg et al., 1964; Seminario et al., 1964; Brunngraber et al., 1967). A report of the occurrence of proteolipid in synaptosome membrane fractions has appeared (Lapetina and de Robertis, 1968). These workers consider that the proteolipid is located in the junctional complex (post-synaptic membrane), and furthermore that the cholinergic receptor presumed to be present in the junctional complex is composed of proteolipid (de Robertis et al., 1967a; see also next section). The acetylcholine stimulated incorporation of phosphate into phosphatidic acid in brain (Hokin and Hokin, 1958) is found principally in the synaptosome fraction (Durell and Sodd, 1966).

Gangliosides have been implicated in a number of neural phenomena: the restoration of the metabolic response of stored brain slices to electrical stimulation (Balakrishnan and McIlwain, 1961), the binding of tetanus toxin (van Heyningen, 1963), and other pharmacological agents (Albers and Koval, 1962). The location of gangliosides in the synaptosome is therefore of some interest. Burton et al. (1964) proposed that the synaptic vesicle fraction is rich in gangliosides, and suggested a role for them in the binding of acetylcholine to or within the vesicles (see Section III. C. 2b). However, Whittaker (1966a), Wiegandt (1967) and Lapetina et al. (1967) were able to demonstrate significant ganglioside concentrations only in the separated external membrane fraction.

The proteins of synaptosome membranes and other subcellular fractions from rat brain have been separated by acrylamide gel electrophoresis. Most fractions showed a complex spectrum of proteins and it is interesting that the protein composition of synaptic vesicles was found to have similarities with that of the microsomal fraction (Cotman and Mahler, 1967). The turnover time of the proteins of synaptic membranes and synaptic vesicles has been investigated by von Hungen *et al.* (1968). Of particular interest is the observation that the proteins of both synaptic membranes and synaptic vesicles have similar turnover times of about 21 days. This indicates that the protein of synaptic vesicles is not usually destroyed during the process of discharge of transmitter substance.

c. Drug binding

The post-synaptic membrane, and associated structures which are often found adhering to synaptosomes, have been the object of some recent studies in this respect. By treating the nerve ending membrane fraction with Triton X-100 the nerve ending membrane is solubilized, and the post-synaptic membrane may be separated (de Robertis, 1967). The separated post-synaptic membrane fragments retain the capacity to bind cholinergic blocking agents such as dimethyl-D-tubocurarine-^{14}C, but the acetyl-cholinesterase activity is lost. The implication is that this preparation of postsynaptic membrane is enriched in the cholinergic receptor site. However, the evaluation of this interesting finding should be undertaken with caution since the ability of a fraction to bind tubocurarine derivatives does not necessarily indicate the presence of cholinergic receptor substances (Ehrenpreis, 1964). It is noteworthy that in cat cerebral cortex dimethyl-D-tubocurarine and hexamethonium are ineffective in preventing the excitatory effects of acetylcholine applied iontophoretically to cholinoceptive cells (Krnjević and Phillis, 1963); thus one would not expect to find tubocurarine-sensitive cholinergic receptor sites in cortex. Finally, if the tubocurarine binding material were the cholinergic receptor it would be expected that the binding of tubocurarine would be inhibited by acetylcholine at a concentration ratio of acetylcholine to D-tubocurarine similar to that found necessary to overcome the tubocurarine block in more intact preparations. A concentration of acetylcholine of 60 μM is necessary to cause a 50% contraction of the frog rectus abdominis muscle in the presence of 5 μM D-tubocurarine; thus the concentration ratio of acetylcholine necessary to overcome D-tubocurarine blockade is of the order of 10 (van Maanen, 1950). The ratio of acetylcholine concentration to that of dimethyl-D-tubocurarine necessary to cause 50% inhibition of the dimethyl-D-tubocurarine binding observed by de Robertis *et al.* is about 10^6 (Azcurra and de Robertis, 1967).

C. Chemical transmitter systems

1. General considerations

At least three processes are envisaged as taking part in chemical transmitter metabolism: (i) synthesis, which may or may not occur in the preterminal region; (ii) storage in some form readily available for release on the arrival of an action potential in a manner consistent with the physiological observations (including quantal release); (iii) inactivation or removal of transmitter substance after release, in order to terminate transmitter action.

The synaptosome preparation has been used as a source material in the search for unknown transmitters (Krnjević and Whittaker, 1965), but the principal line of investigation has been to examine the properties of the components of known transmitter systems, particularly acetylcholine. This approach involves the demonstration that the putative transmitter is present in synaptosomes; this in itself is not, however, particularly good evidence for a role in chemical transmission since the synaptosome contains numerous compounds as a consequence of its content of soluble cytoplasm. Further fractionation, principally of hypo-osmotically disrupted synaptosomes on an "O–I" density gradient (see Section II. B) gives information regarding the intraterminal localization. In the case of acetylcholine (see next section) a sharp localization is found in the synaptic vesicle fraction. In most investigations of other putative transmitter substances a specifically vesicular location is not nearly so clear cut.

Acetylcholine is rather a special case. It cannot exist in brain homogenates in other than a bound form because of its rapid destruction by acetylcholinesterase, unless an anti-cholinesterase is present. Other putative transmitters are not destroyed anything like so rapidly as acetylcholine. It may be that failure to observe clear-cut localization in vesicles of other transmitters is due to the large amount of free transmitter present which might bind to membranes nonspecifically and in other ways obscure the true localization. In such cases more rigorous criteria of vesicular binding might profitably be adopted. Acetylcholine-containing vesicles will carry their acetylcholine through Sephadex columns (see Section III. C. 2b), and this test could usefully be employed in investigations of the state of vesicular binding of other putative transmitters.

2. *Acetylcholine*

a. *Subcellular distribution*

As briefly explained in the Introduction, acetylcholine exists in the synaptosome in two compartments. This was recognized when it was found that hypo-osmotic disruption of synaptosomes released most of the lactate dehydrogenase but only about 50% of the total acetylcholine (Johnson and Whittaker, 1963). This easily releasable acetylcholine has been called "labile bound" acetylcholine. Further density gradient fractionation of hypo-osmotically disrupted synaptosomes revealed a bimodal distribution of acetylcholine. The acetylcholine was associated with small vesicles (vesicular acetylcholine) approximately 500 Å in diameter found at a sucrose density of 0·4–0·5 M (fraction *D*) and with a fraction which contained incompletely disrupted synaptosomes still containing their vesicles, at sucrose densities of 1·0–1·2 M (fraction *H*) (Whittaker *et al.*, 1964; see Section II. B. 3).

Reports that the acetylcholine-like activity in brain subcellular fractions is due to acetylcarnitine derivatives (Hosein and Proulx, 1964) have not been confirmed. Whittaker and Dowe (1964) separated acetylcarnitine from acetylcholine on ion exchange columns and showed that the acetylcholine-like activity in synaptosomes behaved as acetylcholine on the columns. Material extracted from synaptosomes has actions on the Renshaw cells in the cat spinal cord which are indistinguishable from those of authentic acetylcholine (Ryall *et al.*, 1964a; see also Ryall *et al.*, 1964b).

b. Compartmentation

The gel filtration method described earlier has been used to study the compartmentation of acetylcholine within the synaptosome (Marchbanks, 1967b). The "labile bound" acetylcholine is released from synaptosomes when they are passed through a hypo-osmotic column. It is also released when the synaptosomes are submitted to ultrasonication (Marchbanks, 1968a). In this respect it is similar to the K^+ found in the cytoplasmic space of synaptosomes. The "labile bound" acetylcholine is exchangeable with added radioactive acetylcholine. It seems therefore that "labile bound" acetylcholine is in a free state occupying the cytoplasmic space of synaptosomes. From estimates of the volume of the cytoplasmic space, and assuming that only 15% of the synaptosome population is derived from cholinergic neurons (Whittaker and Sheridan, 1965) the concentration of "labile bound" acetylcholine is estimated at about 0·4 mM (Marchbanks, 1968a).

The number of synaptic vesicles in pure fractions obtained from hypo-osmotically disrupted synaptosomes by sucrose density gradient fractionation has been estimated by a bead-tagging procedure (Whittaker and Sheridan, 1965). From a knowledge of the acetylcholine content of the preparation, and again assuming that 15% of the vesicles are derived from cholinergic neurons the amount of acetylcholine per vesicle is calculated to be about 2000 molecules. This amount is within the range proposed for the number of acetylcholine molecules per quantum (MacIntosh, 1959; Krnjević and Mitchell, 1961).

The main evidence that the acetylcholine found in the synaptic vesicle fraction is actually inside the vesicles and not simply bound to a macromolecule present in the fraction but not detectable in the electron microscope is that the acetylcholine of vesicles may be released by osmotic shock. After isolation on the sucrose density gradient the vesicles are suspended in 0·5 M sucrose. They will carry their acetylcholine through a Sephadex column if the column is equilibrated with 0·4 M sucrose, but they lose their acetylcholine and it is retained on the column if the Sephadex is equilibrated with water (Marchbanks, 1967b). The reason that the vesicles retain their acetylcholine during the initial hypo-osmotic disruption of synaptosomes is presumably that in this circumstance the synaptosome membrane protects the vesicles from the suddenness of the change in osmolarity.

Although it seems clear that the acetylcholine is actually inside the vesicles the possibility cannot be excluded that it is in a bound form inside the vesicles. It can be calculated that the concentration of acetylcholine within the vesicles is about $0 \cdot 1 – 0 \cdot 2$ M. This is some 200–500 times the concentration in the surrounding cytoplasm, and the problem of how this concentration difference is maintained arises.

There has been a report of the uptake of [^{14}C]acetylcholine into vesicles (Burton, 1964), and since gangliosides were present in the preparation, a model involving a ganglioside-acetylcholine complex was proposed to describe acetylcholine storage in vesicles. The weight of evidence is now that gangliosides are not present in synaptic vesicles in significant amounts and it seems likely that the acetylcholine uptake observed was into synaptosomes contaminating the preparation. Synaptosomes or fragments of occluding membrane derived from synaptosomes contain ganglioside and this would thus account for the observation. Attempts in this laboratory to incorporate radioactive acetylcholine into the acetylcholine of vesicles have not met with success. The rate of exchange of vesicular acetylcholine is hardly measurable and certainly much lower than the rate of exchange of labile-bound acetylcholine (Marchbanks, 1968a). This is true under a variety of conditions, e.g. addition of ATP and Mg^{2+}, and elevated temperatures. Even when the "labile bound" pool is labelled and the synaptosomes incubated with glucose, etc., very little exchange is observed. It seems from this that the acetylcholine is not retained within the vesicle by an active transport mechanism and the most likely explanation is that either the acetylcholine exists within the vesicle in a bound non-exchangeable form or that the vesicle membrane is impermeable to acetylcholine. The exact mechanism remains unknown, and it is pertinent at this stage to consider a related problem, the intrasynaptosomal location of choline acetyltransferase.

c. Choline acetyltransferase

This enzyme completes the last stage of synthesis of acetylcholine by transferring the acetyl group from acetyl-CoA to choline. The enzyme is present in relatively high concentration in synaptosomes (Hebb and Whittaker, 1958; de Robertis et al., 1963), and is in an occluded form. However, when the synaptosomes from guinea pig are hypo-osmotically disrupted and the fragments separated by density gradient centrifugation the enzyme is principally in the soluble fraction unassociated with synaptic vesicles (Whittaker et al., 1964). On the other hand, de Robertis et al. (1963), using their differential centrifugation technique for isolating synaptic vesicles from rat brain, found the enzyme associated with the synaptic vesicle fraction. McCaman et al. (1965) suggested that species differences in the degree of binding of choline acetyltransferase to synaptic vesicles would account for the disagreement. Saelens and Potter (1966) using a Ficoll density gradient procedure to separate synaptic vesicles from rat cerebrum also reported that choline acetyltransferase was bound to the synaptic vesicles. Tuček (1966*a*) observed that the degree of binding of choline acetyltransferase to particulate fractions depended on the species investigated. This being so the amount of choline acetyltransferase found in the synaptic vesicle fraction would depend *inter alia* on the degree of contamination of the vesicle fraction by larger membrane fragments (Tuček, 1966*b*). The resolution of these discordant findings is due to Fonnum (1967). He showed that choline acetyltransferase is bound nonspecifically to membrane fragments after hypo-osmotic disruption of synaptosomes. This binding is dependent on ionic strength. At the high ionic strengths presumed to be present inside the presynaptic nerve terminal *in vivo*, most of the enzyme is soluble irrespective of the species studied. However, at the low ionic strengths at which subcellular fractionation is carried out a proportion of enzyme is nonspecifically bound to membrane fragments. Species differences in the amount of enzyme bound also manifest themselves at low ionic strength. Clearly small differences in the ionic strength during hypo-osmotic disruption and the degree of contamination of the vesicle fraction would account for the discrepancies. Therefore, as far as can be determined from subcellular fractionation the enzyme is soluble under conditions expected inside the presynaptic nerve terminal *in vivo*. A similar nonspecific binding at low ionic strength has been observed with the most basic of the five isoenzymes of lactate dehydrogenase (Fonnum, 1967). However, the possibility cannot be entirely discounted that choline acetyltransferase is soluble, but exists loosely bound to the synaptic vesicles, some of which are partially damaged during the preparative procedure, thus releasing the enzyme into the cytoplasm of the synaptosome.

An approach to this problem is to investigate the compartmentation of synthesized acetylcholine. Synaptosomes incubated *in vitro* with glucose, etc., take up radioactive choline by a carrier mediated process (cf. Section III. B. 1). Whether this is a property of synaptosomes derived from cholinergic terminals only is at present not clear. A proportion of the radioactive choline taken up is converted to radioactive acetylcholine. This acetylcholine is found exclusively in the cytoplasmic compartment; very little incorporation of radioactivity has been observed into the acetylcholine of synaptic vesicles (R. M. Marchbanks, unpublished observations). More compelling evidence comes from studies in which radioactive choline is injected intracerebrally into cats which after 1 hr are sacrificed and the synaptosomes and synaptic vesicles isolated. The specific activity of acetylcholine in the synaptosome cytoplasm is consistently higher than that found in the synaptic vesicles (L. W. Chakrin, personal communication). This implies that a major capability to synthesize acetylcholine in the synaptosome resides in the soluble cytoplasmic compartment, although it cannot be excluded that *de novo* synthesis of acetylcholine may also take place at a lower rate in synaptic vesicles.

The role of the cytoplasmic acetylcholine in synaptic transmission remains unknown.

d. Release and inactivation

The factors affecting the release of acetylcholine from either synaptosomes or synaptic vesicles have not been intensively investigated although there are reports of exploratory studies (Takcho et al., 1965; Barker et al., 1967; Marchbanks, 1968a).

The inactivation of acetylcholine is carried out by the enzyme acetyl-cholinesterase, which as already noted is found associated with membrane fragments after hypo-osmotic disruption of synaptosomes (Section III. B. 2a). The enzyme is synthesized within the cell body of the cholinergic cells and is confined within the lumen of the rough-surfaced endoplasmic reticulum (Lewis and Shute, 1966). The enzyme thus appears to be functionally on the outside of the cell which accounts for the stability of free cytoplasmic acetylcholine.

On homogenization of brain and subsequent fractionation the enzyme is found to have rather a broad distribution, occurring in the synaptosome (de Robertis et al., 1962) and microsomal fractions (Aldridge and Johnson, 1959; Toschi, 1959; Hanzon and Toschi, 1961). de Robertis et al. (1962) claim that the distribution of the enzyme indicates two separate populations of synaptosomes in their density gradient. Lighter synaptosomes having greater amounts of acetylcholinesterase are considered to be derived from cholinergic nerve cells, and heavier synaptosomes having less acetyl-cholinesterase are regarded as being derived from non-cholinergic nerve cells. At all events there is agreement that acetylcholinesterase is associated with the neuronal plasma membrane, a localization consistent with its role in the inactivation of acetylcholine. A recent report (Schuberth and Sund-wall, 1967) has suggested that there is an active transport mechanism for uptake of acetylcholine. These authors found that in the presence of the anticholinesterase Sarin acetylcholine is taken up by mouse brain cortex slices. The system has many features in common with that of the choline transport system observed in mouse cerebral cortex slices (Schuberth et al., 1966). The extent to which this process contributes to the physiological inactivation of acetylcholine is at the moment obscure since any acetylcholine outside the cell is rapidly hydrolysed by acetylcholinesterase.

3. Noradrenalin

a. Distribution

Noradrenalin can be visualized in situ in the presynaptic terminals of catecholaminergic neurons by fluorescent histochemical techniques (Hillarp et al., 1965). However, investigations of the content and compartmentation of noradrenalin in synaptosomes has been less extensive than in the case of acetylcholine. Chruściel (1960) observed that the amine was present in the synaptosome fraction from dog hypothalamus; it was also found to be concentrated in the synaptosome fraction from rat brain stem (Potter and Axelrod, 1963; Levi and Maynert, 1964). Masuoka (1965), using a fluorescent histochemical method visualized it in synaptosomes from rat brain stem. Inouye *et al.* (1963*a*) claim that its distribution in rabbit brain fractions parallels that of succinic dehydrogenase (E.C. 1.3.99.1) in the sucrose density gradient (i.e. peaks at a sucrose molarity greater than 1·2). By contrast the peak of acetylcholine activity was found at a sucrose molarity of 1·0.

The existence of a vesicular pool of noradrenalin within the synaptosome has been investigated by several workers. A significant amount of the amine was lost from the particulate material of synaptosomes when they were hypo-osmotically disrupted, but there is no sharp concentration in the small vesicle fractions (Michaelson *et al.*, 1963). Essentially similar results were observed by de Robertis *et al.* (1965) although a rather higher proportion of the total was found to be present in the soluble (supernatant) fraction after hypo-osmotic disruption of synaptosomes from brain and hypothalamus. Maynert *et al.* (1964) used ultrasonication to disrupt synaptosomes, and found a small vesicle fraction containing noradrenalin, although, depending on the degree of ultrasonication considerable amounts of noradrenalin were found either in the heavy particulate fraction or the soluble fraction. The general impression gained from these studies is that there certainly exists a soluble and a particulate pool of the amine in the synaptosome but that the morphological characteristics of the particulate pool are less well defined than in the case of acetylcholine.

b. Compartmentation

The properties of these pools have been investigated by Maynert and Kuriyama (1964) in synaptosomes from rat brain stem and bovine hypothalamus (see also Mirkin *et al.*, 1964). Uptake of noradrenalin into both synaptosomes and isolated "vesicles" was observed, the uptake being greater at 37° than 4°, and inhibited by reserpine in both synaptosomes and vesicles. Rather than propose active amine pumps on both synaptosome and vesicle membranes Maynert and Kuriyama (1964) suggest that their results could be explained by the enzymic formation of a non-diffusible complex of noradrenalin inside the vesicle. Some evidence that noradrenalin forms a ternary complex with ATP and a metal in noradrenalin-containing vesicles from mouse brain stem has been provided by the studies of Colburn and Maas (1965). The considerable literature on noradrenalin-containing vesicles from other tissues has been reviewed by Potter (1966). The extent to which the properties of splenic nerve granules (review: Stjärne, 1966) are similar to noradrenalin-containing particles from brain must await better morphological characterization of the latter.

c. Synthesis and inactivation

The first step in the synthesis of noradrenalin from tyrosine involves the enzyme tyrosine hydroxylase, the amount of which appears to be rate limiting for noradrenalin synthesis in perfused heart preparations (Udenfriend, 1966). Unfortunately there is very little information on the sub cellular distribution of this enzyme. Aromatic amino acid decarboxylase (E.C. 4.1.1.26) which also decarboxylates 5-hydroxytryptophan is located in the soluble supernatant (Bogdanski et al., 1957), but it is present in the synaptosomes (Arnaiz and de Robertis, 1964) presumably in the occluded cytoplasm. The final enzyme in the biosynthetic sequence of noradrenalin is dopamine-β-hydroxylase (E.C. 1.14.2.1); little is known about its localization in brain, but in bovine splenic nerve it appears to be localized in the noradrenalin-containing granules (Stjärne and Lishajko, 1967). Noradrenalin is thought to be inactivated by enzymic methylation outside the nerve cell by catechol-O-methyl transferase (E.C. 2.1.1.6). The enzyme is present in brain and is soluble (Axelrod and Tomchick, 1958); some is present in the synaptosome fraction presumably in association with the occluded cytoplasm (Alberici et al., 1965).

Inside the nerve cell monoamine oxidase (E.C. 1.4.3.4) inactivates noradrenalin by deamination to form 3:4-dihydroxymandelic acid and other products (Kopin and Gordon, 1962). The enzyme is localized in mitochondria in brain (Arnaiz and de Robertis, 1962), and there is evidence that it is associated with the outer membrane of the mitochondria (Tipton, 1967). There is some evidence that an additional route of noradrenalin inactivation is by re-uptake into the nerve cell. Intraventricularly injected tritiated noradrenalin is subsequently found concentrated in synaptosomes (Glowinski and Axelrod, 1966), suggesting that the re-uptake process of noradrenalin takes place at central synapses. An energy-dependent, reserpine-inhibited uptake of noradrenalin into cat brain slices has been observed by Dengler et al. (1962), and in a recent report Bogdanski et al. (1968) have observed an Na$^+$-dependent uptake of noradrenalin into synaptosomes.

4. Dopamine

Dopamine occurs mainly in the caudate nucleus and putamen. Dopamine is less sharply concentrated in synaptosomes from caudate nucleus than is acetylcholine from the same tissue. It more closely resembles the distribution of the cytoplasmic marker lactate dehydrogenase (Laverty et al., 1963). Whether this is due to the fact that free acetylcholine is enzymically destroyed more rapidly than free dopamine, or whether it reflects a genuine difference of subcellular location is not clear. On hypo-osmotic disruption of the synaptosomes 80% of the dopamine was recovered in the supernatant fraction. Although de Robertis claims that dopamine is present in his preparations of synaptic vesicles, there is agreement that dopamine occurs more in the soluble fractions than does noradrenalin (de Robertis, 1966).

5. 5-Hydroxytryptamine

a. Distribution

The presence of this substance at presynaptic nerve terminals in the lower brain stem has been demonstrated in situ by histochemical methods (Hillarp *et al.*, 1965). 5-hydroxytryptamine was shown to be present in the synapto-some fraction and to have a distribution similar to that of acetylcholine (Whittaker, 1959; Michaelson and Whittaker, 1963). A high concentration of 5-hydroxytryptamine relative to protein has been observed in the fraction (P_3) sedimenting at higher centrifugal forces than the crude mito-chondrial fraction from which synaptosomes are usually isolated (Zieher and de Robertis, 1963; Ryall, 1964). By contrast Inouye *et al.* (1962) found 5-hydroxytryptamine in particles which migrated below mitochondria in the density gradient. The reasons for these discrepancies may lie in small differ-ences in technique (discussed at greater length by Whittaker, 1965*a*). It seems that although 5-hydroxytryptamine is present in synaptosomes it may also be associated with other particulate material.

On hypo-osmotic rupture of synaptosomes and subsequent density gradient fractionation, 5-hydroxytryptamine did not appear to be clearly bound to any particular fraction, and substantial amounts were found free (Michaelson *et al.*, 1963). Maynert *et al.* (1964) claim to have isolated 5-hydroxytryptamine-containing vesicles from synaptosomes by ultra-sonic disruption, but as with the previous study substantial amounts were found in the soluble fraction.

Little is known about the properties of the soluble fraction of 5-hydroxy-tryptamine or the putative vesicular bound fractions in synaptosomes, but Robinson *et al.* (1965) have observed an uptake of 5-HT into synaptosomes (see also Inouye *et al.*, 1963*b*).

b. Synthesis and inactivation

The first stage in the synthesis of 5-hydroxytryptamine from L-trypto-phan is the enzymic 5-hydroxylation of the amino acid by tryptophan-5-hydroxylase. On homogenisation of brain 40% of the enzyme can be recovered in the mitochondrial fraction of which about 50% is found in the synaptosome fraction (Grahame-Smith, 1967). Its distribution in the mitochondrial subfraction parallels that of lactate dehydrogenase suggesting that the hydroxylase is in the cytoplasm occluded within the synaptosome.

Aromatic amino acid decarboxylase is thought to carry out the conversion of 5-hydroxytryptophan to 5-hydroxytryptamine and as already noted is a soluble enzyme in the cytoplasm occluded within the synaptosome.

Inactivation of 5-hydroxytryptamine is carried out by monoamine oxidase the subcellular location of which has already been discussed. *N*-acetylation, and further methylation of the 5-hydroxy group have also been proposed as mechanisms of inactivation but little is known about the subcellular dis-tribution of these enzymes.

c. Substance P

The polypeptide vasodilator discovered by Gaddum and Schild (1934) and called substance P seems to be concentrated in synaptosomes (Inouye and Kataoka, 1962; Ryall, 1964; Cleugh *et al.*, 1964).

6. GABA and other amino acids

a. Distribution

GABA is of particular interest because of its presence exclusively (in higher animals) in the central nervous system. GABA as well as some other amino acids (notably alanine and glycine) have a depressant effect when applied iontophoretically to central neurons. Glutamate on the other hand has an excitatory effect (review: Krnjević, 1965). The subcellular distribution of GABA has been examined by Weinstein et al. (1963), and along with glutamate by Ryall (1964). Mangan and Whittaker (1966) studied the distribution of GABA together with glutamate, aspartate, glycine, serine, alanine and threonine. All these workers found GABA associated with the synaptosome fraction, but Ryall observed that the distribution throughout the primary fractions of both glutamate and GABA paralleled that of potassium. He suggested that the GABA and glutamate concentration in synaptosomes simply represented cytoplasmic occlusion. Mangan and Whittaker's (1966) study yielded a similar conclusion for all the amino acids studied. When the synaptosomes were hypo-osmotically disrupted and submitted to further density gradient centrifugation the amino acids were recovered almost entirely in the soluble supernatant.

An evaluation of the role of Na^+-dependent binding of GABA to particulate material in brain subcellular fractions (Sano and Roberts, 1963) is complicated by an admitted heterogeneity of the material in the fractions. An Na^+-activated carrier-mediated transport process of GABA into nerve ending fragments, or microsomes is proposed (Weinstein et al., 1965; Varon et al., 1965).

b. Glutamic decarboxylase (GAD)

This enzyme (L-glutamate-1-carboxy-lyase, E.C. 4.1.1.15) forms GABA from glutamate, is unique to nervous tissue and has been the subject of several studies (review: Whittaker, 1965a). The enzyme is found in crude mitochondrial fractions, but it is generally agreed that GAD does not sediment in the same way as free mitochondria (Løvtrop, 1961; Weinstein et al., 1963; van Kempen et al., 1965; Salganicoff and de Robertis, 1965; Fonnum, 1968). Exactly where it does sediment, and the reasons for it are the subject of some disagreement. Weinstein et al. (1963) report that GAD is present mainly in fractions containing synaptosomes, but its distribution does not exactly parallel that of GABA, being found at sucrose densities slightly greater than that of GABA. Salganicoff and de Robertis (1965) find it concentrated in the heavier synaptosome fraction and suggest that this is because a separation of cholinergic and non-cholinergic synaptosomes has occurred. In the studies conducted by van Kempen et al. (1965) the peak of GAD activity was found at a slightly lower sucrose density (1·2–1·3 M) than that at which peak cytochrome oxidase activity was found. However, Balázs et al. (1966) and Fonnum (1968) found the enzyme at sucrose molarities of 1·1–1·2 M. It is difficult to evaluate these results in terms of synaptosome type differences because, as both van Kempen *et al.* (1965) and Fonnum (1968) noted, the peak enzyme activity moves further down the gradient when the centrifugation period is extended. This could be due to failure to reach equilibrium or to a small density change of the carrier particle perhaps as a result of osmotic dehydration. On hypo-osmotic disruption of synaptosomes most of the GAD is released into the soluble form (Salganicoff and de Robertis, 1965; Fonnum, 1968). The presence of Ca^{2+} causes binding of the enzyme to membrane fragments (Salganicoff and de Robertis, 1965; Fonnum, 1968), but since this binding is not reversible by dilution it is unlikely to exist in the intact synaptosome (Fonnum, 1968).

c. Other enzymes

GABA amino transferase (E.C. 2.6.1.19) which deaminates GABA to succinic semialdehyde is located in mitochondria (Salganicoff and de Robertis, 1965; van Kempen *et al.*, 1965; Balázs *et al.*, 1966). Succinic semialdehyde dehydrogenase (E.C. 1.2.1.16) which completes the GABA shunt by dehydrogenating succinic semialdehyde to succinate is also located in mitochondria (Salganicoff and de Robertis, 1965). The localization of several other enzymes taking part in GABA and glutamate metabolism has been studied (cf. particularly Salganicoff and de Robertis, 1965). Aspartate transaminase (E.C. 2.6.1.1), two iso-enzymes of which exist, is located in both the soluble and mitochondrial fractions (Sellinger *et al.*, 1964; Salganicoff and de Robertis, 1965; Balázs *et al.*, 1966; Fonnum, 1968). Many of the enzymes and substances connected with glutamate metabolism have been examined in subcellular fractions from rat brain by Uyemura *et al.* (1963; reviewed by Tsukada, 1966). In general, their results agree with those of other workers, though exact comparison is difficult because of differences in the fractionation procedure. In considering the possible role at the synapse of glutamate and GABA and the enzymes that synthesize them it should be always remembered that glutamate almost certainly, and GABA probably, have a function in the purely oxidative metabolism of the brain.

D. Complex metabolic functions

1. Respiration

a. Enzymes of glycolysis

Johnson (1960) observed that about 20% of the lactate dehydrogenase of a brain homogenate could be sedimented with the mitochondrial fraction, but was separable from mitochondrial markers such as succinoxidase by further Ficoll density gradient centrifugation. Johnson (1960) suggested that reports of glycolytic activity by brain mitochondria (Balázs and Richter, 1958; Abood *et al.*, 1959) were probably due to contamination of the mitochondrial fraction by the lactate dehydrogenase-containing particles. The lactate dehydrogenase-containing particles were identified as synaptosomes by Gray and Whittaker (1962) and Johnson and Whittaker (1963). The latter showed that the lactate dehydrogenase could be readily released by hypo-osmotic shock, and concluded that lactate dehydrogenase was a soluble enzyme present in the cytoplasm occluded within the synaptosome. Fonnum (1968) has, however, shown that the most basic of the five lactate dehydrogenase iso-enzymes may be nonspecifically adsorbed onto membranes at low ionic strength. This is particularly evident in the pigeon, which has an excess of this iso-enzyme.

With the exception of hexokinase (E.C. 2.7.1.1) (Beattie *et al.*, 1963; Bachelard, 1967) and phosphofructokinase (E.C. 2.7.1.11) (Beattie *et al.*, 1963) the other enzymes of glycolysis are also cytoplasmic, and would therefore be expected to be present in the occluded cytoplasm of the synaptosome. Separation of glycolytic from phosphorylative activity by density gradient fractionation of crude brain mitochondrial preparations was achieved by Tanaka and Abood (1963).

b. Oxygen uptake

Between 40 and 70% of the synaptosomes seen in the electron micro-scope contain mitochondria within them (Whittaker, 1968). In principle therefore a substantial proportion of the synaptosome population should be able to oxidatively metabolize glucose, and perhaps other substrates. A systematic investigation of the ability of synaptosomes to metabolize glucose has not been carried out, but preliminary investigations in this laboratory suggest a considerable capability (R. M. Marchbanks, unpublished observations). Synaptosome fractions were found to respire with glucose as sole substrate, this is in contrast to the mitochondrial fraction which will not respire with glucose as substrate but will respire with succinate. The respiration rate of synaptosomes was found to be optimal when glucose and succinate were used as substrates, and it is about 38% (on a protein basis) of that of guinea pig cortex slices. Addition of high potassium concentrations (100 mM) to the medium caused a small increase in the rate of respiration which was abolished when Ca^{2+} (6 mM) was added to the medium. Hypo-osmotic shock reduced the respiratory rate considerably.

c. Adenosine triphosphate (ATP) and phosphocreatine

Nyman and Whittaker (1963) have estimated the ATP content of synaptosomes. About 50% of the ATP which survives degradation during initial homogenization is found in the synaptosome fraction. Thirty-eight per cent of the total nicotine adenine dinucleotide content of guinea pig brain homogenate was found in the synaptosome fraction (Lindall and Frantz, 1967). The distribution of ATP-creatine phosphotransferase (E.C. 2.7.3.2) in brain subcellular fractions has been investigated by Wood and Swanson (1964), and Swanson (1967). A substantial proportion of the enzyme is associated with particulate material after homogenization of the brain in 0·32 M sucrose. About half of this is found associated with synaptosomes, and the rest with mitochondria. When crude synaptosome fractions are hypo-osmotically ruptured approximately equal proportions are found in the soluble and mitochondrial fractions. The distribution of some of the enzymes concerned with acetyl-CoA synthesis and utilization has been examined by Tuček (1967).

Of the requirements for the production of ATP so far investigated all seem to be present within the synaptosome. Preliminary studies in this laboratory (R. M. Marchbanks, unpublished observations) have shown that when synaptosomes are incubated with glucose, etc. both ATP and phospho-creatine are formed within the limiting membrane. Incubation without added substrate or in a high potassium medium causes falls in the amount of ATP and phosphocreatine produced.

2. Protein synthesis

a. Incorporation of labelled amino acids in vivo

The synaptosome preparation has been exploited in an elegant investigation of the problem of axonal flow by Barondes (1964, 1966, 1968). If protein is synthesized in the nerve cell body, and then transported by axonal flow to the nerve ending it should be possible to demonstrate that the incorporation of radioactivity into soluble proteins from the synaptosome is much slower than that of soluble proteins derived from the nerve cell body, i.e. from brain as a whole, or the soluble high-speed supernatant after homogenization. The specific activity of proteins in brain as a whole reached a peak 2–4 hr after injection, whereas the soluble protein from nerve endings reached a peak at 9–10 days after injection. Barondes was able to demonstrate that the reappearance of monoamine oxide (after irreversible inhibition of the enzyme by β-phenylisopropylhydrazine) in the mitochondria from nerve endings had a similar time course to the appearance of radioactively labelled soluble protein. Barondes concludes that at least some of the soluble and mitochondrial protein of the synaptosome is synthesized in the nerve cell body and transported to the nerve ending by axoplasmic flow. A dissent from this interpretation has been registered by Vrba (1967); his results on [^{14}C]glucose incorporation into protein, though less extensive, in essence agree with those of Barondes, but he prefers to interpret them as indicating nonspecific diffusion into the particulate fractions by high specific activity protein from the supernatant fractions. However, this is not apparent from Vrba's own data (his Table 1, box E), where it is shown that the specific activity of protein in all particulate fractions except P_2 (synaptosomes and mitochondria) is less at 93 hr than it is at 7 hr after injection.

b. Protein synthesis in vitro

In the study by Barondes (1966) the mitochondrial protein (in contrast to the soluble protein) of nerve endings was observed to be quite rapidly labelled, suggesting protein synthesis by the nerve ending mitochondria. Austin and Morgan (1967) observed a linear incorporation of [^{14}C]leucine with no lag period into synaptosomal protein when cerebral cortex slices were incubated under appropriate conditions. Campbell *et al.* (1966) have described an *in vitro* mitochondrial protein-synthesizing system with interesting properties. Bachelard (1966) also observed protein synthesis in isolated mitochondria, but found a rather low rate in isolated synaptosomes.

The question arises whether synaptosomes have a protein-synthesizing ability in addition to that of their intraterminal mitochondria. Although ribosomes cannot be seen in synaptosomes, the latter contain RNA, some of which is released into the soluble fraction on hypo-osmotic disruption and the rest found attached to membrane fragments (Austin and Morgan, 1967). Furthermore, synaptosomal RNA is quite rapidly labelled with no lag period when [^{14}C]orotic acid is intracerebrally injected (Baláas and Cocks, 1967). Morgan and Austin (1968) examined protein synthesis in isolated synaptosomes and subsequently fractionated the hypo-osmotically disrupted synaptosomes on a density gradient. There was incorporation of radioactivity into the protein of the membrane fragments, and the soluble fraction, rather less into the protein of the intraterminal mitochondria. Cycloheximide (which inhibits eukaryotic ribosomal protein synthesis) inhibited the incorporation into the soluble and membrane proteins but hardly into the mitochondrial proteins. Chloramphenicol, which inhibits bacterial and mitochondrial protein synthesizing systems, affected only the incorporation of radioactivity into the mitochondrial protein. It seems probable, therefore, that synaptosomes possess the capability to synthesize some of their soluble and membrane protein *in situ*. Von Hungen *et al.* (1968) also conclude that the nerve-ending region has the capacity to synthesize protein.

This raises the question of the relative importance of axonal flow and *in situ* synthesis in the protein economy of the nerve terminal. Gordon *et al.* (1968) suggest that protein may be synthesized in the nerve cell body and then transported to the preterminal region where lysosomal activity would degrade it to amino acids which could then be used for protein synthesis by local mechanisms. They showed that there is some lysosomal (acid phosphatase, E.C. 3.1.3.2) activity in synaptosome fractions as have other workers (Whittaker, 1959; Mordoh, 1965). Although all the components necessary for the scheme proposed by Gordon *et al.* (1968) are present in the synaptosome, it is by no means clear that they function *in situ* in the manner proposed. The simpler assumption is that proteins in the preterminal region arise both by axonal flow and by local synthesis, the type and amounts of protein in each case being at present unknown.

Incorporation of [^{14}C]amino acids into proteolipid *in vitro* has been examined by Mokrasch (1966); the most rapid incorporation was found in what is termed the medium density mitochondrial fraction – which is probably mainly synaptosomes.

The finding that synaptosomes can synthesize protein *in vitro* reveals a different order of biochemical complexity and metabolic competency than was originally envisaged when these particles were first isolated. As a result of these findings the possibility of investigating *in vitro* the relationship of protein synthesis to synaptic function now exists.

IV. Developmental, Pathological and Pharmacological Aspects

There are two approaches by which the synaptosome preparation may be utilized to investigate abnormal conditions in brain. Synaptosomes can be isolated from the brains of animals in which there is some pathological or pharmacologically induced disturbance, and their content of transmitter substances and the relevant enzymes investigated. Alternatively the effects of pharmacological agents on various properties of isolated synaptosomes can be examined *in vitro*. Studies on abnormal aspects of brain function in which synaptosomes have been used have not been extensive, and in general the former approach has been adopted.

The second approach demands a more complete understanding of the properties of the synaptosome preparation than is currently available. However, as knowledge of the biochemistry of synaptosomes progresses it seems likely that useful knowledge about the causes of pathological and pharmacologically induced malfunction will be gained increasingly from studies of pathological agents on the behaviour of isolated synaptosomes *in vitro*.

Abdel-Latif and Abood (1964) studied the glycolytic, phosphorylative and ATPase activity in subcellular fractions from the brain of embryonic and 10-day-old rats. Synaptosomes from embryonic brain did not travel as far down the Ficoll density gradient as did synaptosomes from 10-day-old brain. ATPase activity was concentrated in the synaptosome fraction and was much greater in the synaptosomes from 10-day-old brain than in those from embryonic brain. In a further study (Abdel-Latif *et al.*, 1967) it was observed that although the amount of protein in synaptosomes increased gradually from five days before birth to 25 days after, there was an abrupt increase in the activity of Na^+–K^+activated ATPase during the first 12 days after birth. The increase of Na^+–K^+activated ATPase activity occurred at the same time as the occurrence of detectable electroencephalographic activity. The rates of incorporation of $^{32}P_i$ (Abdel-Latif and Abood, 1965) and [^{14}C]serine (Abdel-Latif and Abood, 1966) into the phospholipids of subcellular fractions from developing rat brain have also been investigated. The lipid composition of subcellular fractions from developing brain has been examined by Cuzner and Davison (1968). Klee and Sokoloff (1965) found that the incorporation of amino acids into the proteolipid of myelin took place in a crude mitochondrial fraction *in vitro*. The mitochondrial fraction from the brains of immature rats was more active in this respect than that from adult animals.

Kurokawa *et al.* (1963) have investigated the compartmentation of acetylcholine in strains of mice with a congenital predisposition to convulsions. Convulsions are accompanied by a decrease in the amount of acetylcholine found in the brain. This decrease in acetylcholine occurs in what they describe as the osmotically "labile" fraction rather than the osmotically stable fraction. It is therefore cytoplasmic rather than associated with vesicles.

The action of the convulsant methionine sulphoximine has been studied by de Robertis *et al.* (1967*b*). After intrathecal injection most of the bound methionine sulphoximine in brain was found in the crude mitochondrial fraction. The isolated synaptosomes appeared swollen and their complement of synaptic vesicles was reduced. They also found that the activities of alanine aminotransferase and glutamine synthetase in the brain were inhibited as a result of methionine sulphoximine administration, and the possible relationship between these observations is discussed.

Levi and Maynert (1964) examined the subcellular localization of brain stem noradrenalin and 5-hydroxytryptamine after treatments such as electric shock, administration of phenobarbital and of the monoamine oxidase inhibitor 1-phenyl-2-hydrazinopropane. There was no change in the subcellular distribution of these amines despite changes in the total levels found in the brain. The binding of 5-hydroxytryptamine to rat brain subcellular fractions *in vitro* has been investigated (Marchbanks *et al.*, 1964; Marchbanks, 1966*b*). A high-affinity 5-hydroxytryptamine-binding component was found principally in synaptosomes from the midbrain region. This binding of 5-hydroxytryptamine was inhibited by D-lysergic acid diethylamide, but the effects of other lysergic acid derivatives on the 5-hydroxytryptamine binding did not suggest any correlation of this effect with the hallucinogenic activity of lysergic acid derivatives (Marchbanks, 1967*c*).

The effect of phenothiazines on the uptake and release of acetylcholine from synaptosomes *in vitro* has been examined by Guth (1962) who found that phenothiazines inhibited both uptake and release. Mellanby *et al.* (1965) examined the binding of tetanus toxin to subcellular fractions from guinea pig brain, and found high capacity to fix the toxin in subfractions containing synaptosomes and myelin. Further studies suggested that the toxin fixing capacity was mainly associated with the external membrane fragments separable after hypo-osmotic disruption of the synaptosomes (Mellanby and Whittaker, 1968). An attempt to produce antisera against synaptosomes from rabbit and cat brain cortex has been made (de Robertis *et al.*, 1966). The antisera were not specific but produced epileptiform discharge when applied to the visual cortex of the cat, and caused lysis of synaptosomes when incubated with them *in vitro*.

V. Concluding Remarks

It is about a decade since the preparation of synaptosomes was first described. Since then numerous investigators have exploited the preparation to examine the preterminal content and compartmentation of putative transmitter substances and the enzymes which synthesize and degrade them.

Perhaps the single most important finding has been the isolation of synaptic vesicles and the demonstration that they contain within them acetylcholine. This provides an important link in the evidence for the theory of "quantal" release of transmitter at the synapse. Without this demonstration the ascription to synaptic vesicles of a role in chemical transmission would be purely hypothetical.

It has become clear that there are a number of problems which must be considered in evaluating the results of analysis of synaptosomes and other brain fractions.

Synaptosome preparations even when substantially free from myelin and mitochondria are contaminated to varying extents with membrane fragments of unknown origin for which markers are not yet available. Synaptosomes are, moreover, heterogeneous with respect to the type of cell of origin. Thus synaptosomes from cholinergic cells would be expected to differ in chemical composition from those derived from non-cholinergic cells.

Artefacts as a result of the subcellular fractionation process include the diffusion of substances out of the synaptosome or vesicles during the preparation. Conversely soluble substances may diffuse into or equilibrate with the particulate material. These processes will obscure the realities of the *in vivo* compartmentation unless appropriate controls are carried out. Additional criteria of occlusion or binding are useful in this respect.

Subcellular fractionation is always carried out at low ionic strength, in contrast to the internal environment of the cell which has a relatively high ionic strength. Many proteins bind non-specifically to membrane fragments, the binding frequently being dependent on ionic strength. The apparent subcellular distribution of enzymes must always be interpreted with the possibility of this artefact kept in mind. Synthesis or destruction of cell constituents may also take place during the subcellular fractionation procedure.

Finally, the fact that a substance is found in a particular subcellular fraction does not necessarily imply that the substance is present in the particles that mainly constitute that fraction. There is always the possibility that it is present in a minor morphological constituent with a high specific activity.

However, these limitations can be overcome by appropriate controls as has already been discussed with respect to specific examples in the text.

The synaptosome hypothesis states that when brain tissue is homogenised, pre-synaptic nerve terminals survive as detached sealed structures that can be isolated by subcellular fractionation. The intraterminal components may be isolated by hypo-osmotic disruption of synaptosomes and further density gradient fractionation. Despite reservations in some quarters the hypothesis seems generally accepted, and it is appropriate here to consider the possibilities for further advances.

Improved methods of centrifugation by using zonal rotors may increase the resolution of subcellular fractionation. This may make it possible to achieve more definitive separations of synaptosomes according to type. The separation of fragments derived from the different types of membranes present in synaptosomes might also be facilitated by zonal centrifugation.

Much remains to be done concerning the exact compartmentation of various putative transmitters within the synaptosome. A principal problem here is the inadequate sensitivity of assay methods. Continuous flow separation using zonal rotors might overcome this by making more preparations available for analysis. The nature of pathological and pharmacological disturbance as reflected in changes in the properties of the synaptosome preparation has not been extensively investigated. As the properties of the synaptosome preparation become more apparent utilization of this approach can be expected to increase.

It is becoming clear from recent work that the synaptosome is rather similar to an anucleate cell. The limiting membrane is fully sealed, and in some respects appears to be functional. The capability of synaptosomes to carry out complex metabolic functions is considerable. It is therefore possible to examine *in vitro* the permeability properties and metabolic characteristics of an isolated part of the nerve cell which is of particular importance for the processes of chemical transmission. The extent of this possibility has to be established and the results must always be evaluated by comparison with the properties of more organized tissues. However, the increased experimental flexibility allowed by synaptosome preparation *in vitro* guarantees the usefulness of this approach.

Acknowledgements

The unpublished work from this laboratory described in this chapter was supported by grants from the U.K. Medical and Science Research Councils. We are grateful to Dr L. W. Chakrin and Miss E. K. Miller for permission to mention unpublished research results, to Mrs Ruth Sanders for help with the literature survey and to Professor F. G. Young for his interest.

References

Abdel-Latif, A. A. and Abood, L. G. (1964). *J. Neurochem.* **11**, 9-15.
Abdel-Latif, A. A. and Abood, L. G. (1965). *J. Neurochem.* **12**, 157-166.
Abdel-Latif, A. A. and Abood, L. G. (1966). *J. Neurochem.* **13**, 1189-1196.
Abdel-Latif, A. A., Brody, J. and Ramani, H. (1967). *J. Neurochem.* **14**, 1133-1141.
Abood, L. G., Brunngraber, E. and Taylor, M. (1959). *J. biol. Chem.* **234**, 1307-1311.
Alberici, M., Arnaiz, G. R. de L. and de Robertis, E. (1965). *Life Sci.* **4**, 1951-1960.
Albers, R. W. and Koval, G. J. (1962). *Biochim. biophys. Acta* **60**, 359-365.
Albers, R. W., Arnaiz, G. R. de L. and de Robertis, E. (1965). *Proc. natn. Acad. Sci. U.S.A.* **53**, 557-564.
Aldridge, W. N. and Johnson, M. K. (1959). *Biochem. J.* **73**, 270-276.
Arnaiz, G. R. de L. and de Robertis, E. D. P. (1962). *J. Neurochem.* **9**, 503-508.
Arnaiz, G. R. de L. and de Robertis, E. D. P. (1964). *J. Neurochem.* **11**, 213-221.
Arnaiz, G. R. de L., Alberici, M. and de Robertis, E. (1967). *J. Neurochem.* **14**, 215-225.
Austin, L. and Morgan, I. G. (1967). *J. Neurochem.* **14**, 377-387.

Axelrod, J. and Tomchick, R. (1958). *J. biol. Chem.* **233**, 702-705.
Azcurra, J. M. and de Robertis, E. (1967). *Int. J. Neuropharmac.* **6**, 15-26.
Bachelard, H. S. (1966). *Biochem. J.* **100**, 131-137.
Bachelard, H. S. (1967). *Biochem. J.* **104**, 286-292.
Balakrishnan, S. and McIlwain, H. (1961). *Biochem. J.* **81**, 72-78.
Balázs, R. and Cocks, W. A. (1967). *J. Neurochem.* **14**, 1035-1055.
Balázs, R. and Richter, D. (1958). *Biochem. J.* **68**, 5P.
Balázs, R., Dahl, D. and Harwood, J. R. (1966). *J. Neurochem.* **13**, 897-905.
Barker, L. A., Amaro, J. and Guth, P. S. (1967). *Biochem. Pharmac.* **16**, 2181-2187.
Barondes, S. H. (1964). *Science, N.Y.* **146**, 779-781.
Barondes, S. H. (1966). *J. Neurochem.* **13**, 721-727.
Barondes, S. H. (1968). *J. Neurochem.* **15**, 343-350.
Beattie, D. S., Sloan, H. R. and Basford, R. E. (1963). *J. Cell Biol.* **19**, 309-316.
Blaschko, H., Hagen, P. and Welch, A. D. (1955). *J. Physiol., Lond.* **129**, 27-49.
Bogdanski, D. F., Weissbach, H. and Udenfriend, S. (1957). *J. Neurochem.* **1**, 272-278.
Bogdanski, D. F., Tissari, A. and Brodie, B. B. (1968). *Life Sci.* **7**, 419-428.
Bradford, H. F., Brownlow, E. K. and Gammack, D. B. (1966). *J. Neurochem.* **13**, 1283-1297.
Brodkin, E. and Elliott, K. A. C. (1953). *Am. J. Physiol.* **173**, 437-442.
Brunngraber, E. G., Dekirmenjian, H. and Brown, B. D. (1967). *Biochem. J.* **103**, 73-78.
Burton, R. M. (1964). *Int. J. Neuropharmac.* **3**, 13-21.
Burton, R. M., Howard, R. E., Baer, S. and Balfour, Y. M. (1964). *Biochem. biophys. Acta* **84**, 441-447.
Campbell, M. K., Mahler, H. R., Moore, W. J. and Tewari, S. (1966). *Biochemistry* **5**, 1174-1184.
Chruściel, T. L. (1960). In *Adrenergic Mechanisms* (J. R. Vane, G. E. Wolstenholme, and M. O'Connor, eds), CIBA Foundation Symposium, pp. 539-543. Little, Brown & Co., Boston.
Clementi, F., Whittaker, V. P. and Sheridan, M. N. (1966). *Z. Zellforsch. mikrosk. Anat.* **72**, 126-138.
Cleugh, J., Gaddum, J. H., Mitchell, A. A., Smith, M. W. and Whittaker, V. P. (1964). *J. Physiol., Lond.* **170**, 69-85.
Colburn, R. W. and Maas, J. W. (1965). *Nature, Lond.* **208**, 37-41.
Cotman, C. W. and Mahler, H. R. (1967). *Archs Biochem. Biophys.* **120**, 384-396.
Cuzner, M. L. and Davison, A. N. (1968). *Biochem. J.* **106**, 29-34.
de Duve, C. (1963-4). *Harvey Lect.* **59**, 49-87.
del Castillo, J. and Katz, B. (1955). *J. Physiol., Lond.* **128**, 396-411.
Dengler, H. J., Michaelson, I. A., Spiegel, H. E. and Titus, E. (1962). *Int. J. Neuropharmac.* **1**, 23-28.
de Robertis, E. (1960). *Proc. 4th Int. neurochem. Symp. Varenna, 1960.* In *Regional Neurochemistry; the Regional Chemistry, Physiology and Pharmacology of the Nervous System* (S. Kety and J. Elkes, eds), pp. 248-258. Pergamon Press, Oxford.
de Robertis, E. (1966). *Pharmac. Rev.* **18**, 413-424.
de Robertis, E. (1967). *Science, N.Y.* **156**, 907-914.
de Robertis, E. D. P. and Bennett, H. S. (1955). *J. biophys. biochem. Cytol.* **1**, 47-58.
de Robertis, E., de Iraldi, A. P., Rodriguez, G. and Gomez, C. J. (1960). *Sesiones Cientificas de Biologia, Mendoza, October 5-8 1960.*
de Robertis, E., de Iraldi, A. P., Rodriguez, G. and Gomez, J. (1961). *J. biophys. biochem. Cytol.* **9**, 229-235.
de Robertis, E., de Iraldi, A. P., Arnaiz, G. R. de L. and Salganicoff, L. (1962). *J. Neurochem.* **9**, 23-35.

de Robertis, E., Arnaiz, G. R. de L., Salganicoff, L., de Iraldi, A. P. and Zieher, L. M. (1963). *J. Neurochem.* **10**, 225-235.
de Robertis, E., de Iraldi, A. P., Arnaiz, G. R. de L. and Zieher, L. M. (1965). *Life Sci.* **4**, 193-201.
de Robertis, E., Lapetina, E., Saavedra, J. P. and Soto, E. F. (1966). *Life Sci.* **5**, 1979-1989.
de Robertis, E., Fiszer, S. and Soto, E. F. (1967*a*). *Science, N.Y.* **158**, 928-929.
de Robertis, E., Sellinger, O. Z., Arnaiz, G. R. de L., Alberici, M. and Zieher, L. M. (1967*b*). *J. Neurochem.* **14**, 81-89.
Durell, J. and Sodd, M. A. (1966). *J. Neurochem.* **13**, 487-491.
Ehrenpreis, S. (1964). *Nature, Lond.* **201**, 887-893.
Eichberg, J., Whittaker, V. P. and Dawson, R. M. C. (1964). *Biochem.J.* **92**, 91-100.
Feldberg, W. (1945). *Physiol. Rev.* **25**, 596-642.
Florey, E. and Winesdorfer, J. (1968). *J. Neurochem.* **15**, 169-177.
Fonnum, F. (1967). *Biochem. J.* **103**, 262-270.
Fonnum, F. (1968). *Biochem. J.* **106**, 401-412.
Gaddum, J. H. and Schild, H. (1934). *J. Physiol., Lond.* **83**, 1-14.
Germain, M. and Proulx, P. (1965). *Biochem. Pharmac.* **14**, 1815-1819.
Glowinski, J. and Axelrod, J. (1966). *Pharmac. Rev.* **18**, 775-785.
Gordon, M. K., Bendi, K. G., Deanin, G. G. and Gordon, M. W. (1968). *Nature, Lond.* **217**, 523-527.
Grahame-Smith, D. G. (1967). *Biochem. J.* **105**, 351-360.
Gray, E. G. and Whittaker, V. P. (1960). *J. Physiol., Lond.* **153**, 35-37P.
Gray, E. G. and Whittaker, V. P. (1962). *J. Anat.* **96**, 79-88.
Guth, P. S. (1962). *Fedn Proc. Fedn Am. Socs exp. biol.* **21**, 1100-1102.
Hanzon, V. and Toschi, G. (1961). *Scient. Rep. Ist. super. Sanita.* **1**, 19-44.
Hebb, C. O. and Whittaker, V. P. (1958). *J. Physiol., Lond.* **142**, 187-196.
Hillarp, N.-Å., Fuxe, K. and Dahlström, A. (1965). In *Mechanisms of Release of Biogenic Amines* (U. S. von Euler, S. Russell and B. Uvnäs, eds), pp. 31-57. Pergamon Press, Oxford.
Hokin, L. E. and Hokin, M. R. (1958). *J. biol. Chem.* **233**, 822-826.
Hosein, E. A. and Proulx, P. (1964). *Archs Biochem. Biophys.* **106**, 267-274.
Hosie, R. J. A. (1965). *Biochem. J.* **96**, 404-412.
Inouye, A. and Kataoka, K. (1962). *Nature, Lond.* **193**, 585.
Inouye, A., Kataoka, K. and Shinagawa, J. (1962). *Nature, Lond.* **194**, 286-287.
Inouye, A., Kataoka, K. and Shinagawa, J. (1963*a*). *Biochim. biophys. Acta* **71**, 491-493.
Inouye, A., Kataoka, K. and Shinagawa, J. (1963*b*). *Nature, Lond.* **198**, 291-293.
Israël, M., Gautron, J. and Lesbats, B. (1968). *C.r. hebd. Séanc. Acad. Sci., Paris* **266**, 273-275.
Johnson, M. K. (1960). *Biochem. J.* **77**, 610-618.
Johnson, M. K. and Whittaker, V. P. (1963). *Biochem. J.* **88**, 404-409.
Jones, D. G. (1967). *J. Cell Sci.* **2**, 573-586.
Katz, B. (1966). *Nerve, Muscle, and Synapse.* McGraw-Hill, New York.
Klee, C. B. and Sokoloff, L. (1965). *Proc. natn. Acad. Sci. U.S.A.* **53**, 1014-1020.
Kopin, I. J. and Gordon, E. K. (1962). *J. Pharmacol.* **138**, 351-359.
Krnjević, K. (1965). *Br. med. Bull.* **21**, 10-14.
Krnjević, K. and Mitchell, J. F. (1961). *J. Physiol., Lond.* **155**, 246-262.
Krnjević, K. and Phillis, J. W. (1963). *J. Physiol., Lond.* **166**, 328-350.
Krnjević, K. and Whittaker, V. P. (1965). *J. Physiol., Lond.* **179**, 298-322.
Kurokawa, M., Machiyama, Y. and Kato, M. (1963). *J. Neurochem.* **10**, 341-348.
Kurokawa, M., Sakamoto, T. and Kato, M. (1965). *Biochem. J.* **97**, 833-844.
Lapetina, E. G. and de Robertis, E. (1968). *Life Sci.* **7**, 203-208.
Lapetina, E. G., Soto, E. F. and de Robertis, E. (1967). *Biochim. biophys. Acta* **135**, 33-43.

Lapetina, E. G., Soto, E. F. and de Robertis, E. (1968). *J. Neurochem.* **15**, 437-445.
Laverty, R., Michaelson, I. A., Sharman, D. F. and Whittaker, V. P. (1963). *Br. J. Pharmacol. Chemother.* **21**, 482-490.
Levi, R. and Maynert, E. W. (1964). *Biochem. Pharmac.* **13**, 615-621.
Lewis, P. R. and Shute, C. C. D. (1966). *J. Cell Sci.* **1**, 381-390.
Lindall, A. and Frantz, I. D. III. (1967). *J. Neurochem.* **14**, 771-774.
Løvtrop, S. (1961). *J. Neurochem.* **8**, 243-245.
MacIntosh, F. C. (1959). *Can. J. Biochem. Physiol.* **37**, 343-356.
Mangan, J. L. and Whittaker, V. P. (1966). *Biochem. J.* **98**, 128-137.
Marchbanks, R. M. (1966a). *Biochem. J.* **100**, 65P-66P.
Marchbanks, R. M. (1966b). *J. Neurochem.* **13**, 1481-1493.
Marchbanks, R. M. (1967a). *Biochem. J.* **104**, 148-157.
Marchbanks, R. M. (1967b). *Biochem. Pharmac.* **16**, 921-923.
Marchbanks, R. M. (1967c). *Biochem. Pharmac.* **16**, 1971-1979.
Marchbanks, R. M. (1968a). *Biochem. J.* **106**, 87-95.
Marchbanks, R. M. (1968b). *Biochem. J.* **110**, 533-541.
Marchbanks, R. M., Rosenblatt, F. and O'Brien, R. D. (1964). *Science, N.Y.* **144**, 1135-1137.
Masuoka, D. (1965). *Biochem. Pharmac.* **14**, 1688-1689.
Maynert, E. W. and Kuriyama, K. (1964). *Life Sci.* **3**, 1067-1087.
Maynert, E. W., Levi, R. and De Lorenzo, A. J. D. (1964). *J. Pharmac. exp. Ther.* **144**, 385-392.
McCaman, R. E., Arnaiz, G. R. de L. and de Robertis, E. (1965). *J. Neurochem.* **12**, 927-935.
Mellanby, J. and Whittaker, V. P. (1968). *J. Neurochem.* **15**, 205-208.
Mellanby, J., van Heyningen, W. E. and Whittaker, V. P. (1965). *J. Neurochem.* **12**, 77-79.
Michaelson, I. A. (1967). *Ann. N.Y. Acad. Sci.* **144**, 387-407.
Michaelson, I. A. and Whittaker, V. P. (1963). *Biochem. Pharmac.* **12**, 203-211.
Michaelson, I. A., Whittaker, V. P., Laverty, R. and Sharman, D. F. (1963). *Biochem. Pharmac.* **12**, 1450-1452.
Mirkin, B. L., Giarman, N. J. and Freedman, D. X. (1964). *Biochem. Pharmac.* **13**, 1027-1035.
Mokrasch, L. C. (1966). *J. Neurochem.* **13**, 49-58.
Mordoh, J. (1965). *J. Neurochem.* **12**, 505-514.
Morgan, I. G. and Austin, L. (1968). *J. Neurochem.* **15**, 41-51.
Nyman, M. and Whittaker, V. P. (1963). *Biochem. J.* **87**, 248-255.
Palay, S. L. (1956). *J. biophys. biochem. Cytol.* **2**, suppl. 193-202.
Potter, L. T. (1966). *Pharmac. Rev.* **18**, 439-452.
Potter, L. T. (1968). In *The Interaction of Drugs and Subcellular Components on Animal Cells* (P. N. Campbell, ed.), pp. 293-304. J. & A. Churchill Ltd., London.
Potter, L. T. and Axelrod, J. (1963). *J. Pharmac. exp. Ther.* **142**, 291-298.
Robinson, J. D., Anderson, J. H. and Green, J. P. (1965). *J. Pharmac. exp. Ther.* **147**, 236-243.
Ryall, R. W. (1964). *J. Neurochem.* **11**, 131-145.
Ryall, R. W., Stone, N. and Watkins, J. C. (1964a). *J. Neurochem.* **11**, 621-637.
Ryall, R. W., Stone, N. E., Curtis, D. R. and Watkins, J. C. (1964b). *Nature, Lond.* **201**, 1034-1035.
Saelens, J. K. and Potter, L. T. (1966). *Fedn Proc. Fedn Am. Socs exp. Biol.* **25**, 451.
Salganicoff, L. and de Robertis, E. (1965). *J. Neurochem.* **12**, 287-309.
Sano, K. and Roberts, E. (1963). *Biochem. Pharmac.* **12**, 489-502.
Schuberth, J. and Sundwall, A. (1967). *J. Neurochem.* **14**, 807-812.
Schuberth, J., Sundwall, A., Sörbo, B. and Lindell, J.-O. (1966). *J. Neurochem.* **13**, 347-352.

Sellinger, O. Z. and Verster, F. de B. (1962). *J. biol. Chem.* **237**, 2836-2849.
Sellinger, O. Z., Rucker, D. L. and Verster, F. de B. (1964). *J. Neurochem.* **11**, 271-280.
Seminario, L. M., Hren, N. and Gomez, C. J. (1964). *J. Neurochem.* **11**, 197-207.
Sheridan, M. N., Whittaker, V. P. and Israël, M. (1966). *Z. Zellforsch. mikrosk. Anat.* **74**, 291-307.
Stjärne, L. (1966). *Pharmac. Rev.* **18**, 425-432.
Stjärne, L. and Lishajko, F. (1967). *Biochem. Pharmac.* **16**, 1719-1728.
Swanson, P. D. (1967). *J. Neurochem.* **14**, 343-356.
Takcho, K., Nishio, A. and Yanagiya, I. (1965). *Jap. J. vet. Sci.* **27**, 189.
Tanaka, R. and Abood, L. G. (1963). *J. Neurochem.* **10**, 571-576.
Tipton, K. F. (1967). *Biochim. biophys. Acta* **135**, 910-920.
Toschi, G. (1959). *Expl Cell Res.* **16**, 232-255.
Tsukada, Y. (1966). In *Progress in Brain Research* (T. Tokizane and J. P. Schade, eds), vol. 21A, pp. 268-291. Elsevier, Amsterdam.
Tuček, S. (1966a). *J. Neurochem.* **13**, 1317-1327.
Tuček, S. (1966b). *J. Neurochem.* **13**, 1329-1332.
Tuček, S. (1967). *J. Neurochem.* **14**, 531-545.
Udenfriend, S. (1966). *Pharmac. Rev.* **18**, 43-51.
Uyemura, K., Iida, Y. and Tsukada, Y. (1963). *Shinkei Kenkyu no Shinpo, Jap* **7**, 763-771.
van Heyningen, W. E. (1963). *J. gen. Microbiol.* **31**, 375-387.
van Kempen, G. M. J., van den Berg, C. J., van der Helm, H. J. and Veldstra, H. (1965). *J. Neurochem.* **12**, 581-588.
van Maanen, E. F. (1950). *J. Pharmac.* **99**, 255-264.
Varon, S., Weinstein, H., Kakefuda, T. and Roberts, E. (1965). *Biochem. Pharmac.* **14**, 1213-1224.
von Hungen, K., Mahler, H. R. and Moore, W. J. (1968). *J. biol. Chem.* **243**, 1415-1423.
Vrba, R. (1967). *Biochem. J.* **105**, 927-936.
Weinstein, H., Roberts, E. and Kakefuda, T. (1963). *Biochem. Pharmac.* **12**, 503-509.
Weinstein, H., Varon, S., Muhleman, D. R. and Roberts, E. (1965). *Biochem. Pharmac.* **14**, 273-288.
Whittaker, V. P. (1959). *Biochem. J.* **72**, 694-706.
Whittaker, V. P. (1960). *Proc. 4th Int. Neurochem. Symp. Varenna, 1960.* In *Regional Neurochemistry; the Regional Chemistry, Physiology and Pharmacology of the Nervous System* (S. Kety and J. Elkes, eds), pp. 259-263. Pergamon Press, Oxford.
Whittaker, V. P. (1963). *Biochem. Soc. Symp.* **23**, 109-126.
Whittaker, V. P. (1964). *Prog. Brain Res.* **8**, 90-117.
Whittaker, V. P. (1965a). *Prog. Biophys. molec. Biol.* **15**, 39-96.
Whittaker, V. P. (1965b). In *Mechanisms of Release of Biogenic Amines* (B. Uvnäs and S. Rosell, eds), pp. 147-162. Pergamon Press, Oxford.
Whittaker, V. P. (1966a). *Ann. N.Y. Acad. Sci.* **137**, 982-998.
Whittaker, V. P. (1966b). *Pharmac. Rev.* **18**, 401-412.
Whittaker, V. P. (1967). In *Biokhimiya i Funktsiya Nervnoǐ Sistemi* (Ya A. Vinnikov, N. N. Dëmin and E. M. Kreps, eds), pp. 207-214. Academy of Sciences of the USSR, Leningrad.
Whittaker, V. P. (1968). *Biochem. J.* **106**, 412-417.
Whittaker, V. P. (1969a). In *Structure and Function of Nervous Tissue* (G. H. Bourne, ed.), vol. 2, (In the press). Academic Press, New York.
Whittaker, V. P. (1969b). In *Handbook of Neurochemistry* (A. Lajtha, ed.), Vol. 1, (In the press). Plenum Press, New York.
Whittaker, V. P. and Dowe, G. H. C. (1964). *Int. J. Neuropharmac.* **3**, 593-597.

Whittaker, V. P. and Dowe, G. H. C. (1965). *Biochem. Pharmac.* **14**, 194-196.
Whittaker, V. P. and Sheridan, M. N. (1965). *J. Neurochem.* **12**, 363-372.
Whittaker, V. P., Michaelson, I. A. and Kirkland, R. J. A. (1964). *Biochem. J.* **90**, 293-303.
Wiegandt, H. (1967). *J. Neurochem.* **14**, 671-674.
Wolfe, L. S. (1961). *Biochem. J.* **79**, 348-355.
Wood, T. and Swanson, P. D. (1964). *J. Neurochem.* **11**, 301-307.
Zieher, L. M. and de Robertis, E. (1963). *Biochem. Pharmac.* **12**, 596-598.

CHAPTER 3

Brain RNA

G. P. TALWAR

Department of Biochemistry,
All India Institute of Medical Sciences, New Delhi, India

I. Introduction

During the past ten years, a number of reports have appeared in the literature assigning a special role to RNA in the brain, namely, its possible involvement in processes of learning and storage of memory. These functions are amongst the most intriguing attributes of the central nervous system and have consequently evoked widespread interest. It is perhaps too early to arrive at conclusions on complex problems like memory. Nevertheless, it is worth reviewing and critically evaluating the numerous papers that have appeared on the subject. A part of this chapter will be devoted to the discussion of this important issue.

The general objectives of this chapter are to present in a condensed form the current information on brain RNA. What are the types of RNA present in the brain? Do they differ in any respect from the RNA obtained from other tissues? What are their rates of turnover? How do they compare with other tissues? These and other questions have been raised with the idea of assessing whether any RNA species with distinguishing characteristics are present in the brain.

It was the high content of RNA in the neuron which attracted earlier investigators to search for its role in the central nervous system. Data on the distribution of RNA in different regions of the brain and in neurons and glia have been summarized. The high rate of synthesis of RNA in the glial cells together with observations on the reciprocal relationship of the RNA content in nerve cells and glia provide much scope for speculation on the functional role of glia.

The intraneuronal localization of RNA has been surveyed. Apart from the prominent nucleolus and extensive network of Nissl granules in the neuron, which have been described exhaustively in the earlier literature, more recent findings on the presence of RNA in axons and synaptosomes have been discussed. These observations, which are of considerable interest, have a direct bearing on the possible functions of RNA in the brain. The local synthesis of RNA (and some proteins) in nerve-endings independent of the cell nucleus, questions the established belief that *all* constituents of the axon have their dependence on and origin in the perikaryon.

The developing brain in chicks, rats and other animals has served as a useful experimental system to demonstrate that the rate of synthesis of RNA in the brain is high at the foetal and neonatal stage, but drops considerably at a fairly early period of neonatal development. Observations *in vivo* and *in vitro* on this subject have been included not only for their individual merit but also to place in proper perspective the many lacunae in our knowledge. Factors influencing the rate of RNA synthesis in the brain are poorly understood.

A section of this chapter has been devoted to an analysis of the changes taking place in the content and metabolism of RNA in various functional states. The discussion has been limited to prototype cases falling under the category of electrical, chemical or sensory stimulation. Numerous other examples qualifying for inclusion in the title "functional states" have been omitted either for want of sufficient information or for conserving space. This section (like others) does not claim to be comprehensive in its coverage. No attempt has been made to cite all publications on the subject, though an effort has been made to provide basic information and indicate general trends in research.

The review has not limited itself to the description of facts. An attempt has been made to interpret them and to form a hypothesis wherever feasible. The main purpose of such an exercise has been to raise questions for further research.

II. Concentration of RNA in the Brain

A. *Whole brain*

1. *Brain as compared to other organs*

Pioneer studies by the Scandinavian workers have shown the presence of large amounts of the ultraviolet absorbing material in the neural tissue (for review see Hydén, 1960). The content of RNA in a large neuron was found to be fairly high and equivalent to the RNA content of cells in an exocrine gland, e.g. the pancreas (Hydén), even though the RNA/DNA ratios in the whole brain are much lower than those found in liver or pancreas (Leslie, 1955). This apparent discrepancy is perhaps due to the heterogeneity of the cell types in the brain. As will be discussed later, the RNA content of different cells varies a lot in the brain.

TABLE I

Comparison of the RNA content of particulate fractions in rat brain and liver

	RNA/DNA		RNA/proteins	
	Brain	Liver	Brain	Liver
(1) Whole homogenate	2·11 (A)	3·7 (B)	0·015 (A)	0·056 (B)
(2) Purified nuclear fraction	0·24 (A)	0·22 (B)	0·044 (A)	0·046 (B)
(3) Mitochondrial fraction	13·1 (A)	13·85 (C)	0·010 (A)	0·009 (C)
(4) Ribosomes	—	—	0·71 (D)	0·65–0·9 (E)

References: (A) Balazs and Cocks (1967); (B) Widnell and Tata (1964); (C) Nass *et al.* (1965); (D) Murthy and Rappoport (1965) and (E) Korner (1961).

An interesting observation is the fact that the RNA/DNA ratio in purified nuclei or mitochondria derived from liver and brain cells is very nearly the same, even though the concentration of RNA in whole tissue homogenates is widely different (Table I). The same holds true for RNA/protein ratios in other purified particulate fractions from the two tissues in contrast to the values in the total tissue. These observations show that the RNA per particulate structure is nearly the same and that the differences in the total cellular content of RNA in brain and liver may be a matter of more or less particles (such as ribosomes) in the cell. This interpretation would also be consistent with the observations that the RNA content of liver cells changes in situations (nutritional status, hormones) which influence the synthesis or breakdown of ribosomes.

2. Species variations

RNA-P to DNA-P ratio for the whole brain varies from 0·29 in the case of the newt to 2·11 for the turtle. It is around 1·30–1·39 in rat, guinea pig and rabbit, while the values are 2·00 and 2·06 in the chicken and grass snake brain respectively (Mandel et al., 1964). The RNA-P values computed on the basis of diploid DNA-P content vary between 0·36 and 1·17 from species to species. It is obvious that there are large differences in the RNA content of the brain from animal to animal. Furthermore, the content of RNA in the brain does not seem to bear any relation to the degree of evolution of the animal.

B. Regional distribution

1. Mammalian brain

The highest concentration of RNA per unit fresh weight of the tissue in mammals is found in the olfactory bulb, the cerebral and cerebellar grey matter and the hippocampus; slightly lower values are obtained for the corpus striatum and the hypothalamus; and the lowest concentrations are in the mesencephalon, white matter, the medulla oblongata and the spinal cord (Mandel et al., 1964). The DNA content of these areas, however, differs markedly and the RNA/DNA ratios do not follow the same order. Olfactory bulb and cerebellum have high cellular density, with the result that the RNA/DNA ratios in these areas are lower than 1 (0·72 and 0·39) in rat brain. The regional distribution of RNA in some areas of the human and rabbit brain is given in Table II. The highest content of RNA

TABLE II

Content of RNA in different regions of the brain

Region	Species	RNA (μg/mg dry wt)	RNA/DNA	Reference
Grey Matter				
(1) Frontal cortex	Human	5·47	2·14	(A)
(2) Motor cortex	Human	4·38	1·72	(A)
(3) Caudate nucleus	Human	4·40	1·44	(A)
	Rabbit	—	1·89	(B)
(4) Corpus callosum	Human	1·60	0·87	(A)
	Rabbit	—	1·00	(B)
(5) Pineal gland	Human	15·89	1·58	(A)
(6) Hippocampus	Rabbit	—	2·32	(B)
(7) Hypothalamus	Rabbit		2·04	(B)
(8) Cerebral white matter	Rabbit	—	1·14	(B)
(9) Cerebellum white matter	Rabbit	—	0·77	(B)
grey matter	Rabbit	—	0·70	(B)
(10) Medulla oblongata	Rabbit	—	1·70	(B)
(11) Spinal cord	Rabbit	—	1·20	(B)

References: (A) Landolt et al. (1966) and (B) Mandel et al. (1964).

per unit DNA is in the hippocampus and frontal cortex. All areas of the cerebral cortex do not have an equal content of RNA (viz. frontal and motor cortex of the human brain). The hypothalamus has also a high RNA/DNA ratio. The important role of the hypothalamus in the secretion of polypeptides is discussed elsewhere in this chapter.

Data on the incorporation of [^{32}P]*ortho*phosphate into RNA of different brain regions show that the most active incorporation takes place in the olfactory bulb, the hypothalamus, the grey matter of the brain cortex and the hippocampus (Mandel *et al.*, 1961). These areas of the brain appear to have a higher rate of turnover of RNA than others.

2. *Comparative distribution of RNA in various species*

Mandel *et al.* (1964) have estimated the RNA content of four areas of the brain, namely optic lobe, olfactory bulb, cerebellum and cerebral hemispheres in amphibians, reptiles and mammals. It has been noted by these workers that the RNA/DNA ratio is much lower for the olfactory bulbs of mammals than it is for amphibians and reptiles.

C. *Neurons and glia*

An average human brain has approximately ten billion neurons, and about 8–10 times as many glia cells. RNA per nerve cell varies according to the type of cell. In general the values lie between 50 and 2000 $\mu\mu$g. The spinal ganglion cells of the rabbit have an RNA content of 1070 $\mu\mu$g/cell and the anterior horn cells in man 670 $\mu\mu$g (Hydén, 1960). The content varies also from cell to cell in the same nucleus. A large neuron in the Deiters' nucleus of the rabbit has 1550 $\mu\mu$g of RNA, while a smaller cell in the same nucleus has 770 $\mu\mu$g. Edström and Pigon (1958) have suggested the existence of a proportionality between the area of the cell body surface and the content of RNA in the spinal ganglion cells.

The glia have on the average a much lower content of RNA. Table III gives a relative idea of the distribution of RNA in the two types of cells.

The content of RNA in neurons and associated glia cells fluctuates and may be related to each other. Hydén and Lange (1961) have shown a reciprocal relationship between the content of RNA in the neuron and the glia from the same region. The RNA content of nerve cells increased after vestibular stimulation in the lateral vestibular nuclei, while that of the glia cells decreased. Similar observations have been reported by Pevzner (1965). Electrical stimulation of the superior sympathetic ganglion in the cat for three hours induced a marked increase in nucleic acid and protein in the cytoplasm of the neurons. The RNA content of the glial satellite cells was at the same time shown to decrease.

These reports, if found consistent, have interesting implications. First, they would suggest a close interrelation between the neurons and the glia at the metabolic level. And second, they would also suggest the possibility of transfer of RNA or precursors from glia to the neurons.

D

There seems to be an active synthesis of RNA in the glia. Daneholt and Brattgård (1966) have shown that the incorporation of radioactive precursors into each of the four RNA bases (expressed as μ moles labelled base/mole extracted) was almost twice as great in glia than in the nerve cells of the hypoglossal nucleus. The synthesis as measured from a four-hour pulse was twice as rapid in glia than in nerve cells.

TABLE III

A. RNA content of the neurons and glial cells in the
Deiters' nucleus of the rabbit

	RNA ($\mu\mu$g/Cell)	RNA (% of dry wt)	RNA (% of wet wt)
Neuron soma	1545	7·7	1·6
Glial cell soma	3·5	0·61	0·15

B. RNA content of the Deiters' nerve cells and glia
from controls and from animals after vestibular
stimulation 25 min for 7 days

	RNA	
	$\mu\mu$g/Nerve cell	$\mu\mu$g/Glial cell of the same volume
Control	1545	85
	P = 0·01	P = 0·001
Stimulated	1612	123

Data from Hydén (1960) and Hydén and Lange (1961).

III. Intraneuronal Distribution of RNA

A. *Nucleolus*

Like in other cells, the RNA is present both in the nucleus and cytoplasm of the neuron. Most of the nuclear RNA is in the nucleolus which is a prominent structure in the nerve cells. There are one or more nucleoli in the nerve cells even in the small types of neurons. The nucleoli account for approximately one-fifth of the total RNA of the nerve cell (Table IV). The size of the nucleolus is influenced by external factors. The nucleolus of the ganglion cells of the supraoptic nucleus increases in volume after stimulation with sodium chloride (Edström and Eichner, 1958a). It has also been reported that the RNA content per nerve cell body is proportional to the volume of the nucleolus (Edström and Eichner, 1958b). It is known from other studies that ribosomes which constitute the bulk of cellular RNA originate from the nucleolus. The nucleolus is an active locus for the synthesis and maturation of RNA-containing particles. The size and metabolic activity of the nucleolus in the neuron is influenced by a number of factors.

TABLE IV

Subcellular distribution of RNA in the neurons

	Cell type	RNA $\mu\mu$g/cell	%	Reference
(1) Nucleolus	Supra optic nucleus (rabbit)	1·7/nucleolus	20[CR]	(B)
(2) Cytoplasm cell body	Deiters' nerve cell (rabbit)	1200	77[CR]	(A)
(3) Dendrites	Deiters' nerve cell (rabbit)	100	1·2–1·5[CR]	
(4) Axoplasm	Mauthner neuron (gold-fish)	8000	0·03–0·07[W.W]	(C), (F)
XIth Cranial nerve	Nerve (Adult cat)		0·0015–0·0043	(D)
(5) Myelin	Bovine white matter		2·33[D.W]	(E)

CR, % of total cellular RNA; W.W., % of wet wt; D.W., dry wt.
References: (A) Hydén (1960); (B) Edström and Eichner (1958); (C) Edström (1964); (D) Koenig (1965); (E) Soto *et al.* (1966); (F) Edström (1967).

B. *Nissl substance*

The presence of an extensive network of a substance staining with basic dyes in the cytoplasm of the neuron body has been well recognized ever since the first observations of Nissl about 75 years ago. Palay and Palade (1955) described it as a three-dimensional meshwork of flat channels, tubules and vesicles limited by membranes to which small granules staining intensely with basic dyes are attached. The granules are composed of ribonucleoprotein particles (ribosomes). About 77% of the total RNA in the Deiters' nerve cell of the rabbit is accounted by the Nissl granules (ribosomes on the endoplasmic reticulum), Golgi membranes and mitochondria present in the cytoplasm of the cell body. The ribosomes are present as polysomes of various sizes and are active sites of synthesis of proteins in the nerve cell, as is the case in other types of cells.

C. *Dendrites*

Dendrites contain also RNA particles. In the Deiters' nerve cell, 100 μg of RNA ($\sim 6\%$ of the total cellular RNA) is found in the dendrites (Table IV). The types of RNA in dendrites are similar to those found in the cytoplasm of the cell body.

A highly interesting observation has been reported by Bodian (1965). Electron microscopic studies showed an appreciable concentration of ribosomes and endoplasmic reticulum-like structures (ergastoplasm) in a position subjacent to the large synaptic knobs on the soma and proximal dendrites of motoneurons in the monkey spinal cord. These were situated in close apposition to the cell membrane. The apposition was not random but associated with large size (3–6 μ) synaptic boutons of definable characteristics. In embryonic motoneurons of the monkey, ergastoplasm concentrations are noted on the plasma membrane of the cell body, at a time when impinging boutons are beginning to establish contact. A suggestion has been made that such clusters of ribosomes may have a role in the synthesis of proteins required for the formation of boutons and the establishment of junctional contacts.

D. *Axon*

1. *Evidence for the presence of RNA in the axon*

The axon hillock shows no ultraviolet absorption and is devoid of RNA-containing structures. Palay and Palade (1955) in their original electron micrograph studies had reported the absence of ribosomes in the axon, which led to the view that RNA in nerve cells is present only in the perikaryon and dendrites. In recent years Edström and co-workers (Edström *et al.*, 1962; Edström, 1964) have shown the existence of RNA in the axon and myelin sheath of Mauthner neuron of the gold-fish. The perikaryon and the axon are both very large in this neuron and can be dissected from the surrounding elements. RNA is present in the axons and myelin sheath in about the same concentration. The concentration of RNA in the cell body is considerably larger (about 25 times) than in the axon, although the total amount of RNA in the cell body (2000 $\mu\mu$g) is four times less than the total RNA in the axon (8000 $\mu\mu$g), owing to the much larger volume of the axon (J. E. Edström, 1967).

It may be argued that the Mauthner neuron may not be a typical neuron and the presence of RNA in its axon may only represent a special case. However, similar observations have been made by Grampp and Edström (1963) in lobster stretch receptor preparations. The presence of small quantities of RNA in myelin free axons of the cat has also been reported by Koenig (1965a). Similarly RNA has been shown to be present in the myelin derived from bovine white matter (Soto *et al.*, 1966). There is some scepticism about the possible contamination of the mammalian axon and nerve-ending preparations, especially because of the small amounts of RNA detected in this case. However, no definite proof has yet been provided, and the demonstration of RNA in the Mauthner axon is fairly clear.

2. *Origin of axonal RNA*

The origin of axonal RNA is still debated. Some workers believe that like proteins, RNA reaches the axon from the cell body by axoplasmic flow (see discussion in Neurosciences Research Programme Bulletin 5, no. 4, December 1967). Austin *et al.* (1966) injected [^{14}C]leucine and [^{3}H]orotic acid in chicks and determined the distribution of the isotope at different times up to 22 days after injection. The results indicated a distal flow of proteins and RNA (or their precursors) along the nerve axon. There are numerous other reports on axoplasmic transport of proteins from the cell body (Weiss and Hiscoe, 1948; Droz and Leblond, 1963; Austin *et al.*, 1966; Barondes, 1968).

There is also some evidence for the synthesis of RNA (and proteins) in the axon independent of the perikaryon. The synthesis of cholinesterase in the axons of neurotomized cholinergic nerves has been shown by Koenig (1965*b*). Koenig (1967) has also reported the incorporation of [^{3}H]leucine into axonal proteins *in vitro* and of [^{3}H]orotic acid and [^{3}H]adenine into axonal RNA. A. Edström (1967) has provided evidence indicating a local DNA-directed protein synthesis in the axon and myelin sheath dissected from the giant Mauthner neuron. In his experiments, actinomycin D inhibited markedly the incorporation of radioactive amino acids into proteins in the axon and myelin sheath. This inhibition was obtained in spite of interruption of the connection of the axon to the Mauthner cell bodies. The inference is that there would be DNA in the axon and myelin sheath. This could be DNA in particles like those of mitochondria, or it could be DNA localized in cells like that of oligodendrocytes in the vicinity of the fibre. Were it the latter case, it would be necessary to postulate the transfer of RNA templates, or of proteins to the nerve fibre after their synthesis in the glia cells. There are instances of the transfer of RNA in biological systems. For example, RNA transport has been demonstrated in insect oogenesis (Bier, 1963). The observations of Hydén and Lange, and Pevzner on the reciprocal relationship between the content of RNA in the neurons and glia are discussed elsewhere (p. 81).

3. *Nature of axonal RNA*

At present there is no unanimity on the types of RNA present in the axon. Palay and Palade (1955) were unable to detect ribosomes in the axons. This does not conflict with the findings of J. E. Edström (1967), who observed that the base compositions of the RNA extracted from the axon and cell body of the Mauthner neuron of the gold-fish are distinctly different from one another. The cell body is rich in guanine and cytosine and is similar to ribosomal type of RNA, while the RNA from the axon has a base composition unlike that of the ribosomes. The sedimentation constant of the RNA synthesized in the Mauthner nerve fibre with radioactive uridine pulse *in vitro* was found to be approximately four.

The presence of messenger-like RNA is suggested by the work of some investigators who have reported possible local synthesis of proteins in the axon (A. Edström, 1966, 1967; Koenig, 1967). Another report (Miani *et al.*, 1966) has described the presence of ribosomal and other types of

RNA in the axons of the hypoglossal and vagus nerves of the rabbit. RNA was extracted from the axons six days after an intraventricular injection of [^{32}P]*ortho*phosphate. An analysis of the RNA on density gradients showed the presence of 28 s, 18 s and 4 s RNA.

E. *Synaptosomes*

Synaptosomes prepared from rat brain have been shown to be able to synthesize proteins as a unit (Austin and Morgan, 1967). This property is ascribed to not only synaptosomal mitochondria but also to membrane structures derived from synaptosomes. The association of ribonucleoprotein particles with membrane fragments is indicated by the work of Bodian (1965). D'Monte and Talwar (1967) obtained a non-dialysable extract from three areas of the monkey brain by gentle treatment of the tissues with urea solutions. Its chemical nature was that of ribonucleoprotein and it is likely that this material may correspond to the RNP granules associated with the membrane structures. More recently, Balazs and Cocks (1967) have reported that the synaptosomes contained about 6% of the RNA and about 20% protein of the whole tissue. Most of this RNA (90%) was in particulate material after disruption of the nerve-ending particle fraction, and about half of it was in the fraction containing mitochondria.

F. *Comments on the function of RNA in dendrites, axon and synaptosomes*

An important parameter of the functional maturity of the brain may be conceived in terms of the formation of new circuits. Normal cells in tissue culture have the property of adhering to each other. The contact is not random but a cell is able to recognize its type, with the result that in mixed cultures, distinct colonies of the different types of tissues emerge. The property of adhesion to its own type of cell is "lost" in malignant cells. The nature of surface "markers" and other factors involved in the creation of contacts are not known. They may be proteins (or derivatives such as glyco-proteins, lipoproteins, sialo proteins, etc.) characteristic of the cell type.

In the central nervous system, electron dense areas between membranes (desmosomes) have been described. The presence of some substance at the adhesion spots can not be ruled out. In fact, the establishment of the contact may be related to the synthesis of this material.

The creation of "boutons" again envisages the synthesis of proteins and other structural components. The presence of ribosomes and endoplasmic reticulum in close proximity to the junctional membrane may indeed have the role of synthesizing new proteins required for the establishment of the connections. This argument may be extended to all such cases where RNP particles are observed in association with membrane fragments (synapto-somes).

If the argument for a requirement of protein synthesis for the purposes of the genesis and/or maintenance of a connection is accepted, one may consider the synaptic interconnection established by a long axon of a cell to another cell. The proteins in this case would either be made available by the presynaptic or the postsynaptic cell. If the synthesis of proteins in the nerve cell be restricted to the perikaryon, these proteins will need to migrate to distal parts from the presynaptic cell, a proposition totally feasible by the known observations, and the available information on the rates of axoplasmic flow. On the other hand, contribution by the postsynaptic cell is equally likely, particularly because of the proximity of its perikaryon and dendrite protein-synthesizing machinery. Finally, the possibility of a local synthesis of essential proteins at or around the nerve endings can not be excluded till such time as more clear information is available on this issue.

The source of axonal RNA is still shrouded in mystery. The fact that the axonal synthesis of proteins is subject to inhibition by actinomycin D, would suggest that the axonal RNA would emanate from and be a product of DNA-containing entities. The likely candidates would be the mitochondria and the glia cells. The observation of local synthesis of a key enzyme such as cholinesterase underlines the importance of these additional nonparikaryonal protein-synthesizing units. The contributory role of the glia (and/or mitochondria) towards the metabolic needs of the nerve cell is also indicated by these observations.

IV. Properties of Brain RNA

A. *Physical properties*

1. *MAK columns*

RNA has been extracted from the whole brain, as well as from isolated nuclei and cytoplasm and has been analysed on methylated albumin Kieselguhr (MAK) columns and on sucrose density gradients.

The MAK columns resolve bacterial RNA into three peaks: (i) A broad peak of 4 s transfer RNA (tRNA) intermingled with 5 s RNA eluted at low concentrations of the salt, and (ii) two peaks of ribosomal RNA (rRNA) corresponding to 16 s and 23 s components. DNA, if present as a contaminant, is eluted in between the tRNA and rRNA peaks. The RNA from animal tissues is not easily resolved into three peaks on the MAK. Moreover, a portion of the loaded RNA is tenaciously held on the column requiring the use of high temperatures in addition to high salt concentrations for elution. Using this approach Mahler *et al.* (1966) have obtained three peaks from rat brain RNA. Their sedimentation constants have been found to be 4 s, 17 s and 28 s. The 28 s peak was obtained with 1·5 M NaCl concentration at a temperature gradually raised from 45° to 65°. It was identified as ribosomal RNA on the grounds that RNA extracted from highly purified ribosomes gave also this peak. Since the purified ribosomes are active in a cell-free protein synthesis system to which no exogenous messenger is added, it is likely that there would be a certain amount of tightly bound messenger RNA in these fractions.

Toschi *et al.* (1966) obtained four radioactive peaks on MAK columns from a 5-hr labelled sample of RNA extracted from chick embryo ganglion incubated with radioactive uridine *in vitro*. These were 4 s, 18 s, 28 s and a peak eluting after the ribosomal RNA peaks, presumably a type of RNA more tenaciously held than the tRNA and rRNA on MAK.

2. *Sucrose density gradients (S.D.G.)*

On sucrose density gradients, Toschi *et al.* (1966) observed about five species of RNA, with which radioactivity was associated. These were 4 s, 18 s, 28 s, the region between 7 s and 14 s and another minor component of 30–50 s. The heavy component (30–50 s) was specially discernible when the chick embryo ganglia were incubated *in vitro* with the precursor for one hour.

Mahler *et al.* (1966) also analysed rat brain RNA on S.D.G. They obtained three peaks of ultraviolet absorbing material corresponding to 28 s, 17 s and 4 s. The observations of Mahler *et al.* and Toschi *et al.* are not necessarily contradictory. In the latter case, radioactivity permits the detection of quantitatively minor components whose ultraviolet absorption may not be important. The region between 4 s and 18 s gets highly labelled in most tissues and is believed to correspond to messenger RNA species of different sizes. The presence of a rapidly labelled RNA fraction having a sedimentation constant higher than 28 s has also been observed by Vesco and Giuditta (1967) and by Jacob *et al.* (1966). This component is inhibited by actinomycin D (Jacob *et al.*, 1966). Vesco and Giuditta find that the proportion of this fast-moving heavier component is appreciably higher in brain than in other mammalian cells.

Vesco and Giuditta (1967) have also analysed the labelled RNA from rabbit brain nuclei. The sedimentation pattern and the base composition of the newly synthesized RNA shows the presence of at least two classes of components. One of them represents the precursors of ribosomal RNA with sedimentation constants of 45 s and 32–35 s. There may also be a minor amount of mature ribosomal RNA. The second category represents a species of RNA with a wide range of sizes ranging approximately from 8 s to 80 s. It has a DNA-like base composition and may represent the messenger or template type of RNA.

In the cytoplasm, ribonucleoprotein particles of various sizes have been detected showing the presence of polysomes of different sizes. There are also free ribosomes present.

3. *Hybridization*

MAK columns and sucrose density gradients permit only the classification of RNA into broad type of categories characterized on the basis of the size of the molecule and to some extent on the base composition. These methods do not permit distinction between the molecular species within the same class of RNA. In recent years hybridization of RNA to DNA has evolved as an interesting experimental approach to assess the RNA species transcribed by different cistrons in a cell. When RNA is prepared from brain and another organ of the rat such as liver and examined for the homology of their molecular species by hybridization to rat DNA, it is observed that the brain RNA competes only partially with the liver RNA and that in the two cases there would be non-identical species of RNA present in the respective tissues (Fig. 1).

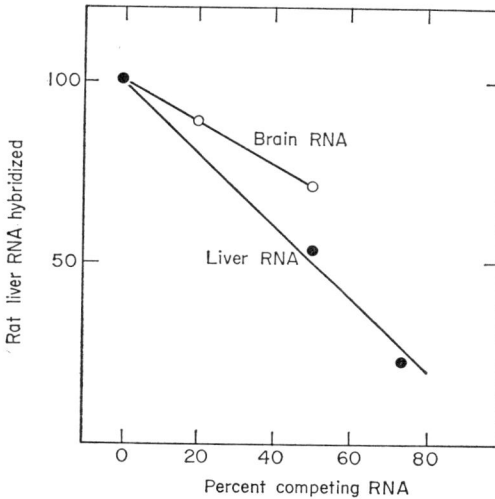

FIG. 1. Competition by unlabelled RNA from rat liver and rat brain for the hybridization of ^{32}P-labelled rat liver RNA to rat liver DNA. 1 g of DNA-agar, containing 46 μg of denatured DNA was incubated with a total of 9·3 mg of liver RNA which consisted of ^{32}P-labelled rat liver RNA and unlabelled rat liver RNA in different proportions in separate vials. For testing the competition by rat brain RNA, the incubation mixtures contained 1·8 g of DNA-agar (29 μg of DNA) and a total of 12·0 mg of RNA which consisted of ^{32}P-labelled rat liver RNA and unlabelled rat brain RNA in different proportions. The hybridization in the absence of competing RNA is taken as 100.

To sum up, an examination of the whole brain and the nuclear and cytoplasmic fractions of RNA on MAK and SDG has demonstrated the presence of the usual categories of RNA encountered in other mammalian tissues. There are no apparent qualitative differences between the RNA from the brain and other tissues as far as their sedimentation patterns and adsorption properties on MAK columns are concerned. Short pulse labelling experiments, however, show a quantitatively higher proportion of a component heavier than 28 s in the brain RNA as compared to other tissues.

Hybridization of rat brain RNA and rat liver RNA to rat DNA demonstrates only partial identity of the molecular species of RNA in the two cases. Brain would have some species of RNA which are not present in the liver and are characteristic of the organ.

4. *Ultraviolet absorption characteristics and hyperchromicity*

The guinea pig brain ribosomal RNA has an absorption maxima at 258 mμ and a minima at 230 mμ. The ratio of E258/E230 is 2·16. The E260/280 ratio is 2·07. The molar extinction coefficient at 258 mμ is between 8150 and 8700, and at 230 mμ 3350 and 3570 (Yamagami *et al.*, 1965).

Brain ribosomal RNA, like liver ribosomal RNA, is partially hydrogen bonded and shows a hyperchromicity. Heating of the goat brain rRNA to 85°C for 20 min gives an increase of about 12–13% in absorption at 260 mμ. Hydrolysis with KOH produces an increase of 30–40% in absorption, while treatment of the guinea pig brain rRNA with 8 M urea gives an increase of 16–19% in absorption (Yamagami *et al.*, 1965; Datta, 1966).

B. *Chemical base composition*

Hydén and Egyhazi (1963, 1964) have reported changes in base composition of the RNA in neurons and glia of specific brain areas in rats when the animal has undergone a learning task. In their experiments, a non-learning stimulus only increases the amount of RNA without causing any change in base composition of the RNA. It has been considered useful to document some information on the base composition of the different types of RNA in the brain, as illustrated by Table V. It may be seen that the ribosomal RNA from rat cortex and guinea pig brain have very nearly the same base

TABLE V

Base composition of RNA

Source	A	G	C	U	Reference
(1) Rat cortex rRNA	18·4	32·3	31·2	18·1	(A)
(2) Guinea pig brain rRNA	19·5	32·1	29·0	19·3	(B)
(3) Rat liver rRNA	18·7	33·8	29·6	18·9	(C)
(4) Mouse brain tRNA	18·2	31·5	25·0	25·3	(D)
(5) Mouse brain rRNA	18·7	32·4	27·2	21·8	(D)
(6) Mouse brain					
^{32}P–2 hr	21·9	26·9	20·9	30·2	(D)
^{32}P–17 hr	17·3	32·8	28·8	20·0	(D)
(7) Nerve cells (rabbit hypoglossal nerve)	21·1	24·8	31·9	22·2	(E)
(8) Glia cells (rabbit hypoglossal nerve)	28·1	23·5	21·8	26·6	(E)
(9) Rat DNA	28·6 (including 5 Me C)	21·4	21·5	28·4 (Thymine)	(F)

References: (A) Mahler *et al.* (1966); (B) Yamagami *et al.* (1965); (C) Magasanik (1955); (D) Kimberlin (1967); (E) Daneholt and Brattgård (1966); (F) Comb *et al.* (1965).

composition, which is again similar to that of the rat liver rRNA. All ribosomal RNAs are rich in GC content.

The analysis of RNA from neurons and glia of the hypoglossal nuclei of the rabbit shows that the neuronal RNA is rich in cytosine nucleotides and relatively poor in adenine nucleotides. Glial RNA, on the other hand, is rich in A and U. It would appear that the nerve cell RNA is predominantly of GC type and the glial RNA of AU type. This is so because the quantity of cytoplasmic RNA present in nerve cells is greater than the nuclear RNA, which is not the case in glia; hence the apparent dominance of GC and AU in the overall composition of RNA in these two cases.

The nuclear RNA in the brain has a lower GC content than the cyto-plasmic RNA (Yamagami et al., 1964), as is also apparent from the base composition of newly synthesized RNA after a short pulse of radioactive precursor.

V. RNA in Developing Brain

A. Content of RNA

Neither the content of RNA nor its rate of synthesis remains constant in the brain in the course of development. In developing rabbit pups, the RNA content of most areas of the brain increases at a rapid rate from day one to about the tenth day (Fig. 2). The pups in this colony opened their eyes on or about the eleventh day. The RNA content (RNA/DNA) of the occipital

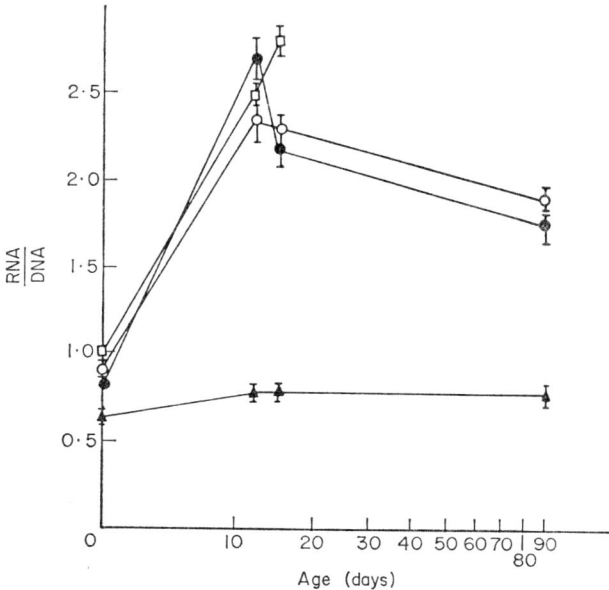

FIG. 2. RNA content of various areas of rabbit brain at different ages. ●, Occipital cortex; ○, cerebral cortex; ▲, cerebellar cortex; □, hippocampus.

cortex (areas 17, 18 and 19) decreased slightly but significantly following the opening of the eyes. Prior blinding of the animal prevented the fall of RNA in the occipital cortex following the opening of the eyes. The changes occurring in other parts of the cerebral cortex resembled to some degree the changes in the occipital cortex of the rabbits during this period. Other parts of the brain, for example the cerebellar cortex, or the hippocampus, were not influenced in the same manner (Talwar et al., 1964). In the occipital cortex there is a rise in the proteins during this period (two days before and two days after opening of the eyes), which is prevented to a significant extent by prior blinding of the animal (Fig. 3). It is possible that a fall in

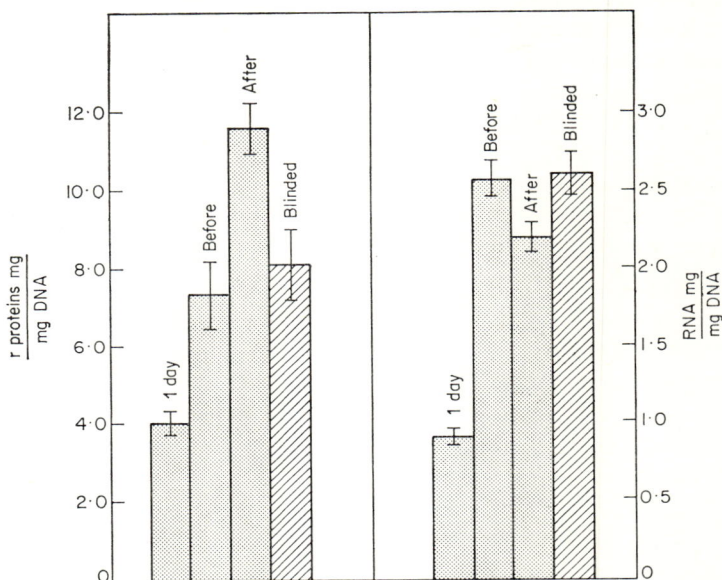

FIG. 3. RNA and protein content of the occipital cortex of rabbit brain at age 1 day and at periods two days before and two days after opening of the eyes. A set of litter-mates was blinded on day four and analysed at the same time as the non-blinded litter-mates two days after opening of the eyes (13th–15th day of age).

total cellular RNA at this stage is related to the synthesis of structural components. Several proteins or enzymes are formed rapidly at defined stages of development, e.g. the $Na^+ - K^+ -$ activated ATPase activity rises rapidly in the chick embryo brain between day ten and twelve, after which its specific activity remains constant (Zaheer et al., 1968). The increase in the activity of this enzyme bears a temporal relationship to the maturation of spontaneous and evoked electrical activity in the chick embryo brain.

B. Rate of RNA synthesis

In developing rats, Orrego (1967) observed that the incorporation of [2^{14}C]uridine into RNA of the brain decreased appreciably from three-day-old to adult rats. The apparent rate of RNA synthesis was reduced by almost five-fold. Johnson (1967) who has made similar observations in mice, used cell suspensions from brain which incorporate radioactive precursors actively into RNA *in vitro*. He found the synthesis of RNA to be rapid in brain cells prepared from newborn mice, and as the mice matured, nucleic acid metabolism diminished progressively. The synthesis of nuclear RNA appeared to diminish after the animals were approximately six days old.

These observations would be consistent with the report of Barondes (1964), showing that the RNA-polymerase activity assayed in nuclear aggregate preparations was higher in immature rat brain as compared to adult brain tissue. However, Bondy and Waelsch (1964) were able to obtain contradictory results on the RNA-polymerase activity in nuclei isolated from rabbit brain. They observed the activity of the cerebral cortex nuclei of rabbit brain to be higher in adults than in newborn. The RNA-polymerase activity varied from area to area in the brain. The cerebral cortex had a high activity, while the activity in the corpus callosum and the thalamus was approximately half as much. The activity in brain nuclei was much higher than in nuclei obtained from liver, indicating a higher potential rate of synthesis of RNA in the brain.

Yamagami *et al.* (1966) have reported that mRNA from young rat brain tissue was more active in stimulating the incorporation of amino acids into proteins in a cell-free system than preparations from adult animals.

VI. Metabolism of Brain RNA

The biosynthesis and the breakdown of RNA in the neural tissue has been followed both *in vivo* and *in vitro*. The main aims of these studies have been to define the kinetics, subcellular distribution and probable turnover rates of RNA in the brain. Moreover, a few *in vitro* systems have been evolved which are capable of incorporating radioactive precursors into RNA and which simulate to some extent the properties of the *in vivo* system. There have also been a few studies in which the incorporation of radioactive precursors (e.g. [³H]uridine) into polymeric constituents in different parts of the cell has been followed by autoradiography (Hancock, 1965; Shimada and Nakamura, 1966).

A. In vivo *metabolism*

1. *Incorporation into different subcellular fractions*

In analogy with the results obtained with other tissues, most workers have observed that the radioactive precursors are incorporated predominantly into the nuclear fractions of RNA of the brain in the first instance. In course of time the cytoplasmic fractions show also the labelling, suggesting a precursor role of the nuclear RNA in their formation. Bondy (1966) injected [2¹⁴C]cytidine intracisternally into rats and found that 80% of the labelled

RNA was localized in the nuclear fraction within the first hour. The radio-activity of nuclear RNA declined rapidly in the first few hours, while the radioactivity in ribosomal and transfer RNA increased. The transfer rate slowed down after about two days. On the 25th day, 16% of the total radioactivity was present in the nuclear fractions, while the radioactivity in ribosomal fractions represented about 60% of the total.

The finding of an appreciable fraction of labelled RNA in the nuclei some three weeks after a single injection of the radioactive precursor is not without significance. This may be due to the re-utilization of breakdown products of RNA, or it could indicate increased stability of a portion of RNA synthesized in the nucleus. Factors regulating the transfer of nuclear RNA to cytoplasmic fractions are little understood. There are indications that all species of RNA synthesized in the mammalian cell nuclei may not be transferred to the cytoplasm. The cytoplasmic RNA from the rat liver competes only partially with the RNA prepared from purified nuclei for hybridization against homologous DNA (Shearer and McCarthy, 1967). In the regenerating phase following partial hepatectomy, more of the nuclear RNA species are transferred to the cytoplasm as tested by hybridization techniques (Church and McCarthy, 1967). There is also evidence of the synthesis of large aggregates of RNA in the duck reticulocytes; the size of this RNA is far greater than the calculated size of the messenger RNA for haemoglobin (Houssais and Attardi, 1966; Scherrer et al., 1966). It is also known that the precursors of 28 s and 18 s ribosomal RNA are molecules of 45 s RNA in the nucleus (Scherrer et al., 1963; Girard et al., 1965). Several of the RNA molecules synthesized in the nuclei may therefore require either partial cleavage or transformation before passage to the cytoplasm.

The early concentration of labelled precursors into nuclear RNA of the brain is also supported by other studies. Hancock (1965) showed by auto-radiography the heavy concentration of radioactivity in the nuclei of the pyramidal cells of the hippocampus of mice after an injection of [^{3}H]uridine. Balazs and Cocks (1967) showed rapid incorporation of [6^{14}C]orotic acid into RNA of the nuclear fractions of rat brain. The nuclei contained more than 80% of the total [^{14}C]incorporated up to 1·5 hr after injection.

A lag period is usually observed in the labelling of RNA in the cyto-plasmic fractions. The incorporation of radioactivity into rRNA was clearly seen at 90 min after injection. An RNA fraction of high specific radioactivity and of heterogenous sedimentation properties was noticed in the 4 s–20 s region. The highest rate of incorporation of [^{14}C]orotic acid was in the RNA of the supernatant fraction (Balazs and Cocks, 1967). These workers have also given evidence for the incorporation of radio-active precursors into RNA of the synaptosomes *in situ* independent of the axoplasmic flow from the cell body.

Jacob et al. (1967) have demonstrated the presence of polysomes in rat brain. Eighty per cent of the ribosomes were in the form of polysome aggregates mostly in the range of 100–120 s and some up to 250 s. These aggregates were presumably composed of 80 s ribosomes linked together by an RNA chain. According to these workers, about 80% of the total labelled RNA was represented by messenger RNA 1 hr after the injection of the radioactive precursor. After 2 hr about 70% of the total radioactivity was in mRNA. A lag period was noticed for the synthesis of ribosomal RNA.

2. Turnover rates

Tracer experiments have shown an appreciable turnover of ribosomal RNA *in vivo* in mouse brain which amounts to approximately 0·2% per hr. Bondy (1966) has computed a half-life of about 12·5 days for brain ribosomal and tRNA. This is of the same order as the half-life time of 13–15 days, reported by Khan and Wilson (1965) for the major fractions of rat brain microsomes.

Dawson (1967) has reported an apparent half-life of six days for brain ribosomal RNA. Their studies, however, do not rule out the re-utilization of precursors; hence these values would be a minimum, and possibly rRNA with longer half-lives would be present in the brain. The half-life of liver ribosomal RNA have been found to be about 5–7·2 days and of liver tRNA 5·2 days (Gerber *et al.*, 1960; Loeb *et al.*, 1965). These figures, if true, would indicate a significant difference in the turnover rates of RNA in the liver and brain. At best the rRNA of the brain would be turning over at the same rate as liver RNA but *more probably* at half of the rate of the liver RNA.

3. Messenger RNA

Data on the turnover rates of messenger RNA in cortex and subcortex of rat brain shows the presence of at least two populations of mRNA (Appel, 1967). A more labile fraction representing most of the template RNAs has a half-life of less than four hours, and another smaller population of molecules is stable for longer than 20 hr. The data also suggest a population of relatively stable molecules in the cortex with a turnover rate of less than 10–12 hr. Orrego and Lipmann (1967) estimated a mean half-life of 2·6 hr for the unstable template RNA in brain slices.

B. In vitro *metabolism*

Incorporation of a wide variety of precursors into RNA has been obtained in three types of brain preparations: (i) tissue slices, (ii) cell cultures, and (iii) cell suspensions.

An incorporation of [^{32}P]*ortho*phosphate into RNA fractions of cat brain slices was demonstrated by DeLuca *et al.* (1953) and Findlay *et al.* (1954); and in guinea pig brain slices by Heald (1957). More recently, Cain (1967) has described the characteristics of the incorporation of [^{3}H]uridine and [^{3}H]uridine-5′-monophosphate into adult guinea pig cortex slices. The incorporation of these precursors is better than that of [³H]orotic acid or of [¹⁴C]adenine or of uracil. The fact that UMP is incorporated and also that the relative specific activity of RNA is more or less identical for [³H]uridine and [³H]UMP suggests that UMP is dephosphorylated before uptake by the cell. The uptake in tissue slices soaking in a tris-HCl phosphate medium (with various salts) was of the order of 5·4–5·8% of that present in the medium in 30 min. The reaction is linear over a 90-min period of observation. There is a negligible conversion of [³H]uridine into cytidine of the RNA, hence the terminal incorporation in tRNA does not vitiate the results when [³H]uridine is employed as a precursor. Uptake into RNA is inhibited 40% with 1·5 μg/ml. actinomycin D and by as much as 70% with 6 μg/ml. The inhibition curve levels off beyond a 6 μg/ml. concentration of the inhibitor to reach 85% inhibition with 39 μg/ml. Orrego and Lipmann (1967) have been able to obtain 98% inhibition of RNA synthesis in brain slices with actinomycin D. They have also postulated that all measurable synthesis of proteins *in vitro* is directed by an unstable template RNA, whose mean half-life was estimated by them as 2·6 hr. Singh (1965) observed that a major portion of the [8¹⁴C]adenine radioactivity incorporated into RNA in brain slices of young rats is localized in soluble RNA (4 s) and in relatively small amounts of highly labile fractions in the region between 10 s and 20 s. Smaller peaks with s values > 30 s are also observed.

Toschi *et al.* (1964, 1966) have grown *in vitro* sympathetic and sensory ganglia from chick embryo in the presence of a specific nerve growth factor (NGF). NGF stimulates in the first instance the synthesis of RNA in tissue that is inhibited by actinomycin D, but its synthesis is not prevented by puromycin. The types of RNA synthesized in the presence or absence of NGF are the same, and it would appear that NGF influences primarily the rate of RNA synthesis in these tissues.

Johnson (1967) has employed brain cell suspensions for *in vitro* studies on RNA and protein synthesis. The incorporation of radioactive precursors into RNA and proteins in this system is both good and rapid, the rate of incorporation being linear for 60 min. The amount of precursor incorporated into RNA was reported as being sensitive to the amount of tissue present and to the concentration of oxygen employed in the incubation atmosphere.

VII. Neuron as a Secretory Cell

Besides receiving, propagating and transmitting impulses, neurons are also secretory cells. A number of neurohumours are synthesized by these cells, and are continuously required for synaptic transmission and/or inhibition. There are also some nuclei, which synthesize and secrete polypeptides of great physiological significance. The posterior pituitary hormones oxytocin and vasopressin, both octapeptides, are elaborated in the neurons of the hypothalamus. In recent years a number of other polypeptides have been identified in hypothalamic extracts which stimulate the secretion of several hormones of the anterior pituitary. It is through these products that integration is achieved between neuronal and endocrine activities of the body.

Many of these "release factors" have been obtained in semipurified form. They appear to be peptides of a probable chain length involving 8 to 20 amino acid units. No precise information is yet available on their mode of synthesis. Does their synthesis take place in the same way as the synthesis of larger polypeptides and proteins? Would there be short-length messenger RNAs for these release factors? Are these polypeptides cleaved from larger proteins, as is the case with angiotensin? Or would there be multi-enzyme complexes for synthesis of short length polypeptides by mechanisms different from the conventionally known mechanisms for the synthesis of proteins? There are more questions than answers in this area. There is some suggestive evidence pointing to the presence of a larger precursor protein for the formation of vasopressin (Sachs, 1963; Sachs and Takabatake, 1964). Investigations are also being done to detect in cerebral tissue the presence of different types of peptidases (Lajtha and Marks, 1966; Marks et al., 1967), which may have a role in the cleavage of polypeptides.

VIII. Alterations in Functional States

A. *Stimulation*

Numerous investigators have reported changes in the content or composition of RNA of the neural tissue under a wide variety of conditions (for review see Einarson, 1957; Hydén, 1960; Pevzner, 1966; Talwar et al., 1966a). At times the observations are conflicting, which emphasizes the complexity of the problem. It is difficult to state at this stage whether there is any *direct* relation between RNA and the functional activity of the brain, even though changes in RNA metabolism have been noticed in different situations.

1. *Moderate stimulation*

In general, stimuli of moderate intensity have been observed to cause an increase in the RNA content of the whole brain or of cells in specific areas of the nervous system. The earlier and most extensive work has been done by Hydén and co-workers (see Hydén, 1960). A sizeable increase was found in the content of cytoplasmic RNA in rabbit spinal ganglion cell following electrical stimulation of exposed ganglion for 5 min. Acoustic stimulation increased the RNA content of rabbit cochlear ganglion cell by 50–100%. Light rotation increased the RNA concentration of the vestibular ganglion cells and Deiters' cells by 30–100%. Other workers have obtained similar results. Attardi (1957) obtained 70–80% stimulation of RNA in rat cerebellar Purkinje neurons on gradual rotation of the animals. Edström and Eichner (1958b) found an increase in the cytoplasmic and nucleolar content of RNA in the ganglion cells of the supraoptic nucleus after stimulation with sodium chloride. Vraa-Jensen (1957) observed that the nerve cells were more chromophilic at the onset of functional activity (see also Einarson, 1957). Several other reports including the work of Russian scientists have been reviewed elsewhere (Pevzner, 1966).

There are also some reports in the literature where investigators have failed to observe any change in the RNA content of the nerve cells on moderate stimulation. Grampp and Edström (1963), working with an isolated lobster stretch receptor organ, noticed that the generation and conduction of about 100 000 spike potentials over a period of several hours did not alter the total amount of RNA of the nerve cell body. However, there were some changes in the base composition of cellular RNA, namely an increase in the A/U ratio and purine to pyrimidine ratios. This result does not rule out the possible influence of electrical activity on the metabolism of RNA in the cell, even though the total RNA content remains essentially unchanged.

There are also reports on a decrease in RNA of the brain on stimulation. Geiger (1957) found that the stimulation of the brain cortex of the cat via the brachial plexus, or by directly applied electrodes caused a breakdown of nucleic acids and lipids with a concomitant rise in non-protein nitrogen. The breakdown was proportional to the number of stimuli. The process was reversible within a few minutes.

2. *Intense stimulation*

Intense stimulation of cortical tissue by electrical, chemical (e.g. convulsants) or motor activity has been *invariably* found to cause a fall in the RNA content of the tissue. Hydén and co-workers (for references see Hydén, 1960; Pevzner, 1966; Talwar, 1966a) have reported a decrease of RNA of the brain following convulsions induced by insulin, electrical stimulation of spinal ganglion cells, intense muscular work or intense acoustic stimulation. Vrba and Folbergrova (1959) reported that strenuous physical exercise (compulsive swimming) in rats led to a decrease in nucleic acids, proteins and orcinol positive substances. Metrazol convulsions caused a fall in brain RNA in rats (Talwar *et al.*, 1961; Chitre *et al.*, 1964). Topical application of metrazol on neuronally "isolated" cerebral cortex slabs also caused a depletion of RNA in the cortical tissue during the spike phase of electrical activity as compared to contralateral gyri in dogs (Chitre and Talwar, 1963). A significant fall was observed in the RNA content of isolated Purkinje cells of rats after administration of large doses of insulin to the animals (Barbato and Barbato, 1965).

Orrego (1967) who stimulated brain slices electrically (1·5 V for 10 min) *in vitro*, observed a fall of about 40% in the rate of synthesis of RNA. But there was no change in the rate of RNA breakdown.

The probable reason for a net depletion of RNA during strenuous exercise or sustained stimulation is a slowing down of the synthesis of RNA caused by decreased availability of the triphosphates of the four nucleosides. Most of the experimental systems used in these studies are reversible in character. On withdrawal of the stress, the tissue returns to its normal state, which suggests (*a*) that no irreversible damage is done to the cerebral tissue on curtailment or inhibition of the synthesis of RNA over short periods, and (*b*) the existence of fine regulatory mechanisms which permit the restoration of cellular RNA levels during the recovery period.

3. *Sensory stimulation*

In this section experimental data on two sensory systems will be examined.

a. *Visual system*

The visual cortex of mammals and primates presents a high degree of complexity. Five different types of neurons have been described on the basis of their response to light and darkness (Jung, 1958). Type A neurons do not react to retinal afferent impulses. In cats they constitute about half of the total visual cortex neurons and give a continuous background discharge independent of retinal stimuli. Type B and D are antagonistic neurons, B neurons being activated by light-on and D by light-off. C neurons are inhibited after light-on and light-off, and E neurons show a short pre-excitory stimulation by light-on followed by activation and stronger activation by light-off. In the context of this intricate organization pattern, it is difficult to design an experimental system, in which all neurons of the visual cortex can be synchronized and brought in "activated" or inhibited state. However, by using a rhythmically flickering light, activation can be obtained over the high basal values. Type D and E neurons show a maximal response at a flicker frequency of 7 per sec. B neurons show a maximal response at a flicker frequency of 10 per sec. The average response of all light sensitive neurons is maximal between the flicker frequency of 7 and 12 per sec (Jung, 1958).

Talwar *et al.* (1966*b*) observed a higher incorporation of radioactive amino acid precursors into proteins of the occipital cortex in rabbits which were exposed to a rhythmically flickering light of a flicker frequency of seven per second as compared to those kept in darkness. Singh and Talwar (1967) made similar observations in monkeys. Monkeys exposed to light of 1614 lumen/m^2 intensity and a flicker frequency of seven/sec for 45 min showed a higher incorporation of intracisternally administered [U^{3}H]lysine into proteins of the occipital cortex (areas 17, 18 and 19) as compared to animals maintained in darkness. In parallel experiments the incorporation of [^{32}P]*ortho*phosphate or [^{3}H]uridine into RNA of the occipital cortex was higher in monkeys kept in darkness, as compared to those exposed to a rhythmically flickering source of light (Talwar *et al.*, 1966*a*; Goel and Talwar, to be published). There is an appreciable difference in the relative specific radioactivities in the two cases. The rate of synthesis of RNA in the occipital cortex is low in monkeys exposed to flickering light. The rate is several fold higher in monkeys kept in darkness. Data is also available on the types of RNA synthesized in the occipital cortex in the phase of darkness.

The radioactivity is identified with almost all peaks of RNA (28 s, 17 s, >4 s and 4 s) including some with a sedimentation constant >28 s. The highest proportion of the newly synthesized RNA was however in the RNA fractions with sedimentation constants of 4 s and 4 s–17 s. There are indications that the incorporation of [^{32}P]*ortho*phosphate into phospholipids of the occipital cortex may also be higher in monkeys kept in darkness as compared to those exposed to the rhythmically flickering light.

The physiological significance of these results is not yet understood. Some speculations can however be made. In the first instance, it is likely that the rate of RNA synthesis is *not* uniform in all cells of the occipital cortex under physiological conditions. Second, it is possible that, in normal circumstances, RNA is synthesized in the occipital cortex of the monkey in only a limited category of neurons and if these neurons are inhibited by the flickering light, the synthesis of RNA (along with other metabolic activities) is also diminished. An alternative possibility is that a lower synthesis of RNA during photic stimulation results from an inhibition of RNA synthesis in cells activated by the flickering light. This is a conceivable postulate as intensive photic stimulation can limit the availability of the RNA precursor tri-phosphates by diversion of ATP to other metabolic needs of the cells. If this hypothesis be true, the RNA isolated from the occipital cortex of the monkeys kept in darkness would in fact represent the RNA synthesized normally in those cells which are sensitive to hyperactivation by the flickering light. Autoradiographic studies are in progress to verify these hypotheses.

The messenger RNA of rat brain is sensitive to environmental changes of light and darkness (Appel *et al.*, 1967). Kupfer and Downer (1967) have also reported an initial rise in the RNA content of lateral geniculate nucleus (LGN) in monkeys after afferent denervation. The optic tract was sectioned in these monkeys and the contralateral area of LGN served as a control.

b. Olfactory stimulation

Studies have been undertaken to correlate the changes in the synthesis of nuclear RNA in the brain of fishes to olfactory stimulants. Salt-water catfish (*Galeichthys felis*) was allowed to swim for one hour in sea-water containing different odorants. Morpholine at a concentration of 10^{-4}M–10^{-6}M induced an increase in brain nuclear RNA in comparison to controls maintained in plain sea-water. There were also changes in the base composition of the brain RNA. These changes were reversed within 24 hr to the levels of unstimulated controls on transfer of the stimulated fish to fresh sea-water (Rappoport and Daginawala, 1968). Similar experiments using split brain preparations with amyl acetate as the odorant also elicited an increase in brain nuclear RNA and a change in base ratios of RNA. The change in base ratios was distinctly different from that induced by morpholine. Two other odorants were also tried. Camphor induced an increase in brain nuclear RNA while menthol caused a decrease. However, neither of these odorants changed the base ratios of the nuclear RNA to any appreciable extent. Shrimp and red fish skin extracts caused no change in the amount of brain nuclear RNA, but the base ratios showed a definite change and were different from those elicited by other odorants.

B. *Drugs and RNA*

With the belief that RNA is related to the processes of learning, there has been a surge of research into chemical agents which can help stimulate the synthesis of RNA in the brain. Conversely, in order to verify the part played by RNA in learning and storage of memory, inhibitors of RNA synthesis have been extensively used for experimental purposes.

1. *Stimulants of RNA synthesis*

Malonitril was one of the first compounds discovered by Hydén and Hartelius (1948) to increase the content of RNA in rabbit motor neurons. A derivative of the same compound, viz. tricyanoaminopropene has been used by Chamberlain *et al.* (1963) with apparently good results in terms of stimulation of nucleic acid levels in the brain. More recently, Glasky and Simon (1966) have reported another compound, magnesium pemoline, to cause the activation of the RNA polymerase of rat brain after a single intraperitoneal injection (20 mg/kg). The compound stimulated also the homopolymer synthesizing activity in rat brain nuclei. However, *in vitro*, the compound activated only the true RNA polymerase. Other psychotropic agents such as imipramine, methamphetamine, methylphenidate, pargyline, piradol and trimethadione failed to produce a similar selective activation of the brain RNA polymerase system.

Caffeine (500 mg/kg) and camphor (400 mg/kg) produced within 4 hr a rise in the RNA of the visual cortex of rats, especially in the outermost and innermost layers (Baranov and Pevzner, 1963). These workers also found that hexenal (100 mg/kg) induced an increase in the RNA content of the outer layers of the motor cortex.

2. *Inhibitors of RNA synthesis*

Actinomycin D has been the drug of choice for inhibition studies, presumably because of its specific action in blocking DNA-dependent RNA synthesis. This compound which has a high affinity for guanine residues of the DNA, is thought to fit into the minor groove of the DNA helix, thus offering steric hindrance, and in turn, preventing the migration of the polymerase along the DNA strand (Hamilton *et al.*, 1963).

Actinomycin D is active both *in vivo* and *in vitro*. Its high toxicity limits its systemic utilization. However, by giving multiple intracerebral injections, an inhibition up to 96% of the total RNA synthesis can be achieved (Cohen and Barondes, 1966).

Pyrimidine and purine analogues have also been used, but only to a limited scale. [2^{14}C]8-Azaguanine was incorporated by as much as 0·05% into RNA of rat brain (Dingman and Sporn, 1961).

IX. RNA in Learning Processes and Memory

A. *Molecular basis of long-term memory*

Rapid advances made in molecular genetics in the past two decades have led to theories about information storage in the brain. The known ability of nucleic acids and proteins for encoding the genetic, enzymatic and immunological memory have rendered them as likely candidates for exploration. A number of excellent reviews have been written on the subject (Dingman and Sporn, 1961, 1964; Hydén, 1966; Eigen, 1966; Roberts, 1966; Gaito, 1966; Appel, 1966; Agranoff, 1967; Schmitt, 1967), so that the problem will be discussed here only very briefly.

Psychologists have distinguished two types of memory, viz., short-term and long-term memory. While short-term memory may reside in reverberating circuits, it is highly likely that long-term memory has a structural basis. The following hypothesis can be formulated:

(i) The psychological information is stored in the form of a subcellular molecular structure. It may be a sequence of polynucleotides in DNA or RNA, a spatial configuration as in a protein molecule or a molecular array as in a lipid membrane. The experimental input is translated by the cells to produce a specific macromolecule. This macromolecule would have the ability to "respond" by a conformational change when challenged by an appropriate stimulus.

(ii) Learning and sensory experience are consolidated by the establishment of new junctions. Molecules are synthesized by cells to negotiate intercellular connection, and information storage in this case would be essentially at the cellular or synaptic level.

(iii) Lastly, it may be postulated that an input is stored neither in the form of a specific molecular engram, nor in the form of specific intercellular contacts, but its role may reside in activating or inhibiting existing pathways by causing the release of neurohumours.

The initial processes connected with the processing of an electrical impulse in the nerve cell (and glia) are poorly understood. One may postulate a molecular structure of labile nature, which is perturbed by a change in electric fields or by electrochemical factors such as concentration of electrolytes and other charged molecules, pH, etc. This conformation change may activate a single or a chain of metabolic events, thus rendering the transduction of an electric message into chemical components.

The impulse signal has a time constant in the range of milliseconds. The "consolidation" of the experience usually requires minutes and sometimes hours. If electric shock is applied after a few seconds of learning, it does not interfere in the consolidation process, which suggests that the information content of the impulse is fixed and processed beyond the point sensitive to electrical shocks after about ten seconds. There is a transfer of information from an electrical or electrochemical pattern to a spatial pattern within this short time. The synthesis of macromolecules may well be involved. In bacteria enzymes are induced within minutes. A polynucleotide chain of about 3×10^6 mol. wt can grow in 1 sec in *E. coli* and a protein of about 10^4 mol. wt can be synthesized in 1 sec. These orders of magnitude fulfil the theoretical temporal requirements for fixation of electrical information into structural macromolecular components.

It is further observed that if inhibitors of protein synthesis are given immediately after learning trials, the experience is not fixed as memory (Agranoff, 1967). On the other hand, if the inhibitors are given one hour after the learning trials, no interference is observed in consolidation of the learnt experience. The inhibitors of protein synthesis do not suppress the learning act. These experiments help to distinguish two distinct phases, the initial phase of learning independent of the synthesis of macromolecules (like proteins) and the consolidation phase where synthesis of macro-molecules e.g. proteins, is required.

B. *Arguments in favour of RNA*

1. *Changes in the content and composition of RNA*

Hydén and collaborators have been the pioneer group in suggesting the involvement of RNA in learning and storage of experience. Amongst their many observations, the following may be cited. When rats were trained to balance on a wire perched at 45° in order to obtain food, it was found that there was a significant increase in the nuclear RNA of both neurons and glia from the Dieters' nucleus. The base ratios of the nuclear RNA were also altered with an increase in A/U ratio. Plain vestibular stimulation caused only an increase in the nuclear RNA, but no change in the base composition of the RNA (Hydén and Egyhazi, 1962, 1963). Similar results were obtained by them in rats which were trained to use the other hand (Hydén and Egyhazi, 1964).

An increase in the RNA content of neurons has been observed in many cases following moderate stimulation. In catfish, various odorants were found to elicit a change in nuclear RNA and/or changes in the base compo-sition of RNA (Rappoport and Daginawala, 1968). In stretch receptor preparations of the lobster, spike potentials caused changes in the base composition of RNA though there was no alteration in the content of RNA (Grampp and Edström, 1963). To sum up, it may be stated that inconsistent changes in either content, composition (or both) of RNA have been reported in many instances.

2. *RNA as a vehicle for transfer of learnt experience*

This approach has been perhaps inspired by the epoch-making experi-ments of Avery *et al.* (1944) in which transformation of genetic charac-teristics was achieved with DNA. The first observations were reported on planaria. The feeding of trained planaria to untrained ones was seen to result in transfer of learnt experience (McConnell et al., 1959; Corning and John, 1961). Babich et al. (1965) reported the transfer of a response to naïve rats by injection of RNA extracted from trained rats. Similar results were obtained by Fjerdingstad et al. (1965) and Albert (1966). Brain extracts have been used by Rosenblatt et al. (1966) and by Ungar and Cohen (1966) for transfer of conditioned responses from trained rats to untrained rats, or for transfer of morphine tolerance ability.

3. *Action of RNA stimulating drugs*

Magnesium pemoline, a compound which is claimed to increase RNA-polymerase activity in the brain, has been reported to cause an enhancement of learning and memory in a conditioned avoidance response (Plotnikoff, 1966). Frey and Polidora (1967), who have extended these studies, find that the effect of magnesium pemoline is more to facilitate the acquisition of training rather than on its retention. Chamberlain et al. (1963) have reported the beneficial effect of tricyanoamino-propene on acquisition rates of conditioned avoidance responses.

C. *Arguments against RNA*

Though changes in content and/or composition of RNA have been observed, there is no evidence that these changes represent either unique or specific events in transduction of electrical impulses into molecular engrams.

The data on the transfer of learnt experiences through RNA is still not well established. A letter signed by 24 investigators has reported their failure to repeat these results (Byrne et al., 1966). Similarly, Smith (1967) has failed to obtain either a facilitation of learning or memory with magnesium pemoline in human beings.

The work on planaria is also disputable. Bennett and Calvin (1964) have discussed the non-reliabillty of planarians for training experiments.

Finally, an inhibition (up to 96%) of RNA synthesis in the brain of mice with actinomycin D has not influenced either the learning of mazes or retention of learned experience by the mice (Cohen and Barondes, 1966).

X. Summary and Conclusions

This chapter has summarized some facts (and fallacies) on brain RNA. Neurons have a variable content of RNA (50–2000 $\mu\mu$g), even though the RNA content of large neurons in some areas of the brain may be very high; the overall RNA/DNA ratios in the brain are lower than those of liver and pancreas. Comparative studies in various species show that the RNA content of the brain does not bear any relation to the degree of evolution of the animal.

Glia have a relatively low RNA content but the rate of RNA synthesis is twice as rapid in glia as in the neurons. Like neurons, glia are sensitive to the functional states of the animal. Similar or reciprocal types of changes are registered in glial RNA following diverse types of stimuli. There are also indications of a possible transfer of RNA from glia to the neurons.

Neurons have prominent nucleoli and a well-developed network of endoplasmic reticulum. Most of the nerve cell RNA is localized in these structures. Recent observations on clusters of ergastoplasm in proximal dendrites lying in close apposition to membranes, and in a position subjacent to "boutons" of 3–6 μ in size, suggest a possible role of these RNP particles in the formation of "boutons" and in the genesis of junctional contacts.

There is evidence suggesting the presence of RNA in the axon. A considerable amount of RNA is found in the axon of the Mauthner neuron of gold-fish, whereas small amounts have been shown in the myelin-free axon of the 11th cranial nerve of the cat. There is still controversy on the general issue of RNA in the axons of mammalian neurons. A local synthesis of some proteins (and enzymes like acetyl cholinesterase) has also been shown to take place at the nerve endings independent of the perikaryon. The possible role of these additional *in situ* mechanisms in the modulation and plasticity of synapses cannot be ignored.

RNA in brain resembles and differs from the RNA found in other tissues. The broad categories of RNA synthesized in brain have sedimentation constants of 4 s, 4 s–17 s, 18 s and > 28 s as in other tissues. Their relative proportions differ slightly in the brain. Hybridization experiments show the presence of tissue specific species of RNA in the brain which do not compete with liver RNA.

Brain ribosomal RNA has a slower turnover rate (a half-life of 12–13 days) than liver RNA (5–6 days). Amongst the messenger RNAs, two broad categories of populations are discernible. The major portion of template activity is associated with a rapid turnover rate (half-life less than 4 hr). The second category of population is stable for more than 20 hr. The base composition of neuronal, glia and newly synthesized nuclear RNA has been given and discussed.

The rate of RNA synthesis in brain is high in foetal and neonatal life but falls considerably at a fairly early stage of neonatal development. A part of the RNA synthesized at this stage seems to be programmed for structural development of the cell.

Attention has been drawn to the fact that neurons in some areas of the brain, e.g. the hypothalamus, have also an important secretory function. The mechanisms underlying the synthesis of these polypeptides of short length are little understood, but if the established mechanisms of protein synthesis in animal and bacterial cells are applicable here, RNA in these cells will have a role in the synthesis of release factors which integrate the nervous and endocrine activities of the body.

Changes have been observed in the RNA content, base composition (or both) of neurons and glia in the brain in response to various types of stimuli.

In general, stimuli of moderate intensity tend to raise the total content of RNA in specific areas of the brain. Intense stimulus on the other hand causes a net fall, probably due to the inhibition or slowing down of the synthesis of RNA by diversion of ATP to other metabolic needs of the cell. These changes do not *per se* indicate direct involvement of RNA in any of the brain functions. An almost total inhibition of RNA in the brain over short yet appreciable periods does not impair mental function nor cause any irreversible damage to the tissue.

The role of RNA in the processes of learning and storage of memory has been discussed. Though the available information does not permit a tenable conclusion, it is almost axiomatic to assume that long-term memory has a structural basis, and that in the establishment of new circuits, RNA must have some part to play at some stage.

Acknowledgements

The work carried out in my department has been supported by research grants from the Indian Council of Medical Research, The Population Council Inc., New York, and the World Health Organization, Geneva.

References

Agranoff, B. W. (1967). *Scient. Am.* **216**, 115-122.
Albert, D. J. (1966). *Neuropsychologica* **4**, 79-92.
Appel, S. H. (1966). In *Enzymes in Mental Health* (G. J. Martin and B. Kisch, eds), pp. 186-193. J. B. Lippincott Co., Philadelphia, Pa., U.S.A.
Appel, S. H. (1967). *Nature, Lond.* **213**, 1253-1254.
Appel, S. H., Davis, W. and Scott, S. (1967). *Science, N.Y.* **157**, 836-838.
Attardi, G. (1957). *Expl Cell Res., Supp.* **4**, 25-53.
Austin, L., Bray, J. J. and Young, R. J. (1966). *J. Neurochem.* **13**, 1267-1269.
Austin, L. and Morgan, I. G. (1967). *J. Neurochem.* **14**, 377-387.
Avery, O. T., MacLeod, C. M. and McCarty, M. (1944). *J. exp. Med.* **79**, 137-158.
Babich, F. R., Jacobson, A. L., Bubash, S. and Jacobson, A. (1965). *Science, N.Y.* **149**, 656-657.
Balazs, R. and Cocks, W. A. (1967). *J. Neurochem.* **14**, 1035-1055.
Baranov, M. N. and Pevzner, L. Z. (1963). *J. Neurochem.* **10**, 279-284.
Barbato, I. W. M. and Barbato, L. (1965). *J. Neurochem.* **12**, 60-61.
Barondes, S. H. (1964). *J. Neurochem.* **11**, 663-669.
Barondes, S. H. (1968). *J. Neurochem.* **15**, 343-350.
Bennett, E. L. and Calvin, M. (1964). *Neuroscience Res. Progr. Bull.* **2**, No. 4, 3-24.
Bier, K. (1963). *J. Cell Biol.* **16**, 436-439.
Bodian, D. (1965). *Proc. natn. Acad. Sci. U.S.A.* **53**, 418-425.
Bondy, S. C. (1966). *J. Neurochem.* **13**, 955-959.
Bondy, S. C. and Waelsch, H. (1964). *Life Sci.* **3**, 633-636.
Byrne, W. L., Mamuel, D., Bennett, E. L., Rosenzweig, M. R., Wasserman, E., Wagner, A. R., Gardner, F., Galambos, R., Berger, B. D., Margules, D. L., Fenichel, R. L., Stein, L., Corson, J. A., Enesco, H. E., Chorover, S. L., Holt, C. E., Schiller, P. H., Chiappetta, L., Jarvik, M. E., Leaf, R. C., Dutcher, J. D., Horovitz, Z. P. and Carlson, P. L. (1966). *Science, N.Y.* **153**, 658-659.
Cain, D. F. (1967). *J. Neurochem.* **14**, 1175-1185.
Chamberlain, T. I., Rothschild, G. H. and Gerard, R. W. (1963). *Proc. natn. Acad. Sci. U.S.A.* **49**, 918-924.

Chitre, V. S. and Talwar, G. P. (1963). *Ind. J. med. Res.* **51**, 80-91.

Chitre, V. S., Chopra, S. P. and Talwar, G. P. (1964). *J. Neurochem.* **11**, 439-448.

Church, R. B. and McCarthy, B. J. (1967). *J. molec. Biol.* **23**, 459-475.

Cohen, H. D. and Barondes, S. H. (1966). *J. Neurochem.* **13**, 207-211.

Comb, D. G., Sarkar, N., DeVallet, J. and Pinzino, C. J. (1965). *J. molec. Biol.* **12**, 509-513.

Corning, W. C. and John, E. R. (1961). *Science, N.Y.* **134**, 1363-1365.

Daneholt, B. and Brattgård, S. O. (1966). *J. Neurochem.* **13**, 913-921.

Datta, R. K. (1966). *Brain Res.* **2**, 301-322.

Dawson, D. M. (1967). *J. Neurochem.* **14**, 939-946.

De Luca, H. A., Rossiter, R. J. and Strickland, K. P. (1953). *Biochem. J.* **55**, 193-199.

Dingman, W. and Sporn, M. B. (1961). *J. Psychiat. Res.* **1**, 1-11.

Dingman, W. and Sporn, M. B. (1964). *Science, N.Y.* **144**, 26-29.

D'Monte, B. and Talwar, G. P. (1967). *J. Neurochem.* **14**, 743-753.

Droz, B. and Leblond, C. P. (1963). *J. comp. Neurol.* **121**, 325-345.

Edström, A. (1964). *J. Neurochem.* **11**, 309-314.

Edström, A. (1966). *J. Neurochem.* **13**, 315-321.

Edström, A. (1967). *J. Neurochem.* **14**, 239-243.

Edström, J. E. (1967). *Neurosciences Res. Prog. Bull.* **5**, 355-357.

Edström, J. E. and Eichner, D. (1958a). *Z. Zellforsch. mikrosk. Anat.* **48**, 187-200.

Edström, J. E. and Eichner, D. (1958b). *Nature, Lond.* **181**, 619.

Edström, J. E. and Pigón, A. (1958). *J. Neurochem.* **3**, 95-99.

Edström, J. E., Eichner, D. and Edström, A. (1962). *Biochim. biophys. Acta* **61**, 178-184.

Eigen, M. (1966). In *Neurosciences Research Symposium Summaries* (F. O. Schmitt and T. Melnechuk, eds), pp. 267-277. M.I.T. Press, Cambridge, Massachusetts.

Einarson, L. (1957). In *Metabolism of the Nervous System* (D. Richter, ed.), pp. 403-421. Pergamon Press, London.

Findlay, M., Majee, W. L. and Rossiter, R. J. (1954). *Biochem. J.* **58**, 236-242.

Fjerdingstad, E. J., Nissen, T. and Roigaard-Petersen, H. H. (1965). *Scand. J. Psychol.* **6**, 1-6.

Frey, P. W. and Polidora, V. J. (1967). *Science, N.Y.* **155**, 1281-1282.

Gaito, J. (1966). In *Macromolecules and Behavior* (J. Gaito, ed.), pp. 3-9, 89-102. Appleton-Century-Crofts, New York.

Geiger, A. (1957). In *Metabolism of the Nervous System* (D. Richter, ed.), pp. 245-256. Pergamon Press, London.

Gerber, G., Gerber, G. and Altman, K. I. (1960). *J. biol. Chem.* **235**, 2682-2686.

Girard, M., Latham, H., Penman, S. and Darnell, J. E. (1965). *J. molec. Biol.* **11**, 187-201.

Glasky, A. J. and Simon, L. N. (1966). *Science, N.Y.* **151**, 702-703.

Grampp, W. and Edström, J. E. (1963). *J. Neurochem.* **10**, 725-732.

Hamilton, L. D., Fuller, W. and Reich, E. (1963). *Nature, Lond.* **198**, 538-540.

Hancock, R. L. (1965). *Experientia* **21**, 152-153.

Heald, P. J. (1957). *Biochem. J.* **66**, 659-663.

Houssais, J. F. and Attardi, G. (1966). *Proc. natn. Acad. Sci. U.S.A.* **56**, 616-623.

Hydén, H. (1960). In *The Cell* (J. Brachet and A. E. Mirsky, eds), Vol. IV, pp. 215-324. Academic Press, New York.

Hydén, H. (1966). In *Neurosciences Research Symposium Summaries* (F. O. Schmitt and T. Melnechuk, eds), pp. 278-293. Massachusetts Institute of Technology, Cambridge, Massachusetts.

Hydén, H. and Egyhazi, E. (1962). *Proc. natn. Acad. Sci. U.S.A.* **48**, 1366-1373.

Hydén, H. and Egyhazi, E. (1963). *Proc. natn. Acad. Sci. U.S.A.* **49**, 618-624.

Hydén, H. and Egyhazi, E. (1964). *Proc. natn. Acad. Sci. U.S.A.* **52**, 1030-1035.

Hydén, H. and Hartelius, H. (1948). *Acta Psychiat. neurol. scand. Supp.* **48**, 1-117.
Hydén, H. and Lange, P. (1961). In *Regional Neurochemistry* (S. S. Kety and J. Elkes, eds), pp. 190-199. Pergamon Press, London.
Jacob, M., Samec, J., Stevenin, J., Garel, J. P. and Mandel, P. (1967). *J. Neurochem.* **14**, 169-178.
Jacob, M., Stevenin, J., Jund, R., Judes, C. and Mandel, P. (1966). *J. Neurochem.* **13**, 619-628.
Johnson, T. H. (1967). *J. Neurochem.* **14**, 1075-1081.
Jung, R. (1958). *Expl Cell Res. Suppl.* **5**, 262-271.
Khan, A. A. and Wilson, J. E. (1965). *J. Neurochem.* **12**, 81-86.
Kimberlin, R. H. (1967). *J. Neurochem.* **14**, 123-134.
Koenig, E. (1965a). *J. Neurochem.* **12**, 357-361.
Koenig, E. (1965b). *J. Neurochem.* **12**, 343-355.
Koenig, E. (1967). *J. Neurochem.* **14**, 437-446.
Korner, A. (1961). *Biochem. J.* **81**, 168-178.
Kupfer, C. and Downer, J. L. de C. (1967). *J. Neurochem.* **14**, 257-263.
Lajtha, A. and Marks, N. (1966). In *Protides of the Biological Fluids* (H. Peeter, ed.), pp. 103-114. Elsevier, Amsterdam.
Landolt, R., Hess, H. H. and Thalheimer, C. (1966). *J. Neurochem.* **13**, 1441-1452.
Leslie, I. (1955). In *The Nucleic Acids* (E. Chargaff and J. N. Davidson, eds), Vol. II, pp. 1-50. Academic Press, New York.
Loeb, J. N., Howell, R. R. and Tompkins, G. M. (1965). *Science, N.Y.* **149**, 1093-1095.
Magasanik, B. (1955). In *The Nucleic Acids* (E. Chargaff and J. N. Davidson, eds), Vol. 1, pp. 373-407. Academic Press, New York.
Mahler, H. R., Moore, W. J. and Thomson, R. J. (1966). *J. biol. Chem.* **241**, 1283-1289.
Mandel, P., Harth, S. and Borkowski, Th. (1961). In *Regional Neurochemistry* (S. S. Kety and J. Elkes, eds), pp. 160-174. Pergamon Press, London.
Mandel, P., Rein, H., Harth-Edel, S. and Mardell, R. (1964). In *Comparative Biochemistry* (D. Richter, ed.), pp. 149-163. Pergamon Press, Oxford.
Marks, N., Datta, R. K. and Lajtha, A. (1967). *Neurology*, **17**, 302-303.
McConnell, J. V., Jacobson, A. L. and Kimble, D. P. (1959). *J. comp. physiol. Psychol.* **52**, 1.
Miani, N., Di Girolamo, A. and Di Girolamo, M. (1966). *J. Neurochem.* **13**, 755-759.
Murthy, M. R. V. and Rappoport, D. A. (1965). *Biochim. biophys. Acta* **95**, 132-145.
Nass, S., Nass, M. M. K. and Hennix, U. (1965). *Biochim. biophys. Acta* **95**, 426-435.
Orrego, F. (1967). *J. Neurochem.* **14**, 851-858.
Orrego, F. and Lipmann, F. (1967). *J. biol. Chem.* **242**, 665-671.
Palay, S. L. and Palade, G. E. (1955). *J. biophys. biochem. Cytol.* **1**, 69-88.
Pevzner, L. Z. (1965). *J. Neurochem.* **12**, 993-1002.
Pevzner, L. Z. (1966). In *Macromolecules and Behavior* (J. Gaito, ed.), pp. 43-70. Appleton-Century-Crofts, New York.
Plotnikoff, N. (1966). *Science, N.Y.* **151**, 703-704.
Rappoport, D. A. and Daginawala, H. F. (1968). J. Neurochem. **15**, 991-1006.
Roberts, E. (1966). *Brain Res.* **2**, 109-144.
Rosenblatt, F., Farrow, J. T. and Herblin, W. F. (1966). *Nature, Lond.* **209**, 46-48.
Sachs, H. (1963). *J. Neurochem.* **10**, 299-311.
Sachs, H. and Takabatake, Y. (1964). *Endocrinology* **75**, 943-948.
Scherrer, K., Latham, H. and Darnell, J. E. (1963). *Proc. natn. Acad. Sci. U.S.A.* **49**, 240-248.
Scherrer, K. Marcand, L., Zajdela, F., London, I. M. and Gros, F. (1966). *Proc. natn. Acad. Sci. U.S.A.* **56**, 1571-1578.

Schmitt, F. O. (1967). *Archs. Neurol., Chicago* **17**, 561-572.

Shearer, R. and McCarthy, B. (1967). *Biochemistry* **6**, 283-289.

Shimada, M. and Nakamura, T. (1966). *J. Neurochem.* **13**, 391-396.

Singh, U. N. (1965). *Can. J. Biochem. Physiol.* **43**, 1083-1089.

Singh, U. B. and Talwar, G. P. (1967). *J. Neurochem.* **14**, 675-680.

Smith, R. G. (1967). *Science, N.Y.* **155**, 603-605.

Soto, E. F., De Bohner, L. S. and Calvino, M. D. C. (1966). *J. Neurochem.* **13**, 989-998.

Talwar, G. P., Chopra, S. P. and Goel, B. K. (1964). *VI Int. Congr. Biochem., N.Y.* **5**, 419.

Talwar, G. P. Sadasivudu, B. and Chitre, V. S. (1961). *Nature, Lond.* **191**, 1007-1008.

Talwar, G. P., Goel, B. K., Chopra, S. P. and D'Monte, B. (1966a). In *Macromolecules and Behavior* (J. Gaito, ed.), pp. 71-88. Appleton-Century-Crofts, New York.

Talwar, G. P., Chopra, S. P., Goel, B. K. and D'Monte, B. (1966b). *J. Neurochem.* **13**, 109-116.

Toschi, G., Attardi Gandini, D. and Angeletti, P. U. (1964). *Biochem. biophys. Res. Commun.* **16**, 111-115.

Toschi, G., Dore, E., Angeletti, P. U., Levi-Montalcini, R. and De Maen, Ch. (1966). *J. Neurochem.* **13**, 539-544.

Ungar, G. and Cohen, M. (1966). *Int. J. Neuropharm.* **5**, 183-192.

Vesco, C. and Giuditta, A. (1967). *Biochim. biophys. Acta* **142**, 385-402.

Vraa-Jensen, G. (1957). In *Metabolism of the Nervous System* (D. Richter, ed.), pp. 422-424. Pergamon Press, London.

Vrba, R. and Folbergrova, J. (1959). *J. Neurochem.* **4**, 338-349.

Widnell, C. C. and Tata, J. R. (1964). *Biochem. J.* **92**, 313-317.

Weiss, P. and Hiscoe, H. B. (1948). *J. exp. Zool.* **107**, 315-395.

Yamagami, S., Kawakita, Y. and Naka, S. (1964). *J. Neurochem.* **11**, 899-900.

Yamagami, S., Kawakita, Y. and Naka, S. (1965). *J. Neurochem.* **12**, 607-611.

Yamagami, S., Fritz, R. R. and Rappoport, D. A. (1966). *Biochim. biophys. Acta* **129**, 532-547.

Zaheer, N., Iqbal, Z. and Talwar, G. P. (1968). *J. Neurochem.* **15**, 1217-1224.

CHAPTER 4

The Biochemistry of Mental Illness

DEREK RICHTER

*Neuropsychiatric Research Unit, Medical Research
Council Laboratories, Carshalton, Surrey, England*

I. Causal Factors

Early attempts to classify mental disorders led to the recognition of a number of broad classes of conditions which were defined mainly in descriptive terms. The psychoses, which were relatively severe and generally necessitated mental hospital care, were distinguished from the neuroses, which included the milder forms of mental illness such as hysteria, neurotic depression and obsessional states. Mental subnormality (mental retardation or mental defect), which was characterized by an impairment of intellectual ability from the time of birth or from an early age, was distinguished again from forms of mental illness that develop in later life. The psychoses were divided into the "organic" psychoses (such as general paralysis and senile dementia) in which there were pathological changes in the brain, and the "functional" psychoses, in which there was no known organic pathology. The functional psychoses included affective disorders (depressive illness, mania, anxiety states, etc.) in which the central feature was a disturbance of mood, and the schizophrenias (catatonia, hebephrenia, paranoia, paraphrenia, etc.). Schizophrenia implied a disintegration of the personality, with a disorganization of thinking, behaviour and emotional response.

In looking for the causes of mental illness, psychiatrists, like other physicians, tried at first to identify individual diseases attributable to a single cause. This approach was encouraged by the discovery of a mental disease, general paralysis, caused by the spirochaete of syphilis: it was encouraged also by the discovery of phenylketonuria, in which mental subnormality is associated with an inherited biochemical abnormality. Pursuing this line of thought, investigators were led to look for a specific biochemical cause in other forms of mental illness, including schizophrenia. A number of further forms of mental subnormality attributable to "inborn errors" of metabolism were discovered, but this approach has not proved rewarding so far as the functional psychoses are concerned.

In recent years it has come to be recognized that mental illnesses can result from the interaction of a number of different causal factors, some of which are genetic in nature, some constitutional and some deriving directly from the external environment. There can be a continuous interaction extending over many years, between intrinsic predisposing factors and extrinsic factors which include infections, malnutrition, toxic factors and environmental stresses of many kinds. Moreover, in mental illness the predisposing factors and immediate precipitating causes may vary from one case to another. On this view a mental illness such as schizophrenia is not a single unitary disease in the same sense as a physical disease as, for example, diabetes, encephalitis or pellagra.

The genes produce their effects by determining the pattern of enzymes and other proteins formed in the body: they operate in fact through biochemical mechanisms. It is likely therefore that biochemical mechanisms are concerned, not only in the so-called metabolic diseases associated with inborn errors, but also as contributory factors in mental illnesses such as schizophrenia and depressive states, in which genetic factors have been shown to play a part.

To function normally the brain requires an ionic milieu of relatively constant composition. It is protected to some extent from external influence and from toxic substances in the blood by a set of homeostatic mechanisms known collectively as the "blood-brain barrier". Yet the brain is sensitive to changes in the glucose, oxygen, carbon dioxide and electrolyte content of the blood. It is easily influenced by endocrine factors such as thyroid or steroid hormones and by alcohol and other substances of nutritional origin.

In investigating the biochemistry of mental illness we are studying those metabolic factors, intrinsic and extrinsic, which may influence the growth, maturation and normal functioning of the brain. Within the limits of normal biological variation there are large individual differences in the activity of many enzymes, differences in transport mechanisms and differences in the controlling mechanisms which determine the normal levels of metabolites in the tissues. There are also important differences in the ability to adapt in meeting a metabolic challenge under conditions of stress.

There are a number of ways in which this problem can be approached. One way is to study the metabolism of patients who are mentally ill and to look for biochemical abnormalities, such as toxic substances in the blood or biochemical differences from normal controls. We can study the effects of administering enzyme inhibitors and drugs which influence metabolic pathways, and we can test the effect of giving or withholding dietary factors such as individual amino acids or vitamins. It is not generally possible to study the metabolic characteristics of the human brain directly, since only in rare cases is it justifiable for a brain biopsy examination to be made, but tests can be carried out with brain material obtained post-mortem. Further, in animal experiments we can study the special characteristics of brain metabolism and learn how drugs and other factors influence the levels of transmitter substances and other compounds in the brain. The activity of enzyme systems *in vivo* can be tested by carrying out "tolerance tests" in which a chemical compound is administered to a patient and measurements are made of the rate at which it disappears from the blood or at which degradation products appear in the urine. By using compounds labelled with radioisotopes, the sensitivity of these methods can be greatly increased and multiple isotope techniques have opened up many new avenues for research.

II. Mental Subnormality

A. *Biochemical factors*

Mental subnormality forms the largest single diagnostic category among the mental disorders causing severe chronic disablement. The incidence in most countries is of the order of 1% of all children born, but the number is greater if milder cases of mental retardation are taken into account: thus it has been estimated that in the United States as many as 3% of all children born will never achieve the intellect of a 12-year-old child. Some of the known causes of mental subnormality are listed in Table I, which gives also some rough estimates of their relative importance in severely retarded children (I.Q. up to 50) based on figures given by Berg (1962) for children admitted to the Fountain Hospital, London. Mongoloids (Down's disease) formed the largest single clinical group in this series, but clearly there are considerable differences in different communities, depending on the availability of antibiotics and other factors. Thus, cretinism due to iodine deficiency, which has now become rare in most countries, is still prevalent in parts of India and New Guinea. After mongolism, meningitis was found by Berg to be the next commonest known cause of mental retardation: the incidence due to meningitis is reported to be higher in countries which do not have a National Health Service and where treatment therefore tends to be delayed. Of the 68% of cases in which the cause was unknown, some 30% had epileptic seizures which in many cases were probably associated with structural abnormalities of the brain. The known metabolic disorders, such as phenylketonuria, accounted for only a small proportion of cases: but mongolism and certain other conditions are also genetic in origin and therefore biochemically determined. Biochemical factors are concerned again in conditions such as kernicterus due to Rhesus incompatibility and in mental

E

subnormality due to prematurity. On this basis it would appear that some 30% of cases of severe mental retardation are associated with biochemical abnormalities which are either known or capable of being defined.

TABLE I

Possible causal factors of mental retardation. Estimated incidence in severely retarded children (I.Q. up to 50)

Primary cause	Estimated Incidence (%)	
Genetic, Monogenic	Structural (epiloia, etc.)	2
	Phenylketonuria	1
	Carbohydrate errors (galactosemia)	1
	Lipidoses (gargoylism etc.)	1
	Other metabolic errors	
Genetic, Polygenic	Structural (microcephaly etc.)	10
	Metabolic deviants	
Genetic, Chromosomal	Mongolism	22
	Kleinfelter, YY etc.	
Nutritional	Cretinism	—
	Avitaminoses	
	Protein deficiency	
	Toxic encephalopathies	
Infective, Postnatal	Meningitis	3
	Encephalitis	
Infective, Foetal	Rubella	—
	Syphilis	
	Toxoplasma	
Birth Accidents, etc.	Physical injury	
	Prematurity	
	Anoxia	
	Kernicterus	1
	Hypoglycemia	
Psychogenic	Amentia sensoripriva, etc.	—
Unclassified	Epilepsy	15
	Unknown	44
		100

It was formerly thought that the severe forms of mental retardation are different in kind from the milder forms seen in "high grade" defectives at the lower end of the normal range of intelligence; and attempts were made to distinguish "pathological" from "subcultural" forms of mental subnormality. This view has found little support in recent years, for it has been found that under different circumstances factors which produce severe retardation can also cause retardation of lesser degree (Berg and Kirman, 1959). It is now generally believed that similar factors, genetic and environmental, are operative throughout the whole range of mental retardation, but that they vary in relative importance from one case to another.

B. *Phenylketonuria*

The work of Fölling (1934) on phenylketonuria established for the first time a form of mental disorder associated with a specific biochemical abnormality. The condition might have been called "phenylalaninemia", for the central feature is a high level of phenylalanine in the blood. With the demonstration that the blood tyrosine level is abnormally low, it became clear that the primary metabolic defect is a block in the enzymic oxidation of

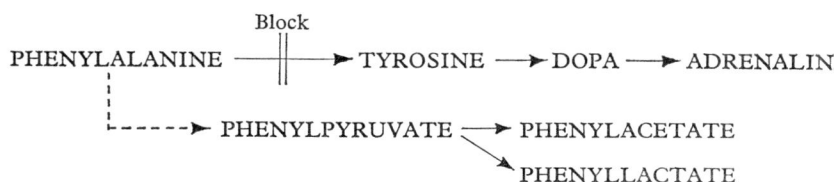

```
                    Block
PHENYLALANINE ——||——► TYROSINE ——► DOPA ——► ADRENALIN
      |
      ┆╌╌╌╌╌► PHENYLPYRUVATE ⇌► PHENYLACETATE
                              ╲
                               PHENYLLACTATE
```

FIG. 1. Metabolism of phenylalanine in phenylketonuria.

phenylalanine to tyrosine (Fig. 1). The excess of phenylalanine is metabolized along a secondary pathway by oxidative deamination and forms phenylpyruvate, which is excreted in the urine together with increased amounts of other deaminated products. The low activity of the enzyme phenylalanine hydroxylase in the liver of phenylketonurics was later confirmed by direct experiments with autopsy and liver biopsy material obtained from patients (Jervis, 1957).

The brains of phenylketonurics are on the average about 20% below the normal weight and in most cases there are pathological changes in the white matter, which has an increased water content and reduced content of cerebrosides and cholesterol (Menkes, 1966; Crome and Stern, 1967). The damage to the brain appears to occur mainly during the first few years of life while the brain is actively developing and myelination is proceeding, but we still do not know the mechanism by which the mental symptoms are produced. The mental deterioration appears to be due to a toxic action of phenylalanine or its metabolites, since it can be halted by giving a diet low in phenylalanine. Some investigators have attributed the mental defect to a deficiency of catecholamines, serotonin or thyroxin; others have thought that phenylalanine may interfere with the transport of other amino acids or with the synthesis of protein (Swaiman *et al.*, 1968). Individual patients differ widely in the severity of the mental symptoms and in their response to dietary treatment. This suggests that phenylketonuria is not a single uniform disease, but a group of similar hereditary disorders in which the hydroxylation of phenylalanine is impaired.

C. Other monogenic disorders

Following the discovery of phenylketonuria the search for other analogous conditions led to the recognition of more than 50 hereditary metabolic disorders associated with mental subnormality. Several of these disorders came to light through the routine testing of urine for amino acids. The conditions so discovered were found to involve carbohydrate, lipid or other aspects of metabolism. In every case the disorder could be attributed to a block in a normal metabolic pathway caused by the relative inactivity of an essential enzyme. In a number of these disorders the enzyme defect has been established by direct tests on tissue samples obtained from patients.

TABLE II

Partial metabolic blocks in heterozygous carriers

Condition	Phenylketonuria	Cystinuria	Galactosemia	Wilson's Disease
Test	Blood phenylalanine after oral dose (mg %)	Cystine in urine (mg/g creatinine)	Galactose-1-P U transferase in blood (Units/gm Hb)	Ceruloplasmin synthesis after test dose (^{61}Cu/ml. serum)
Level in				
(a) Patients	41	453	0·6	0·17
(b) Heterozygotes	19	124	2·9	0·5
(c) Normal controls	9	40	4·3	137

The metabolic disorders of this kind are all relatively rare conditions due apparently for the most part to the homozygous occurrence of a defective recessive gene. Phenylketonuria, which is the commonest, has an incidence in the United States of only about one in 25 000 of the general population. However, this implies an incidence of 1 in 173 of the general population for heterozygous carriers of the recessive gene. In view of the considerable number of known hereditary disorders, the total incidence in the general population of defective genes occurring as recessive must be relatively high. On this basis Muller (1950) has estimated that the average normal person must carry at least eight lethal or seriously deleterious recessive genes.

Biochemists were concerned at first mainly with finding the site of the metabolic block in these disorders and establishing the nature of the enzyme defect. Further biochemical work is now proceeding on the problem of detecting the heterozygous carriers of recessive genes. By applying suitable loading tests and other methods it has been shown that the heterozygous carriers often have a partial enzymic defect, less severe than in the homozygotes and generally insufficient to produce symptoms (Table II). The identification of heterozygotes is of value for determining the gene frequency and for the genetic counselling of parents. There are now about a dozen inherited metabolic diseases associated with mental subnormality in which the heterozygous carriers can be recognized by examining the blood or urine, or applying a loading test (Price Evans, 1965).

The recognition of a metabolic defect still does not tell us how the mental symptoms arise. In most conditions hitherto investigated the primary enzymic defect is in the liver or some organ other than the brain; but evidence has recently been obtained that in homocystinuria the mental retardation which is found in about 60% of cases is due to a reduced activity of the enzyme cystathionine synthase in the brain (Brenton *et al.*, 1965). It was shown that cystathionine is present in relatively high concentration in the normal human brain, but is almost absent from the brains of mentally retarded homocystinurics; this may be the reason for the mental symptoms. Another condition in which the mental retardation may be due to a primary metabolic disorder in the brain is arginino-succinaturia: this is suggested by the relatively high concentration of arginino-succinate found in the cerebrospinal fluid. However, the way in which the mental symptoms arise is still unknown. In galactosemia the metabolic block is due to inactivity of the enzyme galactose-1-phosphate uridyl transferase and the mental symptoms have been attributed by some investigators to the accumulation of galactose-1-phosphate: but recent evidence points rather to a toxic action of galictitol (dulcitol) which has been shown to reach high concentrations in galactosemic subjects after administration of labelled galactose (Egan and Wells, 1966). Evidence has been presented that the mental retardation in gargoylism (mucopolysaccharidosis) is attributable to accumulation in the brain of a glycolipid which is not always present, and not to the mucopolysaccharides which are deposited in many organs including the brain (Young *et al.*, 1966).

Mental retardation has been found in association with metabolic disorders of many different kinds. These conditions may be classified under the following headings:

1. *Aminoacidurias*

The disorders of amino acid metabolism comprise some 14 well-recognized conditions which include phenylketonuria, maple syrup urine disease, homocystinuria, cystathioninuria, Lowe's syndrome, hyperlysinemia, citrullinuria, hyperglycinemia, hyperprolinemia, hyperhistidinemia, kynureninuria and argininosuccinaturia. The amino-aciduria in phenylketonuria is caused by phenylalanine entering the urine by an overflow from the blood where the phenylalanine concentration is many times the normal level. This "overflow" type of amino-aciduria can be distinguished from a "renal" type, found for example in Wilson's disease and galactosemia, in which the blood amino acid concentration is normal but there is defective resorption in the kidney tubules. Defective resorption may be caused by a toxic metabolite or by a defect in the enzymes concerned in amino acid transport.

In many cases the defective enzyme has been identified, but the precise nature of the enzymic defect is not generally known. In a recent investigation of homocystinuria it was found surprisingly in one case that the enzyme cystathionine synthase was present in normal concentration in the lens of the eye (Gaull and Gaitonde, 1966). More recent work has shown that in this condition the essential defect is a reduced ability of the enzyme to combine with the co-factor pyridoxal phosphate (Gaull, 1968). The activity of the enzyme can be increased by administering pyridoxine, an observation of interest in relation to treatment.

2. *Carbohydrate disorders*

These comprise seven main conditions which include galactosemia, sucrosuria, hereditary fructose intolerance, glycogenosis, gargoylism (lipochondrodystrophy or Hurler's disease), progressive myoclonus epilepsy and spontaneous hypoglycemias. It is noteworthy that, as with the amino-acidurias, several of these conditions occur in variant forms: as many as nine variant forms of glycogenosis have been described (Hug *et al.*, 1966).

3. *Lipid disorders*

These conditions include the lipid storage diseases. Besides the various forms of amaurotic idiocy (ganglioside accumulation), they include Gaucher's disease (cerebroside accumulation), Niemann-Pick disease (sphingomyelin accumulation), cholesterinosis (cholesterol accumulation), metachromatic leucodystrophy (sulphatide accumulation) and α-lipo-proteinemia (lipoprotein accumulation). Other lipid disorders associated with mental retardation are cephalin lipidosis, disseminated lipogranulo-matosis and various conditions with myelin defects. The lipid storage diseases are attributable in some cases to a reduced activity of enzymes normally present in the lysosomes.

4. *Other metabolic disorders*

The disorders affecting other aspects of metabolism make up a mixed group which includes Wilson's disease (caeruloplasmin deficiency), acute porphyria, congenital hyperbilirubinemia, hypercalcemia, hyperuricemia and various steroid disorders.

The monogenic disorders are all relatively rare conditions and in most of them the number of patients investigated is small. In some cases the relation between the metabolic disorder and mental retardation is not yet clearly established: thus mental retardation is found in only a proportion of the cases of tyrosinosis and abeta-lipoproteinemia. Information on the biochemical and genetic aspects of the monogenic disorders has been collected by Stanbury *et al.* (1966) and a shorter account of them is given by Crome and Stern (1967). The investigation of the monogenic disorders is actively proceeding in a number of different laboratories and the number of recognized disorders of this kind is increasing at the rate of one or two a year.

If mental retardation can result from the action of one defective gene of large effect, it is likely that it can result also from the combined action of a number of genes of small effect. Such polygenic disorders are more difficult to investigate, since it is harder to identify a number of minor metabolic deviations than a single large metabolic error, but it is generally believed that some forms of mental retardation are polygenic in nature and it should be possible by further work to obtain an understanding of the causal mechanisms concerned.

D. *Chromosomal abnormalities*

In the diseases such as mongolism (Down's disease) associated with chromosomal abnormalities we are dealing with conditions in which a quantity of DNA equivalent to some thousands of genes is added to the normal complement of genes in the cells. This can arise through a faulty cell division (nondisjunction) leading to cells containing an extra chromosome, so that one of the chromosomes occurs in triplicate (trisomy) instead of the normal pair. It can also arise through a fragment of one chromosome breaking off and adhering to another chromosome (translocation), so that again the cells contain an additional amount of chromatin material. Nondisjunction can occur before fertilization or during the development of the fertilized ovum: it then results in an individual made up of a mosaic of normal and trisomic cells. In the case of mongolism, the clinical appearances of the trisomic and translocation types of mongoloid child are practically identical, but the difference can be important to the parents, since nondisjunction is unlikely to be repeated and there is a good chance that a further child will be normal, whereas translocation mongolism is inherited in 50% of the children.

The biochemical investigation of mongoloid children has led to reports of a number of minor quantitative deviations from the normal. Many patients are found to have an increased γ-globulin and reduced serum albumin. Other reported abnormalities include a raised serum calcium content, lowered serum cholinesterase, raised serum uric acid, lowered blood serotonin and reduced excretion of 17-ketosteroids. It would appear that these are for the most part unspecific deviations due to defective homeostasis or defective transport of metabolites (Crome and Stern, 1967). The leucocytes of mongoloids commonly show morphological abnormalities and mongolism is associated with a relatively high incidence of leukemia. This suggests that the extra chromosome (No. 21) may have something to do with the blood cells. In agreement with this, differences have been reported in the activity of certain enzymes in the leucocytes and in the red cells of mongoloids. Rosner *et al.* (1965) have confirmed earlier reports of increased activity of the leucocyte alkaline phosphatase and they have found also increased activity of the leucocyte 5-nucleotidase and other enzymes. They have suggested the possibility of using the activity of the blood enzymes to differentiate between trisomy and translocation mongoloids. Hypotonia is a characteristic feature of the mongoloid infant and it is of interest that in some cases this is relieved by treatment with 5-hydroxytryptophan, which is a serotonin precursor.

The incidence of chromosomal abnormalities is higher in children born to mothers of advancing age. This may be due to endocrine changes in the mother because the oocytes in the ovary are exposed for a longer time to noxious environmental agents. Genetic and environmental factors both appear to be concerned in the causation of nondisjunction. Thus the incidence of mongolism is higher in certain families and the mothers of mongoloids have been found to have a higher incidence of thyroid auto-antibodies (Fialkow *et al.*, 1965). Viral infection has also been considered as a possible cause of nondisjunction of the chromosomes (Stoller and Collmann, 1965).

A number of conditions are known in which mental retardation is associated with chromosomal abnormalities. The Klinefelter syndrome, in which there is an additional X chromosome, is estimated to have an incidence of about one in 400 males in the general population and it accounts for about 1% of the patients in mental deficiency institutions. The more recently recognized "YY syndrome" has been found with an incidence of over 3% in a group of mentally retarded subjects with criminal records. Some chromosomal abnormalities are normally lethal: a cytogenetic study of human abortions has shown that nearly one-third of early spontaneous human abortions have obvious chromosomal defects (Polani, 1966). On this basis Polani has estimated that as many as 3% of all human conceptions may carry detectable chromosome abnormalities.

E. *Environmental factors*

While the potential characteristics of an individual are laid down in the DNA of the chromosomes, their development depends to a large extent on the environment. The normal maturation of the brain depends on an adequate supply of glucose, amino acids and other nutritional factors, and also on appropriate stimulation in a continuous interaction with the environment. The brain suffers less as a rule than other organs of the body under conditions of malnourishment, but it is more vulnerable during the earlier stages of rapid growth. Undernourishment affects the weight and development of the foetal brain. Fasting in pregnant mice has been shown to lead to the birth of offspring with congenital malformations: this could be prevented by a dietary supplement of glucose or amino acids given up to the ninth day of fasting (Kalter and Warkany, 1959). In some species a deficiency or excess of vitamin A at early stages of development can lead to a high incidence of neurological disorders including hydrocephalus, spina bifida and anencephaly (Millen and Woollam, 1959). It is of interest that abnormal plasma vitamin A levels have been found in the mothers of children born with spina bifida (Gal, 1968). Even after birth an ill-balanced protein-deficient diet has been found to affect the balance of enzymes in the rat brain and lead to an impairment of goal-seeking behaviour (Rajalakshmi *et al.*, 1965). Studies in several countries have given evidence of an association of mental retardation with severe malnutrition, but with human subjects it is difficult to carry out a controlled experiment and show whether there is a causal relationship. It is also hard to say to what extent an observed mental deficit is due to protein deficiency, lack of vitamins or to lowered resistance to viral and other infections. Stoch and Smythe (1963) applied intelligence tests and found that severe undernourishment was associated with a reduced head circumference and lower I.Q. in comparison with normally fed children who served as controls. It is well established that neurological and mental symptoms can result from deficiency of the B-group vitamins, as in pellagra and in infantile convulsions due to lack of pyridoxine. The mental symptoms most commonly noted in undernourished children are apathy and listlessness.

TABLE III

Treatable causes of mental retardation

Causal Condition	Treatment
(a) *Infections*	
Syphilis	Antibiotics
Meningitis	Antibiotics
Encephalitis	Immunization
Maternal Rubella	γ-Globulin
Toxoplasmosis	Antibiotics
(b) *Perinatal conditions*	
Rhesus incompatibility	Blood transfusion
(c) *Dietary disorders*	
Avitaminoses	Vitamins
Protein deficiency	Protein diet
Cretinism	Iodide. Thyroxin
Lead encephalopathy	Chelating agents
(d) *Metabolic disorders*	
Phenylketonuria	Low phenylalanine diet
Galactosemia	Low galactose diet
Maple syrup urine disease	Low leucine, isoleucine and valine diet
Wilson's disease	Penicillamine
Diabetes insipidus (Nephrogenic)	Esacrinic acid
Cystathioninuria	Pyridoxine
Pyridoxine dependency	Pyridoxine
Homocystinuria	Low methionine diet: pyridoxine
Histidinemia	Low histidine diet
Lactose intolerance	Low lactose diet
Tyrosinosis	Low phenylalanine and tyrosine diet
Hartnup disease	Riboflavin and nicotinamide
Spontaneous hypoglycemia	Glucose

Nutritional factors are of special importance in subjects with inborn metabolic disorders and in some cases it is possible to prevent the development of mental symptoms by suitable dietary treatment. The value of a low phenylalanine diet for phenylketonurics has sometimes been questioned, but there is evidence that in certain cases it is effective in reducing the extent of the mental deterioration. Conditions now treatable by special diets include galactosemia, maple syrup urine disease, homocystinuria, histidinemia, tyrosinosis and lactose intolerance. Other metabolic diseases such as Wilson's disease, Hartnup disease, pyridoxine dependency and spontaneous hypoglycemia can also be treated by specific biochemical methods (Table III).

Besides nutritional factors the developing brain needs essential metabolites elaborated by the thyroid and other organs of the body. The thyroid hormones have been shown to exert a stimulant action on protein synthesis in the brain whereas thyroid deficiency retards the development of the nerve cells and particularly the growth of the dendrites (Sokoloff and Kaufman, 1961). Thyroidectomy reduces the activity of the succinate dehydrogenase and glutamate decarboxylase in the rat brain (Balázs et al., 1968). The evidence suggests that the mental retardation in the cretin is due to a failure of the nerve cells to synthesize the specific proteins needed for the growth of the dendritic tree. Steroid hormones also play a part in the normal growth and maturation of the brain, but there is evidence that abnormal amounts of steroid hormones in the maternal blood can lead to maldevelopment of the foetal brain (Gal et al., 1967).

III. Depressive Illness

A. *Classification*

Patients suffering from depressive illness differ widely in the pattern of symptoms they present. Depression of mood is a central feature, but the presenting syndrome may include symptoms such as insomnia, inability to concentrate, feelings of unworthiness or physical complaints. The patient may be tense and anxious or apathetic and indifferent. Some patients experience only depression, whereas in others depression may alternate with periods of manic excitement or euphoria. The older clinical classifications into "agitated" and "retarded" or "neurotic" and "psychotic" types are mainly descriptive and the underlying causes are still very little understood. The terms "endogenous depression", for conditions caused mainly by constitutional factors and "reactive depression" for those judged to be due to environmental factors, continue in common use, although in practice the distinction is not always easy to make. "Involutional melancholia" is descriptive of depressive illness occurring at about the time of the menopause, or middle age: but there is little evidence that this represents a distinct nosological entity. Depressive illness tends to run in families, and twin studies have given strong support for the view that genetic factors are important. Perris (1966) concluded that manic-depressive (bipolar) psychosis and recurrent (monopolar) depression are separate entities, since the relatives of manic-depressives have a higher expectation of affective illness, and it generally takes the same (bipolar) form in blood relations as in the patient. Hopkinson (1964) found the incidence of depression higher in the relatives of patients with depressive syndromes commencing early in life.

The view is now widely held that depressive illnesses form a continuum of conditions of mixed aetiology in which "endogenous" and "reactive" depression represent extremes: but genetic and environmental factors are both operative to some extent in every case. It is likely that depressive illnesses can arise in a number of different ways: the existence of different genetic factors is suggested by evidence that members of the same family, who suffer from depression, tend to respond to the same form of treatment by specific antidepressant drugs such as monoamine oxidase inhibitors and imipramine (Pare et al., 1962).

B. *Electrolytes*

Water and electrolyte metabolism are of interest in view of the sensitivity of the brain to changes in cation concentration. It is known that mental disturbances with depression of mood are caused by hyponatremia due to sodium depletion or water intoxication. The mental state is affected also by the tissue levels of potassium, calcium and magnesium ions: potassium deficiency is associated with weakness and malaise.

Information about the electrolyte distribution in the body can be obtained by the isotope dilution method. If, for example, a known amount of the labelled ion, $^{24}Na^+$, is allowed to exchange for a period of 24 hours with the sodium (^{23}Na) in the body, the amount of "exchangeable sodium" can be measured by the dilution of the isotope. Most of the exchangeable sodium is in the blood and extracellular fluid but a smaller amount, contained mainly in the cells, is known as the "residual sodium". Coppen and Shaw (1963) investigated severely depressed patients soon after admission to hospital and again after they had recovered, so that each patient served as his own control. Using a multiple isotope technique, with ^{82}Br to measure extracellular fluid and tritium to measure total body water, they found that depression was associated with a significant decrease in total body water due mainly to a decrease in extracellular fluid. The main finding, however, was a considerable increase of nearly 50% in the "residual" sodium. In other words, there was no evidence of an overall loss or retention of sodium in depression, but the distribution of water and electrolytes between extracellular and intracellular compartments was altered. Their findings agree with an older report by Altschule and Tillotson (1949), who found that the thiocyanate space was decreased in depressive illness. These changes were reversible on recovery, but it was noted also by Coppen and Shaw that the intracellular potassium levels before and after recovery were lower in their patients than in a group of normal control subjects. This is of interest as representing a possible constitutional difference in these subjects.

Further investigations carried out by similar methods on a series of 22 manic patients showed that manics also differed from the normal in the distribution of water and sodium between intra- and extracellular compartments (Coppen et al., 1966). The changes found were similar in kind but greater in magnitude than those found in depression. It appeared, therefore, that the changes in water and electrolytes are not specific for depression, but they are found also in association with other abnormal affective states.

The earlier workers reported changes in water and electrolyte excretion related to the periodic swings of mood in patients with rapidly changing cyclical psychoses. Crammer (1962) studied a patient of this kind who showed a marked retention of water and sodium during the depressive phase: but he was unable to alter the mental state by restricting the sodium or water intake. A causal relation between sodium retention and depressive mood appeared unlikely, since treatment with chlorpromazine altered the time relation between the retention of sodium and the swings of mood. In a somewhat similar case of cyclical manic-depressive psychosis, Goodwin et al. (1965) were able to dissociate the rhythm of the psychosis from that of electrolyte excretion by keeping the patient in a chamber with an artificial 22-hour day and night. These observations suggest that the changes in mental state and in electrolyte retention in these patients both reflect a primary disturbance in the hypothalamic centres which control the natural rhythms of the body.

Although of considerable interest, such cases of rapidly changing cyclic psychosis are relatively uncommon and they may not be directly comparable to the types of depressive illness more commonly seen. Some evidence that electrolytes may play a part in affective illness has come from studies of the effects of treatment with lithium. Lithium carbonate has been used for the treatment of mania and it is reported to exert a prophylactic action in reducing the frequency and duration of manic or depressive episodes in patients liable to recurrent attacks (Baastrup and Schou, 1967). The prophylactic action in depressive illness claimed for lithium has been questioned (Blackwell and Shepherd, 1968), but an effect in prolonging the interval between recurrent depressive attacks has been confirmed (Angst, 1968). It is therefore of interest that lithium has been found to increase the total body water – a change opposite to that found in affective illness (Coppen and Shaw, 1967). Lithium administration has also been shown to affect the electrical activity of the cerebral cortex: it was found to delay the recovery of the cortical response to the second of two paired stimuli (Gartside et al., 1966).

C. *Endocrine factors*

Symptomatic depression can occur as a result of almost any kind of physical illness – post-influenzal depression is a common example – but mental disturbances are especially frequent in endocrinological disorders. Thus changes of mood are found in Addison's disease, in Cushing's syndrome, in thyrotoxicosis, in myxoedema and in association with the endocrine changes of the involutional period and the puerperium. It is known that hormones released by the adrenal cortex and hypophysis affect the distribution of water and electrolytes. The question therefore arises: to what extent are endocrine factors concerned in the causation of depressive illness?

Studies with ^{131}I have given little evidence of any significant abnormality of thyroid function in depressive illness, although thyroid activity may be increased in patients with anxiety (Gibbons et al., 1960). Investigations of carbohydrate metabolism by glucose tolerance tests have shown that a decreased glucose tolerance is fairly common in patients suffering from depressive illness: the same result is obtained by intravenous as well as oral glucose tolerance tests (Pryce, 1958). However, this finding is not specific for depression: a reduced glucose tolerance is a frequent finding in patients with other forms of mental illness and especially in those who are malnourished or emotionally disturbed. If the patients are made to take an adequate diet and examined when free from stress, normal values are generally obtained (Herzberg et al., 1968).

A number of workers have reported findings indicative of increased adrenocortical activity in patients with depressive illness: this applies to urinary excretion of 17-ketogenic steroids, plasma cortisol levels and cortisol secretion rate (Gibbons, 1964; Linjaerde, 1964). Of particular interest are reports of an altered diurnal rhythm of plasma cortisol level, with a tendency to abnormally high values in the early-morning hours, in patients who are depressed (Bridges and Jones, 1966). However, a raised plasma cortisol level is in no way specific for depression; and in some patients who are severely depressed normal values are obtained (Brooksbank and Coppen, 1967). It is known that the plasma cortisol level is raised by almost any kind of stress: even admission to hospital or serious loss of sleep may be sufficient to cause a rise. It would therefore appear that a raised plasma cortisol level is not generally a causal factor in depression, but rather a response to a state of stress which often accompanies severe depressive illness. It is also unlikely that the electrolyte changes in depression are attributable to increased cortisol secretion, since normal plasma cortisol levels are found in patients suffering from mania, although in them the electrolyte changes are even more pronounced (Brooksbank and Coppen, 1967).

D. *Biogenic amines*

The discovery of the antidepressant action of the monoamine oxidase inhibitors (MAOI) suggested that the monoamines might be concerned in the aetiology of depressive states. The two catecholamines, dopamine and noradrenalin, are both present in significant amounts in subcortical areas of the brain, but noradrenalin and 5-hydroxytryptamine (5-HT or serotonin) are of particular interest since they are present in relatively high concentration in the hypothalamus, a region containing centres which control the autonomic functions involved in emotional expression (Vogt, 1962). The MAOI drugs such as iproniazid increase the levels of amines in the brain and relieve depression. Conversely, reserpine, which reduces amine levels, causes sedation and in some cases it has even been found to induce a depressive psychosis. It therefore appeared that depression might be associated with a deficiency in the brain of one or both of the amines, noradrenalin or 5-HT.

Pharmacological studies with another antidepressant drug, imipramine, suggested that noradrenalin is the amine primarily concerned in depressive illness, since it potentiates certain actions of noradrenalin (Kety, 1966). The central excitant effects of amphetamine have also been attributed to an increase in noradrenalin concentration in the brain. These considerations led to the formulation by a group of workers at Bethesda of the "low catecholamine" hypothesis, according to which depression is associated with an absolute or relative deficiency of catecholamines in functionally important sites in the brain, while elation may be associated with an excess of such catecholamines (Durell and Schildkraut, 1965). Clinical studies of catecholamine metabolism in depressed patients by Rosenblatt and Chanley (1965) revealed an apparent difference in the proportions of the different degradation products of noradrenalin excreted in the urine: they found that the ratio of amine-containing products to de-aminated products was relatively higher in manic-depressive patients than in controls. The interpretation of this finding is not easy, but it suggests a possible difference in catecholamine metabolism in patients who are depressed.

Another group of investigators working in England approached the problem by administering to patients relatively large amounts of amine precursors together with a MAOI, so as to raise the levels of the different amines in the brain. Administration of DOPA (dihydroxyphenylalanine), which is a precursor of the catecholamines, proved to be ineffective in relieving depression, although it reverses reserpine-induced sedation in animals. However, in a controlled trial tryptophan, which is a precursor of tryptamine and 5-HT, produced a striking alleviation of depression (Coppen et al., 1963). This observation has been confirmed in several other centres. More recently, it has been found in a controlled trial that treatment of depression with tryptophan and a MAOI is very nearly as effective as ECT (electroshock therapy) in the treatment of depressive illness (Coppen et al., 1967). Attempts to treat patients with tryptamine or with 5-hydroxytryptophan which is the immediate precursor of 5-HT, were not successful; but only relatively small doses of these compounds could be given because of their undesirable peripheral side-effects (Coppen, 1967).

These observations pointed to 5-HT rather than noradrenalin as the amine most likely to be deficient in the brain in depression. Further evidence on this point has come from determinations of amines and their derivatives in the CSF. Dencker et al. (1966) found the level of noradrenalin in the CSF to be relatively high in a group of depressed patients: the level fell to a normal level after recovery. Conversely, the level of 5-hydroxyindole acetic acid (5-HIAA), which is the main degradation product of 5-HT, was found to be significantly low in the CSF of patients suffering from depression.

These findings run contrary to the "low catecholamine" hypothesis. Direct evidence of the levels of biogenic amines in the human brain has recently been obtained by post-mortem studies of the brains of people who have committed suicide: levels of 5-HT in the hind brain of people who committed suicide during attacks of depression were significantly lower than in a comparable series of accident cases who served as controls (Shaw et al., 1967).

The high content of 5-HT and noradrenalin in the hypothalamus and in other subcortical regions of the brain suggests that these amines may be concerned in some way in the regulation of emotional expression. It is believed that they may act as modulators of synaptic transmission, but the precise way in which they operate is still unknown. An indication of the way in which they work was obtained by Feldberg and Myers (1965), who found that in certain animals the regulation of body temperature depends, not on the absolute level of any individual amine, but on the *ratio* of 5-HT to noradrenalin. By changing the ratio of amines in the anterior hypothalamus they were able to raise or lower the temperature at will. If similar mechanisms operate in the control of emotional state, a disturbance affecting the metabolism either of 5-HT or of catecholamines could lead to an elevation or depression of mood. These considerations led to the hypothesis that depression is associated with a reduced ratio of 5-HT to catecholamines at certain sites in the brain. This view and the "low catecholamine" hypothesis are both current at the present time.

The mechanisms determining the level of 5-HT in the brain include the transport of tryptophan into the central nervous system, the hydroxylation of tryptophan and the subsequent decarboxylation of 5-hydroxytryptophan to form 5-HT. Some evidence of a general disturbance of tryptophan metabolism in depressive illness is given by the observation that in depressed subjects the excretion of tryptamine is greatly reduced: it returns to normal on recovery (Coppen et al., 1965). In this connection it is of interest that in some patients the excretion of kynurenic acid and other metabolites of tryptophan is apparently increased (Cazzullo et al., 1966): this implies that the available tryptophan may be metabolized to a greater extent along the kynurenine pathway which depends on the activity of the enzyme tryptophan pyrrolase. This enzyme is induced by cortisone which is present in increased amounts in some patients. Clearly different mechanisms may operate in different cases in altering the normal ratios of amines in the brain.

Further evidence relating to the biochemistry of depressive illness has been reviewed by Kety (1966) Coppen (1967), and Richter (1969).

E. *Relation of biochemical findings to clinical state*

Attempts to differentiate on biochemical grounds between "reactive", "endogenous" and other clinical types of depression have not hitherto had great success. Since the mechanisms operating in the development of depressive states are still unknown, any attempt to explain the biochemical

findings must be speculative at the present time: but it may be useful nevertheless to consider possible ways in which the biochemical findings may be
related to the general clinical state in patients suffering from depressive
illness.

A number of reported findings are listed in Table IV. In trying to assess
their significance it would appear that the findings fall into a number of
distinct groups. Some of them are nonspecific in the sense that they are
found also in other conditions. That is true, for example, of the reduced
glucose tolerance, which is found in some cases of depression but not in

TABLE IV

Findings in depressive illness

Relating to subcortical controlling mechanisms

Disturbance of mood
Loss of appetite
Sleep rhythm disturbed
Plasma cortisol cycle changed
Salivary secretion cycle changed
Diurnal rhythm of electrolyte excretion changed
Altered distribution of water and electrolytes
Arousal sensitivity increased
Alpha blocking prolonged
Autonomic changes: (*a*) salivary secretion decreased
                                  (*b*) sweat secretion decreased
                                  (*c*) insensible weight loss reduced
                                  (*d*) gastric secretion reduced
                                  (*e*) skin temperature lowered

Relating to amine metabolism

5-HT in hind brain reduced
5-HIAA in CSF reduced
Tryptamine excretion low
Xanthurenic acid excretion high
Antidepressant action of tryptophan
Antidepressant action of MAOI and imipramine
Depressant action of reserpine
Noradrenalin level in CSF high
High N/O ratio in excreted noradrenalin metabolites

Associated with malnutrition and stress

Body weight reduced
Reduced plasma folate and vitamin B_{12}
Cortisol secretion increased
Plasma corticoids increased
Urinary ketogenic steroids increased
Glucose tolerance reduced
Plasma acetoin level raised
Plasma triglycerides raised

others. It can result from malnutrition or from stress, both of which are of fairly frequent occurrence in patients who are severely depressed. In this connection it is relevant that recent surveys have shown a significant incidence of folic acid and vitamin B_{12} deficiency attributable to defective diet in patients with depressive illness (Reynolds, 1968).

That depression is often associated with a generalized stress reaction is suggested by the raised plasma cortisol and increased urinary excretion of steroid metabolites also found in certain cases. It is significant that other characteristic stress responses such as raised plasma triglycerides are also among the reported findings. One of the most frequent findings in depressive illness is a disturbance of sleep. The disturbance of diurnal rhythms, which is seen also in the plasma cortisol, electrolyte excretion and salivary secretion, points to a dysfunction of the controlling centres in the hypothalamus. This applies also to a number of the other common symptoms of depression which are mediated by the autonomic nervous system, such as reduced sweating, dryness of the mouth and reduced gastric secretion. It would appear that other biochemical findings, such as the altered distribution of water and electrolytes, may be attributable to the same cause. The view that affective disorders are associated with hypothalamic dysfunction was suggested many years ago by Zondek (1935), who drew attention to the frequent occurrence of depression and euphoria in patients with primary disease of the hypothalamus. More recent work implicates a somewhat larger region described as the "limbic system", but the basic idea remains the same, that depressive illness is associated with a dysfunction of subcortical centres concerned in the control of autonomic functions and mood.

The work of Feldberg and Myers (1965) has provided evidence of the way in which autonomic activity may be controlled by the balance of amines at specific sites in the brain. It indicates also the importance of the biochemical mechanisms determining the levels in the brain of noradrenalin and 5-HT. If it is taken that similar mechanisms are operative in relation to mood, a disturbance of amine metabolism may be expected to influence the control, not only of autonomic activity, but also of the affective state. It is relevant to point out that two of the biochemical findings reported in depressive illness relate to the metabolism of noradrenalin (CSF level high; increased N/O ratio in metabolites) and six of them relate to 5-HT (CSF 5-HIAA level low; 5-HT in hindbrain reduced; antidepressant action of tryptophan; tryptamine excretion low; tryptophan decarboxylation low; xanthurenic acid excretion high). Changes of the kind reported could result from changes in membrane permeability, altered amino acid transport, altered activity of enzymes, lack of co-enzymes and in many other ways: the primary causal factors are still obscure.

In considering the mechanisms concerned in the causation of depressive illness, there is evidence that environmental and endogenous factors both play a part. The biochemical evidence suggests that among the endogenous factors are metabolic disturbances affecting amine levels at certain subcortical centres in the brain.

IV. Schizophrenia

A. *Different clinical types*

The term "schizophrenia" was introduced by Bleuler (1911) to describe a group of psychiatric conditions of unknown aetiology characterized by a disintegration of the personality, as shown by disorganization of thinking, altered behaviour and abnormal emotional response, but without significant disturbance of memory, clouding of consciousness or gross intellectual impairment. Associated with the mental disharmony is a failure to adapt to events in the outside world and to respond normally to other people. Delusions and hallucinations are among the commonest symptoms.

A schizophrenic psychosis may take the form of one of the four classically recognized syndromes (simple, hebephrenic, catatonic and paranoid), but often the patient shows different clinical features at different stages of the illness. Many other clinical forms of schizophrenia have also been described (pseudoneurotic, schizo-affective, paraphrenic) as well as symptomatic schizophrenia, which is a schizophrenia-like psychosis induced by physical illness or a drug or other known agent. In a rare form of schizophrenia, known as periodic catatonia, there are recurrent periods of psychosis with lucid periods in between. There is no sharp line of demarcation between the main clinical forms of schizophrenia, nor can a sharp distinction be made between the milder forms of schizophrenia and the non-psychotic condition of the person of schizoid personality (withdrawn, autistic, paranoid) described by Bleuler as schizoid psychopathy. Some psychiatrists (notably in the United States of America) use the term schizophrenia in a relatively wide sense to include all the milder forms: others (especially in Europe) use the term in a more restricted sense ("true schizophrenia", "nuclear schizophrenia") for a more virulent form of psychosis corresponding more nearly to the older term dementia praecox, which did not include paranoia or other "atypical schizophrenias". The difference in the meaning attached to the word schizophrenia is important in interpreting the experimental findings reported by groups of workers in different countries.

Studies by conventional neuropathological techniques have failed to show any specific structural abnormalities in the brains of schizophrenics. However, more recent work, as yet unconfirmed, has suggested the possibility of a developmental failure in the arborization of the dendrites of certain types of nerve cells (Schadé, 1968). These observations are of interest since the development of the dendrites has been shown to be influenced by the thyroid and adrenocortical hormones. The frequent commencement of schizophrenia during adolescence points to the endocrine system as a possible aetiological factor; this is supported by evidence of a tendency to an immature or female type of body-build in patients suffering from schizophrenia. However, no consistent endocrine abnormality has hitherto been established. Some investigators have confirmed, and others have failed to confirm, the early findings of Mott (1922), who reported testicular atrophy and pathological changes in the endocrine organs of schizophrenics. A possible explanation is that Mott's experimental material included patients who today would be recognized as cases of Klinefelter's syndrome, a condition in which an extra X-chromosome is associated with various endocrine abnormalities and with a mental disorder which may resemble schizophrenia.

Another condition frequently diagnosed as schizophrenia is temporal lobe epilepsy. In some cases the clinical picture (symptoms of de-personalization, delusions, emotional incongruity, hallucinations, etc.) is so similar to that of schizophrenia that the differential diagnosis presents considerable difficulty and a firm diagnosis can be made only on the basis of a special EEG investigation with sphenoidal electrodes.

B. *Genetic factors*

Schizophrenia is a relatively common condition occurring in most countries with an expectancy of about 1 in 100 of the general population. The incidence is reported to be higher in certain isolated communities living in the arctic north. Many investigations have shown that the likelihood of developing a schizophrenic psychosis increases with increasing closeness of blood relationship to an individual suffering from schizophrenia. In the classical study of Kallmann (1950) the expectancy increased from 2·6% in first cousins to 11·5–14·3% in sibs, 16·4% in children, 17·6% in dizygotic twins of the same sex and 86% in monozygotic twins. The large difference in expectancy between mono- and dizygotic twins is of particular interest, since it is difficult to attribute this to environmental factors.

Figures similar to those of Kallmann were obtained by a number of other investigators. Some studies on a small number of cases by Scandinavian and Finnish workers led to reports of relatively low concordance rates in monozygotic twins. However, a more recent investigation by Gottesman and Shields (1966), using improved techniques, has again confirmed the essential finding of a much higher concordance rate in mono- than in dizygotic twins. It would appear that the differences between the results of different investigations are largely accounted for by differences in the type of schizophrenia in the samples studied. The patients in Kallmann's series were long-stay hospital cases with schizophrenic psychoses of the severest kind, whereas the Scandinavian and Finnish investigations included mild cases not even admitted to hospital. The evidence indicates that genetic factors are important, and particularly so in the more severe forms of schizophrenia; environmental factors also play a part and they are relatively more important in the milder forms. Further evidence of the importance of genetic factors has come from studies of children adopted at birth and brought up out of contact with their mothers or members of her family: the incidence of schizophrenia was found by Heston (1966) to be much higher in the adopted children of schizophrenic mothers than in those of non-schizophrenic mothers.

The earlier workers thought in terms of a Mendelian type of inheritance of a single gene of large effect, which carried the predisposition to schizo-phrenia. The data on expectancy rates cannot easily be attributed to the action of a recessive gene, but they would fit a monogenic type of inheritance in which a schizophrenic psychosis developed in all the homozygous and 26% of the heterozygous carriers (Slater, 1965). However, the expectancy rates could also be explained on the basis of a polygenic type of inheritance and this explanation is favoured by a number of authorities at the present time (Shields, 1967).

Evidence that genetic factors play a part raises the question: what exactly is inherited? The genes determine the potential activity of enzymes, but their effects may be manifested at various different organizational levels: they may be expressed in the molecular configuration of chemical com-pounds, in the structural characteristics of neuronal systems or in character-istics shown at a behavioural level. Studies of the relatives of schizophrenics have suggested that the parents show an increased incidence of schizoid abnormalities of character: these were found also in the adopted children of schizophrenic mothers, who did not develop a psychosis (Heston, 1966). On a polygenic hypothesis it is reasonable to believe that some of the deviant genes may carry the characteristics of a schizoid personality, while others are concerned more directly with the development of a psychosis. Factors of the latter kind may well operate at a molecular level: there is ample evidence for example that schizophrenia-like psychoses can be produced in suceptible individuals by chemical substances as simple as amphetamine or LSD. On the other hand, it must also be remembered that the genetic factors may be of an entirely different kind: the Russian investigators could be right in believing one of the predisposing factors to be the susceptibility to infection by a neurotropic virus (Malis, 1961; Romasenko, 1967). The number of possible genetic mechanisms is clearly very great. If there are 50 known metabolic abnormalities that can lead to mental retardation, there could be as many or more different metabolic abnormalities that can result in the group of behavioural syndromes described as schizophrenia.

C. *Biochemical investigations*

1. *Early investigations*

The earlier biochemical investigations failed to show the existence of any gross abnormalities in the body fluids of schizophrenics: no evidence could be found of any metabolic disturbance in the blood or urine of the kind found in the monogenic metabolic diseases. Many minor deviations from the normal in the concentration of metabolites were reported, but generally on further investigation they turned out to be of a secondary or artifactual nature: the abnormalities found could be attributed to factors such as dietary habits, incidental infections, emotional stress, lack of exercise or administration of drugs. Although the results were mainly negative, these investigations gave some evidence of a greater individual variation in schizophrenic patients than in similar groups of matched controls: this suggested the possibility that schizophrenia might be a condition of mixed aetiology rather than a single homogeneous condition.

Gjessing (1932) pointed out that attempts to establish a consistent biochemical deviation by the statistical analysis of larger numbers could be misleading in studying a condition such as schizophrenia, since individual variations, which might be important for the individual patient, would tend to be missed. He chose for special investigation patients suffering from a recurrent form of schizophrenia, periodic catatonia, and studied each patient individually over a long period extending in some cases over several years. By carrying out repeated physiological measurements and metabolic studies, he was able to establish that the recurrent periods of mental disturbance in his patients were regularly associated with changes in autonomic function and metabolic balance. This was shown by cyclic changes in blood pressure, pulse rate and body temperature as well as in blood glucose level, alkali reserve, metabolic rate, liver function and excretion of nitrogenous and other metabolites. Retention of nitrogen was a significant finding in every case, generally in the period immediately preceding the mental disturbance, although the individual patients differed to some extent in the time relations of the changes. Since nitrogen retention appeared to be a possible causal factor, Gjessing tried reducing this by restricting the nitrogen intake and treating with large doses of thyroid: this treatment relieved the nitrogen retention and in many cases relieved the mental symptoms as well.

Gjessing's work was important in establishing for the first time a form of schizophrenic psychosis definitely associated with a metabolic disorder. His essential findings have now been confirmed in many other laboratories. However, further work has shown that nitrogen retention is not generally the main cause of the mental symptoms: both appear to result from a primary disorder in which the neuroendocrine system as well as the higher centres of the brain are both involved. Periodic catatonia is a comparatively rare condition and the relevance of these observations to the commoner forms of schizophrenia may not be very great: but they point once again to a relation between a disturbance of mental state and the activity of controlling centres in subcortical regions of the brain. Gjessing's investigations also established the value of the longitudinal type of investigation in which patients are studied over a long period of time: they drew attention to the fact that the biochemical findings in the early acute stages of schizophrenia, and during exacerbations of the psychosis, might differ from those in the chronic "burnt out" schizophrenic.

The earlier biochemical work on schizophrenia has been reviewed by Richter (1957a; 1957b; 1960) and by Kety (1960).

2. *Plasma proteins*

It is commonly found that some 10–15% of patients admitted to hospital with a diagnosis of schizophrenia have a raised erythrocyte sedimentation rate (ESR). This implies an alteration in the plasma proteins, which is generally a reaction to a toxic factor in the blood. On further investigation a site of chronic infection, such as an abscess, may be found; and when this is treated the psychosis may quickly disappear. The importance of looking for septic foci in all psychiatric patients is now well known; but not so long ago such patients were left untreated and allowed to deteriorate. These cases suggest that a schizophrenic psychosis can be evoked in a person who is predisposed to it by the action of a toxic factor in the blood.

The idea that schizophrenia might be caused by a toxic blood metabolite has led to many attempts to obtain a biological or other test that would enable an abnormal blood constituent to be detected. Heath (1959) reported the isolation from the blood of schizophrenics of a protein fraction ("taraxein") which produced behavioural abnormalities when injected into monkeys or into human volunteers, but several attempts to confirm this report have not been successful (Robins et al., 1957). More recently, Heath and Krupp (1967) have produced evidence that their protein fraction contains an antibody which reacts with an antigen in the brains of schizophrenics: they have suggested that schizophrenia is a single disease entity depending on an auto-immune process in which "taraxein" acts as a specific antibody.

Workers at the Worcester Foundation hold the view that Heath's "taraxein" may be the same as a protein factor described by them which interferes with the climbing behaviour of trained rats. They have characterized the factor as an α_2-globulin, which may be a carrier of a biologically active amine (Pennell et al., 1967). Frohman et al. (1961) independently reported the presence in the serum of schizophrenics of a protein factor which influences the metabolism of glucose: this was shown by an increase in the ratio of lactate to pyruvate produced during the aerobic glycolysis of glucose by the chicken erythrocyte. Subsequent work revealed that this factor is probably the same as the rat climbing factor studied by the workers at the Worcester Foundation (Cooperative Study, 1968). Since its concentration in the plasma of patients is influenced by stress or by physical exercise, and since it is present in a considerable proportion of normal subjects, the specificity for schizophrenia cannot be upheld. It has been suggested that the presence of this factor may depend on the conditions of chronic hospitalization rather than on the occurrence of a schizophrenic psychosis (Kety, 1967).

Reports of effects produced by blood plasma from schizophrenic patients on evoked cortical responses in experimental animals could not be confirmed (German et al., 1965). Amongst other factors reported to be present in the plasma proteins of schizophrenics are heterophile haemolysins which haemolyse mouse, chicken and rabbit erythrocytes (Turner and Chipps, 1966; Ryan et al., 1966). These factors do not appear to be specific for schizophrenia and there is no evidence that they are directly related to the mental state.

3. *Toxic amines*

In view of the known pharmacological actions of the biogenic amines, Pollin *et al.* (1961) studied the effects of treating schizophrenic patients with different amino acids administered together with a MAOI. Most of the amino acids tested produced little or no effect. Tryptophan produced an unspecific intoxication, but methionine appeared to act specifically in producing an exacerbation of the symptoms of schizophrenia. This observation was of special interest because methionine is a methylating agent: a number of hallucinogenic drugs, such as mescaline, are methyl derivatives of phenolic amines, and it had previously been suggested that schizophrenia might be caused by the toxic action of an abnormal metabolite produced endogenously by the methylation of derivatives of adrenalin (Harley-Mason *et al.*, 1958). Interest in this hypothesis was increased when Friedhoff and van Winkle (1962) reported that dimethoxyphenylethylamine (DMPE) was present in the urine of 60% of schizophrenic patients but not in the urine of non-schizophrenic controls. The evidence was consistent with the view that schizophrenia was associated with excessive methylation, or with an inability to demethylate a toxic compound such as DMPE.

The excretion of DMPE by schizophrenics was indicated by a "pink spot" produced when the urines were examined by paper chromatography. While some investigators were able to confirm the production of a "pink spot" by urine from schizophrenics, some failed to find it and others reported it to be produced also by urine from non-schizophrenic controls. The confusion was increased when it was found that some urines contained unknown compounds other than DMPE which also produced "pink spots" on paper chromatograms (Williams, 1967). Some of these unknown compounds were apparently phenothiazine derivatives and others were shown to be of dietary origin, since the "pink spots" disappeared when patients or controls were given diets free of fruit and vegetables, or when they were put on a pure carbohydrate regimen (von Studnitz and Nyman, 1965). The hypothesis that the mental symptoms of schizophrenia might be caused by DMPE became less probable when it was found that doses of up to 600 mg of DMPE were without effect on human volunteers. Studies carried out by administering labelled [³H]adrenalin to schizophrenics also failed to show any abnormality of adrenalin metabolism or any abnormal excretion of methylated products (LaBrosse *et al.*, 1961).

The observation of an association between schizophrenia and homocystinuria is of interest in this connection, since in homocystinurics the plasma methionine level is abnormally high: in several cases patients diagnosed as suffering from schizophrenia have been found to have homocystinuria and there is a relatively high incidence of schizophrenia in the blood relations of homocystinurics (Spiro *et al.*, 1965). However, it may be questioned whether the symptoms observed when methionine is administered to schizophrenics really represent a specific exacerbation of schizophrenia: they may be no more than an unspecific response to a compound which is toxic when given in excess. Many schizophrenics show spontaneous changes in mental state and it has been found that just before and during a phase of emotional excitement ("exacerbation of schizophrenia") the excretion of tryptamine and of creatinine may be increased (Brune and Himwich, 1962a): but there was no evidence of an increased excretion of toxic methylation products. Brune and Himwich (1962b) have reported that administration of betaine, which is another methylating agent, also exacerbates the symptoms of schizophrenia. There would therefore appear to be some evidence that methylating agents can influence the mental state of schizophrenic patients, but that is still a long way from establishing that faulty methylation is a common causal factor in schizophrenia.

Recent biochemical investigations of schizophrenia have been reviewed by Kety (1967) and by Smythies (1967).

D. *Conclusions*

A number of biochemical deviations from the normal have been reported in schizophrenic patients and several speculative hypotheses have been proposed, but there are as yet no specific biochemical abnormalities which can be accepted as characteristic of schizophrenia. There is evidence that genetic as well as environmental factors play a part: some abnormalities referable to the DNA of the chromosomes may be inferred from this, and it may be significant that the symptoms of schizophrenia are mainly referable to a disordered function of the temporal lobes, but the nature of the genetic factors concerned is still unknown.

The term "schizophrenia" was introduced by Bleuler (1911) to describe by exclusion a group of behavioural syndromes which fell outside the other known forms of mental illness. In the course of time the group of schizophrenias has gradually become smaller as improved methods of investigation have enabled further specific forms of mental illness within the group to be identified. Thus a proportion of the patients who formerly would have been diagnosed as suffering from schizophrenia can now be included in other categories such as temporal lobe epilepsy, myxoedema, Klinefelter's syndrome, folate deficiency, homocystinuria, bromidism and various toxic psychoses. It would be unwarranted to conclude that the remaining forms of schizophrenia constitute a single unitary disease. The genetic evidence suggests rather that schizophrenia is genetically heterogeneous and that genetic factors are relatively more important in the severer forms than in those which take a milder course. There is little evidence for the hypothesis that schizophrenia is attributable to any single biochemical cause: it is more likely that a number of different biochemical factors which have yet to be discovered are concerned in the development of the various syndromes of schizophrenia. It would appear that further progress may depend on developing methods for identifying homogeneous subgroups of schizophrenia, in which consistent biochemical deviations can be defined.

References

Altschule, M. D. and Tillotson, K. J. (1949). *Am. J. Psychiat.* **105**, 829-833.

Angst, J. (1968). Personal Communication.

Baastrup, P. C. and Schou, M. (1967). *Archs gen. Psychiat.* **16**, 162-172.

Baastrup, P. C. and Schou, M. (1968). *Lancet i*, 1419-1422.

Balázs, R., Kovács, S., Teichgräber, P., Cocks, W. A. and Eayrs, J. T. (1968). *J. Neurochem.* **15**, 1335-1349.

Berg, J. M. (1962). *Proc. Mental Deficiency Conf., London*, 1960, (B. W. Richards, ed.) pp. 160-164. (Sponsored by American Association on Mental Deficiency).

Berg, J. M. and Kirman, B. H. (1959). *Br. med. J.* **2**, 400-404.

Blackwell, B. and Shepherd, M. (1968). *Lancet i*, 968-971.

Bleuler, E. (1911). *Dementia Praecox oder die Gruppe Schizophrenien.* Franz Deuticke, Leipzig.

Brenton, D. P., Cusworth, D. C. and Gaull, G. E. (1965). *Pediatrics* **35**, 50-56.

Bridges, P. K. and Jones, M. T. (1966). *Br. J. Psychiat.* **112**, 1257-1262.

Brooksbank, B. W. L. and Coppen, A. (1967). *Br. J. Psychiat.* **113**, 395-404.

Brune, G. G. and Himwich, H. E. (1962*a*). *Archs gen. Psychiat.* **6**, 324-328.

Brune, G. G. and Himwich, H. E. (1962*b*). *J. nerv. ment. Dis.* **134**, 447-450.

Cazzullo, C. L., Mangoni, A. and Mascherpa, G. (1966). *Br. J. Psychiat.* **112**, 157-167.

Co-operative Study (1968). *Archs gen. Psychiat.* **18**, 471-476.

Coppen, A. (1967). *Br. J. Psychiat.* **113**, 1237-1264.

Coppen, A. and Shaw, D. M. (1963). *Br. med. J.* **2**, 1439-1444.

Coppen, A. and Shaw, D. M. (1967). *Lancet ii*, 805-806.

Coppen, A., Shaw, D. M. and Farrell, J. P. (1963). *Lancet i*, 79-81.

Coppen, A., Shaw, D. M. and Malleson, A. (1965). *Br. J. Psychiat.* **111**, 105-107.

Coppen, A., Shaw, D. M., Malleson, A. and Costain, R. (1966). *Br. med. J.* **1**, 71-75.

Coppen, A., Shaw, D. M., Herzberg, B. and Maggs, R. (1967). *Lancet ii*, 1178-1180.

Crammer, J. L. (1962). In *Aspects of Psychiatric Research* (D. Richter, ed.), pp. 401-419. University Press, Oxford.

Crome, L. and Stern, J. (1967). *The Pathology of Mental Retardation*, pp. 260-266. Churchill, London.

Dencker, S. J., Malm, V., Roos, B.-E. and Werdinius, B. (1966). *J. Neurochem.* **13**, 1545-1548.

Durell, J. and Schildkraut, J. J. (1965). In *The American Handbook of Psychiatry* (S. Arieti, ed.), pp. 1-74. Basic Books Inc., New York.

Egan, T. J. and Wells, W. W. (1966). *Am. J. Dis. Child.* **111**, 400-405.

Feldberg, W. and Myers, R. D. (1965). *J. Physiol., Lond.* **177**, 239-245.

Fialkow, P. J., Uchida, I., Hecht, F. and Motulsky, A. C. (1965). *Lancet ii*, 868-870.

Fölling, A. (1934). *Hoppe-Seyler's Z. physiol. Chem.* **227**, 169-173.

Friedhoff, A. J. and Van Winkle, E. (1962). *Nature, Lond.* **194**, 897-898.

Frohman, C. E., Tourney, G., Beckett, P. G. S., Lees, H., Latham, L. K. and Gottlieb, J. S. (1961). *Archs gen. Psychiat.* **4**, 404-412.

Gal, I. (1968). Personal Communication.

Gal, I., Kirman, B. and Stern, J. (1967). *Nature, Lond.* **216**, 83.

Gartside, I., Lippold, O. C. J. and Meldrum, B. (1966). *Electroenceph. clin. Neurophysiol.* **20**, 382-390.

Gaull, G. E. (1968). Personal Communication.

Gaull, G. E. and Gaitonde, M. K. (1966). *J. med. Genet.* **3**, 194-197.

German, G. E., Antebi, R. N., Dear, E. M. A. and McCance, C. (1965). *Br. J. Psychiat.* **111**, 345-347.

Gibbons, J. L. (1964). *Archs gen. Psychiat.* **10**, 572-575.

Gibbons, J. L., Gibson, J., Maxwell, A. and Willcox, D. (1960). *J. psychosom. Res.* **5**, 32-41.

Gjessing, R. (1932). *Archs Psychiat.* **96**, 319.

Goodwin, J. C., Jenner, F. A., Lobban, M. C. and Sheridan, M. (1965). *J. Physiol., Lond.* **176**, 16-17.

Gottesman, I. I. and Shields, J. (1966). *Br. J. Psychiat.* **112**, 809-818.

Harley-Mason, J., Laird, A. H. and Smythies, J. R. (1958). *Confinia neurol.* **18**, 152-155.

Heath, R. G. (1959). *Int. Rev. Neurobiol.* **1**, 299-331.

Heath, R. G. and Krupp, Iris, M. (1967). *Archs gen. Psychiat.* **16**, 1-33.

Herzberg, B., Coppen, A. and Marks, V. (1968). *Br. J. Psychiat.* **114**, 627-630.

Heston, L. L. (1966). *Br. J. Psychiat.* **112**, 819-825.

Hopkinson, G. (1964). *Br. J. Psychiat.* **110**, 244-254.

Hug, G., Garancis, J. C., Schubert, W. K. and Kaplan, S. (1966). *Am. J. Dis. Child.* **111**, 457-474.

Jervis, G. A. (1957). *J. Neuropath. exp. Neurol.* **16**, 308-320.

Kallmann, F. J. (1950). *Congrès Internat. de Psychiatrie, Rapports VI*, pp. 1-27. Hermann, Paris.

Kalter, H. and Warkany, J. (1959). *Physiol. Rev.* **39**, 69-115.

Kety, S. S. (1960). In *Chemical Pathology of the Nervous System* (J. Folch-Pi, ed.), pp. 684-704. Pergamon Press, Oxford.

Kety, S. S. (1966). *Pharmac. Rev.* **18**, 787-798.

Kety, S. S. (1967). *New Engl. J. Med.* **276**, 325-331.

LaBrosse, E. H., Mann, J. D. and Kety, S. S. (1961). *J. psychiat. Res.* **1**, 68-75.

Linjaerde, P. S. (1964). *Br. J. Psychiat.* **110**, 423-432.

Malis, G. Y. (1961). *Research on the Etiology of Schizophrenia*, pp. 1-195. Consultants Bureau, New York.

Menkes, J. H. (1966). *Pediatrics* **37**, 967-978.

Millen, J. W. and Woollam, D. H. M. (1959). *J. ment. Defic. Res.* **3**, 23-32.

Mott, F. W. (1922). *J. ment. Sci.* **68**, 333-339.

Muller, H. J. (1950). *Am. J. hum. Genet.* **2**, 111-176.

Pare, C. M. B., Rees, L. and Sainsbury, M. J. (1962). *Lancet ii*, 1340-1343.

Pennell, R. B., Pawlus, C., Saravis, C. A. and Scrimshaw, G. (1967). In *Molecular Basis of Some Aspects of Mental Activity* (O. Walaas, ed.), pp. 269-282. Academic Press, London.

Perris, C. (1966). *Acta psychiat. neurol. scand.* **42**, Supp. 194, 1-189.

Polani, P. E. (1966). *Devl med. Child Neurol.* **8**, 67-70.

Pollin, W., Cardon, P. V. and Kety, S. S. (1961). *Science, N. Y.* **133**, 104-106.

Price Evans, D. A. (1965). In *Biochemical Approaches to Mental Handicap in Children* (J. D. Allan and K. S. Holt, eds), pp. 21-26. Livingstone, Edinburgh.

Pryce, I. G. (1958). *J. ment. Sci.* **104**, 1079-1092.

Rajalakshmi, R., Govindarajan, K. R. and Ramakrishnan, C. V. (1965). *J. Neurochem.* **12**, 261-271.

Reynolds, E. H. (1968). *Br. J. Psychiat.* **113**, 911-919.

Richter, D. (1957a). In *Schizophrenia: Somatic Aspects* (D. Richter, ed.), pp. 53-75. Lewis, London.

Richter, D. (1957b). *Congress Report of IInd Internat. Cong. for Psychiatry,* Zurich, Vol. 1, pp. 285-295.

Richter, D. (1960). In *Chemical Pathology of the Nervous System* (J. Folch-Pi, ed.), pp 505-522. Pergamon Press, Oxford.

Richter, D. (1969). In *Melancholie.* (W. Schulte, ed.), Thieme Verlag, Stuttgart (In the press)

Robins, E., Smith, K. and Lowe, I. P. (1957). In *Neuropharmacology: Fourth Conference* (H. A. Abramson, ed.), pp. 123-135. Josiah Macy Jr. Foundation, New York.

Romasenko, V. A. (1967). *Hypertoxic Schizophrenia*, pp. 1-239. Meditsina Press, Moscow.

Rosenblatt, S. and Chanley, J. D. (1965). *Archs gen. Psychiat.* **13**, 495-502.

Rosner, F., Ong, B. H., Paine, R. S. and Mahanand, D. (1965). *New Engl. J. Med.* **273**, 1356-1361.

Ryan, J. W., Brown, J. D. and Durell, J. (1966). *Science, N Y.* **151**, 1408-1410.

Schadé, J. P. (1968). Personal Communication.

Shaw, D. M., Camps, F. E. and Eccleston, E. G. (1967). *Br. J. Psychiat.* **113**, 1407-1411.

Shields, J. (1967). In *Recent Developments in Schizophrenia* (A. Coppen and A. Walk, eds), pp. 25-41. Headley Bros., Ashford, Kent.

Slater, E. (1965). In *Biochemical Aspects of Neurological Disorders* (J. N. Cummings and M. Kremer, eds), pp. 271-285. Blackwell, Oxford.

Smythies, J. R. (1967). In *Recent Developments in Schizophrenia* (A. Coppen and A. Walk, eds), pp. 61-68. Headley Bros., Ashford, Kent.

Sokoloff, L. and Kaufman, S. (1961). *J. biol. Chem.* **236**, 795-803.

Spiro, H. R., Schimke, R. N. and Welch, J. P. (1965). *J. nerv. ment. Dis.* **141**, 285-290.

Stanbury, J. B., Wyngaarden, J. B. and Fredrickson, D. S. (1966). *The Metabolic Basis of Inherited Disease*, pp. 1-1434. McGraw-Hill, New York.

Stoch, M. B. and Smythe, P. M. (1963). *Archs Dis. Childh.* **38**, 546-552.

Stoller, A. and Collmann, R. D. (1965). *Lancet ii*, 1221-1223.

Studnitz, W. von, and Nyman, G. E. (1965). *Acta psychiat. neurol. scand.* **41**, 117-121.

Swaiman, K. F., Hosfield, W. B. and Lemieux, B. (1968). *J. Neurochem.* **15**. 687-690.

Turner, W. J. and Chipps, H. I. (1966). *Archs gen. Psychiat.* **15**, 373-377.

Vogt, M. (1962). In *Aspects of Psychiatric Research* (D. Richter, J. M. Tanner, S. Taylor and O. L. Zangwill, eds), pp. 343-360. Oxford University Press, London.

Williams, C. H. (1967). *Proc. R. Soc. Med.* **60**, 558-560.

Young, G. F., Wolfe, H. J., Blennerhasset, J. B. and Dodge, P. R. (1966). *Devl med. Child Neurol.* **8**, 37-44.

Zondek, H. (1935). *The Diseases of the Endocrine Glands*, pp. 298-301. Arnold, London.

Part II
The Liver and Gall Bladder

CHAPTER 5

The Correlation of Structure
with Function in the Liver

JAN L. E. ERICSSON

*Department of Pathology, Sabbatsberg Hospital,
Karolinska Institutet Medical School, Stockholm, Sweden*

I. Introduction

Vertebrate liver has a wide variety of important functions, many of which are vital to the survival of the organism. There are different cell types in liver, but the parenchymal cells form not only the bulk of the tissue but also are involved in most of the diverse functions of this organ.

Many important contributions have been made to our knowledge of the functional significance of the various subcellular structures in the liver. This is a field which has been comprehensively reviewed by Novikoff and Essner (1960), Aterman (1963), Benacerraf (1964), Moulé and Chauveaux (1963), Rouiller and Jézéquel (1963), Wachstein (1963), David (1964) and others.

This chapter is mainly concerned with recent developments in the study of the ultrastructure of hepatic cells in relation to function. Biochemical studies carried out with liver homogenates have provided increasing insight into the chemistry of the organelles. This information is now correlated wherever possible with observations obtained from studies based on histochemical, cytochemical, and autoradiographic methods. Clearly, it is beyond the scope of this chapter to give a full account of these various techniques. Nor is it possible to cover all aspects of the correlation between structure and function in liver cells. For more detailed information in these respects the reader is referred to monographs and reviews by de Duve *et al.* (1959), Dallner (1963), Dallner and Ernster (1968), and Moulé and Chauveaux (1963) dealing with fractionation procedures for the isolation of subcellular organelles; Trump and Ericsson (1965*a*), and Ericsson and Biberfeld (1967) dealing with fixation techniques; de Duve and Wattiaux (1966), and Novikoff (1961) dealing with lysosomes; Lehninger (1964), and Parsons (1965) dealing with mitochondria; de Duve and Baudhuin (1966) dealing with microbodies; Dallner (1963), and Dallner and Ernster (1968) dealing with microsomes; Bernhard and Granboulan (1968), and Hay (1968) dealing with the nucleus; Ericsson (1969*a*) dealing with cellular autophagy; Novikoff *et al.* (1962), Sabatini *et al.* (1963), and Scarpelli and Kanczak (1965) dealing with electron microscopic histochemical methods; Beams and Kessel (1968) dealing with the Golgi apparatus; and Benedetti and Emmelot (1968), Robertson (1966), and Sjöstrand (1968) dealing with the plasma membrane.

II. Structural Organization of the Liver under the Light Microscope

A. *Hepatic lobule*

The basic histological unit of the mammalian liver is the lobule, a polygonal prism of liver tissue, measuring up to 2 mm in maximal diameter. In cross-sections, the lobule has the appearance of a hexagonal structure whose central portion contains a terminal branch of the hepatic vein – the central vein. At the corners of the hexagon are the portal areas containing the portal triads, i.e. the branches of the portal vein, the hepatic artery, and the bile duct (and also the usually inconspicuous lymphatic vessels) and the surrounding connective tissue. In most mammals the cells of the hepatic lobules form a continuous network from one lobule to the other. Within the liver the parenchymal cells are arranged in a spongework consisting of plates which are usually one cell layer thick extending radially from a central vein to the peripheral portal area of the lobule. These plates of cells branch and anastomose and are surrounded by fluid derived from the portal vein and the hepatic artery. Hence, the liver may be considered as a sac filled with fluid in which a spongework of liver tissue is suspended. During the flow of the fluid through the liver, the supply is obtained from the portal vein and hepatic artery while drainage is by way of the hepatic vein. It follows that the cells located nearest the portal vein receive blood first and consequently gain access to food and oxygen before the cells that are situated in the central area of the lobule. This means the supply of food and oxygen diminishes continuously as the blood passes from the periphery toward the centre of the lobule, and a gradient of the metabolic activity is thereby created in the liver plate. This gradient is morphologically represented by the zonation seen in the light microscope following application of stains to liver parenchyma in normal and pathologically altered tissues for the demonstration of glycogen or fat.

B. *The blood vessels*

The main afferent blood vessel of the liver is the portal vein. The hepatic artery in all mammals supplies less blood than the portal vein. It enters the liver together with the portal vein and the bile duct. The three vessels branch together as they penetrate the liver mass. The fine branches occupy the portal areas at the periphery of each lobule. The details of the terminal branching of the portal vein and the renal artery have been studied by injection and corrosion experiments. The portal venule sends off lateral branches from which terminal branches entering the sinusoids arise. Likewise, the artery sends off branches which subdivide and end up in the sinusoids. The blood leaves the lobule through the central vein which represents a terminal radicle of the hepatic vein. The wall of the central vein is penetrated by numerous pores which open directly into the sinusoidal area of the lobule.

C. *The sinusoids*

The sinusoids function as the blood vessels of the lobule. They are larger than capillaries and differ from capillaries in that their lining cells are immediately associated with the epithelial cells of the liver parenchyma (there is no intervening tissue). The component cells of the sinusoids are of two types: one is a typical endothelial cell whose cytoplasm extends as a thin film in the wall of the sinusoids and that has a small, compact, elongated nucleus. The other cell type is the Kupffer cell which functionally is equivalent to a fixed macrophage. This is a large cell with a big, oval nucleus and a small prominent nucleolus; its cytoplasm includes granules of pigment which often contain iron. Droplets of fat may also be present in the cytoplasm of this cell. Kupffer cells are known to phagocytoze particulate materials injected into the blood stream, and hence they are intensely stained with vital dyes. They also take up carbon particles and particles of india ink and thorotrast. Such materials are also taken up by the endothelial cells but in much smaller quantity. Following repeated injections of colloidal materials, such as thorotrast and particles of india ink, the phagocytic cells in the sinusoids become greatly enlarged and more numerous than in the livers of untreated animals. It has been suggested that the endothelial-like cells may transform into phagocytic cells following exposure to colloidal material which is not metabolized for long periods of time (several months and even years). Light microscopists have long debated the possible

F

existence of a space between the cells lining the sinusoid and the underlying parenchymal cells. Electron microscopy (see later) has convincingly
demonstrated the presence and boundaries of such a space (the space of
Disse). This space is frequently observed in human postmortem material
when studied with the light microscope, but the evidence indicates that
this space is artifactually enlarged under such circumstances.

D. *The parenchymal cells*

The liver cells are polygonal in shape and have six or more surfaces. Three
different types of surfaces are recognized: (*a*) those exposed to the subsinusoidal space; (*b*) those bordering the lumen of the bile canaliculus; and
(*c*) those adjacent to other parenchymal cells. The nuclei are large and round
with a smooth outline. There is some variation in size between the nuclei.
This variation is due to difference in ploidy. Most parenchymal cells have a
single nucleus, but binucleate ones are not uncommon. In conventionally
fixed tissue – excised and immersed in the fixative (usually formaldehyde) –
the nuclei are typically vesicular with scattered chromatin granules and one
or more prominent nucleoli. However, in livers fixed by perfusion fixation
(Ericsson and Biberfeld, 1967) the chromatin is much more evenly distributed within the nuclei. Mitosis is extremely rare in the normal liver.

The cytoplasm of the liver cell has a variable appearance, to some extent
reflecting the functional state of the cell. The main reason for this is the
presence of stored material such as glycogen and fat. In conventionally
prepared histologic sections (fixation in formaldehyde, dehydration in
ethanol and xylene, embedding in paraffin and staining with hematoxylin
and eosin) both fat and glycogen have been removed and/or are not properly
visualized, and the presence of glycogen is suggested by the appearance of
irregular empty spaces in the cytoplasm. Staining with the PAS technique
(or other stains for glycogen) makes it possible to demonstrate the polysaccharide at the light microscope level provided the material has been fixed
efficiently. Aldehyde-containing fixatives such as formaldehyde and glutaraldehyde are sufficient fixatives for glycogen. When using these fixatives,
care must be taken to ensure penetration of all cells in the tissue, i.e. by
perfusion fixation or fixation of thin pieces (not thicker than approximately
1 mm). The antecedent presence of fat is indicated by the presence in the
cytoplasm of round vacuoles of varying size. Droplets of neutral fat can be
shown histologically in the tissues by staining fixed frozen sections with Oil
Red O or other fat stains. The content of fat and glycogen in the liver varies
widely with the diet. Small amounts of glycogen are present following a
12–16 hr fast while there is abundant glycogen in non-fasted animals.

Provided thin sections are used, different subcellular organelles can be
visualized with light microscopic staining methods. For instance, with
phospholipid stains, the mitochondria appear as rod-shaped or rounded
structures. The size and shape of the mitochondria vary considerably in
different areas of the liver lobule. This has been attributed to different

degrees of metabolic activity. The mitochondria in the central area of the lobule (i.e. the zone of permanent repose) are thin, elongated and comparatively few. On the other hand, those located in the periportal areas are large, broad and abundant. These mitochondria are located in cells representing the zone of permanent function in which the supply of nutrients and other materials by the blood stream is greatest.

With basophilic stains (such as methylene blue or toluidine blue) coarse, irregular aggregates of basophilic material can be demonstrated in the hepatic parenchymal cells. These stains define the location and extent of ribonucleic acids in the cytoplasm, and the stainable material corresponds most likely to accumulations of rough surfaced endoplasmic reticulum (see below).

The Golgi apparatus is observed as a network, usually at the periphery of the cell, i.e. in the vicinity of the bile canaliculi. In the same region are also gathered small granules, up to 1 μ in diameter, which appear to correspond to the lysosomes. These granules are PAS-positive in reaction, and the staining material is resistant to digestion with diastase or amylase. Thus these granules can be readily differentiated from glycogen.

E. *The bile canaliculi*

These are fine tubular canals that run between liver cells throughout the parenchyma. Usually, they occur singly between each adjacent pair of cells. Since there are many anastomosing branches of the plates of liver cells, the canaliculi form a three-dimensional net with polygonal meshes. The bile canaliculi are not very conspicuous in regular histologic preparations, but are well visualized with certain histochemical procedures, e.g. the procedure used for the localization of adenosine tri-phosphatase (see Fig. 3). The junction of the bile canaliculi with the bile duct system is not readily demonstrable at the light microscope level. The terminal branches of the bile ducts appear as fine canals lined by a thin layer of flattened cells which can only be recognized with difficulty. The relationship between the bile canaliculi and the bile duct system is morphologically described in the electron microscopy section (see Section V).

F. *The bile ducts*

The fine radicles of the bile ducts are 15–20 μ in diameter and have a small lumen surrounded by cuboidal epithelial cells. These small ducts are located intralobularly and are surrounded by a thin basement membrane. They have rounded nuclei and a cytoplasm containing scant organelles. Hence, the cytoplasm is comparatively pale. These small ducts communicate directly with the interlobular bile ducts in the portal areas which form a richly anastomosing network which closely surrounds the branches of the portal veins. In progressing to the common hepatic duct, the lumens of the bile ducts become gradually larger and the epithelium taller. The cells now contain large numbers of fat droplets and occasionally cholesterol crystals. At the transverse fossa of the liver, the main ducts from the different lobes of the liver fuse to form the common hepatic duct.

G. *The lymph spaces*

These produce large amounts of lymph that differs from the rest of the lymph in that it contains a large amount of plasma protein. The origin of the liver lymph is currently the subject of active investigation. The network of the lymphatic canals follow the portal vein to its finest terminal branches in the connective tissue sheath of the periportal area. No lymphatics have been found inside the liver lobules. It appears most likely that the lymph comes from the subsinusoidal space of Disse which may freely communicate with the tissue space around the interlobular twigs of the bile duct and portal vein, and their accompanying lymphatics.

H. *The connective tissue*

The liver has an unusually small amount of connective tissue. Within the portal canals, the connective tissue forms a common sheath around the branches of the portal veins, the hepatic artery, the bile duct, and the lymphatics.

III. Fine Structure and Function of the Parenchymal Cell

The low magnification picture in Fig. 2 shows the overall fine structural organization of hepatic parenchymal cells and their relationship to a sinusoid and a bile capillary.

A. *The interphase nucleus*

The fine structure of the interphase nucleus varies considerably, depending on the type of fixative used and the mode of application of the fixative. Unless stated otherwise, the nomenclature used applies to structures visible in the interphase nucleus in glutaraldehyde-fixed and "post-osmicated" tissues in sections doubly stained with lead containing solutions and uranyl acetate (Fig. 1). The appearance is essentially similar in different vertebrate species provided the fixation method is the same.

For the interpretation of the functional significance of the structures observed, reference will be made to studies in which the chemical composition of the nuclear components has been revealed by enzymatic digestion and/or electron microscopic autoradiography (for review see Bernhard and Granboulan, 1968). Two procedures may be utilized for enzyme digestion studies. In the first of these, small blocks of tissues or frozen sections of aldehyde-fixed tissues are incubated in the enzyme solutions (protease, DNAse, RNAse, or other compounds). After postfixation in osmium tetroxide, the material is embedded according to routine techniques for electron microscopy. The second method consists of embedding aldehyde-fixed tissues in water soluble embedding media (such as Durcupan and glycolmethacrylate).

Adaptation of autoradiographic methods to electron microscopy was first performed by Caro (1962). The localization of radioactive precursors to DNA and RNA (tritiated thymidine and tritiated uridine) can now be detected at the fine structural level with comparatively high resolution (Granboulan, 1963, 1965; Bernhard and Granboulan, 1968). Ultrastructural cytochemistry and electron microscopic autoradiography can be combined on the same cellular material to correlate the data of enzymatic treatments and dynamic studies.

1. *Nuclear envelope*

The nuclear envelope consists of two roughly parallel membranes separated by a 200–300 Å wide empty space (Watson, 1955, 1959). The outer nuclear membrane is studded with particles which are approximately 150 Å in diameter, and which are similar in appearance to the cytoplasmic ribosomes. The membrane is in direct continuity with the endoplasmic reticulum and the thickness of the membrane is approximately 50 Å. High resolution electron microscopy shows that the membrane is triple-layered and has the general characteristics of a "unit membrane". The perinuclear space is bounded by the inner and outer nuclear membranes. The nuclear pores are formed by the junction of the two nuclear membranes at more or less regular intervals around the nuclear perimeter. They are 300–1000 Å in diameter (Watson, 1955, 1959). Each pore is associated with an assembly of nuclear and cytoplasmic structures which have been designated as the pore complex (Watson, 1959). These units consist of a channel, measuring approximately 1200 Å in width, and formed by a cylindrical arrangement of the nucleoplasm and the cytoplasm. The nucleoplasmic portion is referred to as the intranuclear channel, and the cytoplasmic portion as the cytoplasmic cuff (Watson, 1959). The intranuclear channel, bounded by a zone of condensed chromatin (see later) diffuses into the nucleoplasm as the concentration of the adjacent chromatin diminishes. The cytoplasmic cuff is delimited by a small zone of hyaloplasm which is denser than the remainder of the cytoplasmic ground substance. It is not completely clear whether the nuclear pores are closed by a diaphragm, or fused and compacted by the outer and inner nuclear membranes (Miyai and Steiner, 1965). When nuclear pores are sectioned obliquely or tangentially to the axes of the pore complex, the pores appear as rings or annuli which contain a central mass of dense material (Watson, 1955, 1959). This mass is often referred to as the central knob.

The function of the nuclear envelope is to separate the nucleoplasm from the cytoplasm. Present evidence suggests that the interchange of materials including mRNA, sRNA and ribosomal RNA takes place across the nuclear pores (for reviews, see Bernhard and Granboulan, 1968; and Hay, 1968).

2. *Nucleoplasm*

a. *Chromatin*

It is now generally agreed that the chief structural feature of chromatin is that it is filamentous rather than granular. Most authors agree that the individual filaments are coiled and do not form an interconnected meshwork. Ris (1956) described fibrils of approximately 500 Å in diameter which were composed of double, closely associated fibrillar subunits, each measuring roughly 200 Å in diameter. Subsequently, Ris (1962) showed that the subunits were composed of approximately 100 Å thick fibrils which in turn were made up of 40 Å fibrils. There may of course be some variation in the thickness of the fibrils in different species. Differences may also be due to different fixation techniques. X-ray diffraction studies (Huxley and Zubay, 1961) indicate that osmium tetroxide fixation does not distort the structure of nucleoproteins. Neither does glutaraldehyde fixation. Hence, the measurements indicating a thickness of the unit fibril in the order of 40 Å appear to be reasonably reliable.

The distribution of chromatin in the nucleus is usually fairly even in perfusion fixed hepatic parenchymal cells (Ericsson and Biberfeld, 1967) and also in cells fixed primarily in s-collidine buffered osmium tetroxide (Ericsson *et al.*, 1965a). Some condensation occurs along the nuclear envelope and round the nucleolus. However, in aldehyde-fixed tissues fixed by immersion a more irregular distribution of the chromatin material is noted. In such cells, occasional randomly scattered concentrated aggregates of chromatin elements are found and are referred to as chromatin centers (Hay and Revel, 1963). These areas probably correspond to the heterochromatin observed under the light microscope. With most fixation procedures, chromatin is condensed around the nucleolus as nucleolus-associated chromatin (heterochromatin), and occurs also as intranucleolar chromatin.

b. *Interchromatin granules*

Single or clusters of granules ranging in diameter from 150–500 Å occur rather randomly in the interchromatinic areas (Fig. 1). They may form chains or may be separated from one another. They are highly electron-dense, but are less dense than perichromatin granules (see later). It is not yet clear whether these granules contain RNA, although they do not disappear after digestion with ribonuclease (Granboulan and Bernhard, 1961). Possibly they contain a type of RNA which is inextractable with ribonuclease or with hydrochloric acid (Swift, 1963), or they are surrounded by a protein shell. It has been suggested that both interchromatin and perichromatin granules may represent "nuclear ribosomes" (Alfrey, 1963; Bernhard and Granboulan, 1963).

c. *Perichromatin granules*

These granules are usually found singly next to chromatin areas. They are spherical in shape and have a high electron density. They measure 300–

350 Å in diameter and are separated from the surrounding chromatin by a clear halo approximately 250 Å wide. The overall diameter of the halo with its central granule is about 750 Å (Swift, 1962; Watson, 1962; Bernhard and Granboulan, 1963). According to Watson (1962), each liver cell nucleus contains 500–2000 such granules. As pointed out already, these granules may represent nuclear ribosomes, or, as has also been suggested, they might contain both RNA and DNA (Watson, 1962; Bernhard and Granboulan, 1963).

d. Interchromatinic substance

This occupies the interchromatinic areas and consists of a fine fibrillar material of low electron density, which appears to be mainly composed of protein (Bernhard and Granboulan, 1963). It probably corresponds to the nuclear sap of light microscopy.

e. Nucleolus

The nucleolus appears to contain two relatively well-defined regions: the *nucleolonema* and the *pars amorpha* (Fig. 1) (Bernhard and Granboulan, 1963; Swift, 1963). The nucleolonema is an irregular tortuous structure which probably forms a sponge-like configuration. Several components can be identified within it. One component in the so-called "*pars granulosa*" (Hay, 1968) is the ribonucleoprotein (RNP) granule which is approximately 150 Å in diameter and hence is slightly smaller than cytoplasmic ribosomes. The nucleolar granules vary somewhat in size and it is often difficult to measure them accurately because they are connected by thin filaments (Hay, 1968). The filaments on which the nucleolar granules seem to reside appear to be continuous with intranucleolar and perinucleolar chromatin fibrils and also with the ill-defined filaments of the *pars fibrosa* (see later).

The second part of the nucleolonema is the *pars fibrosa* or filamentous part of the nucleolus. When viewed at low magnification this component may appear as a dense, structureless mass. Closer examination at higher magnification reveals, however, that the underlying fine structure of this region is a filamentous meshwork. The filaments that comprise the *pars fibrosa* and form the skeleton of the granulosa are in the order of 40–50 Å in diameter and thus resemble the filaments of deoxyribonucleoprotein. At first it was speculated that the filaments in the *pars fibrosa* might contain DNA but later it was shown that the filaments were digested by RNAse and hence they are considered a form of ribonucleoprotein (Bernhard and Granboulan, 1968; Hay, 1968).

Less dense "amorphous" regions of the nucleolus consist of microfibrillar elements 40–50 Å in diameter. They usually lack any sort of polarized pattern, and are interspaced between the nucleolonema and found in the peripheral portion of the nucleolus. It has been shown that the amorphous region consists of chromatin (Swift, 1963) which has been designated as intranucleolar chromatin (Bernhard and Granboulan, 1963). The same material in the nucleolar periphery is referred to as heterochromatin or nucleolus associated chromatin. Since the *pars amorpha* is mainly composed of chromatin material, it has also been referred to as the *pars chromosoma* (Hay, 1968). Cytochemical studies (Bernhard and Granboulan, 1963; Swift, 1963) have indeed shown that the nucleolus associated chromatin and the intranucleolar chromatin have DNA in them.

The significance of the various morphologic components of the nucleolus has been elucidated by histochemical and autoradiographic studies. In the light of present concepts of nuclear control over both cytoplasmic and nuclear synthetic mechanisms, the findings indicate that the nucleolus associated and intranucleolar "DNA fibrils" operate as templates for nucleolar RNA synthesis. It is well known from light microscopic auto-radiographic studies that RNA synthesis occurs within the nucleolus of vertebrate cells. These studies have also shown that the incorporation of tritiated precursors of RNA is greater in the nucleolus than in the remainder of the nucleus. From kinetic studies it appears that the RNA synthesized in the nucleolus is transferred to the cytoplasm. By combining enzymatic digestion and electron microscopic autoradiography of cultivated monkey-kidney cells labelled with short pulses of tritiated uridine, it was possible to demonstrate that the synthesis of nucleolar RNA occurs in nucleolar associated and intranucleolar chromatin (Bernhard and Granboulan, 1968), and that there exists an interrelationship between the fibrillar and the granular component of the nucleolonema. After 5 min of labelling the newly synthesized RNA was already present in the fibrillar areas and at later intervals, it began to appear in granular areas. These results indicate that the RNA fibrils represent the origin of the ribonucleoprotein granules. At present the biochemical, genetic, and cytological findings strongly suggest that the nucleolus is the source of the ribosomal RNA (rRNA). The RNA fibrils of the fibrillar areas in nucleolar nucleolonema can be the morpho-logical substrate of the 45 s obligatory precursor of ribosomal RNA. The granular area could represent complete nucleolar ribosomes but more probably 60 s subribosomal particles. It appears likely that the nucleolus produces ribosomal RNA in the form of 45 s precursor corresponding to the fibrillar area of the nucleolonema and that after breakage into 35, 28 and 18 s molecules and linkage with protein, RNA particles are formed. Bio-chemical evidence amply suggests that these ribosomes are transferred to the cytoplasm. Supporting evidence for the view that this transfer occurs through the nucleolar pores is both fragmentary and unconvincing.

The principal products of the nuclear chromatin outside nucleolar areas appear to be messenger RNA and soluble RNA.

B. *Plasma membrane and associated structures*

The plasma membrane (plasmalemma) forms the interphase between the cell interior and the extracellular space. It is apparent that the plasma-lemma is of utmost importance for general function and structural integrity of the cell, since the exchange of water, solutes and macromolecules – including bile constituents, nutrients as well as waste products – occur across this membrane. This key role of the plasma membrane in the maintenance of the intracellular milieu makes it likely that various factors concerned with control mechanisms are located within, or in close proximity to, the membrane. Such factors may include the organization of the structural "backbone" as well as the associated enzymes, and other molecules and compounds.

1. *Canalicular cell membrane*

The cell membrane in bile canaliculi is thrown into numerous finger-like projections or microvilli extending into the canalicular lumen (Figs 4, 5, 11 and 12). The length and width of these microvilli vary somewhat between different species. They may be up to $0\cdot2$ μ in diameter. The appearance of the canalicular membrane varies according to the fixation and staining procedures employed (Biava, 1964). In osmium tetroxide-fixed tissues where the thin sections have been stained with uranyl acetate and lead hydroxide or other lead-containing solutions the membrane is approximately 100 Å thick (see Fig. 5). The membrane characteristically shows a triple-layered unit membrane structure, which seems to be compatible with the Danielli-Davson (1935) model for the chemical constitution of cell membranes. According to this model the cell membrane is composed of a central bimolecular layer of phospholipids and neutral lipids, bounded on both sides by a layer of protein. The two electron-dense bands in the cell membrane correspond to the binding sites occurring between phospholipids and proteins; the pale, intermediate zone is thought to be composed of the bimolecular lipid layer.

As the canalicular membranes of adjacent liver cells converge and come in contact at the sides of the bile canaliculi, *junctional complexes* are formed which are similar to those described by Farquhar and Palade (1963) under the names of *tight junctions*, *desmosomes*, and *intermediate junctions* (Figs 4, 6 and 11). *Tight junctions* result from the apposition of liver cell membranes at points immediately adjacent to bile canaliculi, and hence directly contribute to the line of the canalicular lumen. These types of junctions appear to be formed by the closely juxtaposed inner leaflets of canalicular membranes separated by a distance of about 100 Å. The outer leaflets of these membranes, after coming into contact, fuse into a single lamella which appears as a fusion line bisecting the space between the juxtaposed inner leaflets.* The tight junctions extend for distances of $0\cdot1$–$0\cdot5$ μ from the canalicular lumen. Thereafter, the fused cell membranes separate again, each membrane regaining its individual outer leaflet. Since tight junctions are constantly present in any random tissue section through the canalicular area, the results suggest that they border each canaliculus and extend as uninterrupted junctional bands along the entire length of bile canaliculi. Similar junctions are also seen, although less often, at variable locations

---

* This fusion is readily visible in $KMnO_4$-fixed tissues but is not apparent following primary fixation in OsO_4 (Biava, 1964).

along the lateral plasma membranes of adjacent liver cells between bile canaliculi and sinusoids. The tight junctions appear to represent water-tight "seals" which prevent direct communication between the lumen of the bile canaliculus and the extracellular space present between adjacent cells. Thus, exchange of water and solutes between these two spaces must probably occur through the cytoplasm of the parenchymal cell and can therefore be controlled by the cell.

Desmosomes are located at variable distances from canalicular tight junctions (Fig. 6). They consist of parallel segments of plasma membranes approximately 0·2 μ in length, separated by a gap of uniform width (approx-imately 250 Å). Characteristically, there is a layer of dense homogeneous material 60–80 Å thick, closely apposed to the inner surface of the plasma membrane in the desmosomal region. A condensation of finely fibrillar material is present in adjacent areas of the cytoplasm of the hepatocytes. Desmosomes are not constantly seen between liver cells in any given section. Hence, they appear to constitute focal specializations of cell surface rather than continuous bands running along the entire length of the cell. Probably their function is to keep adjacent cells together, and like other membrane junctions, they may also be involved in intercellular ion continuity, as suggested by Loewenstein (1966).

Intermediate junctions are less conspicuous in the liver than in other tissues (Biava, 1964). They are usually located between tight junctions and desmosomes and consist of relatively short parallel segments of lateral plasma membranes separated by a gap of more uniform width (approxim-ately 200 Å) than that interposed between such membranes outside junctional complexes (Fig. 4).

Immediately below the plasma membrane in the bile canaliculi the cytoplasmic ground substance forms a 0·1–0·2 μ thick layer devoid of organelles and composed of tightly packed thread-like units 50–70 Å in diameter. This area has been termed the *pericanalicular ectoplasm*. Its functional significance is unknown.

The *lateral cell membranes* are separated by a space 150–300 Å in width which is relatively pale but which contains scattered filamentous strands of moderately dense material. In light microscope preparations stained with PAS, a thin red line which is continuous with the thicker lines surrounding the bile canaliculi and the sinusoidal margin of the cells appears to corres-pond to the lateral cell membranes. It usually exhibits a single inflection ("Kapillarhöckerchen") which is normally seen near the canaliculus. As in the bile canaliculi the membrane is triple-layered and approximately 100 Å thick.

The sinusoidal border of the cell exhibits numerous microvilli, which project into the extracellular space between the parenchymal cells and sinusoidal lining cells (see Figs 2 and 36). The villi at the sinusoidal border are longer than those along the bile canaliculi and project at more irregular angles from the hepatic cell surface. Microvilli are regularly present on cells with absorptive function. The extracellular sinusoidal space is often bordered by junctional complexes similar to those seen near the bile canaliculi. In the extracellular space between the microvilli are accumulations of moderately dense, flocculent material which is considered by some investigators to represent a poorly defined basement membrane.

In the cytoplasm immediately below the membrane of the sinusoidal surface there are numerous small vesicles often exhibiting a bristle-coat on their cytoplasmic side. Similar bristle-coated vesicles have been shown in other tissues to represent endocytosis vesicles in which absorbed macromolecules and other substances are transported into the cell. Indeed, in hepatocytes, marker protein e.g. horse-radish peroxidase and other materials, including thorotrast particles, can be shown to be absorbed by such vesicles (Ericsson, 1968b; Hampton and Rosario, 1967). Larger vacuolar structures containing liposomes (see Section D on endoplasmic reticulum) are present near the sinusoidal surface of hepatocytes. Free liposomes are sometimes seen in the extracellular space (the space of Disse) and, as mentioned below, the evidence suggests that liposomes are released into this space by fusion of the vacuolar membrane to the plasma membrane (a process termed exocytosis and believed to represent the reverse of endocytosis). Hence, the process is regarded as secretion.

Successful attempts have been made to isolate plasma membrane fractions from the liver of experimental animals. This subject has been reviewed by Benedetti and Emmelot (1968). The isolated plasma membrane from rat liver constituted a fraction distinct from and free from other cellular membranes and one that was representative of the plasma membrane *in situ*. In the electron microscope the isolated fraction contained bile spaces with microvilli and also the various junctional complexes already described. The membranes were triple-layered and 80–100 Å wide. Negative staining of the plasma membrane revealed a temperature-dependent hexagonal subunit pattern and 50–60 Å globular knobs on certain areas of the membrane surface which were smaller and distinct from mitochondrial knobs (see Section C). The evidence suggests that the globular knobs of the membrane surface (probably representing microvilli) contain active leucine-aminopeptidase (Emmelot *et al.*, 1968).

Compared with other organelles of the rat liver, plasma membrane was found to have more cholesterol, saturated fatty acids, sphingomyelin, hexosamine and sialic acids per unit weight of protein while RNA was virtually absent and cytochrome P_{450} could not be demonstrated. Mg^{2+}- and Na^+-K^+-activated-ATPase, 5'-nucleotidase, alkaline glycerophosphatase, and leucyl-β-naphtylamidase were shown to be present in high concentration. These observations strengthen the view that the fraction contains reasonably pure samples of plasma membrane. Histochemically, ATPase (Fig. 3) and alkaline phosphatase can be demonstrated on the plasma membrane of hepatocytes (Novikoff *et al.*, 1962). It appears that the enzymes mentioned above and found in the isolated fractions participate in cellular transport. In the case of the Na^+-K^+-activated-ATPase, the available data indicate that this enzyme is concerned with the active transport of ions between the interior of the cell and the extracellular space.

Colloidal iron and thorium dioxide at low pH selectively stains the acidic groups of carbohydrates (Mowry, 1963; Revel, 1964). Incubation of glutaraldehyde-fixed plasma membranes isolated from rat liver, with colloidal iron hydroxide (CIH) revealed the binding of electron dense CIH granules on only one side of the membrane elements (Benedetti and Emmelot, 1968). Pretreatment with neuraminidase prevented the subsequent CIH staining almost completely. CIH thus stains the neuraminidase-sensitive sialic acid which comprises the major part of the sialic acid present in liver membranes. The sialic acid appears to be bound to the PAS-positive glycoprotein on the outer membrane leaflet of the triple-layered unit membrane (Benedetti and Emmelot, 1968). A possible function of sialic acid as "contact site" for calcium ions in cementing desmosomes and intermediate junctions has been suggested (Benedetti and Emmelot, 1968). The glycoprotein coat is probably similar to that of other cell types and appears to contain specific antigens (Emmelot and Benedetti, 1967). The function of the coat is to facilitate the binding of macromolecules and other compounds to the cell membrane before absorption (through endocytosis) by the cell.

C. *The mitochondria*

A mitochondrion is defined as a cytoplasmic organelle which is enveloped by a double membrane and which in thin sections shows one or more pairs of internal membranes termed *cristae*. The outer limiting membranes are termed the *mitochondrial envelope*; the area between them is the *envelope space*. The envelope is in some areas continuous with the cristal membranes. The space between the leaves of the cristae – *the intercristal space* – is therefore continuous with the envelope space. In hepatocyte mitochondria the cristae appear as flattened lamellae which are moderately abundant and usually arranged more or less perpendicularly to the envelope. Studies of serial sections of mouse hepatic cell mitochondria indicate that the attachment of the *cristae mitochondriales* to the inner mitochondrial membrane is confined to a round stem with a varying length and a diameter of about 300 Å (Daems and Wisse, 1966) (see Fig. 7). This stem has been termed the *pediculus cristae*. The membranes forming the outer and inner mitochondrial envelope as well as the membranes creating the cristae are of the unit membrane type, i.e. they are trilaminar. Their thickness is approximately 50 Å.

The space enclosed by the inner membrane of the envelope and the membranes of the cristae is termed the *matrix*. The matrix appears as a fairly homogeneous material of moderate electron density. Its appearance is, however, partially dependent on the fixative and embedding method utilized. Scattered within the matrix are small dense granules termed the *matrix granules*. They are approximately 300 Å in diameter.

The mitochondria in hepatic cells are abundant and one single cell may contain as many as 2000 mitochondria. It has been calculated that rat liver contains about $5 \cdot 10^{11}$ mitochondria per gram; this corresponds to a volume of $0 \cdot 14$ ml./g and to an area of $2 \cdot 5$ and 1 m^2/g for the inner and outer membranes respectively (Baudhuin and Berthet, 1967). Morphometric analyses indicate that the mitochondria in hepatic parenchymal cells occupy approximately 20% of the volume of each cell (Loud, 1968).

The mitochondria are randomly dispersed in the cytoplasm and often closely surrounded by a cisterna of the rough surfaced endoplasmic reticulum. In thin sections the mitochondria appear as rounded or elongated profiles and they are described as sausage-shaped, approximately $0 \cdot 5$ μ wide and of various length (up to 2 μ or more). Both size and shape are, however, quite variable in different species. According to Elias and Cohen (1965) the average volume of mitochondria of rat liver varies between $0 \cdot 27$ and $4 \cdot 19$ μ^3.

Application of negative staining techniques to the study of biochemically isolated fractions of mitochondria from the liver and other organs has disclosed the presence of approximately 85 Å in size particles, attached along the matrix surface of the cristae and inner membrane of the envelope by slender stalks 40–50 Å wide (Fernandez-Morán, 1962; Parsons, 1963; Stoeckenius, 1963; Fernandez-Morán et al., 1964) (Fig. 7). These particles are usually not visualized in conventionally fixed and embedded material.

There are indications from biochemical studies of isolated fractions containing reasonably pure samples of mitochondria from liver and other tissues that the primary function of mitochondria is to supply energy for the production of ATP in the cell. This evidence is consistent with the view that the function of mitochondria is to couple aerobic oxidation, via the citric acid cycle, with the synthesis of ATP. Mitochondria are also capable of oxidizing fatty acids and amino acids, some of which give rise to members of the citric acid cycle. In addition to these primary functions, mitochondria appear to exhibit other functional properties including synthesis of protein, phospholipid, citrulline and hippuric acid. There is good evidence that the enzymes of the electron transport system (the chain of respiratory enzymes, including flavoproteins and cytochromes b, c_1, c, a, and a_3) are localized in or on the mitochondrial membrane (Ball and Joel, 1962).

It was tentatively suggested by Fernandez-Morán (1962) that the particles 85 Å in size along the matrical surface of the cristae and in the membrane of the envelope might correspond to the elementary particles described by Green and Fleischer (1962), and that they might contain the enzymes of the electron transport system. Subsequent studies, however, have suggested that these particles represent artefacts (Sjöstrand et al., 1964; Sjöstrand, 1968) and that they may not contain the electron transport system which appears to be more intimately associated with the membrane. Recent studies by Racker and his associates (see Racker, 1968) are compatible with the notion that the particles may represent sites of the enzyme adenosine triphosphatase which is essential for the hydrolysis of ATP.

Recent evidence derived from experiments based on swelling and shrinking of mitochondria, followed by sonication and density gradient centrifugation, indicate that the rotenone-insensitive NADH-cytochrome c reductase system is associated with the outer mitochondrial membrane (Sottocasa *et al.*, 1967).

Our knowledge of the matrix is still very sparse. It appears that the matrix contains the enzymes involved in the substrate-level transformations of the citric acid cycle, nucleotides, and inorganic electrolytes (de Duve *et al.*, 1962; Lehninger, 1962, 1964). The matrix may also contain ribonucleic acids (RNA) and deoxyribonucleic acids (DNA) (Nass and Nass, 1963a, b).

The chemical composition and function of the matrix granules (Fig. 8) is not yet certain. However, there is a growing body of evidence implicating these granules in ion transport by mitochondria (Weiss, 1955; Peachy, 1962, 1964). The granules are present as negative images in tissue quenched in propane or isopentane and freeze-substituted in acetone (Rebhun, 1965) or in tissues fixed in acroleine without postfixation in osmium tetroxide (Trump and Ericsson, 1965a). More recently, Ashworth *et al.* (1966) showed that the granules could be extracted with lipid solvents if pieces of aldehyde-fixed liver tissue were exposed to such compounds. There is thus strong evidence that the granules may, at least in part, be composed of lipid or lipoprotein materials, which may perhaps serve as matrix material for cationic binding.

Disappearance of the matrix granules appears to be an early reaction to anoxic cellular injury (Trump and Ericsson, 1965b).

Mitochondria with cristalloid matrix and various aberrations of their cristae have been observed in normal liver of man and experimental animals (David, 1964; Stephens and Bils, 1965; Spycher and Rüttner, 1968). It is presently not clear whether such appearances should be regarded as variants of the normal or evidence for mitochondrial damage.

D. *The endoplasmic reticulum and Golgi apparatus*

The term *endoplasmic reticulum* is used to refer to a series of membranous profiles that are present in the cytoplasm of hepatic parenchymal cells and other cell types. These profiles appear in several forms: some are elongated and others are circular. Most of these images probably represent oblique or transverse sections through anastomosing tubular and cisternal systems. The endoplasmic reticulum is usually divided into the so-called rough- (granular) and smooth-surfaced (agranular) varieties, the rough having ribosomes apposed to the surface of the membrane. The appearance of the endoplasmic reticulum is illustrated in Figs 6, 8, 9, 10, 13, 14 and 33–35.

In the mammalian hepatocyte, the *rough-surfaced endoplasmic reticulum* is largely confined to the middle portions of the cytoplasm while the areas along the bile canaliculi and sinusoids are usually free of this organelle. As a rule approximately parallel arrays of rough-surfaced profiles (up to 10 or more) are found within the mid-region of the cell. Rough-surfaced profiles may also occur singly among the other cytoplasmic organelles. The exact disposition of the rough-surfaced reticulum is probably dependent on the precise position of a cell within the lobule, on the dietary status, and on several other factors. Mitochondria are often partially surrounded by curving profiles of rough-surfaced endoplasmic reticulum. Micrographs showing direct contact between the reticulum and the mitochondria have not been seen, however. Neither is there evidence for continuity between the endoplasmic reticulum and the plasma membrane. On the other hand, a close structural relationship appears to exist between the microbodies and both smooth- and rough-surfaced areas of the endoplasmic reticulum. In some cases, tubular protrusions from the microbody surface appear to be in continuity with the reticulum and it has been suggested that microbodies may, in fact, form within the lumen of the reticulum (Novikoff and Shin, 1964; Essner, 1966; Tsukada *et al.*, 1968). Continuity is often observed between the rough- and smooth-surfaced varieties of the endoplasmic reticulum.

The *smooth-surfaced endoplasmic reticulum* is more difficult to separate from other cytoplasmic structures and organelles than the rough-surfaced variety since there are numerous smooth membrane profiles throughout the cytoplasm of hepatic cells. In high resolution electron micrographs it can be seen, however, that the thickness of the membrane bordering smooth- (and rough-) surfaced endoplasmic reticulum is thinner (approximately 50 Å) than those bordering endocytosis vesicles, cytosomes and multivesicular bodies (see below). Like the plasma membrane, the membrane is triple-layered. Perhaps the most characteristic portions of the smooth-surfaced endoplasmic reticulum are the cisternae and tubules which appear in areas of glycogen deposits. In animals that have been fasted for periods of 10–20 hr prior to sacrifice, the glycogen areas (see below and Fig. 33) are relatively sparse and are partly replaced by numerous smooth-surfaced profiles of endoplasmic reticulum (compare with Fig. 16). Lipid droplets lying free in the cytoplasmic ground substance are often closely surrounded by tubular images (cisternae?) of smooth-surfaced endoplasmic reticulum (Figs 34 and 35). At the margins of the Golgi apparatus (both at the forming and emitting sides as described below) profiles of smooth-surfaced endoplasmic reticulum seem to blend with the cisternal elements of the Golgi complex. As noted above, continuity is also present between occasional microbodies and smooth-surfaced endoplasmic reticulum.

Ribosomes are arranged along the surface of the rough-surfaced endoplasmic reticulum. These particles are approximately 180 Å in diameter and have an irregular shape. They show the same general appearance as the free ribosomes in the cytoplasmic ground substance, and they seem to be composed of two subunits of which the larger is in contact with the membrane of the reticulum. This larger unit has been thought to contain a central canal continuous with the intracisternal space in the endoplasmic reticulum (Sabatini *et al.*, 1966). Occasional tangential sections of the rough-surfaced cisternae reveal a pattern of spherules and clusters of ribosomes, the so-called polysomes (Fig. 9). As many as 23 such particles have been counted in a single cluster (David and Metzler, 1967).

Most lumens of rough- and smooth-surfaced cisternae and tubules are devoid of content. In a few areas, small homogeneous, rounded, moderately electron dense bodies, up to 600 Å in diameter, can be seen (Figs 13 and 14). These structures have been referred to as liposomes. In addition, a sparse, flocculent material can often be observed in the lumens. The amount of such flocculent material is to some extent dependent on the mode of fixation and more material is usually observed in glutaraldehyde, as compared to osmium tetroxide-fixed tissues (Ericsson *et al.*, 1965a).

The endoplasmic reticulum appears to show *local specializations* in the cytoplasm of hepatic parenchymal cells. One such specialization occurs around the microbodies and has been mentioned previously. Another specialization is observed on either side of the intercellular space immediately below the lateral plasma membrane. It consists of a series of elongated and rounded membranous profiles which in some areas appear to be in continuity with the endoplasmic reticulum proper (Figs 6 and 17). These profiles can be observed along the plasmalemma from the space of Disse to the bile canaliculus. Some of the membranous profiles of this system are studded with ribosomes, while others are devoid of such particles. This series of membrane profiles ceases at a short distance from the bile canaliculus and the space of Disse, respectively. The profiles are arranged in a relatively straight line and the lateral membranes are approximately parallel to the lateral plasma membrane. A similar specialized portion of the endoplasmic reticulum has also been described in renal proximal convoluted tubule cells where it occurs along the lateral plasma membrane. It has been referred to as the *paramembranous cisternal system* (Ericsson, 1964; Trump *et al.*, 1965).

Electron microscopic histochemical studies have revealed the occurrence of nucleoside diphosphatases, β-glucuronidase and glucose-6-phosphatase in the endoplasmic reticulum, both in the rough- and the smooth-surfaced varieties (Fig. 10) (Novikoff *et al.*, 1962; Ericsson, 1965; Fishman *et al.*, 1967). In the case of glucose-6-phosphatase its activity could be demonstrated in the local specializations of the reticulum, i.e. in the paramembranous cisternal system and the reticulum surrounding microbodies (Orrenius and Ericsson, 1966b).

The *Golgi apparatus* is typically located near the bile canaliculus (Figs 2, 11, 12, 13 and 29). Closely associated with the Golgi apparatus are cytosomes, multivesicular bodies and microbodies (Fig. 11). The Golgi apparatus is composed of a series of elongated and rounded smooth-surfaced membranous profiles probably representing cisternae, vesicles and vacuoles, respectively. Often the various membranous elements of the Golgi apparatus form a "polarized" structure in that the cisternae form slightly curved, parallel arrays with the convex side facing smooth-surfaced end portions of rough-surfaced cisternae of endoplasmic reticulum, and the concave side facing an area containing numerous Golgi vacuoles. The convex side is often, though not invariably, facing a bile canaliculus (Figs 11 and 12). Several Golgi regions may be seen in a single cell. Images suggesting budding of Golgi vacuoles from the cisternae are often encountered (Figs 12 and 13). In fasted animals, elements of the Golgi complex usually contain clusters of rounded bodies up to 600 Å in diameter with smooth contour (liposomes) similar to the ones seen in the endoplasmic reticulum, as described above (see Figs 13 and 14). The liposomes appear to be concentrated in some of the Golgi vacuoles budding off from the Golgi cisternae (Fig. 13).

Electron microscopic histochemical studies have indicated the presence of acid phosphatase and thiaminopyrophosphatase in Golgi cisternae, vacuoles and vesicles (Novikoff et al., 1962; Ericsson and Glinsmann, 1966).

According to Novikoff and his associates, a close functional and structural relationship exists between the smooth-surfaced endoplasmic reticulum and the Golgi elements at the concave face of the apparatus (Novikoff et al., 1966; Holtzman et al., 1967). It has been suggested that the formation of primary lysosomes as well as multivesicular bodies and autophagic vacuoles occurs in this general region. This region has been named GERL (Golgi-endoplasmic reticulum-lysosome) (Novikoff et al., 1966).

With biochemical fractionation procedures, a fraction from liver homogenates termed the *microsomal fraction* has been isolated. The microsomes are lighter than mitochondria and hence need a higher centrifugation force for sedimentation than mitochondria. While liver mitochondria can be separated from the remainder of the homogenate by centrifugation at 2×10^5 g/min for 10 min in 0·25 M sucrose, microsomes can be forced to sediment by centrifugation at 6×10^6 g/min for 60 min in the same medium. Comparison between the fine structure of microsomal pellets and intact liver cell cytoplasm suggests that the microsomes represent fragments of the endoplasmic reticulum (Palade and Siekevitz, 1956). From an investigation on sectioned pellets of rat liver microsomes it was concluded that the total microsomal fractions consist almost entirely of closed vesicles which are limited by single, continuous, dense membranes and contain a material of low electron density (Palade and Siekevitz, 1956). The vesicles could be divided into two groups, one consisting of rough-surfaced vesicles, with small (approximately 15 mμ in diameter), dense particles attached to their outer surface, and another group of smooth-surfaced vesicles, devoid of such particles. A number of particles in the non-bound form were also included in the fraction. Deoxycholate was found to solubilize the membranes and the contents of the vesicles, but not the particles, which thus could be isolated as a separate fraction. The dissolved membranes accounted for the major part of the microsomal lipids, and the particles contained the bulk of the RNA. It appeared that the rough-surfaced vesicles were formed as a result of fragmentation of rough-surfaced endoplasmic reticulum, while the smooth-surfaced vesicles seemed to originate, at least partly, from the region of the endoplasmic reticulum which lacked attached ribosomes, i.e. the smooth-surfaced endoplasmic reticulum. Rough-surfaced vesicles of the microsomal fraction are 100–300 μ in diameter while the smooth-surfaced vesicles (Fig. 15) are 100–150 μ in diameter. The density of the rough-surfaced vesicles is 1·17–1·25 while that of the smooth-surfaced vesicles is 1·05–1·17. The RNA to protein ratio is for the former 0·27 and for the latter 0·04. The cholesterol content expressed as a percentage of the total lipid is for rough-surfaced vesicles approximately 6% and for smooth-surfaced vesicles about 13% (Glaumann and Dallner, 1968). The variation in lipid composition of different types of cell membranes has been reviewed by Rouser et al. (1968).

The occurrence of enzymes in liver microsomes was first investigated by Hogeboom and Schneider (1950) (Hogeboom, 1949), who found that microsomes contained DPNH and TPNH cytochrome c reductase.

Hultin (1950) and Borsook et al. (1950) were the first to report that the incorporation of labelled amino acids into liver protein in vivo is most rapid in the microsomal fraction. In 1952 Siekevitz demonstrated the incorporation of labelled alanine into the protein of isolated liver microsomes. It is now firmly established that protein synthesis takes place mainly or exclusively on the ribosomes (polysomes) and that the role, if any, of the endoplasmic reticulum membranes, i.e. the microsomal vesicles, is only secondary. It seems, however, that the membrane is necessary for the transport of the newly synthesized proteins. According to Sabatini et al. (1966), the ribosomes on the rough-surfaced endoplasmic reticulum consist of two subunits, one large particle (with a sedimentation coefficient of 47 s) and one small particle (with a sedimentation coefficient of 30 s). The ribosomes are anchored to the membrane by the larger particle (Sabatini et al., 1966). Studies by Redman and Sabatini (1966) indicate that the 47 s subunit contains a canal through which the newly synthesized protein is transported to the endoplasmic reticulum membrane or through the membrane to the lumen of the reticulum.

One of the important proteins which is synthesized by the liver is albumin. The presence of albumin (and also fibrinogen) in hepatic parenchymal cells has been amply demonstrated with the immunofluorescent technique (Hamashima et al., 1964). By injecting ^{14}C-labelled leucine it is possible to follow the transport of newly synthesized albumin following its formation on the ribosomes. Approximately 10 min after the administration of label to experimental animals in vivo, the tagged protein is concentrated in the rough-surfaced microsomes isolated from liver homogenates. Some 10 min later the protein shows high concentration in the smooth-surfaced microsomes, and 40 min after the injection labelled albumin is present in the blood plasma (Glaumann et al., 1968). Recent observations by Redman (1968) and Takagi and Ogata (1968) indicate that serum albumin is exclusively synthesized on membrane-bound polysomes.

Studies such as these and correlated with those of the fine structure indicate strongly that proteins synthesized on the ribosomes of rough-surfaced endoplasmic reticulum are transported through the canals and cisternae formed by this reticulum, thence into the lumen of smooth-surfaced endoplasmic reticulum (the morphologic evidence is compatible with there being a direct connection between the lumens of rough- and smooth-surfaced endoplasmic reticulum). It appears likely, judging from other tissues such as the pancreas, that newly synthesized proteins are concentrated in the Golgi region, prior to their release to the extracellular space. Clear-cut evidence for such concentration in the Golgi apparatus of liver cells has not been obtained, however. It is, furthermore, not known in which form these proteins are transported to the cell membrane for release into the extracellular space. Possibly this transport occurs via vesicles or vacuoles moving from the Golgi apparatus to the cell membrane, but these presumptive vectors for protein transport have so far not been identified.

Not only proteins for "export" appear to be synthesized on the ribosomes of the rough-surfaced endoplasmic reticulum, but also protein for the cell's own needs. Acid phosphatase for example is probably synthesized by attached ribosomes (de Duve and Wattiaux, 1966). Although the presence of acid phosphatase has not been demonstrated in the endoplasmic reticulum of normal liver cells, there is evidence from other cell types (reviewed by Ericsson, 1969a) that the enzyme is present in the reticulum. The Golgi apparatus of the liver cell shows phosphatase activity (Ericsson and Glinsmann, 1966).

In some instances, synthesized proteins may be complemented by other compounds present in the endoplasmic reticulum. As an example of this, the glycoproteins could be mentioned. The (smooth-surfaced?) membrane itself appears to participate in the synthetic mechanisms by conjugation of the sugar portion to the protein prior to transportation to the blood (Lawford and Schachter, 1966). Such conjugation may also occur in the Golgi apparatus.

In 1950 Hers and de Duve demonstrated that glucose-6-phosphatase – the enzyme catalysing the final step in hepatic glycogenolysis – is located in the microsomes of liver homogenates. The biochemical findings are in agreement with the electron microscopic histochemical demonstration of glucose-6-phosphatase in the smooth- and rough-surfaced endoplasmic reticulum of hepatic parenchymal cells (Orrenius and Ericsson, 1966b) (see Fig. 10). Morphologic evidence indicating a functional relationship between the endoplasmic reticulum and glycogen comes from a comparison of the appearance of hepatic cells isolated from fasted and non-fasted animals. The cells of the non-fasted animals show large areas of cytoplasm containing densely packed glycogen particles (Fig. 33), whereas the cells of fasting animals show smooth surfaced endoplasmic reticulum that penetrates these areas which gradually loose their glycogen particle. The evidence suggests that the glycogen is metabolized during fasting and that the endoplasmic reticulum plays a role, presumably by supplying glucose-6-phosphatase for the final step in the breakdown of glycogen to glucose.

One important function of the liver is its ability to detoxify drugs and toxins. Numerous studies indicate that the microsomes are actively involved in this process. Basically, the reaction involves hydroxylation whereby the different substances are broken down to less lipophilic compounds; this process facilitates excretion and hampers accumulation within the cells. TPNH-cytochrome c reductase and the CO-binding pigment are present in microsomes and are probably involved in oxidative demethylation

(Orrenius *et al.*, 1965). Pretreatment of rats *in vivo* with certain drugs, e.g. phenobarbital, induces an increased rate of drug hydroxylation and also leads to increased numbers of endoplasmic reticulum membranes, mainly the smooth-surfaced variety (Remmer and Merker, 1963) (Figs 16 and 17). Figure 18 shows the effect of phenobarbital on microsomal protein, RNA and phospholipids. Following the injection of 5 doses of phenobarbital into rats, there is a marked increase in phospholipid, and a moderate increase in RNA and protein per gram of liver tissue. The effect of phenobarbital treatment on several microsomal enzymes is shown in Fig. 19. It is apparent that phenobarbital acts by the specific induction of the synthesis of TPNH-cytochrome *c* reductase and the CO-binding pigment both of which are necessary for oxidative demethylation. This substrate induction is sensitive to actinomycin D and puromycin (Orrenius *et al.*, 1965). Electron microscopic studies (Figs 16 and 17) suggest that the newly-formed endoplasmic membranes are continuous with the pre-existing membranes of the endoplasmic reticulum. Hence they appear to represent outgrowths from the reticulum. It is not completely clear whether the new membrane area is formed as an apposition on the ends of pre-existing endoplasmic reticulum, or rather represents a general increase in the total area of the reticulum by diffuse addition of membrane components throughout the reticulum – like the stretching of a rubber band. In the latter case, one must envisage many of the ribosomes as being present on the membranes of the reticulum for only a limited period of time and then leaving them, since most of the induced membranes are smooth-surfaced.

The membranes induced by phenobarbital treatment persist up to 15 days after the last of a series of five inducing injections (Orrenius and Ericsson, 1966a) (cf. Fig. 22). On the other hand, *the enzymes* are only increased for approximately five days (Fig. 20). Disappearance of the membranes is gradual and does not seem to be associated with increased autophagic activity in the cells. The findings indicate that the induced membranes and enzymes are not degraded together in bulk. The theory of differential replacement of the various components of the membranes is supported by studies on the turnover of the various constituents of the endoplasmic reticulum membranes in the normal rat (Omura *et al.*, 1967). These studies show that the total membrane proteins in microsome fractions have half-lives that range from 75 to 113 hours, while in the same experiments total membrane lipids have 10–30% shorter half-lives. The half-life of the NADPH-cytochrome *c* reductase was, in two experiments, almost exactly that of total membrane proteins, while the half-life of cytochrome b_5 was significantly (about 50%) longer. The polar and non-polar components of the lipids had different apparent half-lives, that of fatty acids being much longer than that of the glycerol backbone. The findings show that phospholipid protein complexes are not degraded as a unit. It would thus seem that the endoplasmic reticulum membranes have a continuous existence throughout the lifetime of the differentiated cell and form a framework in which the components proteins and phospholipids are being exchanged at varying rates. Hence, the component molecules have a much shorter and finite existence than the membrane taken as a whole. In the case of phenobarbital induction of membranes and proteins, the effect may be explained on the basis of increased synthesis, diminished turnover rates (decreased breakdown), or a combination of these factors (Holtzman and Gillette, 1968). Although in phenobarbital induction there is a selective increase only in the enzymes participating in oxidative hydroxylation (Fig. 19), the other constitutive enzymes of the endoplasmic reticulum appear also to be present in all the membranes induced by phenobarbital treatment. This is indicated by combined biochemical and electron microscopic histochemical studies in which glucose-6-phosphatase was demonstrated in all the endoplasmic reticulum membranes of phenobarbital-treated animals. In the same experiments, similar patterns of distribution of protein, aminopyrin-demethylation, and glucose-6-phosphatase activity were noted after differential centrifugation of smooth surfaced microsomes in different sucrose gradients (Orrenius and Ericsson, 1966b) (Fig. 21). These observations appear also to support the theory that the proliferation of membranes induced by phenobarbital is the result of the addition and/or slowed down turnover of molecules in the entire area occupied by the endoplasmic reticulum membranes.

Studies by Emans and Jones (1968) have demonstrated that hypertrophy of liver cell smooth surfaced endoplasmic reticulum – resembling that found after phenobarbital injection – can be induced by the administration of progesterone. This finding raises the possibility that enzymes normally occurring in the organism may be of importance in the maintenance of the development of the endoplasmic reticulum.

Hepatic microsomes appear to contain an ethanol-oxidizing system distinct from alcohol dehydrogenase. In vitro it has the characteristics of microsomal drug-detoxifying enzymes. This system has been claimed to be capable in vivo of adaptive increase following the administration of ethanol (Lieber and DeCarli, 1968). The feeding of ethanol to rats has been reported to cause significantly increased activities of hepatic pentobarbital and benzpyrene hydroxylases (Rubin, 1968). These observations may explain at least in part, the increased tolerance of alcoholics to sedatives and alcohol; they further indicate that the endoplasmic reticulum participates in the detoxification of alcohol.

The microsomal fraction of various tissues exhibits an ATPase activity (Novikoff et al., 1952). The tissues studied include livers of various species. The ATPase of liver microsomes is stimulated by sodium and potassium ions (Schwartz, 1963). Such observations suggest that the microsomal ATPase may be involved in active cation transport. It should be kept in mind, however, that the microsomes isolated from the liver may not only contain membranes derived from the endoplasmic reticulum of hepatocytes, but also membrane material from the plasmalemma and from Kupffer cells and other cells. The plasma membranes of several cell types including nerve cells and kidney tubule cells are known to contain a $Na^+ + K^+$-activated

ATPase. Hence, the possibility cannot be ruled out that the $Na^+ + K^+$-activated ATPase in liver microsomes might be a contaminant. Such a possibility is rendered likely by the finding of 5'-nucleotidase activity in microsomal fractions.

Evidence based upon electron microscopic histochemical studies suggests that several nucleoside-di-phosphatases (adenosine-, cytidine-, guanosine-, uridine-, and inosine-5-diphosphatases) are present in the endoplasmic reticulum of hepatic parenchymal cells. These observations are in general supported by biochemical data demonstrating the same enzymes in microsomes. The functional significance of these enzymes is not yet clearly understood. It is likely that the enzymes have mainly hydrolytic functions (Novikoff et al., 1962).

Other enzymes present in liver microsomes are actively engaged in the biosynthesis of phospholipids, triglycerides and cholesterol (Tchen and Bloch, 1955; Wilgram and Kennedy, 1963). The phospholipids are components of different cytomembranes, while triglycerides and cholesterol, besides being constituents of membranes, also are transported to the blood. An important function of the endoplasmic reticulum appears to be the elaboration of lipoproteins. It is well known that the liver removes free fatty acid (FFA) from the circulation and releases esterified fatty acids in the form of lipoproteins. As shown in perfusion studies, the major portion of esterified fatty acid that is released appears as triglycerides in the very low density lipoprotein (VLDL) (D less than 1·006) (Kay and Entenman, 1961; Heimberg et al., 1965). Increased amounts of FFA in the liver result in accelerated VLDL release. Electron microscopic studies have shown that perfusion with FFA causes an increase in the number, size, osmiophilia and distribution of electron-dense particles with the dimensions of VLDL. Such particles are 300–600 Å in diameter and appear to be represented by the particles described previously in the endoplasmic reticulum and the Golgi apparatus and associated elements (Figs 13 and 14) (Jones et al., 1966; Hamilton et al., 1967; Parks, 1967; Stein and Stein, 1967). Lipid solvent extraction of aldehyde fixed hepatic tissue of rats caused the disappearance of all intravascular and hepatocellular osmiophilic droplets similar to those described above, thus indicating their lipid content (Ashworth et al., 1966). Thin-layer chromatography of the lipid solvents used in extracting aldehyde-fixed tissue revealed that triglyceride, phospholipid, and cholesterol and other lipids had been removed. Liposomes are not only present in the endoplasmic reticulum and the Golgi apparatus, but also in vesicular structures closely related to the plasma membrane at the sinusoidal surface of the liver cell. Images suggesting continuity between the plasma membrane at this site and the membrane of vesicles have been obtained (Parks, 1967). Thus, the available evidence suggests that lipoproteins are formed and transported in the following manner: FFA is taken up from the blood at the sinusoidal surface of the liver; and lipoprotein synthesis occurs in the endoplasmic reticulum, perhaps both in the smooth and rough-surfaced types. It appears likely that the protein component of lipoprotein is elaborated in the rough-surfaced ER. The liposomes thus formed appear as 300–600 Å spheres which are transported to, and concentrated within, the Golgi apparatus. Golgi vacuoles budding off from the cisternae contain concentrated liposomes. The vacuoles containing the liposomes move toward the sinusoidal surface and release their phospholipids into the space of Disse. From there the liposomes move through the sinusoidal lining into the blood stream.

Finally, it should be mentioned that the microsomes appear to contain the enzymes that are involved in the conjugation of bile pigment, the synthesis of bile acids, the synthesis of vitamin C, and the reduction of fatty acids (for review of the functions of microsomes, see Smuckler and Arcasoy, 1969).

There is little information about the structural basis of the uptake and transport of bilirubin by the parenchymal liver cell. Unconjugated bilirubin is apparently absorbed at the sinusoidal surface of the cell. It is not clear whether this absorption occurs by way of endocytosis (as in the case of proteins and macromolecules) or by some kind of transmembrane transport, or possibly by a combination of these routes. Following uptake by the cell, bilirubin appears to become associated with the endoplasmic reticulum, where conjugation is accomplished. Further transport must involve movement of the conjugated bilirubin molecules to the cell surface at the bile capillary. This transport may either be channelled through the endoplasmic reticulum – Golgi system, and via moving vesicles to the plasma membrane. Alternatively, the molecules may move freely through the cytoplasm to reach the plasma membrane. The sparsity of vesicular structures under the plasmalemma bordering the bile capillaries is evidence supporting the latter notion. In cholestasis, intracellular accumulation of bilirubin has been reported to occur in the cytoplasmic ground substance.

E. Cytosomes and cytosegresomes

1. Cytosomes

Hepatic cell cytosomes have a characteristic, yet variable appearance. They can be demonstrated by (a) light microscopy with the aid of toluidine blue staining of Epon or Vestopal embedded tissues, (b) in paraffin sections stained with the PAS method before or after diastase digestion, (c) by their autofluorescence, (d) by the Perls technique for iron, and (e) by the Gomori technique for acid phosphatase (see below and Fig. 23), or by techniques for demonstration of β-glucuronidase and aryl sulfatase activities.

Under the electron microscope cytosomes appear as rounded or elliptical bodies up to 1 μ in diameter and enveloped by a single, triple-layered membrane, 90–100 Å in thickness (cf. Fig. 30). The bodies contain a variety of dense, granular and filamentous or lamellar material dispersed in a rather uniform matrical substance (Figs 2, 6, 11, 13, 17 and 27). The appearance of the granular and filamentous material varies and the enclosed structures include dense linear profiles of different thickness, and large, rounded dense bodies; structures resembling myelin figures, and small particles resembling ferritin. The density of the matrix also varies considerably; this seems to some extent to depend on the fixative utilized (Ericsson *et al.*, 1965*a*).

The cytosomes are most abundant in that part of the hepatic parenchymal cell which lies adjacent to the bile capillaries (Figs 2, 6 and 29). For this reason these bodies have been termed peribiliary dense bodies (Palade and Siekevitz, 1956; Novikoff, 1960, 1961). Cytosomes have also been referred to by many other terms including "lysosomes", "residual bodies", "electron dense bodies" and "microbodies" (for review of terminology see Ericsson *et al.*, 1965*b*; Trump and Ericsson, 1965*b* and de Duve and Wattiaux, 1966).

Using the Gomori technique for acid phosphatase with light microscopy, the brownish-black, granular sites (viz. the reaction product) are found along the bile canaliculi, a location corresponding to that of most cytosomes (Fig. 23). When the Gomori technique is combined with electron micro-scopy, it can be shown that the lead phosphate is present in the cytosomes (Fig. 24). In fact, virtually all of the cytosomes are found to contain the final product of the Gomori stain. Similarly, most of the cytosomes contain on the basis of electron histochemical evidence aryl sulphatase and E-600 resist-ant esterase ("acid esterase", probably an acid protease with cathepsin-like action) (Miller, 1964; Ericsson and Helminen, 1967). Taken together, these findings indicate that the cytosomes are actually the lysosomes first isolated and defined biochemically by de Duve and his group (see de Duve, 1959). Biochemical evidence for the identity of isolated lysosomes and the morpho-logically demonstrable cytosomes has been brought forward as the result of combined electron microscopic and biochemical studies in which the fine structure of pellets obtained by both differential centrifugation and sub-fractionation by equilibration in a density gradient was established (Baud-huin *et al.*, 1965). Subcellular fractions isolated from rat liver in this way show high specific activity of several lysosomal enzymes and are composed almost entirely of bodies resembling cytosomes.

Biochemical studies of isolated lysosomal fractions have revealed that there are more than 25 different hydrolytic enzymes in these organelles. Such lytic enzymes include proteases (cathepsins) capable of degrading various proteins and polypeptides, phospholipases capable of degrading phospholipids, acid hyaluronidase, β-glucuronidase, acid phosphatase, acid deoxyribonuclease, acid ribonuclease, aryl sulfatase and other sulfatases, and α-1-4-glucosidase hydrolysing the breakdown of glycogen. Clearly, these enzymes can degrade most of the macromolecules found in liver cells, and in addition hydrolyse many compounds known to be taken up by these cells.

On the basis of the enzyme content of lysosomes, three main functions have been assigned to these organelles. First, segregation and digestion of materials taken into the cells. Second, "physiologic autolysis". Third, "pathologic autolysis". Numerous electron microscopic, histochemical, and biochemical studies have provided strong supporting evidence for the notion that the lysosomes are actively involved in the segregation and digestion of absorbed materials (de Duve and Wattiaux, 1966). These include observations on hepatic parenchymal cells. Similar mechanisms seem to be involved in widely different cell types.

Macromolecules of different types are taken up at the sinusoidal surface of the liver cell where endocytosis is extensive. Before absorption compounds are trapped in small invaginations of the plasma membrane. These invaginations or pits are pinched off from the plasma membrane, thereby imprisoning the material in a small vesicle. These vesicles are enveloped by a membrane which is 90–100 Å in thickness and triple-layered as in the case of the plasma membrane. The endocytosis process can be fruitfully studied by exposing the sinusoidal surface of the liver cell to electron dense marker molecules, such as thorium dioxide (thorotrast) (Hampton and Rosario, 1967). The thorotrast particles are transferred across the endothelial lining of the sinusoids, and hence enter the space of Disse. During the uptake of thorotrast particles in the hepatocytes, small endocytosis vesicles containing the marker substance appear in the cytoplasm immediately below the sinusoidal plasma membrane. Such vesicles often have an external bristle coating, and many of them fuse to form vacuoles with a diameter of up to 1 μ, or even more. Subsequently, the endocytosis vesicles and vacuoles approach the cytosomes at the canalicular region of the cell. Fusion between the endocytosis vesicles and vacuoles with cytosomes is suggested by the presence of thorotrast particles in the cytosomes which show acid phosphatase activity (Ericsson, 1968a; Ericsson and Engberg 1968) (Fig. 29). Since the thorotrast particles resist digestion by the lysosomal enzymes, the marker becomes segregated and stored for long periods in the cytosomes. On the other hand, proteinaceous materials, e.g. hemoglobin, albumin and peroxidase which also seem to be transported to the cytosomes from the sinusoidal surface by way of endocytosis vesicles and vacuoles, are rapidly degraded within the cytosomes (Ericsson, 1968b; Novikoff et al., 1968).

The participation of lysosomes in physiologic autolysis is discussed below in part 2.

Release of lysosomal enzymes from cytosomes is probably a late phenomenon in pathologic conditions involving cell death and necrosis. Digestion of the cytoplasm by lysosomal enzymes is known to occur in these conditions, but it is beyond the scope of this presentation to enlarge upon this aspect of lysosomal function. The subject is treated by Trump and Ericsson (1965b) and de Duve and Wattiaux (1966).

2. Cytosegresomes

These are defined as membrane-limited cytoplasmic bodies containing other recognizable organelles such as mitochondria, microbodies or endoplasmic reticulum (Figs 25, 26 and 28) (Ericsson, 1964; Ericsson and Trump, 1964; Ericsson et al., 1965b). The limiting membrane may be single, triple-layered measuring 90–100 Å in diameter, or a double membrane with each membrane measuring approximately 60 Å and also showing the triple-layered structure (Maunsbach, 1966). Occasionally, the border around the enclosed organelles may occupy several layers.

The results of electron microscopic histochemical studies indicate that in liver and other cells the cytosegresomes contain acid phosphatase and aryl sulphatase (for review see Ericsson, 1969a). As in the case of cytosomes, these bodies have been designated numerous other terms, such as "cytolysomes" (Novikoff, 1960, 1961), "areas of focal cytoplasmic degradation" (Hruban et al., 1963), "lysosomes" (Ashford and Porter, 1962) and "autophagic vacuoles" (de Duve, 1963). It would appear that in the normal hepatic parenchymal cell the cytosegresomes represent areas of the cell's own cytoplasm which had been segregated from the remainder of the cytoplasm. Hence, under these circumstances, the cytosegresomes represent autophagic vacuoles, i.e. bodies in which areas of the cell's own cytoplasm are degraded. The formation of cytosegresomes under normal conditions may thus be the morphologic expression of the turnover in bulk of cytoplasmic constituents.

The idea that the cytoplasmic organelles found in cytosegresomes are degraded is largely favored by evidence from experimentally induced formation of these bodies. Following partial hepatectomy or administration of a number of different hepatotoxic agents, an increased number of cytosegresomes becomes demonstrable in the cytoplasm of these cells. That degradative processes do occur in the cytosegresomes is indicated by the observation that the enclosed organelles undergo structural reorganization with sequential loss of structural integrity, and by the histochemical demonstration of acid phosphatase activity. As degradation continues, the cytosegresomes seem to be gradually transformed into bodies that resemble cytosomes or lipofuscin bodies (Glinsmann and Ericsson, 1966; Ericsson, 1969a) (compare with Fig. 27). The increased occurrence with age of lipofuscin-like bodies in hepatic parenchymal cells may be related to the accumulation of end-products of autodigestive processes in this special type of "lysosome".

The mechanism of formation of autophagic cytosegresomes has been the object of numerous theories in recent years (for review, see Ericsson, 1969a). The possibility of labelling pre-existing cytosomes – corresponding to "secondary lysosomes" – with thorotrast and other electron-dense granular compounds has facilitated the study of the relationship between forming cytosegresomes and pre-existing secondary lysosomes (Ericsson, 1968a, b, 1969b; Ericsson and Engberg, 1968). If de novo formation of cytosegresomes is induced by partial hepatectomy or by the administration of glucagon to rats pretreated with thorotrast, it can then be shown that the early formative stages of cytosegresomes are unrelated to the thorotrast-labelled cytosomes (Fig. 31). Such early cytosegresomes lack acid phosphatase activity (Ericsson, 1969b); subsequently they fuse with pre-existing labelled cytosomes, as evidenced by the presence of marker when enclosed organelles begin to show degenerative alterations (see Figs 31 and 32).

The origin of the membrane surrounding early cytosegresomes remains an enigma. Most likely the membranes derive from the endoplasmic reticulum (for review see Ericsson, 1969a).

The primary lysosome. The primary lysosome is defined as a lysosome which has not yet participated in any kind of digestive event. Electron microscopic histochemical evidence suggests that the primary lysosome is formed in the Golgi region of the hepatocyte. It is not yet certain, however, whether Golgi vesicles correspond to primary lysosomes or whether perhaps these lysosomes are formed by direct budding from the smooth-surfaced endoplasmic reticulum in the Golgi region (the GERL region of Novikoff and his collaborators).

F. *Microbodies*

The term "microbody" was coined by Rhodin (1954) to designate a special type of cytoplasmic organelle found in the convoluted tubule cells of the mouse kidney. These organelles were originally described as having a single limiting membrane and a finely granular matrix. Later, however, bodies resembling the kidney microbodies but containing in addition a dense core with regular crystalloid structure were described by Rouiller and his collaborators under the same name to be present in the parenchymal cells of rat liver (Gänsler and Rouiller, 1956; Rouiller and Bernhard, 1956).

Following these early observations, microbodies have been observed in hepatic parenchymal cells in numerous vertebrate species (for review, see de Duve and Baudhuin, 1966; Hruban and Rechcigl, 1969). The fine structure of microbodies has been most extensively studied in hepatocytes of the rat and the mouse liver. In the rat, the microbodies of hepatic cells are round or oval organelles less than 1 μ in diameter. They are distributed throughout the cytoplasm and occur singly or in clusters, and are almost always in close contact with the endoplasmic reticulum. Tubular extensions from the surface of the microbodies are occasionally observed. Such extensions may possibly in some instances represent connections with the endoplasmic reticulum. The microbodies are limited by a single triple-layered membrane approximately 50 Å thick and hence thinner than the membrane-bordering cytosomes but similar in appearance to the membrane limiting the endoplasmic reticulum. They contain a finely granular or amorphous matrix which is somewhat denser than the matrix of mito-chondria. The central portions of most microbodies contain an electron-dense area termed "core", "nucleoid" or "crystalloid" (Figs 6 and 17) of a highly organized substructure. In longitudinal sections the crystalloid is formed by 8–15 parallel pairs of electron dense lines, separated by inter-spaces of lower electron density, with a mean spacing of about 110 Å.

In the mouse hepatic parenchymal cell the nucleoids have laminated, serpentine, stellate or irregular thread-like shape. The laminae of the nucleoid are 400–600 Å in diameter and 0·2–0·5 μ long. A detailed analysis of the laminae shows the presence of a row of cylinders the lumen of which is about 50 Å wide. These cylinders have a diameter of about 95 Å.

In the human liver, microbodies are round or oval up to 0·8 μ in diameter.

Nucleoids are usually absent from the microbodies of the human liver. However, they have been demonstrated in a few instances, but it is not completely clear whether or not they are present under normal conditions.

There are indications that the microbodies do not contain acid phosphatatase. Neither do the microbodies appear to participate in the uptake or sequestration of exogenous material taken up by the cells. These observations and the fact that the microbodies are limited by a membrane thinner than that bordering cytosomes indicate that the microbodies are functionally different from lysosomes.

Attempts at purifying rat liver microbodies with good yield have met with success by taking advantage of the finding that a considerable decrease in the equilibrium density of lysosomes in a sucrose gradient can be achieved by intravenous injection of triton WR-1339 into experimental animals prior to sacrifice. In this way microbodies in liver homogenates can be separated from lysosomes which otherwise appear to have sedimentation coefficients very similar to those of microbodies. Preparations isolated by this technique (for details of technique see de Duve and Baudhuin, 1966) are probably little more than 40% pure, and when examined in the electron microscope, they contain microbodies as their major recognizable component.

The enzymes found in hepatic microbodies include catalase and a certain number of hydrogen peroxide – producing oxidases. Catalase alone accounts for as much as 40% of the total microbody protein in microbodies isolated from rat liver and is therefore present in these particles at enormously high concentrations. The oxidases identified so far in the hepatic microbodies include a cupro-protein, urate oxidase, a flavoprotein, D-aminooxidase, and a third enzyme, possibly also of flavoprotein nature, L-α-hydroxyacid oxidase.

Biochemical observations indicate that the microbodies are important sites of hydrogen peroxidase metabolism and it appears that the association of oxidases with catalase is biologically meaningful. Thus, the microbodies have been termed *peroxisomes* by de Duve and Baudhuin (1966).

Attempts at correlating fine structure with enzyme localization have been made. It appears that the insoluble urate oxidase is associated with the nucleoid and that the soluble catalase and D-aminoacidoxidase are present in the structureless sap in which the nucleoid is embedded and which appears to leak out from injured particles.

The finding of microbodies that have apparent connections with the endoplasmic reticulum suggests that these organelles are formed within the endoplasmic reticulum. Supporting evidence for this has been obtained from studies of the intracellular distribution of labelled catalase following the injection of ^{14}C-leucine (Higashi and Peters, 1963). The enzyme appears to be synthesized by rough surfaced microsomes and subsequently transferred to the microbodies within 30 min.

The possible metabolic role of microbodies has been discussed by de Duve and Baudhuin (1966). Suggested functions include the disposal of hydrogen peroxide, participation in specific metabolic pathways (gluconeogenesis), and energy production for oxidative metabolism. However, the precise role of microbodies remains unknown.

G. *Multivesicular bodies*

These organelles are single membrane-limited vacuolar structures containing multiple, small internal vesicles which are dispersed in a rather homogeneous matrical material of relatively low density. They are rare in hepatic parenchymal cells. The multivesicular bodies are usually surrounded by a swarm-like cluster of vesicles, resembling the ones they contain. These vesicles are surrounded by dense condensations of cytoplasmic ground substance. At least some of the surrounding vesicles probably represent oblique sections through tubular invaginations of the limiting membrane of the multivesicular body.

The chemical and enzymatic composition of the multivesicular bodies is essentially unknown. Acid phosphatase has not been convincingly demonstrated in multivesicular bodies of hepatic parenchymal cells but may be present in similar bodies in other cell types. In rat kidney proximal tubules, transitional images between multivesicular bodies and cytosomes have been observed (Ericsson *et al.*, 1965*b*; Maunsbach, 1966). In some cells the multivesicular bodies are functionally closely related to endocytosis vacuoles.

H. *Cytoplasmic ground substance*

The cytoplasmic ground substance represents the continuous phase of cytoplasm (the cytoplasmic matrix or cell sap) which forms the "intracellular milieu". The cell sap itself appears relatively structureless in electron micrographs. Suspended within this matrix is a population of ribosomes, aggregations of glycogen particles forming typical rosettes, droplets of neutral fat (triglycerides), and arrays of fine filaments and microtubules.

The fat droplets have a homogeneously dense appearance except when fixation is inadequate and dehydration results in extraction. In the latter case, the fat droplets appear as pale "holes" in the cytoplasmic ground substance. Although the fat droplets are not limited by a membrane, they show a sharp limitation against the cell sap. Often the droplets are surrounded by smooth-surfaced endoplasmic reticulum (Figs 34 and 35). In some instances mitochondria are also closely associated with the droplets (Fig. 34). It has been suggested that the droplets of triglyceride are formed as the result of a condensation and packing of liposomes derived from the endoplasmic reticulum and the Golgi apparatus. However, clear evidence for such a mode of formation has not yet been obtained. The close association found between fat droplets and mitochondria may be the morphologic expression of fatty acid oxidation by the mitochondria. Such associations are often seen during starvation when other substrates for mitochondrial energy production are limited.

Embedding of tissue blocks in epoxy resins permits optimal structural preservation of glycogen particles. Following staining of ultrathin sections of epoxy-embedded tissues with lead-containing solutions (usually lead hydroxide or lead citrate), the electron scattering properties of the glycogen particles are greatly enhanced. The data obtained by these methods show that liver cell glycogen consists of large structures formed by aggregated spheroidal particles (β-particles) ranging from 200 to 300 Å in diameter. The aggregates have a characteristic rosette-like appearance (Figs 33–35). In a study on glycogen isolated from rat liver, Drochmans (1962) showed that the β-particles aggregated in the rosettes (α-particles) are composed of unit filaments (γ-particles) about 30 Å in diameter and 200 Å long. It is possible that areas of low electron density between the 30 Å filaments represent sites of some of the enzymic proteins known to be bound to the glycogen particles and to be involved in glycogen synthetic functions (Biava, 1963). According to electron microscopic studies done on purified large particle size glycogen isolated from skeletal muscle, phosphorylase appears to be localized on the outer surface of the glycogen particles (Wanson and Drochmans, 1968).

Recent information on the intracellular localization of other enzymes directly involved in glycogen metabolism indicates that these enzymes are either free in the cytoplasm or, like phosphorylase, firmly bound to the particles themselves. An exception to this is glucose-6-phosphatase which is associated with the endoplasmic reticulum (Fig. 10) and is necessary for the final release from liver cells of glucose liberated in the breakdown of glycogen and is responsible for the vital role played by the liver in the maintenance of blood glucose levels.

The ribosomes which are free in the cell sap probably account for almost half the total number of ribosomes in the hepatic cell cytoplasm (Webb et al., 1964). The free ribosomes appear to show exactly the same structural and functional characteristics as the membrane-bound ones (Loeb et al., 1967) and form helically arranged aggregates (Benedetti et al., 1966). As mentioned earlier (see Section D on endoplasmic reticulum) it is possible that the ribosomes are intermittently attached to the endoplasmic reticulum and that they occur in two states, the membrane-bound state and the free state.

It is assumed that the supernatant fluid of cell fractionation studies represents at least in part the cytoplasmic ground substance. These studies indicate that the cell sap contains a variety of enzymes and enzyme systems, nucleotides, electrolytes and water (for review see de Duve et al., 1962). Of particular importance in the hepatic parenchymal cell are cell sap enzymes involved in the synthesis and breakdown of glycogen, as emphasized above.

IV. The Sinusoids

The structure of the liver sinusoid (Figs 2 and 36) is not the same in various parts of the lobule. The presence or absence of basement membranes and cellular fenestrations are features which determine the morphologic appearance of three distinct zones through which blood flows en route from the periphery of the lobule to the central vein in rat liver (Burkel and Low, 1966).

At the *periphery of the lobule* the sinusoid resembles a capillary with non-fenestrated endothelium enclosed by a continuous basement membrane without any cellular investment. This zone is 10–15 μ in length. The perisinusoidal space of Disse is located between the sinusoidal wall and the parenchymal cells. It contains microvilli of parenchymal cells and bundles of collagen fibres.

The *intermediate zone* comprises approximately 90% or more of the length of the sinusoid. The transition from peripheral to intermediate zones is abrupt. The basement membrane disappears after becoming spotty. The lining cells become somewhat thinner than in the periphery and develop fenestrations. The lining endothelial-like cells have flat, overlapping and interdigitating cytoplasmic processes and between these there are gaps 100 Å to 1 μ in width (Fig. 36). The cell boundary towards the sinusoid is smooth, while short processes are found towards the space of Disse. The gaps between the processes establish connections between the blood stream and the space of Disse. A direct connection between the blood stream and the parenchymal cells is thereby created. Little endoplasmic reticulum and some free ribosomes are found in the cytoplasm.

The *Kupffer cells* (Figs 36 and 37) are usually located in the corners of the sinusoids between parenchymal cells and possess short processes interdigitating with those of the endothelial-like cells (Fig. 36). It appears that the endothelial-like and the Kupffer cells belong to the same cellular lineage and that under certain circumstances endothelial cells can be transformed into Kupffer cells (Nicolescu and Rouiller, 1967). The Kupffer cell cytoplasm contains numerous endocytosis vesicles and also several larger vacuoles. Some small mitochondria and comparatively abundant endoplasmic reticulum, mostly of the smooth-surfaced variety, are present. In addition there are numerous cytosomes of highly variable size most of which contain rounded or more irregular densities, membranous profiles, myelin-figure-like materials and 50–100 Å granules, some of which have the structural characteristics of ferritin and appear to be responsible for the positive iron staining in light microscopic preparations. Cytosegresomes are occasionally encountered. The Golgi regions are large and mainly composed of arrays of smooth-surfaced cisternae.

In the *central zone*, the endothelium becomes continuous and a basement membrane appears. The space of Disse becomes a typical tissue space and is continuous with this space around the central vein.

The *space of Disse* (Figs 2 and 36) itself contains microvilli, reticular fibres and bits of cytoplasm. The microvilli almost fill the space in many areas and sometimes project into the sinusoid through fenestrations. Liposomes lying free in the space of Disse are often observed.

Apart from their sentinel duties, Kupffer cells and endothelial cells have mainly a phagocytic and endocytic function. Apparent transitional stages between the two types of cells are sometimes known to occur (Fig. 2). The Kupffer cells, and to a lesser extent the endothelial cells, absorb all kinds of macromolecular and small particulate materials by means of endocytosis. As in the parenchymal cells of the liver, endocytosis vesicles and vacuoles appear to fuse with the cytosomes, thereby releasing their contents to the latter organelles. Fig. 38 provides an example of the enormous amounts of thorotrast particles that can be engulfed by a single Kupffer cell following intravenous injection of the material. All the vacuolar structures containing the thorotrast particles usually show deposition of the final product of the Gomori procedure, provided sufficient time is allowed for the release of the absorbed material to the cytosomes. Hence, the thorotrast-containing cytosomes appear to represent greatly enlarged secondary lysosomes.

Kupffer cells also fulfil a specific task during phagocytosis and disintegration of erythrocytes taken up from the bloodstream. The red blood cells are first enclosed in large vacuoles in the Kupffer cells. Subsequently, they undergo a series of morphologic alterations involving decomposition in several fragments and finally appear to remain as hemosiderin granules and ferritin aggregates in the cytosomes and sometimes also in the ground cytoplasm. The Kupffer cells also play an important role during the synthesis of argyrophilic fibres in the space of Disse.

Although the Kupffer cells are comparatively few and small in comparison with parenchymal cells, it is apparent that subcellular fractions of organelles, e.g. lysosomes, mitochondria and endoplasmic reticulum (microsomes), are "contaminated" with organelles from the Kupffer cells (and the cells lining the biliary tree). The extent of such intermingling of parenchymal and Kupffer cell organelles is not yet known. Moreover, the endoplasmic reticulum fails to show any glucose-6-phosphatase activity and so it may possibly contribute to the inactivity of this enzyme in some microsomal fractions (Dallner, 1963).

V. Bile Preductules and Bile Ductules

As suggested by Steiner and Carruthers (1961), the following terminology for the terminal branches of the biliary tree has been noted: (a) "*bile canaliculi*" or "*bile capillaries*" refer to intralobular passages bounded by parenchymal liver cells (see Section III.B on the plasma membrane); (b) "*bile preductules*" refer to connecting channels between bile canaliculi and bile ductules in portal tracts. These ductules have also been referred to as the ducts of Hering; and (c) "*bile ductules*" and "*bile ducts*" refer to the larger branches of the biliary tree found in extralobular locations.

The intralobular portion of the biliary tree – the *bile canaliculi* or *bile capillaries* – is simply the gap occurring between adjacent parenchymal liver cells. The *bile pre-ductules* (ducts of Hering) are similarly located between two adjacent biliary epithelial cells in portal areas. *Bile ductules* in extralobular areas are formed by rosettes of biliary epithelial cells surrounding a lumen.

Infrequent points of contact between parenchymal cells and the biliary epithelial cells may be found at the periphery of the lobules. A basement membrane is never interposed between a biliary epithelial cell and a parenchymal cell at their point of contact. But higher up the tree, in ductules and ducts, the rosettes of biliary epithelium lining them are completely surrounded by a basement membrane. Both the bile canaliculi and the ducts of Hering form a complex network of channels which probably branch out. It is presently not completely clear whether each duct of Hering corresponds to one canaliculus or whether canaliculi form a confluence before entering the terminal branches of biliary epithelial cells.

The lining cells in the pre-ductules, ductules and bile ducts (Fig. 39) are cuboidal in shape or display a pyramidal form with a slight apical narrowing at the lumen surface. The more distally located cells tend to be taller than those in proximal portions close to the parenchymal cells. The apical plasma membrane forms microvilli which are shorter and farther apart than at the sinusoidal surface of the parenchymal cells. Plump protrusions of the apical cytoplasm into the lumen are relatively common (Fig. 39). The lateral cell walls form closely interlocking cytoplasmic processes. Tight and intermediate junctions and desmosomes are noted around the cell membranes in the immediate vicinity of the lumen. Mitochondria are moderately abundant. The cristae of the mitochondria usually traverse almost the entire width of the corpuscle, dividing the matrix into multiple slit-like intercommunicating compartments. The endoplasmic reticulum is mainly of the smooth surfaced, agranular kind. Free cytoplasmic ribosomes are comparatively sparse. Golgi regions are usually fairly prominent and located on the luminal side of the nucleus. Cytosomes are moderately abundant and up to 1 μ in diameter. Apparent endocytic vacuoles are few and small and located in the apical portions of the cells. The nuclei are situated in the basal half of the cells.

The main function of the biliary epithelium is apparently to form a luminal space for the transport of the bile. The fine structure of the vesicles of these cells is compatible with the view that the cells are capable of endocytosis of luminal fluid. The complex plications of the lateral walls of biliary epithelial cells may serve the purpose of permitting easy extension of the lumen in response to increases of intraluminal pressure. Such plications appear to be common to all cells of the biliary tree, and they are known to occur between the lining cells of the gall bladder. It is possible that these features of the plasma membrane may also be related to mechanisms of active ion pumping. It appears that the cells are highly active metabolically, as evidenced by the comparatively large number of mitochondria and by the well-developed Golgi regions.

References

Alfrey, V. G. (1963). *Histochemie* **11**, 129-131.
Ashford, T. P. and Porter, K. R. (1962). *J. Cell Biol.* **12**, 198-202.
Ashworth, C. T., Leonard, J. S., Eigenbrodt, E. H. and Wrightsman, F. J. (1966). *J. Cell Biol.* **31**, 301-318.

G

Aterman, K. (1963). In *The Liver: Morphology, Biochemistry, Physiology* (C. Rouiller, ed.), Vol. I, pp. 61-136. Academic Press, New York.

Ball, E. G. and Joel, C. D. (1962). *Int. Rev. Cytol.* **13**, 99-133.

Baudhuin, P. and Berthet, J. (1967). *J. Cell Biol.* **35**, 631-648.

Baudhuin, P., Beaufay, H. and Duve de, C. (1965). *J. Cell Biol.* **26**, 219-243.

Beams, H. W. and Kessel, R. G. (1968). *Intern. Rev. Cytol.* **23**, 209-276.

Beaufay, H. (1968). Personal communication.

Benacerraf, B. (1964). In *The Liver: Morphology, Biochemistry, Physiology* (C. Rouiller, ed.), Vol. II, pp. 37-62. Academic Press, New York.

Benedetti, E. L. and Emmelot, P. (1968). In *Ultrastructure in Biological Systems* (A. J. Dalton and F. Haguenau, eds), Vol. 4, pp. 33-120. Academic Press, New York.

Benedetti, E. L., Bont, W. S. and Bloemendal, H. (1966). *Nature, Lond.* **210**, 1156-1157.

Bernhard, W. and Granboulan, N. (1963). *Expl. Cell Res.* Suppl. **9**, 15-53.

Bernhard, W. and Granboulan, N. (1968). In *Ultrastructure in Biological Systems*, The Nucleus (A. J. Dalton and F. Haguenau, eds), Vol. 3, pp. 81-149. Academic Press, New York.

Biava, C. (1963). *Lab. Invest.* **12**, 1179-1197.

Biava, C. (1964). *Lab. Invest.* **13**, 840-864.

Biberfeld, P. and Ericsson, J. L. E. (1968). Unpublished observations.

Borsook, H., Deasy, C. L., Haagen-Smit, A. J., Keighley, G. and Lowy, P. H. (1950). *J. biol. Chem.* **187**, 309-315.

Burkel, W. E. and Low, F. N. (1966). *Am. J. Anat.* **118**, 769-783.

Caro, L. G. (1962). *J. Cell Biol.* **15**, 189-199.

Daems, W. T. and Wisse, E. (1966). *J. Ultrastruct. Res.* 123-140.

Dallner, G. (1963). *Acta path. microbiol. Scand., Suppl.* **166**, 1-94.

Dallner, G. and Ernster, L. (1968). *J. Histochem. Cytochem.* **19**, 611-632.

Danielli, J. F. and Davson, H. (1935). *J. Cellular Comp. Physiol.* **5**, 495-508.

David, H. (1964). *Submicroscopic Ortho- and Patho-Morphology of the Liver.* Pergamon Press, Oxford.

David, H. and Metzler, E. (1967). *Acta biol. med. german.* **18**, 529-540.

Drochmans, P. (1962). *J. Ultrastruct. Res.* **6**, 141-163.

Duve, de C. (1959). In *Subcellular Particles* (T. Hayashi, ed.), pp. 128-159. Ronald Press, New York.

Duve, de C. (1963). In *Lysosomes* (A. V. S. De Reuck and M. F. Cameron, eds), pp. 1-31. Churchill, London.

Duve, de C. and Baudhuin, P. (1966). *Physiol. Rev.* **46**, 323-357.

Duve, de C. and Wattiaux, R. (1966). *Ann. Rev. Physiol.* **28**, 435-492.

Duve, de C., Berthet, J. and Beaufay, H. (1959). *Progr. Biophys. Biophys. Chem.* **9**, 325-369.

Duve, de C., Wattiaux, R. and Baudhuin, P. (1962). *Adv. Enzymol.* **24**, 291-324.

Elias, H. and Cohen, T. (1965). *Z. Zellforsch.* **41**, 407-420.

Emans, J. B. and Jones, S. L. (1968). *J. Histochem. Cytochem.* **16**, 561-571.

Emmelot, P. and Benedetti, E. L. (1967). In *Carcinogenesis: A Broad Critique*, M. D. Anderson Hosp. Tumor Institute Symposium, University of Texas, pp. 471-533. Williams and Wilkins, Baltimore.

Emmelot, P., Visser, A. and Benedetti, E. L. (1968). *Biochim. biophys. Acta* **150**, 364-375.

Ericsson, J. L. E. (1964). *Acta path. microbiol. scand.* Suppl. **168**, 1-121.

Ericsson, J. L. E. (1965). *J. Histochem. Cytochem.* **14**, 361-362.

Ericsson, J. L. E. (1968a). *Acta path. microbiol. scand.* **72**, 451.

Ericsson, J. L. E. (1968b). Unpublished observations.

Ericsson, J. L. E. (1969a). In *Lysosomes in Biology and Pathology* (J. T. Dingle and H. B. Fell, eds). North Holland Publishing Company, Amsterdam. (In press.)

Ericsson, J. L. E. (1969b). *Expl. Cell Res.* (In press.)

Ericsson, J. L. E. and Biberfeld, P. (1967). *Lab. Invest.* **17**, 281-298.

Ericsson, J. L. E. and Engberg, A. (1968). In *Electron Microscopy*. Proceedings of the Fourth European Regional Conference on Electron Microscopy, Rome, September 1-7, 1968 (D. S. Bocciarelli, ed.), Vol. II, pp. 239-240. Tipografia Poliglotta Vaticana, Rome, Italy.

Ericsson, J. L. E. and Glinsmann, W. H. (1966). *Lab. Invest.* **15**, 750-761.

Ericsson, J. L. E. and Helminen, H. (1967). *Histochemie*, **9**, 170-180.

Ericsson, J. L. E. and Trump, B. F. (1964). *Lab. Invest.* **13**, 1427-1456.

Ericsson, J. L. E., Saladino, A. J. and Trump, B. F. (1965a). *Z. Zellforsch.* **66**, 161-181.

Ericsson, J. L. E., Trump, B. F. and Weibel, J. (1965b). *Lab. Invest.* **14**, 1341-1365.

Essner, E. (1966). *Lab. Invest.* **17**, 71-87.

Farquhar, M. G. and Palade, G. E. (1963). *J. Cell Biol.* **17**, 375-412.

Fernandez-Morán, H. (1962). In *The Interpretation of Ultrastructure* (R. J. C. Harris, ed.), Vol. I, pp. 411-427. Academic Press, New York.

Fernandez-Morán, H., Oda, T., Balir, P. V. and Green, D. E. (1964). *J. Cell Biol.* **22**, 63-100.

Fishman, W. H., Goldman, S. S. and DeLellis, R. (1967). *Nature*, **213**, 457-460.

Gänsler, H. and Rouiller, C. (1956). *Schw. Z. allg. Path. Bakteriol.* **19**, 217-243.

Glaumann, H. and Dallner, G. (1968). *J. Lipid Res.* **9**, 720-729.

Glaumann, H. and Ericsson, J. L. E. (1968). Unpublished observations.

Glaumann, H., von der Decken, A. and Dallner, G. (1968). *Life Sci.* **7**, 905-911.

Glinsmann, W. H. and Ericsson, J. L. E. (1966). *Lab. Invest.* **15**, 762-777.

Granboulan, N. (1963). *J. R. microsc. Soc.* **81**, 165-171.

Granboulan, N. (1965). In *The Use of Radioautography in Investigating Protein Synthesis*. Symp. International Soc. Cell Biol. (C. P. Leblond, ed.), pp. 43-63. Academic Press, New York.

Granboulan, N. and Bernhard, W. (1961). *Compt. Rend. Soc. Biol.* **155**, 1767-1779.

Green, D. E. and Fleischer, S. (1962). In *Horizons in Biochemistry* (M. Kasha and B. Pullman, eds), pp. 381-420. Academic Press, New York.

Hamashima, Y., Harter, J. G. and Coons, A. H. (1964). *J. Cell Biol.* **20**, 271-279.

Hamilton, R. L., Regen, D. M., Gray, M. E. and Le Quire, V. S. (1967). *Lab. Invest.* **16**, 305-319.

Hampton, J. C. and Rosario, B. (1967). *Ann. N.Y. Acad. Sci.* **145**, 533-544.

Hay, E. D. (1968). In *Ultrastructure in Biological Systems* The Nucleus (A. J. Dalton and F. Haguenau, eds), Vol. 3, pp. 1-79. Academic Press, New York.

Hay, E. D. and Revel, J. P. (1963). *J. Cell Biol.* **16**, 29-51.

Heimberg, M., Weinstein, I., Dishmon, G. and Fried, M. (1965). *Am. J. Physiol.* **209**, 1053-1060.

Hers, H. G. and Duve, de C. (1950). *Bull. Soc. Chim. Biol.* **32**, 20-29.

Higashi, T. and Peters, Jr., T. (1963). *J. Biol. Chem.* **238**, 3952-3956.

Hogeboom, G. H. (1949). *J. Biol. Chem.* **177**, 847-858.

Hogeboom, G. H. and Schneider, W. C. (1950). *Nature, Lond.* **166**, 302-303.

Holtzman, J. L. and Gillette, J. R. (1968). *J. biol. Chem.* **243**, 3020-3028.

Holtzman, E., Novikoff, A. B. and Villaverde, H. (1967). *J. Cell Biol.* **33**, 419-436.

Hruban, H. and Rechcigl, M., Jr. (1969). *Int. Rev. Cytol.* (In the press.)

Hruban, Z., Spargo, B., Swift, H., Wissler, R. W. and Kleinfeld, R. G. (1963). *Am. J. Pathol.* **42**, 657-683.

Hultin, T. (1950). *Expl Cell Res.* **1**, 376-381.

Huxley, H. E. and Zubay, G. (1961). *J. biophys. biochem. Cytol.* **11**, 273-296.

Jones, A. L., Ruderman, N. B., and Herrera, M. G. (1966). *Proc. Soc. exp. Biol. Med.* **123**, 4-9.

Kay, R. E. and Entenman, C. (1961). *J. biol. Chem.* **236**, 1006-1012.
Lawford, G. R. and Schachter, H. (1966). *J. biol. Chem.* **241**, 5408-5418.
Lehninger, A. L. (1962). In *Horizons in Biochemistry* (M. Kasha and B. Pullman, eds), pp. 421-435. Academic Press, New York.
Lehninger, A. L. (1964). *The Mitochondrion.* Benjamin, New York.
Lieber, C. S. and DeCarli, L. M. (1968). *Science, N.Y.* **162**, 917-918.
Loeb, J. N., Howell, R. and Tomkins, G. M. (1967). *J. biol. Chem.* **242**, 2069-2074.
Loewenstein, W. R. (1966). *Ann. N.Y. Acad. Sci.* **137**, 441-472.
Loud, A. V. (1968). *J. Cell Biol.* **37**, 27-46.
Maunsbach, A. B. (1966). *J. Ultrastruct. Res.* **16**, 197-238.
Miller, F. (1964). *Beit. path. Anat.* **130**, 253-261.
Miyai, K. and Steiner, J. W. (1965). *Expl. molec. Path.* **4**, 525-566.
Moulé, Y. and Chauveau, J. (1963). In *The Liver, Morphology, Biochemistry, Physiology* (C. Rouiller, ed.), Vol. I, pp. 379-447. Academic Press, New York.
Mowry, R. W. (1963). *Ann. N.Y. Acad. Sci.* **106**, 402.
Nass, M. M. K. and Nass, S. (1963a). *J. Cell Biol.* **19**, 593-612.
Nass, S. and Nass, M. M. K. (1963b). *J. Cell Biol.* **19**, 613-630.
Nicolescu, P. and Rouiller, C. (1967). *Z. Zellforsch.* **76**, 313-338.
Novikoff, A. B. (1960). In *Developing Cell Systems and their Control* (D. Rudnick, ed.), pp. 167-203. Ronald Press, New York.
Novikoff, A. B. (1961). In *The Cell* (J. Brachet and A. E. Mirsky, eds), Vol. II, pp. 423-488. Academic Press, New York.
Novikoff, A. B. and Essner, E. (1960). *Am. J. Med.* **29**, 102-131.
Novikoff, A. B. and Shin, W. Y. (1964). *J. Microscopie* **3**, 187-206.
Novikoff, A. B., Essner, E., Goldfischer, S. and Heus, M. (1962). In *The Interpretation of Ultrastructure* (R. J. C. Harris, ed.), Vol. I, pp. 149-192. Academic Press, New York.
Novikoff, A. B., Goldfischer, S. and Biempica, L. (1968). *J. Histochem. Cytochem.* (In the press.)
Novikoff, A. B., Hecht, L., Podber, E. and Ryan, J. (1952). *J. biol. Chem.* **194**, 153-170.
Novikoff, A. B., Roheim, P. S. and Quintana, N. (1966). *Lab. Invest.* **15**, 27-49.
Omura, T., Siekevitz, P. and Palade, G. E. (1967). *J. biol. Chem.* **242**, 2389-2396.
Orrenius, S. and Ericsson, J. L. E. (1966a). *J. Cell Biol.* **28**, 181-198.
Orrenius, S. and Ericsson, J. L. E. (1966b). *J. Cell Biol.* **31**, 243-256.
Orrenius, S., Ericsson, J. L. E. and Ernster, L. (1965). *J. Cell Biol.* **25**, 627-639.
Palade, G. E. and Siekevitz, P. (1956). *J. biophys. biochem. Cytol.* **2**, 171-200.
Parks, H. F. (1967). *Am. J. Anat.* **120**, 253-281.
Parsons, D. F. (1963). *Science, N.Y.* **140**, 985-987.
Parsons, D. F. (1965). *Int. Rev. Exp. Path.* **4**, 1-54.
Peachy, L. D. (1962). In *Proceedings of the Fifth International Congress on Electron Microscopy* (S. S. Breese, Jr., ed.), Vol. 2, p. 3. Academic Press, New York.
Peachy, L. D. (1964). *J. Cell Biol.* **20**, 95-109.
Racker, E. (1968). *Scient. Am.* **218**, 32-39.
Rebhun, L. I. (1965). *Fedn Proc. Fedn Am. Socs exp. Biol.*
Redman, C. M. (1968). *Biochem. biophys. Res. Commun.* **31**, 845-850.
Redman, M. D. and Sabatini, D. D. (1966). *Proc. natn. Acad. Sci. U.S.A.* **56**, 608-615.
Remmer, H. and Merker, H. J. (1963). *Klin. Wochenschr.* **41**, 276-283.
Revel, J. P. (1964). *J. Microscopie* **3**, 535-544.
Rhodin, J. (1954). *Correlation of Ultrastructural Organization and Function in Normal and Experimentally Changed Proximal Convoluted Tubule Cells of the Mouse Kidney*, pp. 1-76. AB Godvil, Stockholm.

Ris, H. (1956). *J. biophys. biochem. Cytol.* **2** (Suppl.), 385-392.
Ris, H. (1962). In *The Interpretation of Ultrastructure* (R. J. C. Harris, ed.), Vol. I, pp. 69-88. Academic Press, New York.
Robertson, J. D. (1966). In Symposia of the International Society for Cell Biology, The Unit Membrane and the Danielli-Davson Model (K. B. Warren, ed.), Vol. 5, pp. 1-31. Academic Press, New York.
Rouiller, C. and Bernhard, W. (1956). *J. biophys. biochem. Cytol.* **2**, 355-359.
Rouiller, C. and Jézéquel, A.-M. (1963). In *The Liver: Morphology, Biochemistry, Physiology* (C. Rouiller, ed.), Vol. I, pp. 195-264. Academic Press, New York.
Rubin, E. (1968). *Science, N.Y.* **162**, 690-691.
Rouser, G., Nelson, G. J., Fleischer, S. and Simon, G. (1968). In *Biological Membranes, Physical Fact and Function* (D. Chapman, ed.), pp. 5-69. Academic Press, New York.
Sabatini, D. D., Bensch, K. and Barrnett, R. J. (1963). *J. Cell Biol.* **17**, 19-58.
Sabatini, D. D., Tashiro, Y. and Palade, G. E. (1966). *J. molec. Biol.* **19**, 503-524.
Scarpelli, D. G. and Kanczak, N. M. (1965). *Int. Rev. exp. Path.* **4**, 55-126.
Schwartz, A. (1963). *Biochim. biophys. Acta* **67**, 329-331.
Siekevitz, P. (1952). *J. biol. Chem.* **195**, 549-565.
Sjöstrand, F. S. (1968). In *Ultrastructure in Biological Systems* (A. J. Dalton and F. Haguenau, eds), Vol. 4, pp. 151-210. Academic Press, New York.
Sjöstrand, F. S., Anderson-Cedergren, E. and Karlsson, U. (1964). *Nature, Lond.* **202**, 1075-1078.
Smuckler, E. A. and Arcasoy, M. (1969). *Int. Rev. Path.* **7**, 305-418.
Sottocasa, G. L., Kuylenstierna, B., Ernster, L. and Bergstrand, A. (1967). *J. Cell Biol.* **32**, 415-438.
Spycher, M. A. and Rüttner, J. R. (1968). *Virchows Arch. Abt. B, Zellpath.* **1**, 211-221.
Stein, O. and Stein, Y. (1967). *Lab. Invest.* **17**, 436-446.
Steiner, J. W. and Carruthers, J. S. (1961). *Am. J. Path.* **38**, 639-661.
Stephens, R. J. and Bils, R. F. (1965). *J. Cell Biol.* **24**, 500-504.
Stoeckenius, W. (1963). *J. Cell Biol.* **17**, 443-454.
Swift, H. (1962). In *The Interpretation of Ultrastructure* (R. J. C. Harris, ed.), Vol. I, pp. 213-232. Academic Press, New York.
Swift, H. (1963). *Expl. Cell Res.* Suppl. **9**, 54-67.
Takagi, M. and Ogata, K. (1968). *Biochem. Biophys. Res. Commun.* **33**, 55-60.
Tchen, T. T. and Bloch, K. (1955). *J. Am. Chem. Soc.* **77**, 6085-6086.
Trump, B. F. and Ericsson, J. L. E. (1965a). *Lab. Invest.* **14**, 1245-1323.
Trump, B. F. and Ericsson, J. L. E. (1965b). In *The Inflammatory Process* (B. W. Zweifach, L. Grant and T. McCluskey, eds), pp. 35-120. Academic Press, New York.
Trump, B. F., Goldblatt, P. J. and Stowell, R. E. (1965). *Lab. Invest.* **14**, 2000-2028.
Tsukada, H., Mochizuki, Y. and Konishi, T. (1968). *J. Cell Biol.* **37**, 231-243.
Wachstein, M. (1963). In *The Liver: Morphology, Biochemistry, Physiology* (C. Rouiller, ed.), Vol. I, pp. 137-194. Academic Press, New York.
Wanson, J. C. and Drochmans, P. (1968). In *Control of Glycogen Metabolism.* Proceedings of the Fourth Meeting of the Federation of European Biochemical Societies, Oslo, 3-7 July 1967 (W. J. Whelan, ed.). Universitetsforlaget, Oslo, and Academic Press, London.
Watson, J. M. (1955). *J. Biophys. Biochem. Cytol.* **62**, 257-270.
Watson, J. M. (1959). *J. biophys. biochem. Cytol.* **6**, 147-156.
Watson, J. M. (1962). *J. Cell Biol.* **13**, 162-167.
Webb, T., Blobel, G. and Potter, V. R. (1964). *Cancer Res.* **24**, 1229-1237.
Weiss, J. M. (1955). *J. expl. Med.* **102**, 783-788.
Wilgram, G. F. and Kennedy, E. P. (1963). *J. biol. Chem.* **238**, 2615-2619.

Note to Figure Legends

The electron micrographs in Figures 1, 2, 4 to 17, 22, and 24 to 39 show the appearance of thin sections of rat liver tissue fixed by perfusion with 1·5% glutaraldehyde in 0·1 M cacodylate buffer (pH 7·4) (Ericsson, 1966) or immersion of small cubes of tissue with a side length not exceeding 1 mm in 2% osmium tetroxide (OsO_4) containing 0·1 M s-collidine buffer. Unless stated otherwise, the animals received drinking water *ad libitum* but were starved for a period of 12–16 hr prior to sacrifice. Perfusion fixation with glutaraldehyde was followed by "post-osmication" in s-collidine buffered OsO_4. Dehydration and embedding was performed according to routine techniques. Three types of embedding media were utilized: Epon, Maraglas, or Vestopal. The thin sections were stained with lead- and/or uranyl-containing solutions before examination in the electron microscope (a Siemens Elmiskop I). The mode of fixation, embedding, and staining is stated in the legend for each figure.

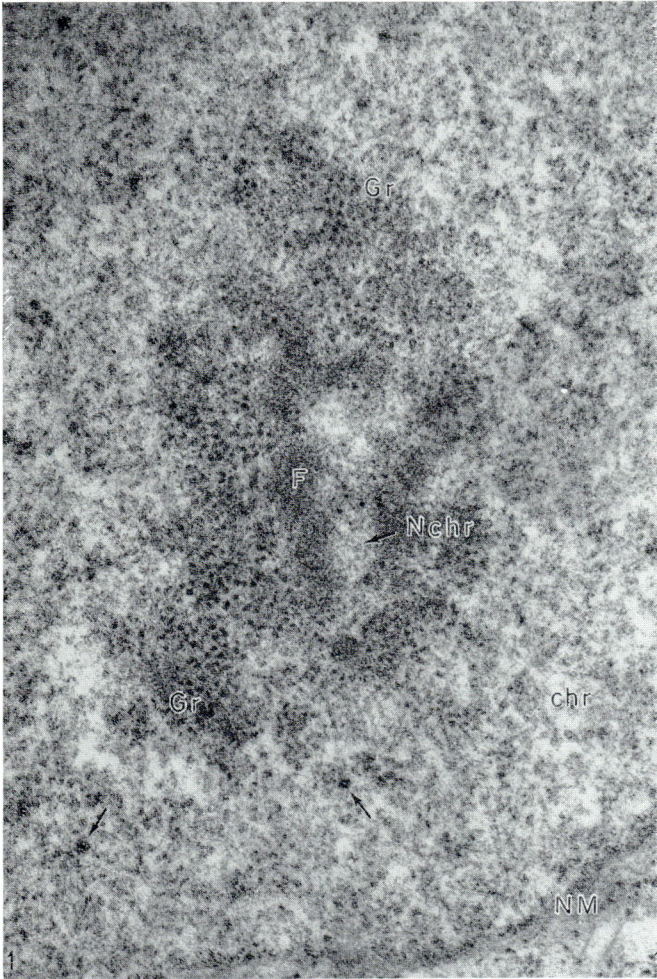

FIG. 1. Portion of the nucleus in a parenchymal cell. The central part of the picture is occupied by the nucleolus. Two components are apparent in the nucleolonema: a granular part (Gr) ("*pars granulosa*") and a dense fibrillar background material (F) ("*pars fibrosa*"). The pale areas in the nucleolus are believed to represent nucleolar chromatin material (Nchr) ("*pars chromosoma*"). Outside the nucleolus the chromatin material (chr) consists of diffusely dispersed filamentous material. *Arrows* indicate interchromatin granules. NM, nuclear membrane. Perfusion fixation; postfixation in OsO_4; Epon; lead citrate. × 39 750.

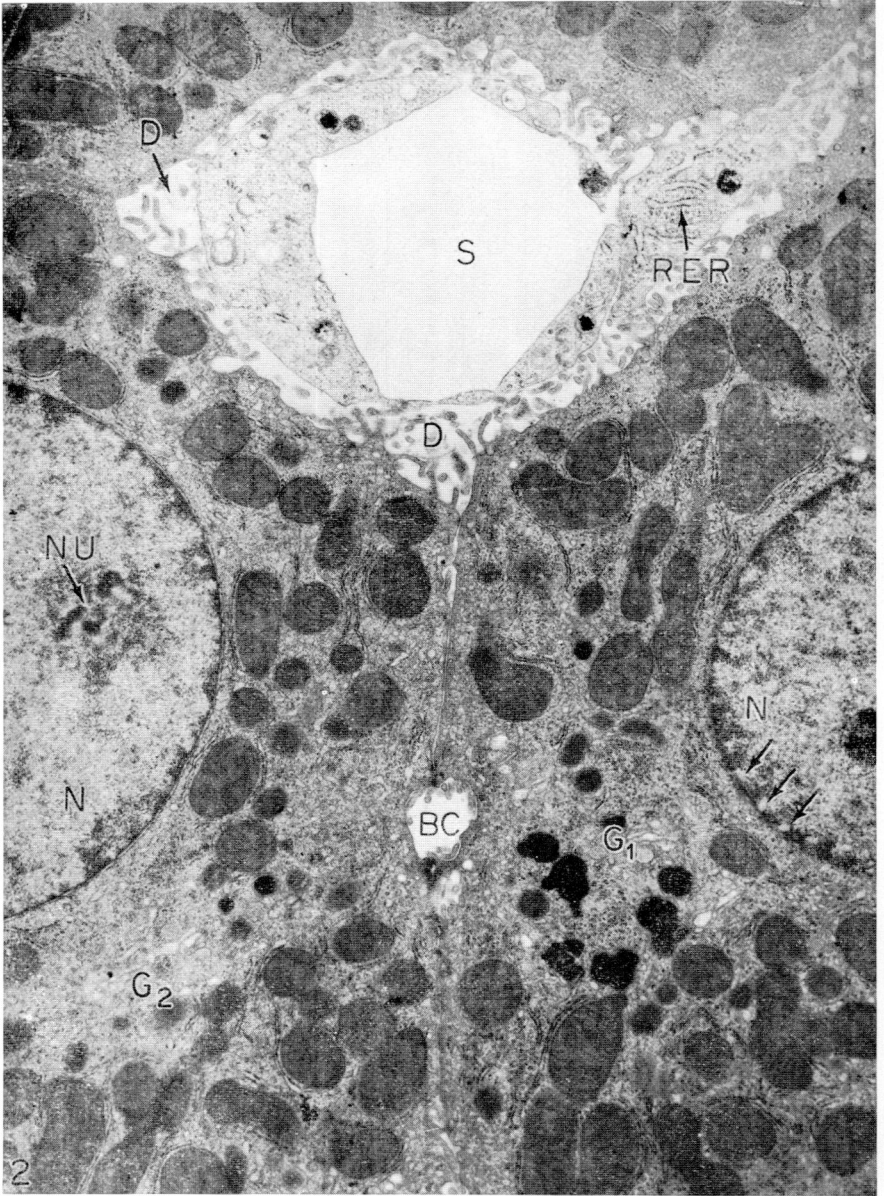

FIG. 2. A low-magnification picture illustrating the interrelationships and overall appearance of parenchymal cells and the cells lining a sinusoid (S). The sinusoid is lined by cells with rather abundant cytoplasm containing – among other organelles – well-developed rough-surfaced endoplasmic reticulum (RER). These cells may represent intermediate stages between endothelial cells and Kupffer cells. The space of Disse (D) is well recognizable between the sinusoidal lining cells and the parenchymal cells. Note abundant microvilli on the surface of the latter projecting into the space of Disse. The lateral cell membranes are closely applied, except where the bile canaliculus (BC) is created. In the Golgi areas (G_1 and G_2) there are numerous electron dense bodies with irregular contours believed to represent cytosomes. The nuclei (N) in the parenchymal cells show accumulation of chromatin material along the nuclear membrane. The pale intranucleolar channels (*arrows*) are clearly evident in the nucleus to the right. NU, nucleolus. Perfusion fixation; postfixation in OsO_4; Epon; lead citrate. $\times 8800$.

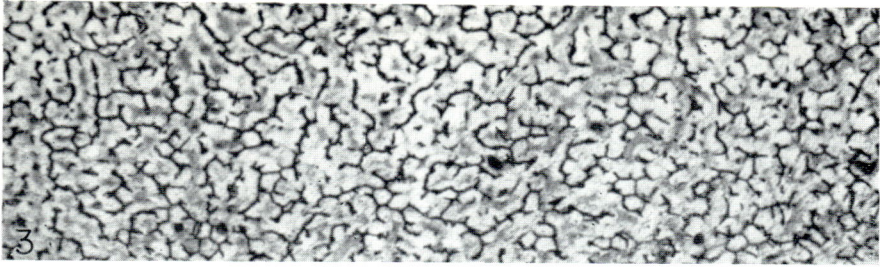

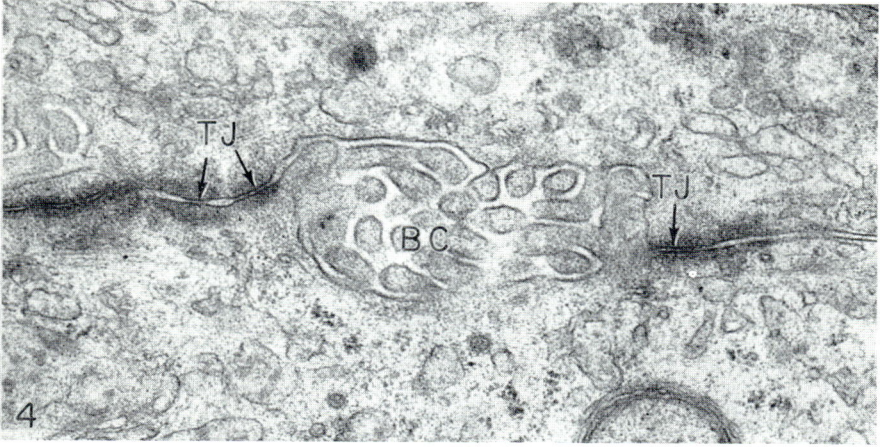

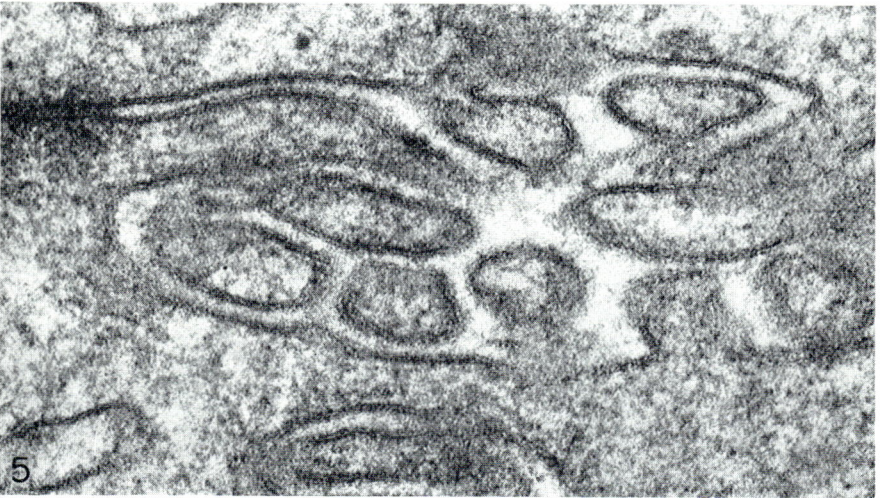

FIG. 3. Light microscopic picture of approximately 5 μ thick frozen section of perfusion fixed liver incubated for the demonstration of adenosine-triphosphatase (ATPase) activity. Sites of activity (lead phosphate precipitate made visible by treatment with ammonium sulphide) delineate the plasma membrane in the bile capillaries. $\times 240$.

FIG. 4. Bile capillary (BC) and adjacent areas of parenchymal cells. The bile capillary is sealed on both sides by tight junctions (TJ). Note the presence of condensed cytoplasmic material in the internal areas of the plasma membranes along the junctional complex. OsO_4; Epon; lead citrate. $\times 36\,000$.

FIG. 5. Portion of bile capillary similar to the one demonstrated in Fig. 4. This high magnification picture illustrates the triple-layered structure of the plasma membrane. OsO_4; Vestopal; lead citrate and uranyl acetate. $\times 120\,000$.

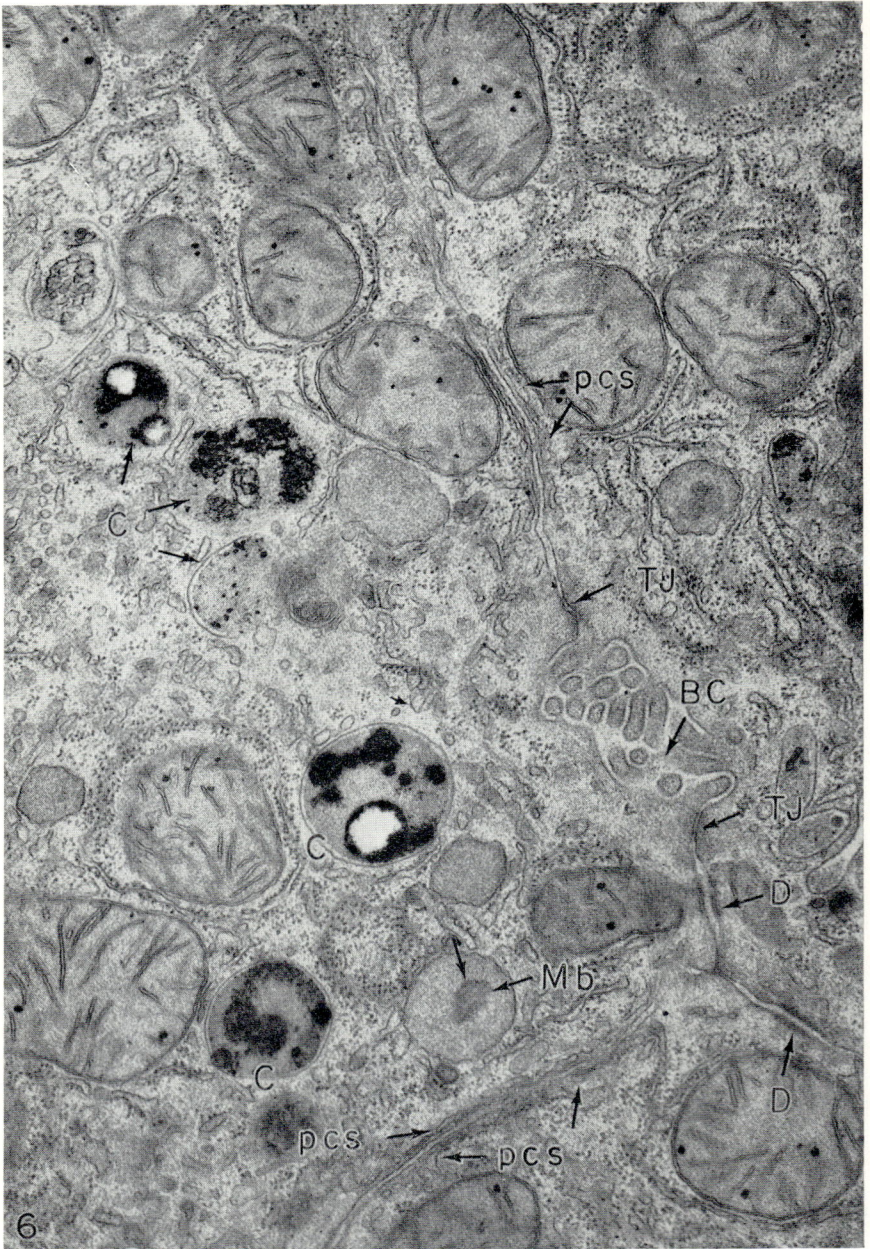

FIG. 6. Bile capillary (BC) and adjacent cytoplasmic structures in three parenchymal cells. C, cytosomes; D, desmosomes; Mb, microbody (unattached *arrow* indicates nucleoid); pcs, paramembranous cisternal system; TJ, tight junctions; OSO_4; Epon; lead citrate. × 24 000.

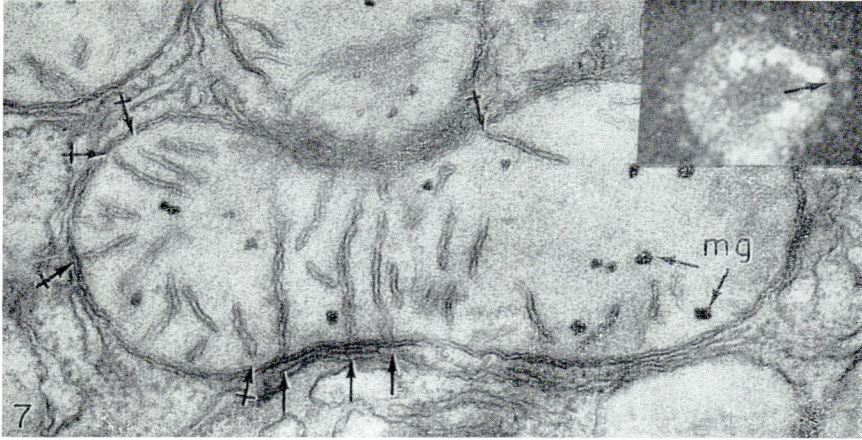

FIG. 7. Micrograph illustrating the appearance of mitochondria in parenchymal cells. Some of the cristae appear to be continuous with the mitochondrial envelope (*arrows*), while other cristae are close to the envelope but do not reach it to establish contact in the plane of the section (cross-marked *arrows*). The appearance of the cristae is compatible with the idea that they are connected with the envelope by narrow stems, the "*pediculi cristae*". mg, mitochondrial matrix granules. × 36 000.

Inset shows a portion of a sonicated mitochondrion negatively stained for the demonstration of the small mitochondrial particles believed to be associated with the inner membranes of the cristae. These particles appear as a row of pale, rounded areas, some of which (*arrow*) are connected with the inner membrane by a thin stalk. OsO_4; Epon; lead citrate. *Inset:* Isolated sub-mitochondrial pellet resuspended and dripped directly onto the grid for subsequent negative staining. × 260 000. (*Inset: Courtesy of Dr A. Bergstrand.*)

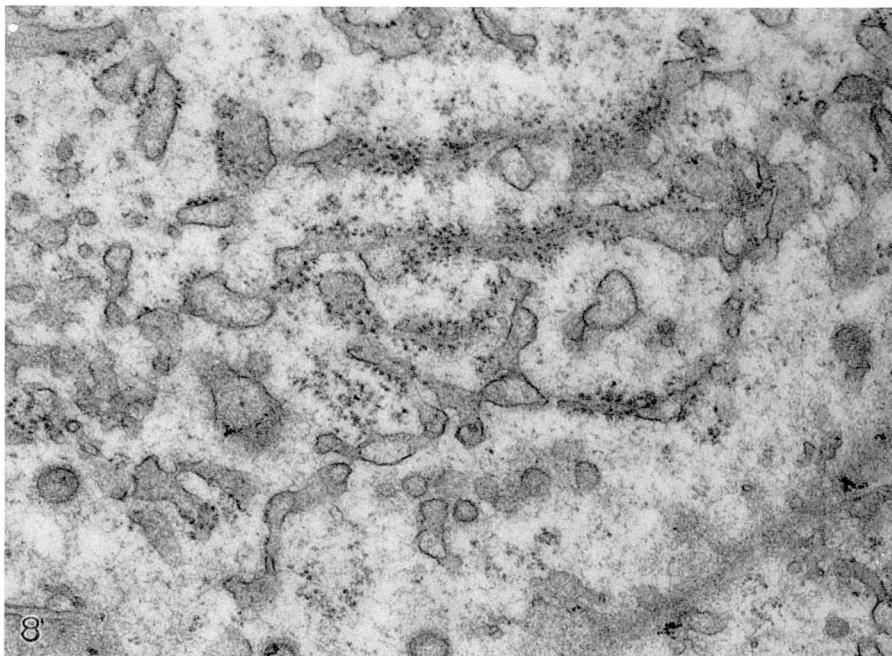

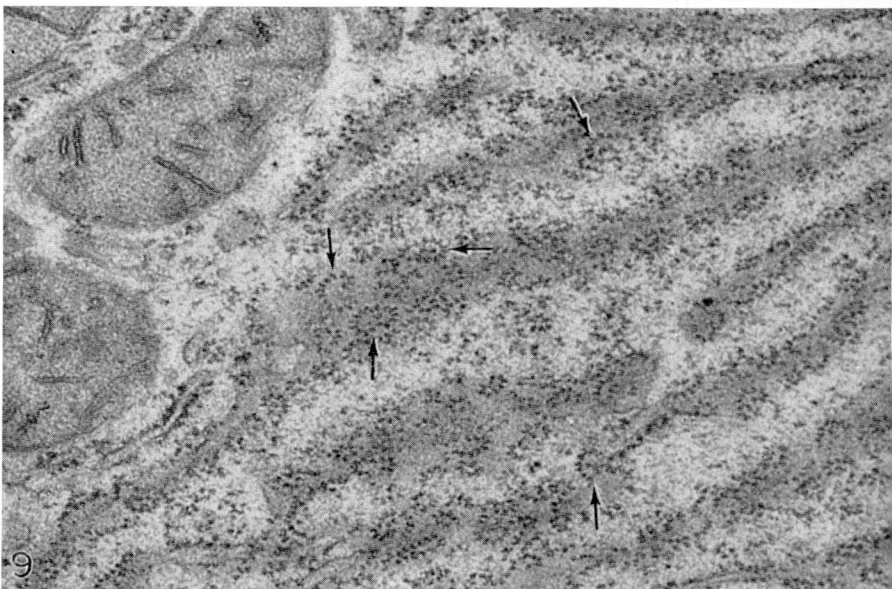

FIG. 8. Portion of parenchymal cell containing both rough-surfaced and smooth-surfaced endoplasmic reticulum with apparent connections between the two. OsO_4; Epon; lead citrate. × 35 000. (From Orrenius and Ericsson, 1966a.)

FIG. 9. Area of parenchymal cell containing several cisternae of rough-surfaced endoplasmic reticulum which have been cut tangentially. The appearance of the polysomes (*arrows*) is readily apparent from this picture. OsO_4; Epon; lead hydroxide. × 42 000.

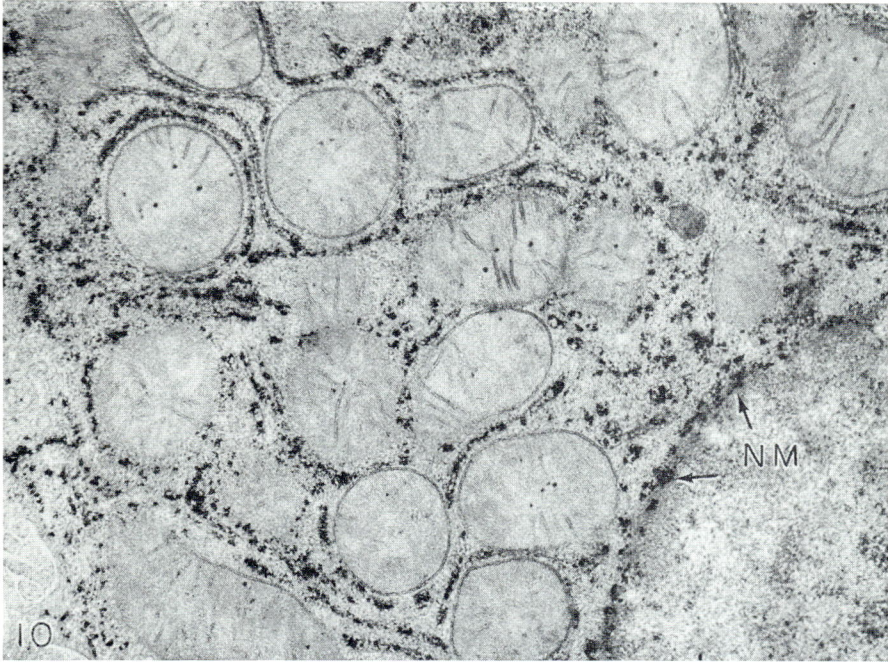

FIG. 10. From tissue fixed by brief perfusion with glutaraldehyde. Frozen section, approximately 50 μ thick, was incubated in a medium containing glucose-6-phosphate and lead ions for the fine structural demonstration of glucose-6-phosphatase (according to Ericsson, 1966). Electron dense deposits composed of lead phosphate are exclusively precipitated on the membranes of the endoplasmic reticulum and on the nuclear membrane (NM). Post-osmication; Epon; lead citrate. × 20 000. (From Orrenius and Ericsson, 1966b.)

FIG. 11. Peribiliary region of two hepatocytes illustrating the polarized structure of the Golgi apparatus (G) and the relationships between Golgi apparatus, cytosomes (C) and the bile capillary (BC). Liposomes are present in vacuoles and expanded regions of Golgi cisternae at the concave face of the Golgi zone (arrows). Among the cytosomes there is one body (CS) which probably represents a cytosegresome (the enclosed organelle may be an altered mitochondrion). LPM, lateral plasma membrane; TJ, tight junction close to the bile canaliculus. OsO$_4$; Epon; lead citrate. × 17 500.

FIG. 12. A similar region as in Fig. 11. The forming face of the Golgi apparatus (the convex side) is directed toward the bile capillary (BC). Liposomes appear to be budding out from Golgi cisternae at the "emitting face" of the Golgi zone and are enclosed in single membrane limited vacuoles or vesicular structures (arrows). Within the Golgi region some vacuoles (GV) appear to be expanded and contain liposomes. OsO$_4$; Epon; lead citrate. × 16 000.

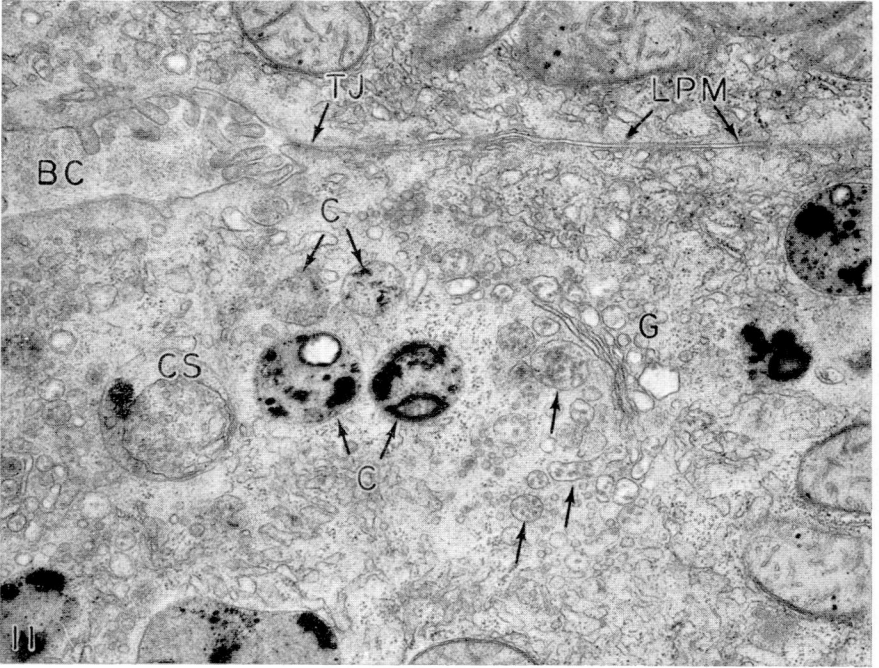

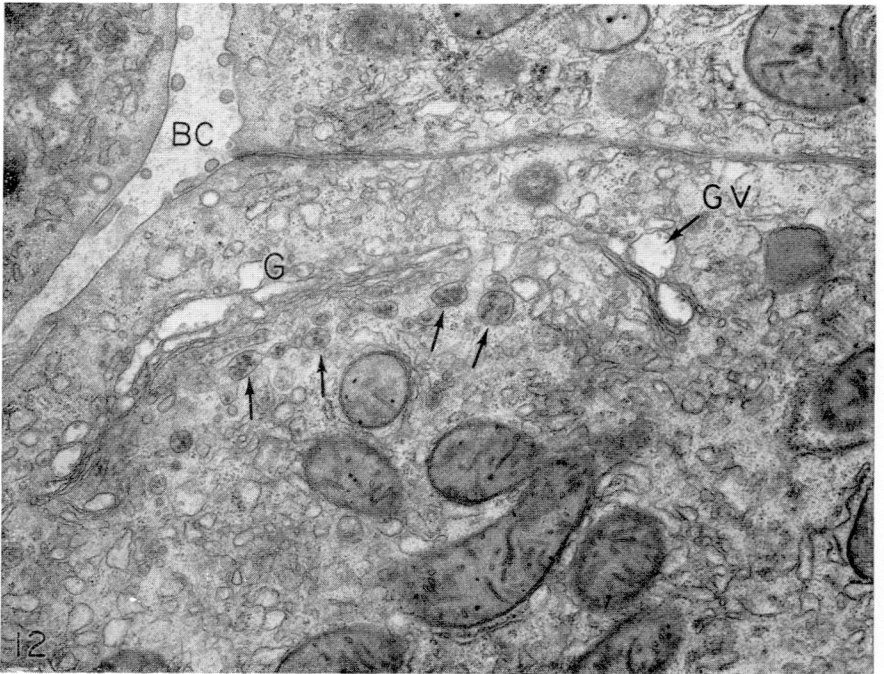

(See p. 189 for legends.)

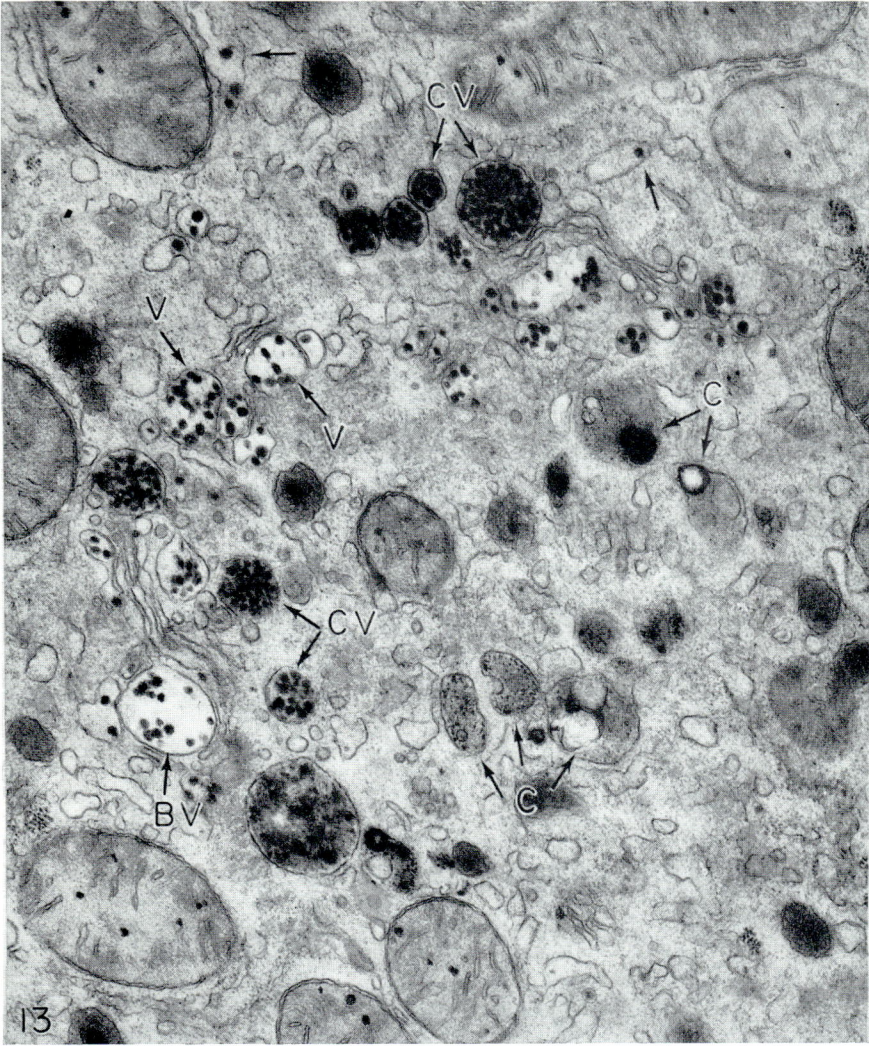

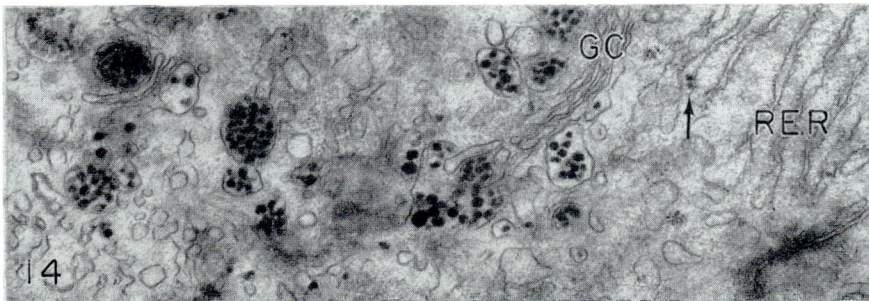

(See p. 192 for legends.)

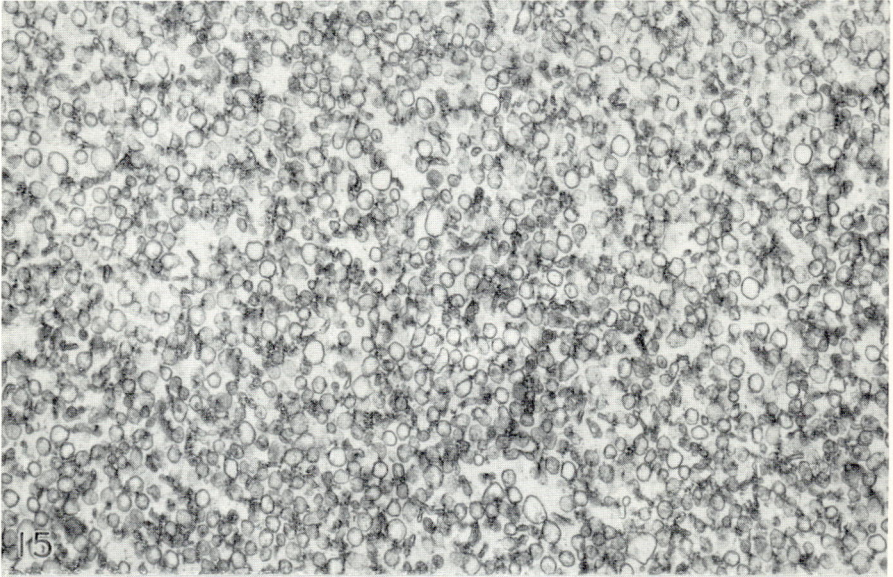

Fig. 15. Section through a pellet of a smooth microsomal fraction isolated from rat liver. Note complete absence of ribosomes on the membranes, and the fairly homogeneous population of vesicles. OsO_4; Vestopal; lead citrate. $\times 25\,000$. (From Glaumann and Ericsson, 1968.)

Fig. 13. Portion of parenchymal cell from 10-day-old rat. This picture illustrates the greatly increased number of liposomes present in the Golgi region and associated organelles during suckling. Unattached *arrows* point to endoplasmic reticulum containing liposomes. The latter appear to be most numerous in "condensing vacuoles" (CV) probably formed by dehydration of Golgi vacuoles (V). One apparent formative stage (a vacuole, BV, budding off from a Golgi cisterna) is shown in the left-hand part of the picture. C, cytosomes. OsO_4; Maraglas; lead citrate. $\times 24\,500$. (From Biberfeld and Ericsson, 1968.)

Fig. 14. The same tissue as in Fig. 13. Picture illustrating the relationships of endoplasmic reticulum and Golgi components in an area with a typically polarized structure of the Golgi region. Liposomes are present in the peripheral elements (*arrow*) of the rough-surfaced endoplasmic reticulum (RER) near the forming face of the Golgi region. The liposomes appear to be channelled through (only some?) Golgi cisternae (GC) and are further transported in Golgi vacuoles which are budded off at the emitting face (left-hand part of the picture). OsO_4; Maraglas; lead citrate. $\times 24\,500$. (From Biberfeld and Ericsson, 1968.)

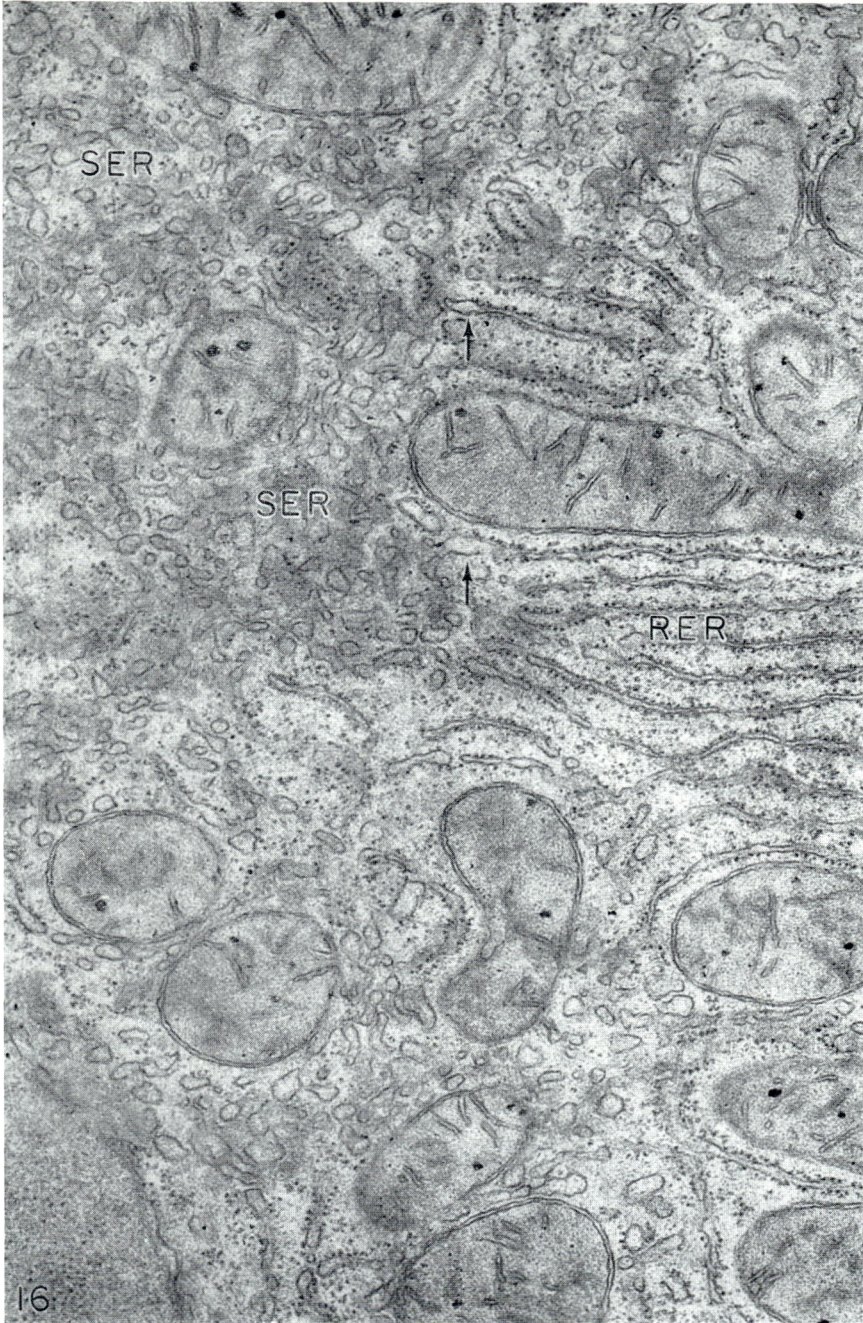

FIG. 16. Increased amount of smooth-surfaced endoplasmic reticulum (SER) in paren-chymal cell following two intraperitoneal injections of phenobarbital (100 mg pheno-barbital per kg body weight). The rough-surfaced endoplasmic reticulum (RER) is arranged in roughly parallel cisternae, some of which appear to be in direct continuity with the smooth-surfaced variety (*arrows*). OsO$_4$; Epon; lead hydroxide. × 30 000.

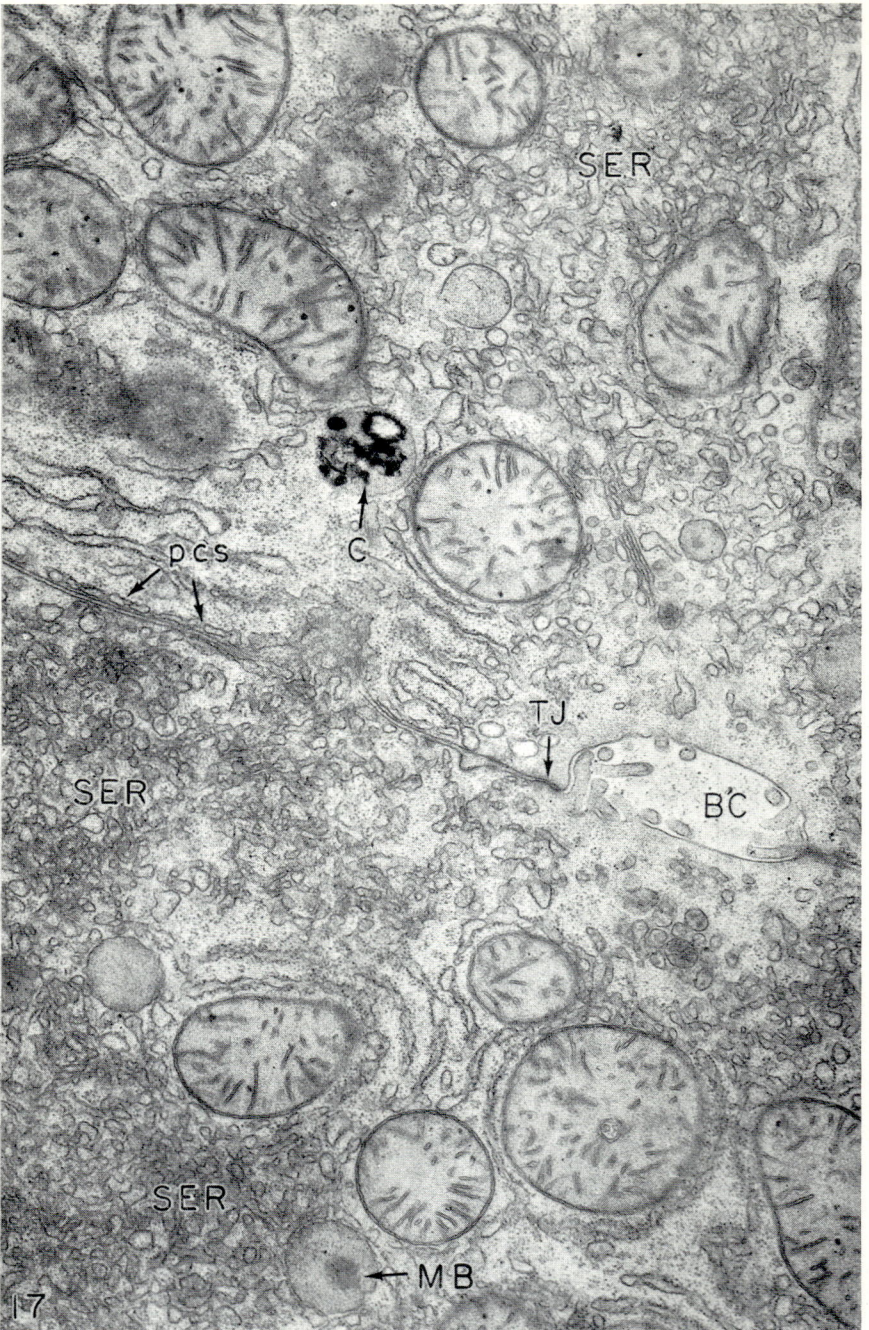

FIG. 17. Peribiliary portions of parenchymal cells after five injections of phenobarbital (given to the animal on consecutive days). The amount of smooth-surfaced endoplasmic reticulum (SER) is greatly enhanced. Other cytoplasmic organelles are unaltered. BC, bile capillary; C, cytosome; MB, microbody; pcs, paramembranous cisternal system; TJ, tight junction. OsO_4; Epon; lead hydroxide. ×18 000. (From Orrenius and Ericsson, 1966a.)

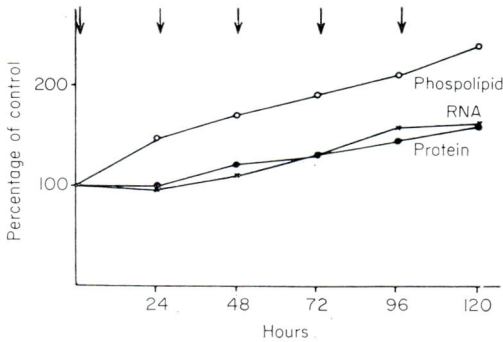

FIG. 18. Effect of phenobarbital treatment on microsomal protein, RNA and phospholipid in rat liver. Mean values (in mg per gm liver) of six phenobarbital-treated rats are plotted, and expressed as percentage of the mean values obtained from a control group of six rats. Phenobarbital injections are marked with *arrows*. (From Orrenius *et al.*, 1965.)

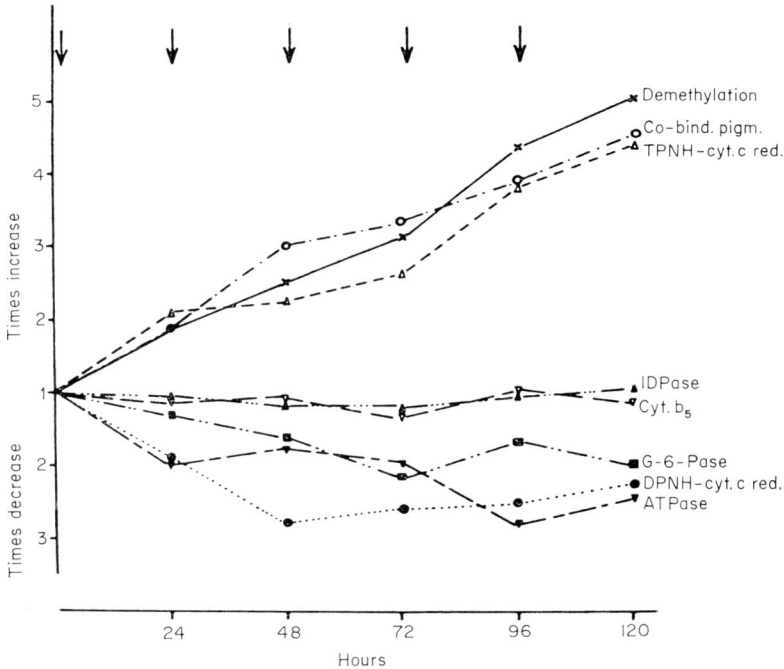

FIG. 19. Effect of phenobarbital treatment on certain microsomal enzymes. The mean values of the specific activities of the enzymes of the phenobarbital-treated group (six ra's) are plotted in relation to the same values of the control group (six rats). *Arrows* indicate phenobarbital injections. (From Orrenius *et al.*, 1965.)

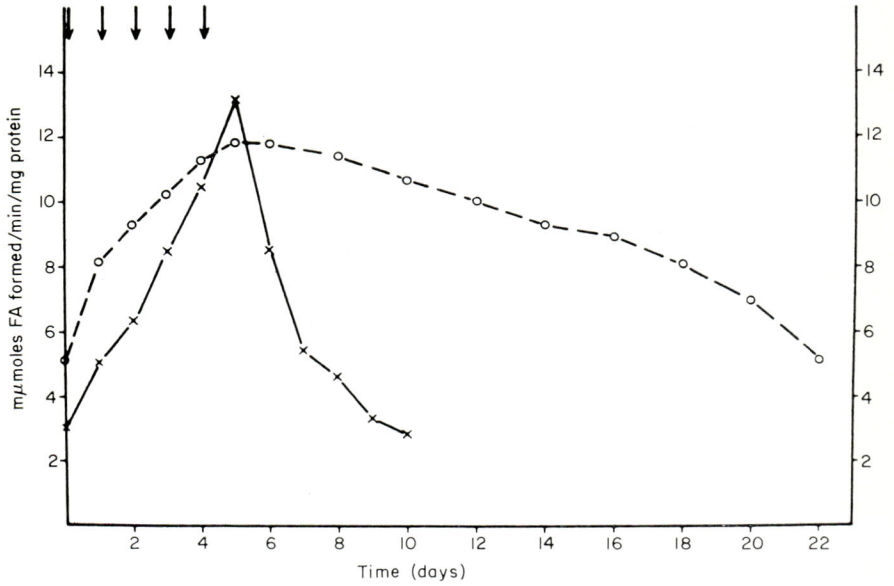

FIG. 20. Effect of phenobarbital treatment on the oxidative demethylation activity and on the amount of liver microsomal lipid phosphorus. The *arrows* indicate phenobarbital injections. FA, formaldehyde. Oxidative demethylation activity, X ——— X. Phospholipid mg/gm liver, O - - - O. (From Orrenius and Ericsson, 1966*a*.)

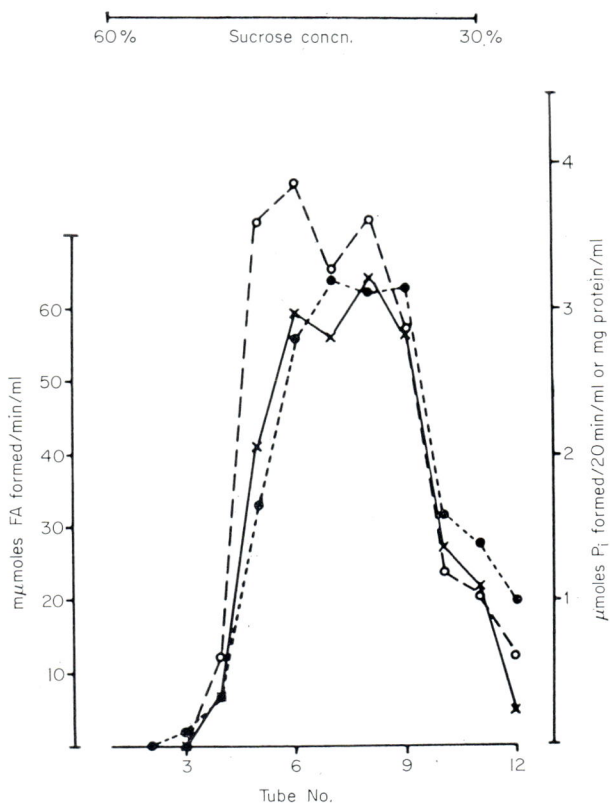

FIG. 21. Patterns of distribution of protein, amino-pyrine, demethylation, and glucose-6-phosphatase activities after the density gradient centrifugation of smooth-surfaced microsomes isolated from phenobarbital-treated rats. Smooth-surfaced microsomes were isolated from the livers of rats treated with three injections of phenobarbital, by means of density gradient centrifugation in the presence of CsCl, suspended in 3 ml of 0·25 M sucrose, and layered on top of a continuous sucrose density gradient ranging from 30 to 60% sucrose concentration. After centrifugation for 15 hr at 22 000 rpm in the Spinco SW rotor, the gradient was divided into 2 ml portions which were analyzed. ● - - - ●, protein; X —— X, aminopyrine demethylation activity (FA, formaldehyde); O - - - O, glucose-6-phosphatase activity. (From Orrenius and Ericsson, 1966b.)

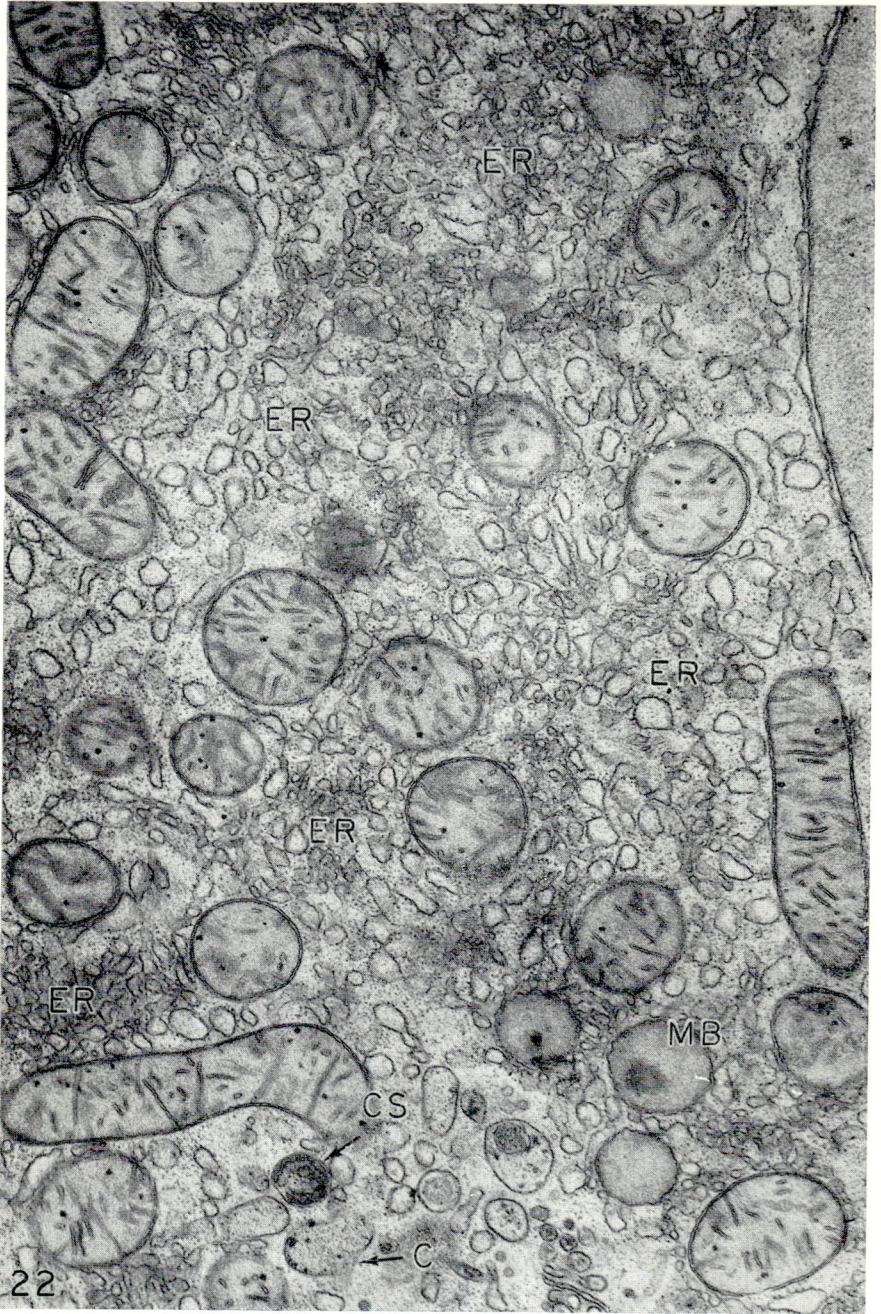

FIG. 22. Portion of parenchymal cell 9 days after the last of a series of 5 phenobarbital injections. Although the induced enzymes show normal activity at this time (compare with Fig. 20), there is still abundant smooth-surfaced endoplasmic reticulum present in the cytoplasm (areas indicated by "ER"). C. cytosome; CS, cytosegresome; MB, microbody, OsO_4; Epon; lead hydroxide. $\times 17\,500$.

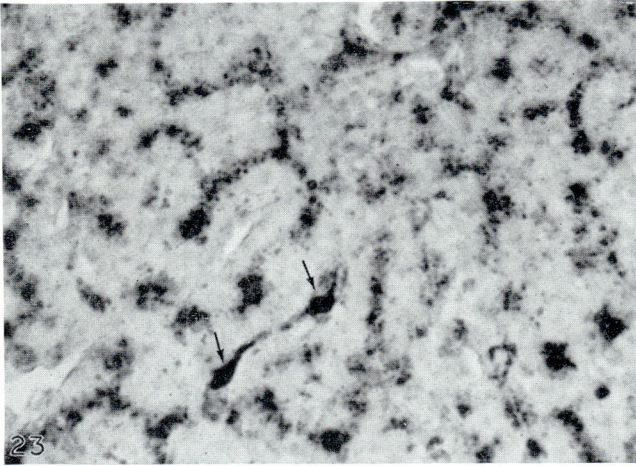

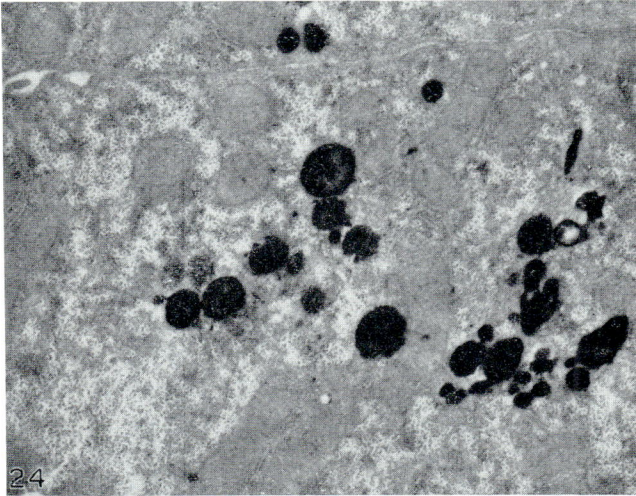

FIG. 23. Light microscopic picture of approximately 5 μ thick frozen section of perfusion fixed liver tissue incubated in a modified Gomori medium for the demonstration of acid phosphatase. Sites of activity appear as black granules mainly located in peribiliary regions. Note heavy staining of Kupffer cells (*arrows*). × 585.

FIG. 24. Thin section of approximately 50 μ thick frozen section prepared from perfusion fixed liver and incubated for the fine structural demonstration of acid phosphatase (according to Ericsson and Trump, 1965). The reaction product (lead phosphate precipitate) specifically delineates cytosomes, and indicates their identity as lysosomes. Post-osmication in OsO_4; Epon; lead hydroxide. × 13 500.

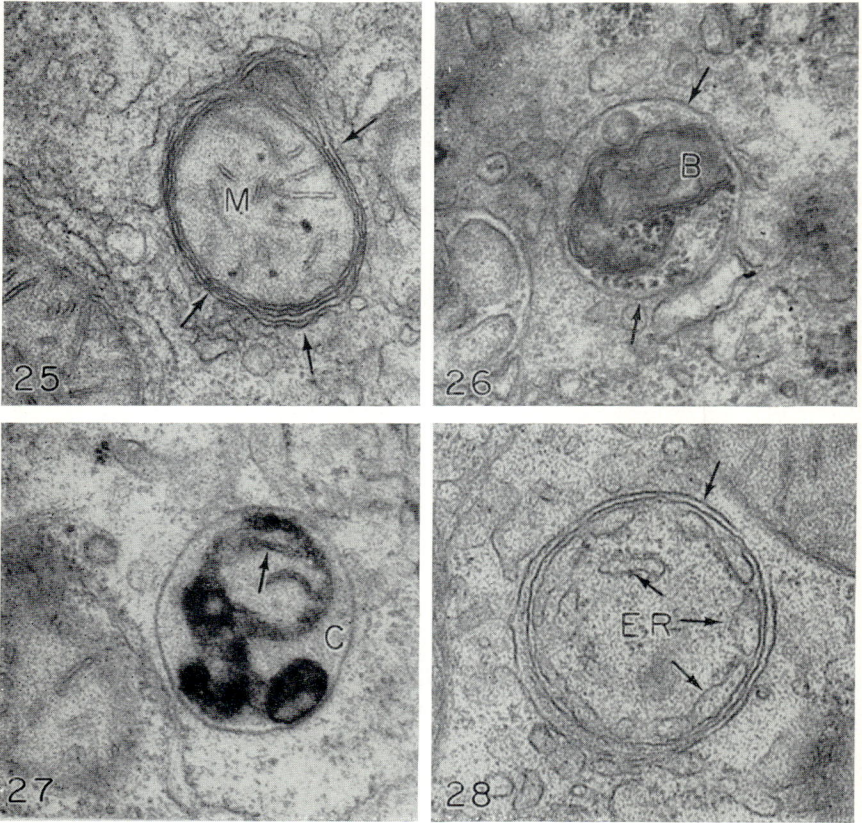

Fig. 25. Apparent early cytosegresome surrounded by two membranes (*arrows*) and containing, as its main component, a mitochondrion which appears unaltered. OsO_4; Epon; lead citrate. $\times 27\,500$.

Fig. 26. Stage of cytosegresome development which is presumably later than in Fig. 25. A cytoplasmic vacuole bordered by a single (at high magnification triple-layered) membrane (*arrows*) contains a body (B) which probably represents an altered mitochondrion. OsO_4; Epon; lead citrate. $\times 33\,000$.

Fig. 27. A cytosome (C) containing an irregularly shaped body possibly representing a profoundly altered mitochondrion. Note area with two membranes possibly representing remnants of mitochondrial cristae (*arrow*). OsO_4; Epon; lead hydroxide. $\times 38\,500$. (From Ericsson and Glinsmann, 1966.)

Fig. 28. Apparent early cytosegresome bordered by two membranes (*arrow*) and containing endoplasmic reticulum (ER) and cytoplasmic ground substance. OsO_4; Epon; lead citrate. $\times 38\,500$.

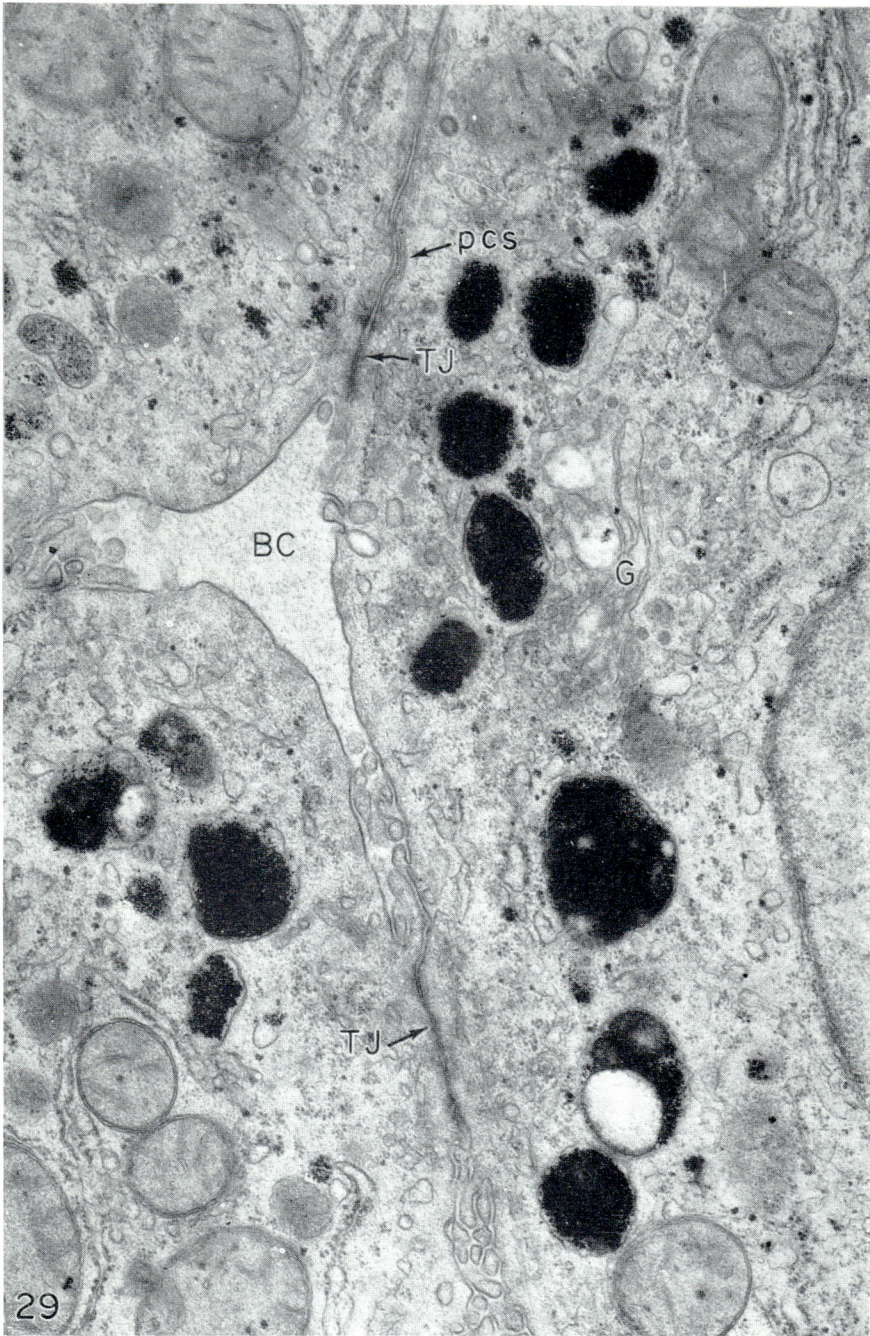

(See p. 202 for legend.)

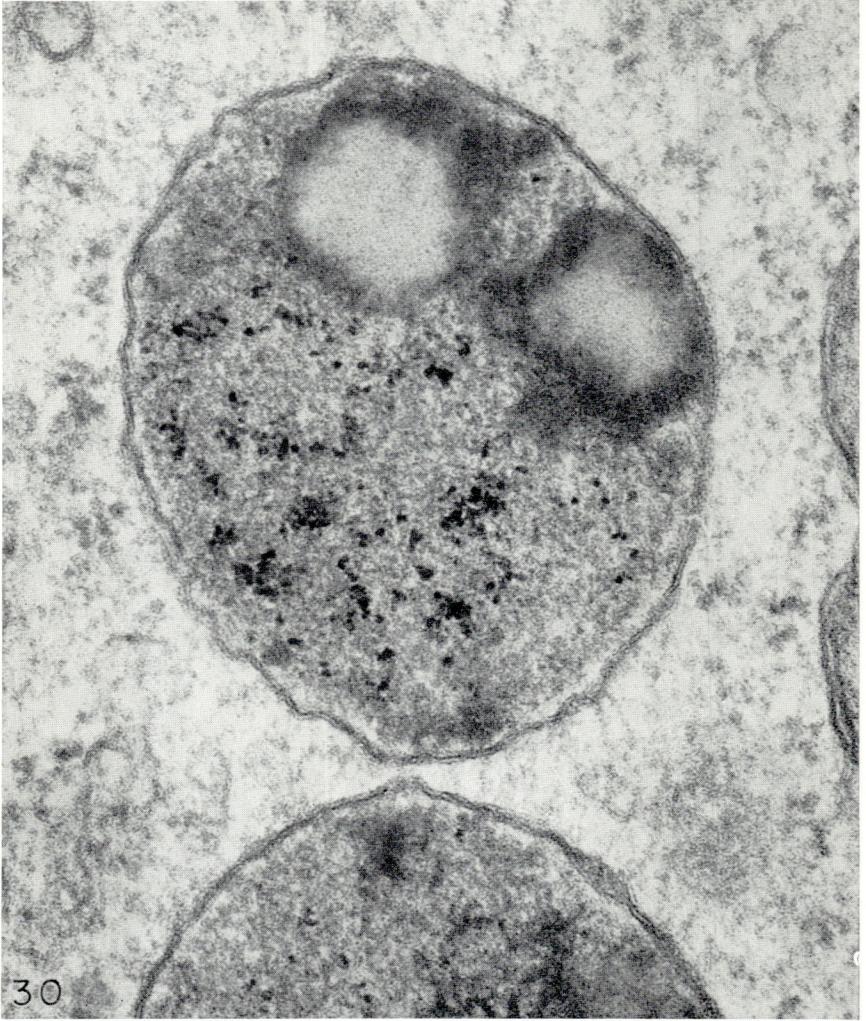

FIG. 30. Cytosomes in hepatocytes from rat treated as indicated in Fig. 29. This high magnification picture shows the appearance of thorotrast particles and triple-layered structure of the membranes bordering the cytosomes. OsO_4; Epon; lead citrate. × 110 000.

FIG. 29. Peribiliary region of three parenchymal cells from rat pre-treated with thorotrast (3 intravenous injections of a 25% solution of thorotrast, 0·5 ml per 100 gm of body weight on consecutive days; animal sacrificed 24 hours after the last injection). All the cytosomes are filled with the electron dense thorotrast particles. BC, bile capillary; G, Golgi apparatus; pcs, paramembranous cisternal system; TJ, tight junction. OsO_4; Epon; lead citrate. × 22 500.

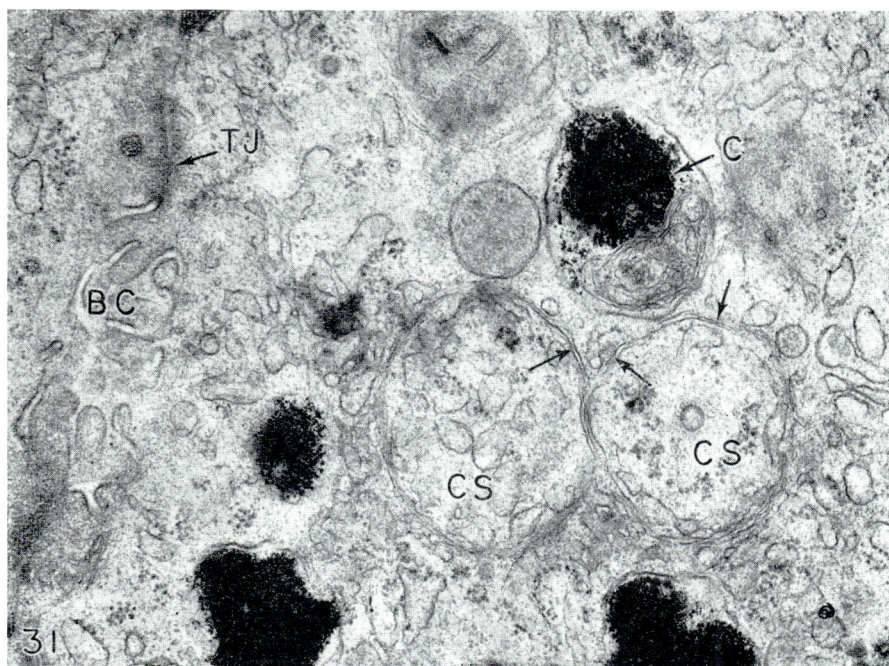

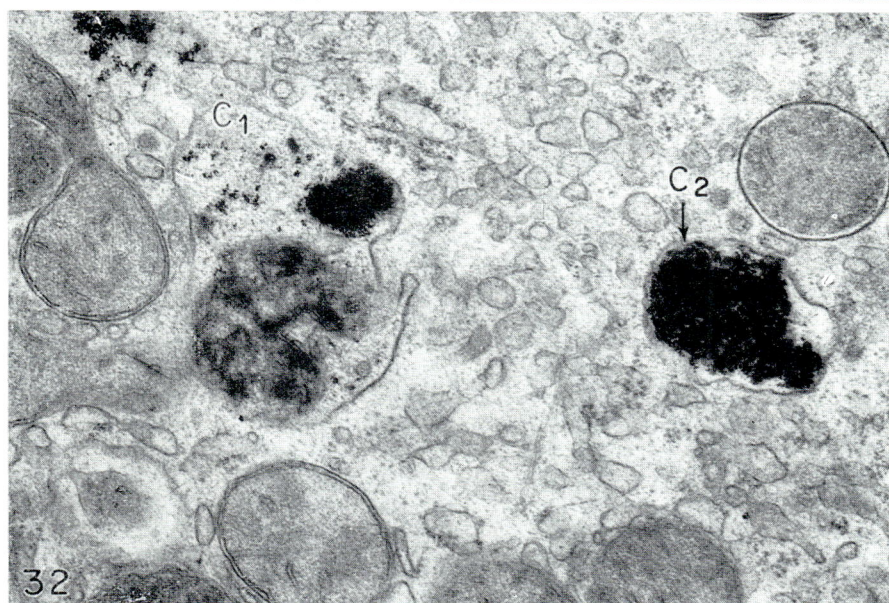

(See p. 204 for legends.)

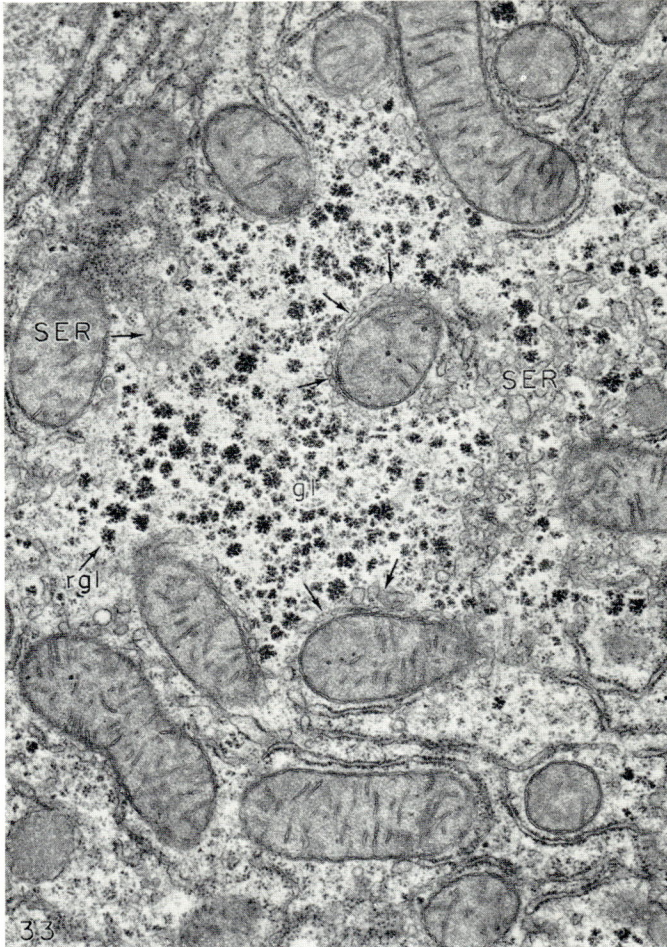

FIG. 33. Portion of parenchymal cell from an unfasted animal. The appearance of a glycogen area (gl) and its relationship to smooth-surfaced endoplasmic reticulum (SER) is shown. Unattached *arrows* indicate tubular profiles of smooth-surfaced endoplasmic reticulum bordering the glycogen area. The glycogen particles are arranged to form rosettes (rgl). Perfusion fixation with glutaraldehyde; postfixation in OsO₄; Epon; lead citrate. × 18 000.

FIG. 31. Peribiliary region of parenchymal cells from rat pretreated with thorotrast for *in vivo* labelling of secondary lysosomes, and given glucagon two hours prior to sacrifice in order to induce cellular autophagy. (Glucagon was administered intra-peritoneally, 50 micrograms per 100 gm of body weight). Apparent early cytosegresomes (CS) fail to show the marker. Thorotrast particles are, however, present in a cytosome (C) in which irregular membrane profiles are also present and probably represent a disintegrating organelle. The cytosegresomes are clearly bordered by a double membrane (*arrows*). BC, bile capillary; TJ, tight junction. OsO₄; Epon; lead citrate. × 32 000.

FIG. 32. Five hours after glucagon. Otherwise same tissue and treatment as in Figure 31. Two thorotrast-labelled cytosomes (C₁ and C₂) are present. Besides the label, cytosome C₁ contains an irregularly shaped dense body, possibly a severely altered organelle. The formation of cytosegresomes and early cytosegresomes were not seen during this period of time. Tissue was processed as in Fig. 31. × 32 000. (From Ericsson, 1969a.)

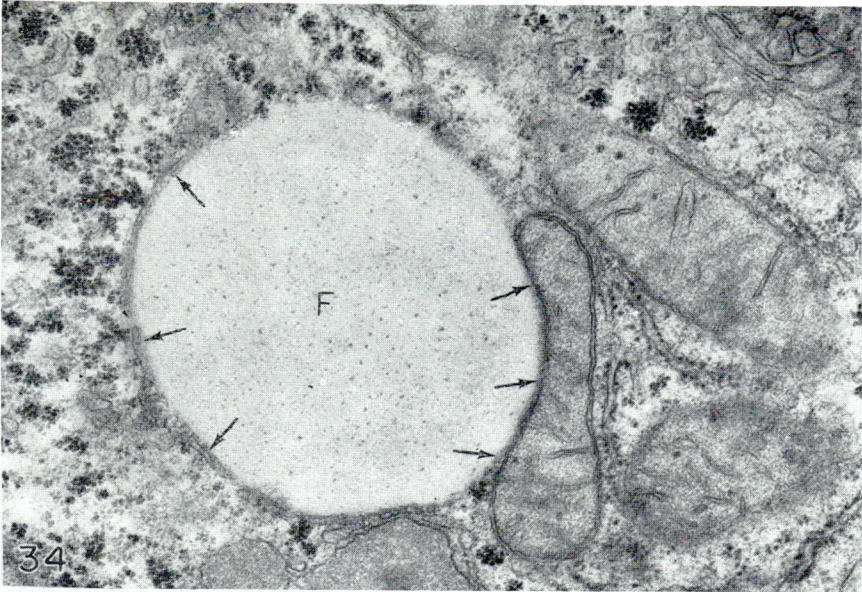

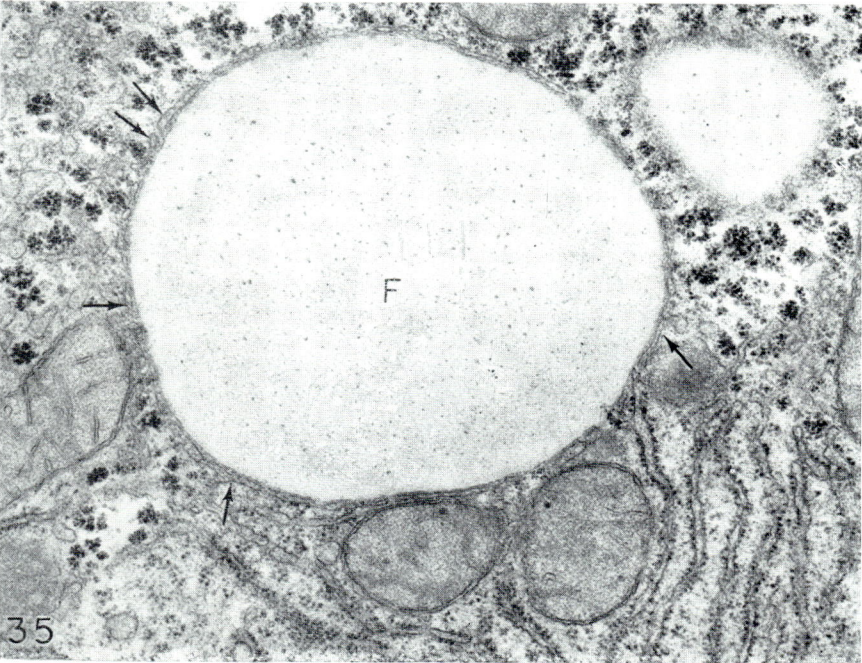

FIG. 34. From an unfasted animal. The parenchymal cell cytoplasm contains a large fat droplet (F), on one side closely applied to a mitochondrion (the border line area is indicated by the *arrows*), and on the other side to smooth-surfaced endoplasmic reticulum (*free arrows*). Note presence of glycogen rosettes in the cytoplasmic ground substance. Perfusion with glutaraldehyde; postfixation in OsO_4; Epon; lead citrate. × 34 000.

FIG. 35. Same tissue and treatment as indicated in Fig. 34. Another large fat droplet (F), along its whole circumference surrounded by closely applied tubular profiles of smooth-surfaced endoplasmic reticulum (*free arrows*). Tissue processed as mentioned in Fig. 34. × 28 000.

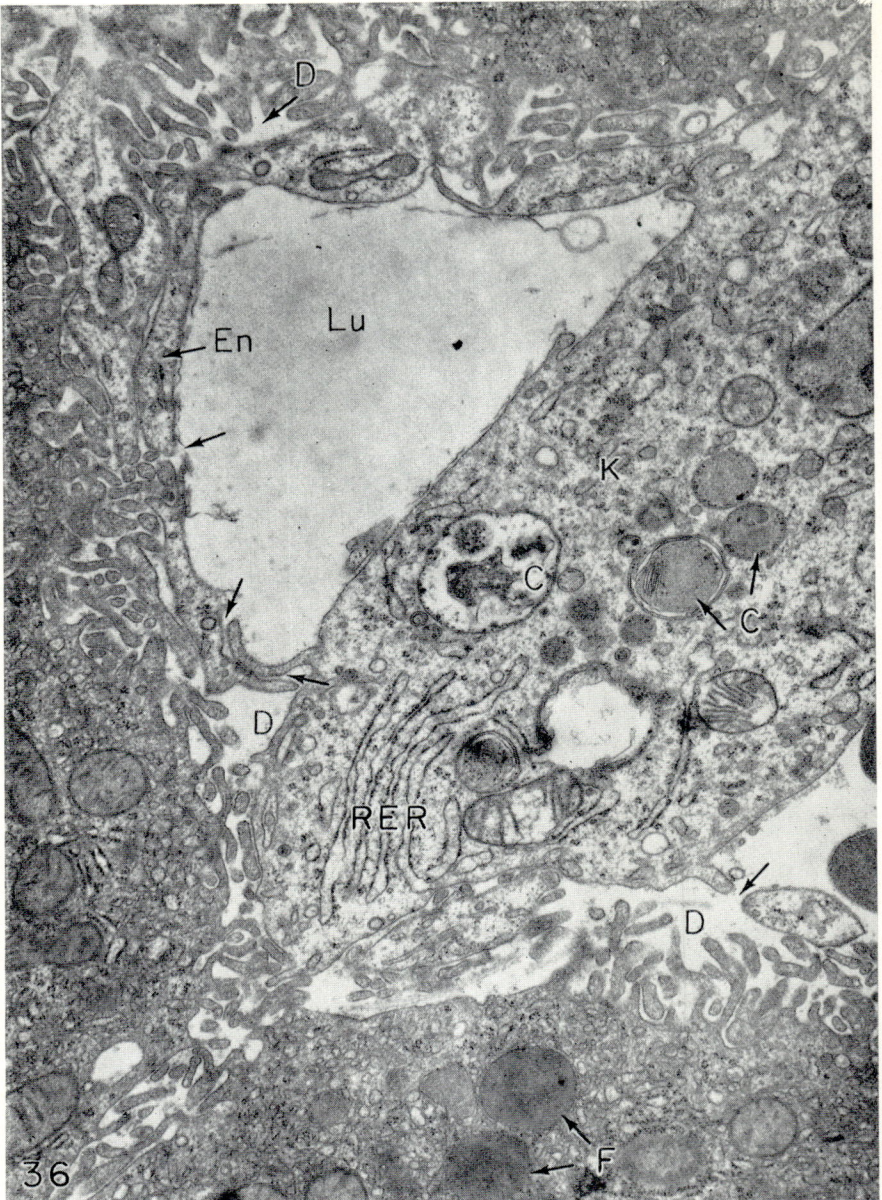

Fig. 36. Sinusoid with Kupffer cell (K) and adjacent portions of parenchymal cells. The lumen of the sinusoids (Lu) is bordered by two types of cells: an endothelial-like cell (En), and the Kupffer cell. These cells separate the lumen from the space of Disse (D). The space of Disse communicates with the sinusoidal lumen through channels of variable width (*arrows*) situated between adjacent endothelial cells, and between endothelial cells and the Kupffer cells. The Kupffer cell cytosomes (C) are relatively numerous, and some are large. Rough-surfaced endoplasmic reticulum (RER) in the Kupffer cell is well developed. F, fat droplets in parenchymal cells. Perfusion with glutaraldehyde; postfixation in OsO_4; Epon; lead citrate. $\times 15\ 000$.

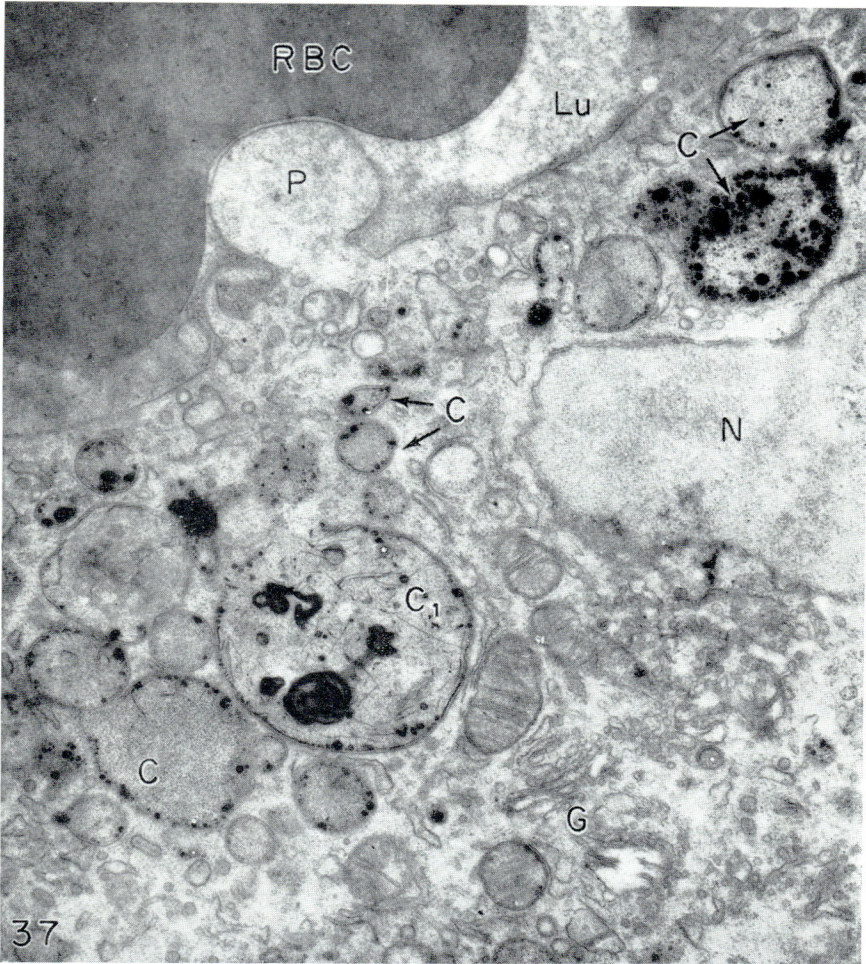

FIG. 37. Portion of a Kupffer cell forming a protrusion (P) toward the lumen (Lu) of the sinusoid which contains an erythrocyte (RBC). Note the variable appearance of the cytosomes (C) in the Kupffer cells. C_1 is particularly big and contains thread-like material in addition to irregular densities and dense membranous elements. G, Golgi apparatus; N, nucleus. OsO_4; Epon; lead citrate. $\times 15\,000$.

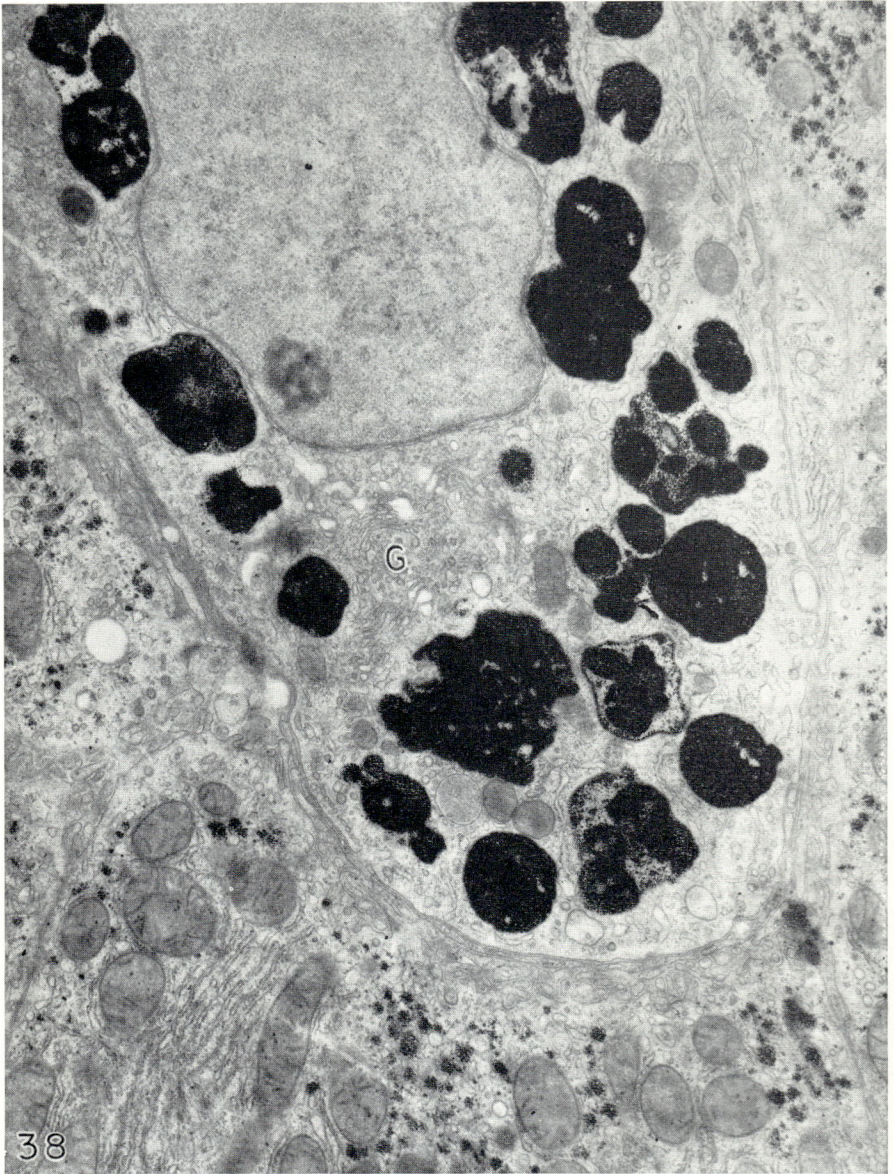

FIG. 38. Portion of a Kupffer cell and adjacent parenchymal cells from rat given three injections of thorotrast. All the Kupffer cell cytosomes are packed with dense thorotrast particles. G, Golgi apparatus; OsO$_4$; Epon; lead citrate. × 11 300.

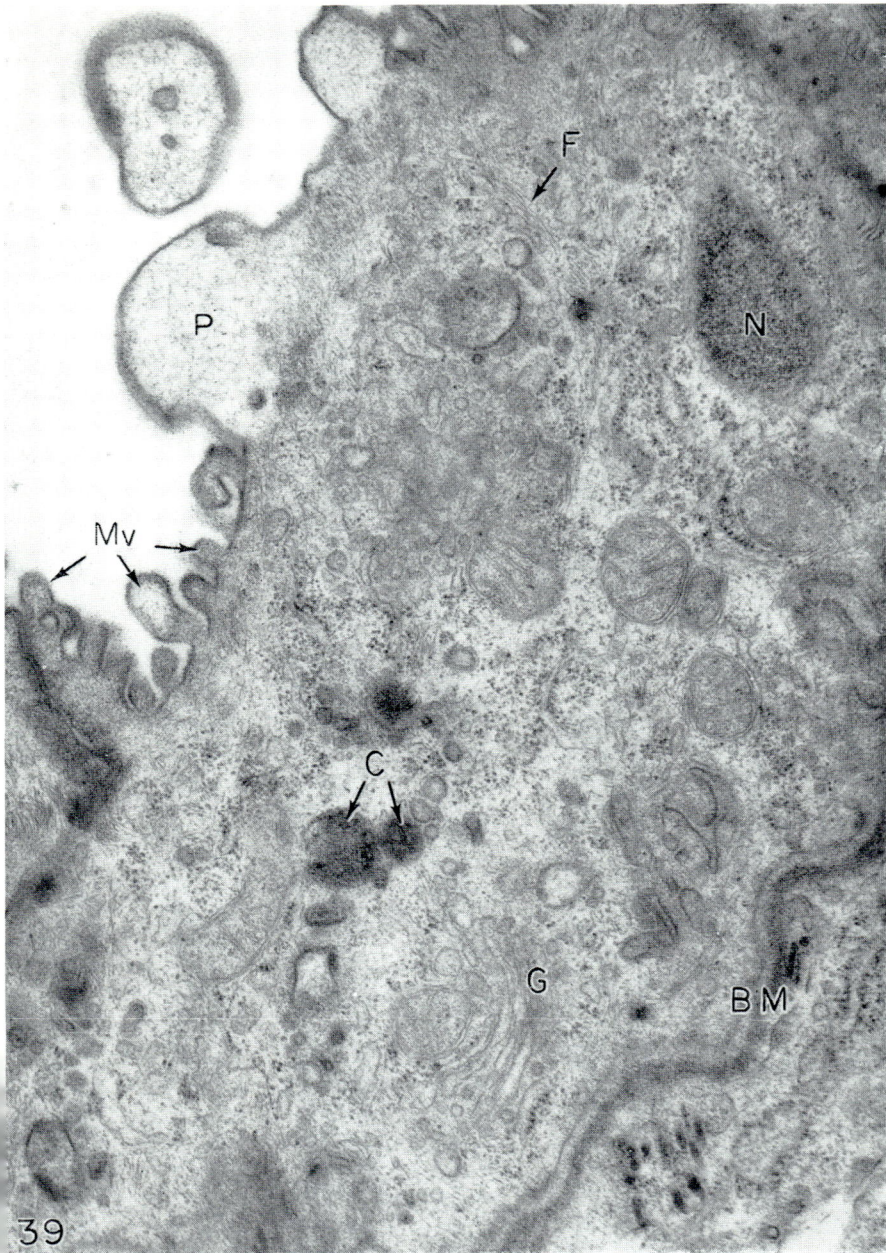

FIG. 39. Portion of bile ductule. The apical plasma membrane forms small plump micro-villi (Mv) and a broad protrusion (B). Note the presence of filaments (F) in the ground cytoplasm. BM, basement membrane; C, cytosomes; G, Golgi apparatus; N, nucleus. Perfusion fixation with glutaraldehyde; postfixation in OsO_4; Epon; lead citrate. $\times 15\,000$.

H

CHAPTER 6

Hepatic Cell Metabolism

FRANK LUNDQUIST

Department of Biochemistry, University of Copenhagen,
Copenhagen, Denmark

I. Introduction

The liver is an organ with such a large number of metabolic potentialities
that a comprehensive treatment of the biochemical processes in liver tissue

would include most of what is known in the field of dynamic biochemistry today, except plant and microbial biochemistry. Indeed, biochemists have been classified into two groups, those who work with rat liver and those who study *E. coli*. However, apart from metabolic processes which occur also in most other tissues, the liver displays a number of metabolic features, which justifies a separate description – especially with the viewpoint in mind that the liver is a center for coordination of the whole biochemical machinery of the mammalian organism.

II. Methods Employed in the Study of Liver Metabolism

Liver tissue is exceptionally well suited for biochemical study as the organ is predominantly built up of one type of cell, the liver cell or parenchyma, which constitutes some 90% of the weight of the organ. However, in terms of number of cells, the parenchymatous cells account for only 65% of the total (Moulé and Chauveau, 1963). The remaining cells include the endothelial lining of the capillaries and liver sinusoids, including or identical with the so-called Kupffer cells, and connective tissue elements which may be present in amounts varying according to the age of the individual and the species studied.

In order to arrive at a complete and integrated picture of the functioning of the liver, it is necessary to consider the results of investigations at many levels of complexity ranging from the intact organism to isolated, crystalline enzymes. In these kinds of study it is not possible to say where biochemistry stops and physiology takes over. In the final analysis all physiological mechanisms can be described in biochemical terms. This truism is perhaps most evident in the case of the liver, the function of which has often been referred to as the biochemical laboratory of the organism.

A. *Intact organisms*

The most physiological method employed in the study of liver is presumably the measurement of the changes which take place in the chemical composition of the blood perfusing the liver in the intact individual. This is done by means of the catheterization technique, in which samples of arterial and hepatic venous blood are withdrawn and analysed. The total blood flow through the organ can be measured simultaneously by suitable methods. However, in the methods developed so far the composition of the portal blood which constitutes a major part of the blood passing the liver is not determined. Another drawback is the lack of information concerning changes in the liver cells with respect to the concentration of intermediary metabolites. Utilization of the biopsy technique when feasible may, however, furnish valuable data in such instances.

B. *Perfused liver preparation*

More experimental freedom is provided by the perfusion technique, in which an artificial circulation is established through the liver alone.

Recirculation of the perfusion medium permits a more accurate evaluation of the changes in composition of the circulating blood caused by the organ. Also the unpredictable influence of hormones and other active substances released into the blood by other organs is eliminated in the perfused liver. A variety of technical modifications (Staib and Scholz, 1968) including double perfusion through both the arterial and portal blood supply have been elaborated to simulate as far as possible physiological conditions. It must be admitted, however, that isolated liver preparations used at present do not resemble exactly in behaviour the liver of the intact animal. For instance, the oxygen uptake decreases rapidly after isolation of the liver (see Schimassek, 1968) to about half that observed *in situ*. Also leakage of a number of enzymes and of potassium ions into the perfusion medium is known to occur.

Improved perfusion media and operation procedures in which transient anoxia is prevented may possibly bring the performance of extracorporeally perfused livers nearer to the physiological level.

Treatment of patients in hepatic coma by circulation of their blood through suitable, isolated animal livers (e.g. from the pig) has been attempted (Eiseman, 1967). This promising practical application of the perfusion technique may give impetus to the development of better experimental methods.

C. *Liver slices*

For studies of the metabolic processes in liver tissue simpler preparations have played a much more important part. This is especially true of liver slices. The leakage of enzymes and cofactors from slices suspended in a suitable artificial medium of a composition more or less similar to that of the extracellular fluid is much more pronounced than for perfused preparations. Another difficulty is caused by the problem of obtaining a uniform concentration of oxygen and other substances throughout the tissue, because slices must have a considerable thickness (generally about 0·3 mm). However, although it may not be permissible to draw conclusions of a quantitative nature from experiments with liver slices, this technique is well suited for work in which the relative importance of different processes and pathways is being evaluated. Much of the most important and unambiguous basal work on liver metabolism has been carried out with slices.

D. *Isolated cells*

Although isolated liver cells have not been employed to the same extent, it is now possible to prepare with relative ease suspensions of apparently intact liver cells in good yield (Jacob and Bhargava, 1962). The liver is perfused *in situ* with a solution containing citrate, EDTA or a similar complex binder, and subsequently homogenized gently. After filtration through a suitable material and fractional centrifugation a suspension is obtained which consists of more than 90% isolated parenchymatous cells.

It might be expected that such a preparation would be ideal for the study of liver cell metabolism. However, it appears that the isolated cells behave in many ways differently from the intact liver or liver slices. For instance, the oxygen uptake expressed per cell or per unit of dry weight depends on the cell density of the suspension and declines rapidly (Gardner and Kay, 1967). Apparently mutual influence of the cells on each other is of importance. Also it has been shown that some soluble enzymes are lost during the isolation procedure (Henley et al., 1959). Some authors have concluded that isolated liver cells as currently prepared are useless in the study of liver metabolism (Friedmann and Epstein, 1967). However, the use of a complex, protein-containing medium improves the performance of the cells to a surprising extent (Hayek and Tipton, 1966).

E. *Liver homogenates*

A still simpler system is the homogenate, a suspension of crushed liver tissue in which the majority of the cells are disintegrated with liberation of the cytoplasm and the various cell organelles into the suspension medium. Crude homogenates contain all the enzymes and cofactors present in the original material, but as dilution to various degrees is always used, cofactors (e.g. adenosinephosphates, cytochrome *c*, and nicotinamide coenzymes) are generally added.

It must be kept in mind that the physical disintegration of the cell causes liberation of enzymes which may destroy vital compounds. For instance, a powerful hydrolase which attacks nicotinamide adenine dinucleotide (NAD) is present in liver homogenate. On the other hand, dilution of the liver tissue may abolish the effect of natural inhibitors of a number of reactions, in this way increasing the velocity of the processes in question.

Notwithstanding the "unphysiological" nature of homogenates, such preparations have furnished very valuable information on the metabolic potentialities of liver.

F. *Isolated cell components*

A further step towards simplification of the system is the use of isolated cell components, mitochondria, nuclei, cytoplasm and others. Preparation of such cellular components in a quasi physiological state is again a goal which has only been partially obtained. It should therefore be remembered that all such preparations even when made by the best methods available may differ seriously from the corresponding structures in the intact cell. This is apparent alone from the lability observed *in vitro* of such preparations. Work with isolated cell components is, however, necessary in order to gain an insight into the coordination of the metabolic processes inside the cell, as will be described later.

G. *Single enzymes*

Finally, individual enzymes have been isolated in a pure state and the kinetic and chemical properties have also been studied. Such investigations have revealed unexpected and very important features of the catalytic action of several enzymes, which are shown to be modified in different ways by reaction with small molecules which are not substrates for the enzyme.

Studies at all these levels of complexity are necessary before a coordinated picture of the biochemical function of the liver can be put together. When pure enzymes are used to throw light on molecular mechanisms in biological material, it should be kept in mind that while the usual type of kinetic experiment employs substrate concentrations, which are high compared to the molecular enzyme concentration, this is far from always the case in living cells (Srere, 1967).

The results so far obtained by means of the methods already outlined have provided only a crude view of the functioning of liver cells, but the work carried out at present with great intensity on regulatory mechanisms, and especially on the mechanisms of hormonal action on metabolic processes seems to bring a far more complete understanding within reach.

III. The Liver as the Central Organ in Biochemical Homeostasis

The numerous and varied functions of the liver require that liver cells have a considerably wider range of metabolic potentialities than other cells of the body. Thus, besides the nearly ubiquitous enzyme systems necessary for deriving energy from the breakdown of the predominant fuel substances in the body, glucose and lipids, and for the synthesis of proteins from amino acids, the liver performs a large number of more specialized functions.

1. Elaboration of bile, the external secretion of the liver. The bile contains a number of specific substances such as bile acids and bile pigments.
2. A variety of nutrients or digestion products of nutrients absorbed from the intestine are converted into a limited number of substances utilizable in most tissues of the body. These substances are liberated into the blood.
3. Regulation of the level in the blood of a multitude of substances including glucose, amino acids, various vitamins, and proteins.
4. Detoxication by means of several different processes of foreign substances taken up by the body.

All these functions may be considered as instrumental in the maintenance of constant chemical conditions for the organism as a whole, namely, chemical homeostasis. Substances which are not part of the normal environment of the tissues are converted into a form which is. Substances which are foreign or noxious to the organism are converted into a less harmful form. The concentration of the circulating blood plasma with respect to a number of important constituents is kept constant by removal or addition, as the case may be.

The problems relating to bile secretion and bilirubin metabolism are treated in subsequent chapters of this volume. Some of the other functions will for practical reasons be considered under the headings of carbohydrate, fat and protein metabolism, although the current trend in metabolic research emphasizes the coordination of these processes rather than their separation.

IV. Carbohydrate Metabolism

A. *Uptake in the liver of monohexoses absorbed from the intestine*

The quantitatively most important sugars released in the gut by digestion of nutrients in human subjects are glucose, fructose, and galactose. On an average diet the amount of glucose is much larger than that of the other two hexoses, but the amount of fructose and galactose are by no means negligible, as about 50 and 25 g respectively are furnished daily in the form of sucrose and lactose. Some fructose is also present in the diet as the free hexose, e.g. in fruits and honey. Other sugars including pentoses are of small importance.

Of the glucose absorbed from the intestine a considerable part is taken up by the liver, but perhaps the largest amount is deposited in peripheral organs as fat. Likewise in the case of fructose a large part of the quantity absorbed (about half, depending on the concentration in the blood) is removed by the liver (Tygstrup *et al.*, 1965). Galactose, on the other hand, is nearly exclusively metabolized in the liver.

As the liver cell membrane is freely permeable to monohexoses, the first stage in the metabolism of these substances is a chemical change, which seems in all cases to be phosphorylation. Glucose is converted to glucose-6-phosphate in a reaction requiring ATP. The enzyme responsible for by far the largest part of glucose phosphorylation in the liver is glucokinase, which differs from the hexokinases of most other tissues in having a rather large Michaelis constant, about 20 mM (Parry and Walker, 1966). This means that the reaction velocity will be proportional to the glucose concentration within the physiological range of blood glucose concentration.

Fructose is phosphorylated in the 1-position by means of a ketohexo-kinase. This is in contrast to the fate of fructose in other organs, in which fructose-6-phosphate is formed. Fructose-1-phosphate which does not participate in the Embden-Meyerhof pathway is converted to glucose through the reactions shown in Fig. 1. In human subjects about half the amount taken up is recovered as lactate and pyruvate in the hepatic venous blood, indicating that the phosphorylation of glyceraldehyde to glyceraldehyde-3-phosphate is not very important in man.

Galactose is phosphorylated in the 1-position, apparently by a specific galactokinase (Cuatrecasas and Segal, 1965). The phosphate compound is further converted to glucose-1-phosphate through the following reactions

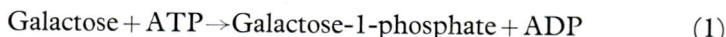

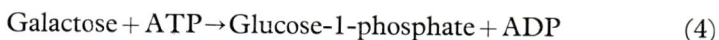

$$\text{Galactose} + \text{ATP} \rightarrow \text{Galactose-1-phosphate} + \text{ADP} \tag{1}$$

$$\text{Galactose-1-phosphate} + \text{UDPG} \leftrightharpoons \text{Glucose-1-phosphate} + \text{UDPGal} \tag{2}$$

$$\text{UDPGal} \leftrightharpoons \text{UDPG} \tag{3}$$

$$\text{Galactose} + \text{ATP} \rightarrow \text{Glucose-1-phosphate} + \text{ADP} \tag{4}$$

This process takes place nearly exclusively in the liver. The capacity of the organism to produce glucose from galactose has been used as a measure of hepatic function (see Tygstrup, 1964). The transferase catalysing reaction (2) is absent in patients with hereditary galactosaemia, a condition in which galactose cannot be utilized by the organism. As the individuals grow older the reaction

$$\text{Galactose-1-phosphate} + \text{UTP} \rightarrow \text{UDPGal} + \text{PP} \qquad (5)$$

is able to substitute partly for reaction (2).

All the ordinary monohexoses thus contribute to the pool of glucose-1-phosphate and glucose-6-phosphate which are in equilibrium in the liver cells.

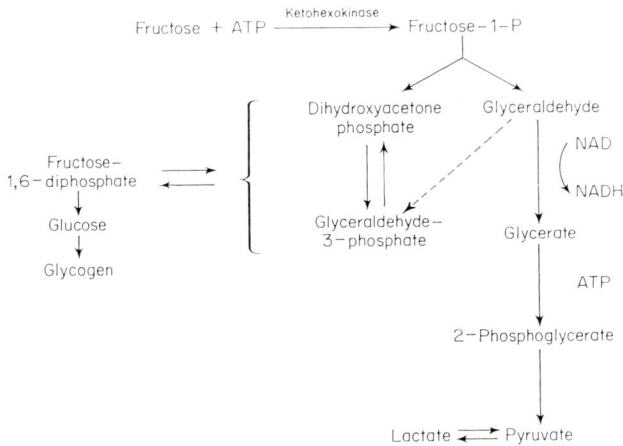

FIG. 1. Pathway of fructose metabolism in the liver.

B. *Formation and breakdown of glycogen*

After conversion to glucose phosphates the hexoses mentioned can enter into a number of reactions, one of which is transformation into glycogen. This polysaccharide consisting of glucose units linked together by glycosidic bonds may be present in the liver in very large amounts (up to 10%) and constitutes a buffer of glucosyl units which can be utilized to replete the blood glucose, when the concentration falls. In the event of a high blood glucose concentration, part of the excess glucose may be deposited as glycogen. As an energy store glycogen is, however, of much less importance than is fat.

Formation of glucose from glycogen takes place predominantly through the following sequence of reactions.

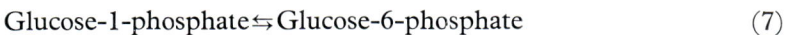

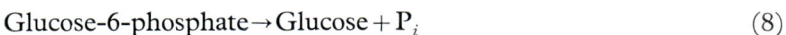

$$(\text{Glucosyl})_n + \text{P}_i \leftrightarrows \text{Glucose-1-phosphate} + (\text{Glucosyl})_{n-1} \qquad (6)$$

$$\text{Glucose-1-phosphate} \leftrightarrows \text{Glucose-6-phosphate} \qquad (7)$$

$$\text{Glucose-6-phosphate} \rightarrow \text{Glucose} + \text{P}_i \qquad (8)$$

The first reaction proceeds until a branching point in the glycogen molecule, having a 1·6-α-glucosidic linkage, is reached. Further breakdown is possible after the interference of an enzyme (debranching enzyme, amylo-1,6-glucosidase), which removes the last part of the branch as free glucose. The phosphorylase is an enzyme the quantity of which is regulated in a special manner as discovered by Sutherland and co-workers (see Sutherland, 1956). An inactive form of the enzyme (phosphorylase *b*) is transformed to the active *a*-form through phosphorylation by ATP (Rall *et al.*, 1956) in a way which is similar to the corresponding process in muscle tissue although the enzymes are different (Henion and Sutherland, 1957). This transformation is part of the mechanism by which certain hormones influence the rate of glycogen breakdown (see later).

The phosphorylase reaction is reversible, as may easily be demonstrated *in vitro*. However, the concentrations of inorganic phosphate and glucose-1-phosphate found *in vivo* are not compatible with glycogen formation. Instead, another pathway is employed by liver and by muscle cells. Glucose-1-phosphate is transformed to uridine-diphosphate glucose by a reaction with uridine-triphosphate

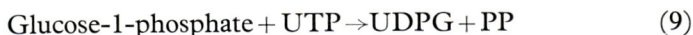

$$\text{Glucose-1-phosphate} + \text{UTP} \rightarrow \text{UDPG} + \text{PP} \qquad (9)$$

UDPG can deliver the glucosyl radical to a molecule of glycogen. Some other primer containing a sequence of glucose molecules bound together by 1,4-α-glucoside linkage may also function as acceptor, but the rate decreases very much when the number of glucose residues in the primer is reduced. In the case of maltotriose it is 5000 times smaller than it is with glycogen. This glucosyl transferase was discovered by Leloir and Cardini (1957). The prolongation of the glucosyl chains proceeds only by a limited number of glucose units. A "branching enzyme" (amylo-1,4:1,6-transglucosidase) then removes part of the chain consisting of about 6 glucose units and places it as a branch in a glucosidic bond to a 6-hydroxy group (Verhue and Hers, 1966). Also glycogen synthetase exists in two forms, one of which the I-form is transformed to the less active D-form through phosphorylation catalysed by a kinase. The reverse process is catalysed by a phosphatase. The D-form of the enzyme requires the presence of glucose-6-phosphate while the I-form is independent of glucose-6-phosphate concentration. The kinases catalysing phosphorylation of phosphorylase *b* and I-glycogen synthetase are very similar, but not identical (Friedman and Larner, 1965).

Whether glycogen is built up or broken down is apparently determined largely by hormonal factors to be considered later, though the concentration of glucose monophosphates may provide the basis of some automatic regulation. The rate of glucose-6-phosphate synthesis in the liver from glucose will increase when the glucose concentration in the blood increases. Conversely glucose-6-phosphatase activity will be higher when the blood glucose concentration is low (Arion and Nordlie, 1964). The relation between glucose uptake and glycogen synthesis is, however, not fully understood (De Wulf and Hers, 1967).

C. *Glycolysis*

The enzymes of the glycolytic breakdown of glucose are all present in the liver, but the overall maximal velocity of glycolysis is small compared to that of other tissues and only about 15% of the maximal rate of gluconeogenesis, i.e. the synthesis of glucose from non-carbohydrate precursors.

It should perhaps be remembered that the glycolytic breakdown of glucose has other potentialities than energy production, as illustrated in Fig. 2 (Sols, 1968), where certain important branch reactions are indicated.

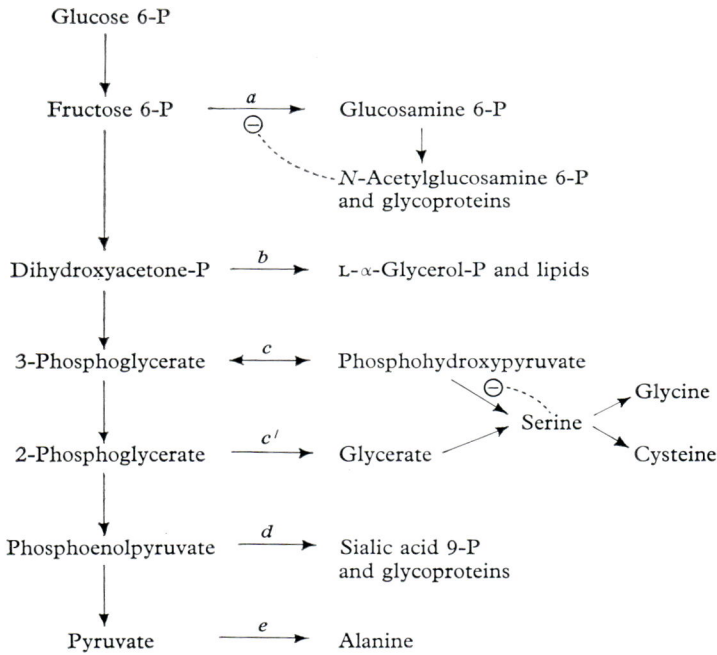

FIG. 2. Important branch reactions of intermediary substances in the Embden-Meyerhof pathway of hexose breakdown.

The limited rate of glycolysis is determined by the relatively small activity of the enzymes catalyzing three irreversible key reactions, viz. glucokinase, phosphofructokinase and pyruvatekinase. These reactions constitute control points which are accurately regulated through the influence of hormones and certain metabolites. The kinetic properties of phospho-fructokinase which is often regarded as the most important regulatory point has been intensively studied with respect to a number of activators and inhibitors involved in cell metabolism (Lowry and Passonneau, 1966; Ferdinand, 1966). Of special importance is the finding that excess of ATP and citrate inhibits the enzyme, while AMP has a pronounced activating (or de-inhibiting) effect.

As the enzyme adenylate kinase catalyzing the reaction

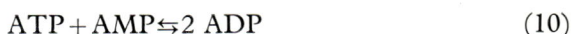

$$ATP + AMP \rightleftharpoons 2\ ADP \tag{10}$$

is believed to have sufficient activity in the liver to establish equilibrium, there will be a relation between the concentration of the three substances involved, determined by the equilibrium constant of this reaction and the ATP concentration, provided that the total adenosine nucleotide concentration, remains constant. As shown in Fig. 3 the AMP concentration is a very sensitive indicator of changes in the ATP/ADP ratio. The system

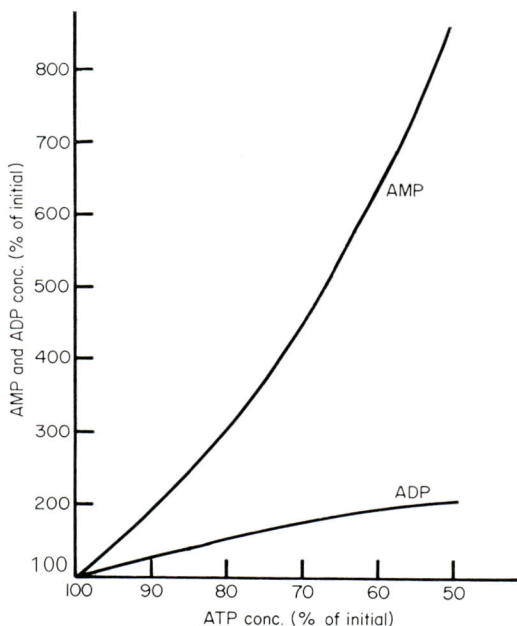

FIG. 3. Relative increases in the concentration of AMP and ADP, when the concentration of ATP is reduced. The total adenosine nucleotide concentration is considered constant at 5 mM. Furthermore, the ATP/ADP ratio in the initial state is taken as 4 and the equilibrium constant of the adenylate kinase reaction as 0·44. (From Grunnet, N., unpublished.)

may be considered a biochemical amplifier which transforms the small changes in the ATP concentration occurring normally into relatively large changes in AMP concentration. This substance therefore is ideally suited as a regulator of energy metabolism. The case of the phosphofructokinase reaction illustrates this. When ATP is drawn upon for anabolic reactions, the AMP concentration rises. This in turn causes increased glycolysis through activation of the fructokinase reaction and energy is furnished in the form of ATP by acceleration of this rate limiting step. This is only one of a number of reactions which are influenced by the AMP concentration (see Fig. 4).

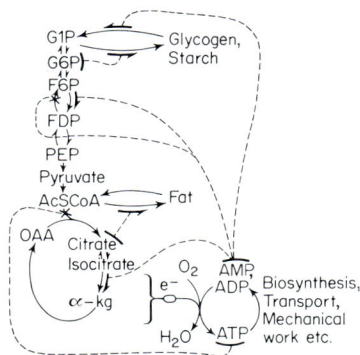

FIG. 4. The role of AMP and ATP in the regulation of important reactions of carbohydrate metabolism. (From Atkinson, 1965.)

D. *Gluconeogenesis*

One of the main functions of the liver is production of glucose, not only from the store of glycogen but also from non-carbohydrate precursors. These include lactate, pyruvate, glycerol, and a large number of amino acids, which are transformed into pyruvate or tricarboxylic acid cycle intermediates. The pathway leading to glucose from pyruvate is not simply a reversal of the glycolytic scheme as was the general belief some years ago. Three of the steps in the Embden-Meyerhof scheme are displaced very much in one direction, as pointed out by Krebs and Kornberg (1957), and reversal of all of them is not thermodynamically feasible under physiological conditions. The steps in question are conversion of glucose-6-phosphate to glucose, conversion of fructose-diphosphate to fructose-6-phosphate and conversion of pyruvate to phosphoenol-pyruvate. In gluconeogenesis these energy barriers are bypassed by other irreversible processes, as illustrated in Fig. 5. The conversion of glucose-6-phosphate to glucose is effected by a specific phosphatase present in liver tissue. Similarly, the phosphofructokinase step is reversed by another specific enzyme removing the phosphate group selectively from the 1-position of fructose diphosphate.

While the effectiveness of these reactions is dependent only on the specificity of the enzymes in question, the pyruvate kinase reaction is circumvented in a more complicated way. Pyruvate is carboxylated in an ATP-requiring reaction, and the oxaloacetate (oxosuccinate, cf. Fig. 5) formed is converted to phosphoenolpyruvate + carbon dioxide by means of phosphoenolpyruvatecarboxykinase with concomitant hydrolysis of one more pyrophosphate bond. While the glycolytic breakdown of one molecule of glucose to lactate results in a net formation of two molecules of

ATP, the synthesis of one molecule of glucose from two molecules of lactate requires the expenditure of six molecules of ATP, two for the formation of two molecules of oxaloacetate, two for phosphorylative decarboxylation to phosphoenolpyruvate, and two for phosphorylation of 3-phosphoglycerate to the 1,3-diphosphate. The complete oxidation of lactate furnishes 18 molecules of ATP, sufficient to convert six molecules of lactate to glucose.

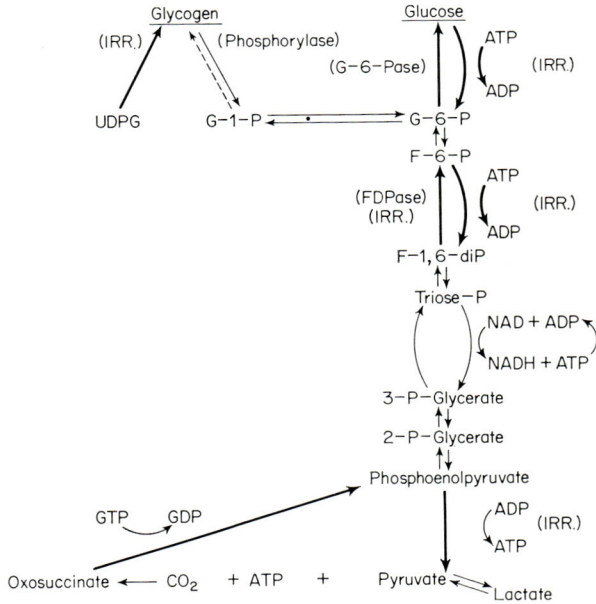

FIG. 5. The Embden-Meyerhof pathway of glucose metabolism. The scheme shows the points at which irreversible steps (IRR) are active.

The four control enzymes involved in gluconeogenesis are regulated in a similar way as the corresponding enzymes of the glycolytic reaction, through the intervention of hormones and metabolites. For instance, the fructose-diphosphatase is inhibited by AMP while the corresponding kinase as mentioned earlier is activated by AMP. It is of vital importance for the energy economy of the cell that the two reverse processes at each control point are not allowed to proceed simultaneously to any significant extent. The simultaneous and equal activity of, for example, glucokinase and glucose-6-phosphatase would achieve only the hydrolysis of ATP to ADP and inorganic phosphate. Exactly the same situation occurs at the two other points. To what extent it is possible to suppress one reaction while activating the other is not known with certainty. One class of metabolites which appears to play an important part in the suppression of glycolysis during gluconeogenesis is unesterified fatty acids. Work by many research groups (for references see Ashmore and Weber, 1968) have shown that these substances and their coenzyme A derivatives have a strong inhibitory influence on a number of enzymes in carbohydrate metabolism in such a way that both the oxydation of carbohydrate and the glycolysis are profoundly influenced while the gluconeogenetic enzymes are unaffected (see Fig. 6). Of special importance is perhaps the inhibition of pyruvate kinase, an enzyme which under optimal conditions has several times the activity of the combined system catalyzing the reverse reaction (Weber *et al.*, 1967).

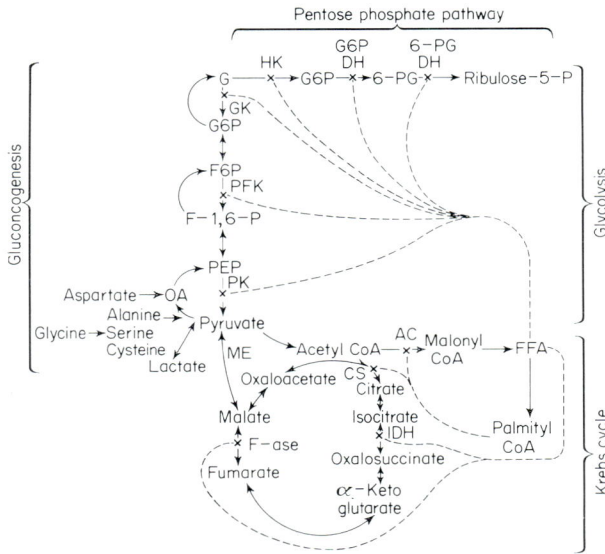

FIG. 6. Influence of unesterified fatty acids and acyl CoA on a number of processes in glucose metabolism. Degradation of glucose is inhibited, while gluconeogenesis is uninfluenced. GK, glucokinase; PFK, phosphofructokinase; PK, pyruvate kinase; HK, hexokinase; G6PDH, glucose-6-phosphate dehydrogenase; 6-PGDH, 6-phosphogluconate dehydrogenase; IDH, isocitrate dehydrogenase; F-ase, fumarase; ME, malic enzyme; AC, acetyl-CoA carboxylase; CS, citrate synthase. (From Ashmore and Weber, 1968.)

The carboxylation of pyruvate to oxaloacetate is a key-reaction in gluconeogenesis from pyruvate and substances which are converted to pyruvate (such as lactate, alanine and serine). The pyruvate carboxylase requires the presence of acetyl-CoA as an activator and the activity is dependent on the concentration of this substance. At the same time acetyl-CoA inhibits the oxydation of pyruvate to acetyl-CoA. This means that when the acetyl-CoA concentration increases as a consequence of fatty acid oxydation, the pyruvate metabolism is deviated from oxydation to carboxylation and concomitant glucose formation. This process is facilitated by the inhibition of the glycolytic steps mentioned above through the presence of the free fatty acids.

The rate of glucose formation from a number of precursors is shown in Table 1. This process in general proceeds markedly better in perfused liver preparations than in slices.

The rate of gluconeogenesis in man may be as high as 420 g per day corresponding to about 1 μmole/min per g liver (Bearn *et al.*, 1952). Other authors have found somewhat lower values. If, however, carbohydrates are not included in the diet, gluconeogenesis will be dependent exclusively on the breakdown of amino acids, and during prolonged fasting the only source of amino acids is the protein of the body itself. Even in this condition a reasonably high glucose concentration is maintained in the blood. Tissues such as the central nervous system which are normally dependent on exclusive carbohydrate metabolism may change their metabolic pattern to one of ketone body utilization (Cahill and Owen, 1968).

TABLE I

The rate of gluconeogenesis from various precursors in rat liver slices and perfused rat liver

Substrate added	Rate of glucose formation (μmoles/min g)	
	Slices	Perfused liver
None	—	0·14
L-Lactate	0·55	1·06
Pyruvate	0·40	1·02
L-Alanine	0·23	0·66
L-Serine	0·20	0·98
Dihydroxyacetone	0·38	2·07
Fructose	0·81	2·68

(From Ross *et al.*, 1967).

E. *The pentose phosphate pathway: the synthesis of pentoses*

The liver like most tissues can metabolize glucose in other ways than through the processes indicated in Fig. 5. The most important of these routes is probably the pentose phosphate or phosphogluconic acid oxidative pathway. Only certain general features, but not the details of the processes involved will be treated here. The breakdown of glucose-6-phosphate by this pathway may be divided into two groups of reactions, two oxidative steps resulting in the liberation of carbon atom 1 as CO_2 and a number of complex rearrangements, catalysed by several enzymes, through which the pentose phosphate formed in the oxidative steps may be converted back to hexose monophosphate. Both oxidation steps require NADP, which is reduced to NADPH. This substance is of vital importance in the reductive synthesis from two carbon units of, for instance, fatty acids and steroids. It may arise from other reactions such as transhydrogenation from NADH, but probably the glucose-6-phosphate oxidation is quantitatively most important. The ketopentose (ribulose-5-phosphate) formed may be converted to ribose phosphate which is needed for nucleic acid synthesis (see Fig. 7). However, it should be made clear that ribose phosphate may be formed also through a series of reversible reactions from intermediates in the Embden-Meyerhof pathway by means of the enzymes which are active in the second part of the pentose phosphate cycle (trans-ketolase, transaldolase and others). Glyceraldehyde-3-phosphate and fructose-6-phosphate are common intermediates in the two pathways (see Horecker, 1968), and indeed through the sequential action of five reversible enzymes the following equilibrium may be established

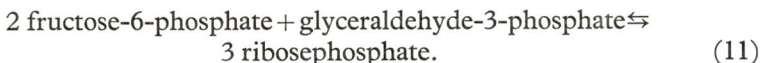

$$\text{2 fructose-6-phosphate} + \text{glyceraldehyde-3-phosphate} \rightleftharpoons$$
$$\text{3 ribosephosphate.} \tag{11}$$

This means that the cell under conditions when NADPH is not needed may still form pentose phosphate for synthesis of nucleic acids and *vice versa*,

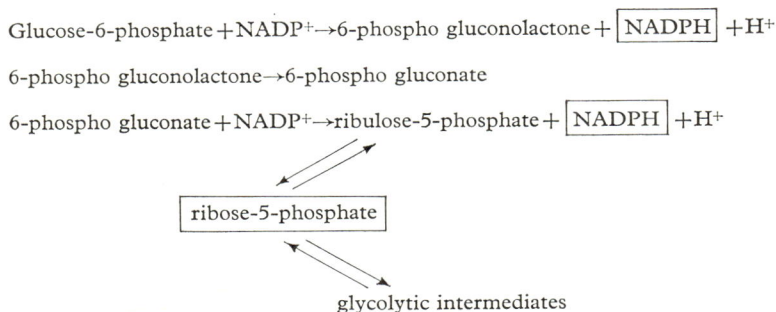

Glucose-6-phosphate $+$ NADP$^+$ $\rightarrow$ 6-phospho gluconolactone $+$ $\boxed{\text{NADPH}}$ $+$H$^+$

6-phospho gluconolactone $\rightarrow$ 6-phospho gluconate

6-phospho gluconate $+$ NADP$^+$ $\rightarrow$ ribulose-5-phosphate $+$ $\boxed{\text{NADPH}}$ $+$H$^+$

$$\boxed{\text{ribose-5-phosphate}}$$

glycolytic intermediates

FIG. 7. Some steps in the pentose phosphate pathway of glucose metabolism, showing the formation of NADPH and ribose phosphate.

when a high rate of formation of NADPH is needed the pentose formed through the steps shown in Fig. 7 may be directed back into hexose and triose phosphate. To what extent the pentose phosphate pathway functions as a cycle resulting in complete oxidation of glucose-6-phosphate is not known. Many attempts have been made to evaluate quantitatively the contribution of the pentose phosphate shunt to glucose metabolism in various tissues including liver. This is done by utilization of glucose labelled in various positions with radioactive carbon (Katz and Wood, 1960, 1963; Katz et al., 1966; Landau and Bartsch, 1966). However, the problem is a very complicated one and fraught with many sources of uncertainty. There is no doubt that the glucose-6-phosphate oxidation pathway plays a considerable role, but the fraction of glucose metabolism taking place in this way is likely to vary with the specific metabolic state of the liver and the metabolic requirements.

F. *The formation of glucuronic acid and other related aspects*

A third cyclic pathway for the metabolism of glucose units has been proposed (Ashwell *et al.*, 1961), as shown in Fig. 8. This pathway is initiated

I

by oxidation of carbon atom number 6 instead of 1. In order to achieve this reaction the reducing end of the glucose molecule is protected through combination with uridine diphosphate (UDPG). This is oxidized to UDPGA (uridine diphosphate glucuronic acid) through a reaction requiring two molecules of NAD. The following steps proceed apparently from free glucuronic acid, but it is not clear how this substance is liberated from the

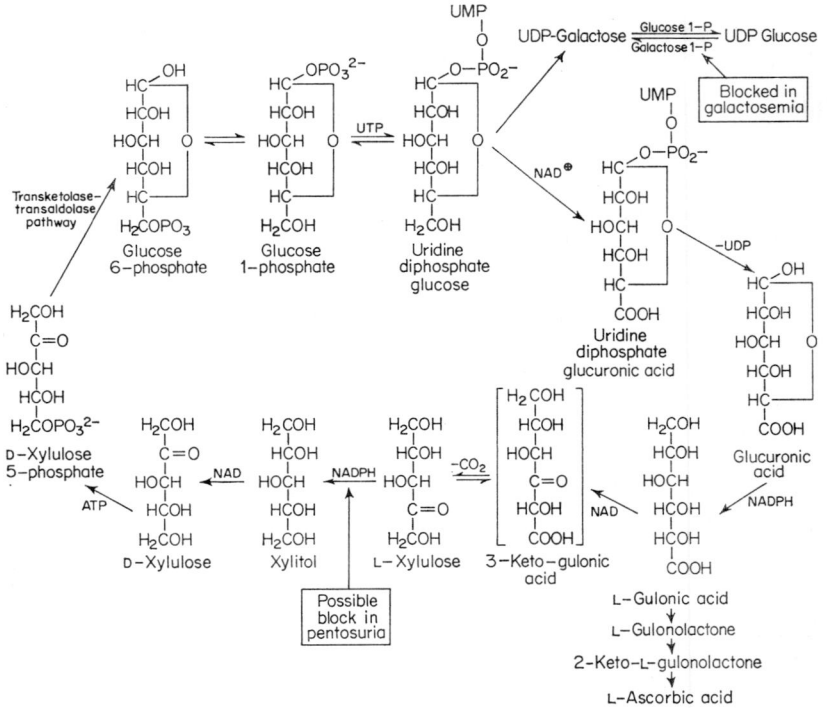

FIG. 8. The glucuronic acid pathway of glucose metabolism. (From Horecker, 1968.)

UDPGA in the liver. A branch from the cycle leads to formation of ascorbic acid in those animals which are able to synthesize this substance. The importance of the cyclic oxidation of glucose along this route in man is not known, but a block in the pathway, probably the reduction of L-xylulose to xylitol (see Fig. 8) is found in the rare congenital disease pentosuria. In this condition no untoward effects are observed apart from excretion of L-xylulose in the urine.

The formation of UDPGA is important as the substance is responsible for glucuronide formation (see Section VII.C). It has, however, also other functions. Through decarboxylation it is transformed to UDP-xylose, and epimerization leads to conversion of UDP-glucuronic acid to UDP-iduronic acid in a reaction resembling the transformation of glucose into galactose. These substances are necessary for the synthesis of a number of complex polysaccharides and glycoproteins.

Another group of important carbohydrate derivatives formed in the liver from glucose is the aminohexoses and neuraminic acids. Glucosamine is made from fructose-6-phosphate through the following reaction

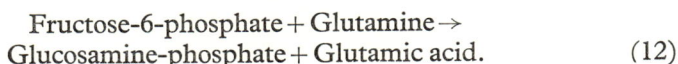

$$\text{Fructose-6-phosphate} + \text{Glutamine} \rightarrow$$
$$\text{Glucosamine-phosphate} + \text{Glutamic acid.} \qquad (12)$$

After acetylation by a reaction requiring acetyl CoA, the acetyl glucosamine may be incorporated into a uridine diphosphate compound, UDP-N-acetylglucosamine (Pontis, 1955). This substance is the source of acetyl galactosamine formed through epimerization analogous to the formation of UDP-galactose. The free acetyl glucosamine can also be converted to acetyl mannosamine, which is a precursor of N-acetyl neuraminic acid. These various amino compounds are components of mucopolysaccharides and glycoproteins produced in the liver. The mechanism by which these various carbohydrate derivatives are incorporated into polysaccharides and proteins is under active study (see for instance Dodgson and Lloyd, 1968).

V. Lipid Metabolism

The part played by the liver in the fat metabolism of higher organisms is significant but largely secondary. Several of the processes in the liver involving lipids have also been shown to be present in other tissues.

Unesterified fatty acid and triglycerides may be utilized in the energy metabolism of the liver. It is in fact generally assumed that under basal conditions some 75% of the energy liberated in the liver originates from the oxidation of fat. Such calculations (see Fritz, 1961) are rather uncertain, but glucose oxidation is very low under basal conditions, as shown in experiments utilizing ^{14}C-labelled glucose (Kruhøffer and Muntz, 1954; Levine and Fritz, 1956). The contribution of the other possible major source of oxidative energy, the amino acids, may be estimated from the nitrogen excretion in the urine. The difference between the total oxygen uptake and that calculated for carbohydrate and amino acid metabolism is assumed to represent fat oxidation, partial or complete. Estimates of fat utilization in the liver based on arteriovenous concentration differences for free fatty acids and ketone-bodies also show that the largest part of the energy metabolism of liver is provided by fatty acid oxidation. Under other conditions, fat oxidation may be very much less; for instance, during alcohol-aemia when nearly all the oxygen uptake of the liver is accounted for through oxydation of ethanol to acetate (Lundquist et al., 1962).

A predominant if not exclusive role is played by the liver in the production of ketone bodies (acetoacetate and β-hydroxybutyrate), in the incorporation of fat (triglycerides, phospholipids and cholesterol) into plasma lipoprotein, in the synthesis of cholesterol and bile acids, and in the metabolism of steroids and some fat soluble vitamins.

Apart from these processes liver cells, like most other cells, contain the machinery for the breakdown and oxidation of fatty acids, and for the synthesis of all groups of lipids. The oxidation and synthesis of fatty acids will not be considered here in detail.

A. *Partial oxidation of fatty acids: formation of acetoacetate and β-hydroxybutyrate*

A long series of reactions are involved in the oxidative breakdown of the ordinary long chain (C_{16}–C_{18}) fatty acids. The first steps include activation by ATP and CoA to acyl-CoA (or possibly other activation systems – see Shapiro, 1967) and conversion of acyl-CoA to acyl-carnitine, a process which presumably is necessary for the passage of fatty acids into the mitochondria. In these cell organelles the complete oxidation takes place through a series of alternate oxidation, hydration, oxidation, and thiolysis reactions, which lead to the liberation of acetyl-CoA units. Formation of the carnitine esters may be the rate-limiting step in the whole process (Shepherd *et al.*, 1966).

The enzymes involved in the usual β-oxidation pathway for fatty acid metabolism are present in large amount in liver cells. In fact more fatty acids may be broken down to acetyl-CoA units than can be oxidized further to CO_2 and H_2O in the tricarboxylic acid cycle. The excess acetyl groups may enter into the synthesis of a number of substances. The first step in the non-oxydative metabolism of acetyl-CoA seems to be a condensation of two molecules to acetoacetyl-CoA with liberation of free CoA. This is a reaction which is known to occur in most tissues. However, in liver acetoacetyl-CoA may be transformed to free acetoacetate in either of two ways. It may be hydrolyzed directly with liberation of acetoacetate in an irreversible process, or it may also be formed through cleavage of β-methyl, β-hydroxy-glutaryl-CoA. The latter pathway is believed to be predominant. β-Methyl, β-hydroxyglutaryl-CoA arises from acetoacetyl-CoA through condensation with one molecule of acetyl-CoA in a reaction resembling citrate synthesis, only the carboxyl group of oxaloacetate is replaced by a methyl group (Fig. 9).

Acetoacetate once formed can not (or only to an insignificant extent) be further oxidized in the liver (see Fritz, 1961) but it is released to the circulating blood and serves as a valuable fuel for many other tissues including muscle. The same is true of β-hydroxybutyrate, which is formed by reduction of acetoacetate in liver mitochondria. The ratio of the reduced and oxidized form of the substance is around 2:1 under most conditions.

The amount of acetoacetate and β-hydroxybutyrate ("ketone-bodies") formed in the liver is dependent on the concentration of free fatty acids in the blood (Hanson *et al.*, 1965). Under normal conditions when the concentration of free fatty acids (unesterified fatty acids) is low only small quantities are released by the liver, but during fasting, fat feeding, or diabetes the rate of lipolysis in peripheral tissues (above all adipose tissue) is much increased, and so is acetoacetate and hydroxybutyrate formation in the liver. These conditions are also those which require an increased gluconeogenesis.

A close relation between the two processes is therefore assumed (Krebs, 1965). One possible mechanism connecting the two pathways is the carboxylation of pyruvate to oxaloacetate, which is needed in gluconeogenesis. For example, acetyl-CoA that is formed by the breakdown of fatty acids is known to accelerate this reaction (see Section IV. D). Also fatty acids inhibit the oxydative decarboxylation of pyruvate and in this way promote gluconeogenesis (Williamson *et al.*, 1966). Under conditions of gluconeogenesis, the activated fatty acids will presumably not form triglycerides and phospholipids at the normal rate, as the glycerophosphate required (see C) originates largely from carbohydrate catabolism, which is inhibited. Some glycerophosphate is, however, formed from glycerol which is liberated through lipolysis in peripheral tissues.

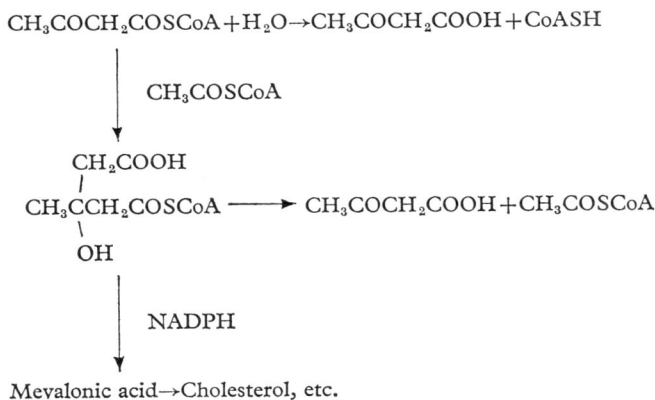

$$CH_3COCH_2COSCoA + H_2O \rightarrow CH_3COCH_2COOH + CoASH$$

$$\downarrow \quad CH_3COSCoA$$

$$\begin{array}{c} CH_2COOH \\ | \\ CH_3CCH_2COSCoA \longrightarrow CH_3COCH_2COOH + CH_3COSCoA \\ \backslash \\ OH \end{array}$$

$$\downarrow \quad NADPH$$

Mevalonic acid→Cholesterol, etc.

FIG. 9. Alternative reactions of acetoacetyl-CoA.

B. *Synthesis and conversion of cholesterol: bile acids*

Cholesterol is generally available in the diet, but many tissues have the ability to synthesize cholesterol from acetate units. The liver synthesizes a large part of the cholesterol formed in the body. The β-hydroxy-β-methyl-glutaryl-CoA mentioned in the previous section is the starting-point for a complex series of reactions leading to cholesterol formation (see for instance the review by Popják and Cornforth, 1960).

Cholesterol synthesized in the liver is partly secreted into the bile and thence into the gut. However, most of the cholesterol excreted in this way is reabsorbed by the intestine and recirculated through the liver. Esterification of part of the cholesterol incorporated into lipoprotein is carried out by the liver. Polyunsaturated fatty acids are predominantly found in the cholesterol esters isolated from plasma lipids. Esterification does, however, also take place in the intestinal mucosa.

Important conversion products of cholesterol in the liver are the bile acids which are produced in quite considerable amounts (500–700 mg per day in man). The details of the reactions leading from cholesterol to cholic and chenodeoxycholic acid, the most important of the cyclic structures found in bile acids, are not completely known (Bergström and Danielsson, 1963).

The rate of bile acid synthesis seems to be homeostatically controlled through feedback inhibition by the concentration of bile acids in the portal blood. In a similar but probably rather complex way, the hepatic cholesterol concentration determines the rate of *de novo* cholesterol synthesis.

The cholic acids are conjugated with amino acids (glycine and taurine) before being excreted into the bile. Conjugation takes place through a reaction between cholyl-CoA and the amino acids just mentioned.

C. *Role of the liver in the maintenance of blood lipid concentration*

The lipids of blood plasma in the post-absorptive state are present exclusively as lipoproteins apart from unesterified fatty acids which are bound to albumin. Two groups of lipoproteins are easily separated (by electrophoresis or ultracentrifugation), α- and β-lipoprotein. They differ among other things in the proportion of lipids relative to protein, β-lipoprotein being the most lipid-rich (containing about 80% lipid). Subdivision of these protein fractions is possible, but the composition of the individual fractions do not seem to be stoichiometrically determined. Triglycerides, phospholipids, and cholesterol are all present in the lipoproteins.

The plasma lipoproteins are believed to be formed exclusively in the liver. Material for their synthesis, apart from the protein part, include firstly, unesterified fatty acids, which are taken up by the liver from plasma or synthesized *de novo* in the liver. Second, chylomicrons, lipid-rich particles containing only a small amount (about 1%) of protein. Chylomicrons are formed in the intestinal mucosa from absorbed digestion products of lipids. Chylomicrons may to some extent be utilized directly by peripheral tissues, for instance, by heart muscle but as a rule they are taken up by the liver cells. The triglycerides are hydrolysed apparently in the plasma membrane of the liver cells and rapidly re-esterified after entering the cell (Green and Webb, 1964; Higgins and Green, 1966). Third, phospholipids, cholesterol and cholesterol esters synthesized in the liver.

A delicately balanced relation between uptake and synthesis of lipids and elaboration and secretion of lipoproteins does exist. When this balance cannot be maintained, fat may accumulate in the liver, predominantly as triglycerides, thereby giving rise to a pathological condition. This may happen if the ability to synthesize the protein moiety or some of the lipid components of lipoproteins is reduced. This is probably the case in many toxic conditions and in choline-deficiency. Fatty liver may also arise from an excessive supply of unesterified fatty acids, or other lipids from plasma, or it may be caused by a block in the oxydative metabolism of fatty acids in the liver. These problems are treated in Chapter 9.

The pathways for the synthesis, interconversion and breakdown of the many complex lipids, phospholipids and glycolipids will not be described here. Although the liver has a considerable capacity for the synthesis of phospholipids, the reactions involved are of widespread occurrence. A schematic representation of the interrelation of the most important classes of lipid is given in Fig. 10.

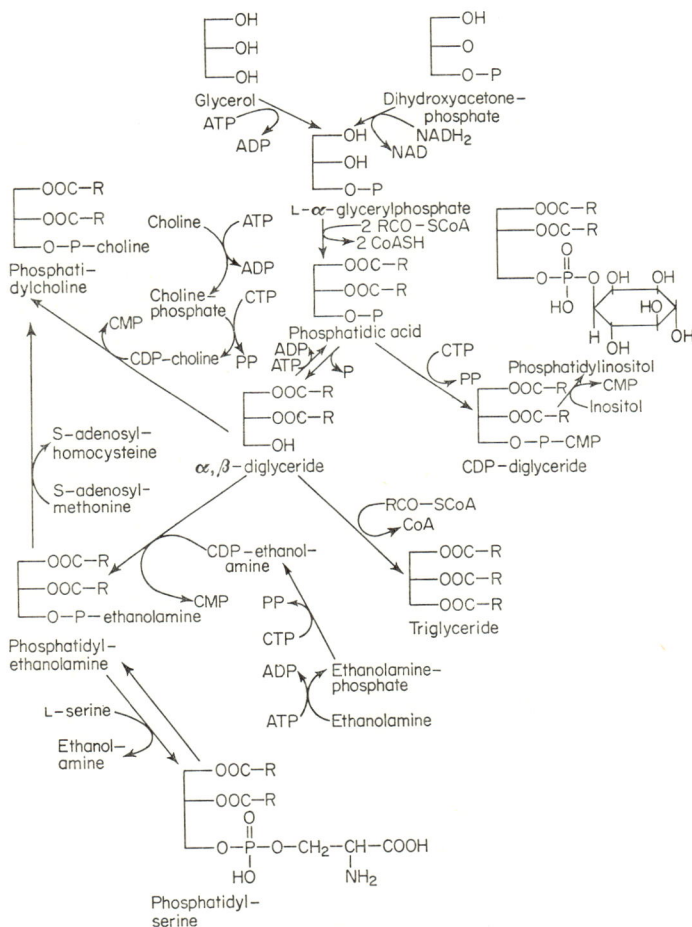

FIG. 10. Interconversion of some important groups of lipids.

VI. Metabolism of Amino Acids and Proteins

One of the vital functions of the liver is to maintain in the blood plasma suitable concentrations of all the amino acids necessary for protein synthesis and other functions in the tissues of the body, in the face of large variations in composition and total amount of the amino acid mixture absorbed from the gut and occasionally during complete absence of an amino acid supply from outside. The problems involved are obviously complex, and a considerable loss of amino acid nitrogen from the organism is apparently unavoidable. The magnitude of this loss is dependent on the amino acid composition of the diet.

It is, however, entirely possible to imagine an organism in which all amino acids and other nitrogen-containing substances derived from the breakdown of proteins and nucleic acids are much more completely re-utilized, resulting in a negligible need for protein in the diet of the adult organism. The non-occurrence of such a mechanism is presumably a consequence of the fact that all natural food does contain protein. Therefore elaborate measures which completely avoid nitrogen loss become superfluous.

A. *Essential and non-essential amino acids*

Higher animals have lost the capacity to synthesize several of the 20 amino acids occurring in ordinary proteins. Consequently these amino acids have become essential nutrients. The synthesis of the essential amino acids, as revealed by biochemical studies on plants and microorganisms, are complicated processes, each requiring many enzymatic steps. This is in sharp contrast to the synthesis of the non-essential amino acids from a number of intermediary metabolites, which in general takes place through few and simple reactions. By renouncing the ability to carry out these syntheses, the animal organism has gained the advantage of being able to spare the production of a considerable number of enzymes.

The liver metabolizes any excess of amino acids absorbed by the organism, and also supplements the essential ones through synthesis of the non-essential amino acids. The synthesis at least of some of the non-essential amino acids also takes place in other organs, but the extent of these processes is not yet known.

The concentration of several amino acids is much higher in the liver than in blood plasma. This is for instance true of glutamate, aspartate, alanine and glycine, but also all the other amino acids are present in higher concentration (see Tarver, 1963). Mechanisms have been postulated which attempt to explain the unequal distribution and, in fact, the uptake of amino acids from the blood against the prevailing concentration gradient. Little is, however, known about this in the case of liver cells.

B. *Reactions involved in the transformation of amino acids*

The major reaction responsible for the synthesis of amino acids is transamination. In this type of reaction the α-amino group is transferred to an α-oxo acid without appearance of free ammonia.

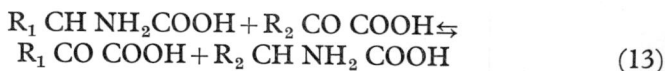

$$R_1 \, CH \, NH_2 COOH + R_2 \, CO \, COOH \rightleftarrows$$
$$R_1 \, CO \, COOH + R_2 \, CH \, NH_2 \, COOH \quad\quad (13)$$

All transamination reactions seem to require pyridoxal phosphate as a coenzyme. The coenzyme passes through a cycle during the catalytic reaction. The aldehyde group accepts the amino group from the amino acid with intermediate formation of a so-called Schiff-base in which an equilibrium is established between the form with the double bond between the coenzyme and nitrogen and another form with this bond between nitrogen and the amino acid carbon. This compound is spontaneously hydrolysed to the oxo acid and pyridoxamine phosphate. Pyridoxamine phosphate in turn reacts with another oxo acid, again forming a Schiff-base, which is now hydrolysed to the second amino acid and pyridoxal phosphate. This type of reaction is known to take place in many tissues (see Meister, 1965), but the enzymes responsible for transamination of essential amino acids are probably mainly located in liver.

α-Oxoglutarate occupies a central position in these reactions. Enzymes catalysing transamination between most amino acids on the one hand and α-oxoglutarate on the other have been demonstrated. However, only in a few cases have they been extensively purified and identified. The specificity of liver transaminases may not be absolute and groups of similar amino acids may react with oxoglutarate by means of the same enzyme. As transamination reactions are reversible it is to be expected that the supply of the α-oxo acid corresponding to the essential amino acid could substitute for these in the organism. This has in fact been shown to be the case in the rat for some amino acids (Wood and Cooley, 1954).

Through these reactions the α-amino groups of the essential and other amino acids present in excess of the need end up as amino groups in glutamic acid, which plays a central role in intermediary metabolism. Several pathways are available for this substance. Three of these are of special interest in this connection. First, formation of non-essential amino acids through transamination with oxo acids formed in the general metabolism of carbohydrates and other substances. Second, the oxydation of glutamate by means of glutamate dehydrogenase to α-oxoglutarate and ammonium ions. And third, conversion to glutamine, the γ-amide of glutamic acid. These 3 pathways will now be dealt with in some detail.

1. The oxo acids which function as acceptors of the amino group are oxaloacetate (forming aspartate), pyruvate (forming alanine), 3-phosphohydroxypyruvate (forming phosphoserine and thence serine) and glutamic semialdehyde (forming proline and ornithine).

   Through aspartate formation the nitrogen group is made available for a number of synthetic processes including those of pyrimidine formation, a step in nucleic acid synthesis, and production of urea. Glutamate oxaloacetate transaminase (GOT) is present in large amount in liver. Determination of this enzyme in plasma is of considerable value in the diagnosis of liver disease as it easily leaks out of the liver cells under certain pathological conditions.

2. Dehydrogenation of glutamic acid is one of the reactions through which ammonia is liberated by the liver. The further metabolism of ammonia is considered in Section D. Glutamate dehydrogenase is

unique among the amino acid deaminating enzymes in requiring NAD^+ (or $NADP^+$) as coenzyme.

$$\text{Glutamate} + NAD^+ \leftrightarrows \alpha\text{-oxoglutarate} + NADH + NH_4^+ \qquad (14)$$

The equilibrium of the reaction is highly in favour of glutamate formation, but the efficient oxidation of α-oxoglutarate in mitochondria (as a step in the tricarboxylic acid cycle) and the effective removal of ammonium ions permit the reaction to proceed to the right.

3. The synthesis of glutamine requires ATP and ammonium ions. This substance is also utilized in a number of vital processes, including synthesis of the purine and pyrimidine bases of the nucleic acids. It is also needed for the synthesis of hexosamines and in a number of detoxication processes.

C. *Fate of the carbon skeleton of essential amino acids*

Space does not permit a detailed discussion of the many interesting reactions involved in the metabolism of the essential amino acids. Most of them are converted through quite complex series of reactions to intermediate metabolites which occur in the tricarboxylic acid cycle. Others [leucine, lysine(?), isoleucine, phenylalanine and tyrosine] are completely [leucine, lysine(?)] or partly metabolized to acetyl groups or acetoacetate, which can not give rise to glucose production.

Methionine deserves special consideration as it is an important source of methyl groups. Through a reaction with ATP *S*-adenosyl methionine is formed. In this compound the methyl group bound to a positively charged sulfur atom is labile and can be transferred in a large number of possible reactions to various methyl acceptors. For instance, choline and creatine are formed through methylation of ethanolamine and guanidoacetic acid, respectively.

D. *End-products of nitrogen metabolism*

Obviously the nitrogen supplied in the food to the adult animal organism must be eliminated again in some way. Several nitrogen-containing substances are excreted in the urine. Quantitatively most important among these is urea which is formed nearly exclusively in the liver. A cyclic reaction in which ornithine functions as a catalytic carrier is responsible for the process as originally discovered by Krebs and Henseleit (1932). Much subsequent work has revealed the details of this reaction (Hall and Cohen, 1957; see also the reviews by Ratner, 1954 and Meister, 1965). The urea cycle may be formulated as a sequence of four reactions leading to synthesis of arginine from ornithine, followed by the hydrolysis of arginine to ornithine and urea, see equations (15)–(19).

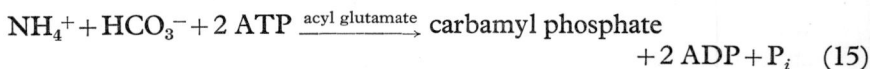

$$NH_4^+ + HCO_3^- + 2\,ATP \xrightarrow{\text{acyl glutamate}} \text{carbamyl phosphate}$$
$$+ 2\,ADP + P_i \qquad (15)$$

ornithine + carbamyl phosphate →citrulline + P_i (16)

citrulline + aspartate + ATP →argininosuccinate + AMP + PP   (17)

argininosuccinate →fumarate + arginine   (18)

arginine + H_2O →*ornithine* + urea   (19)

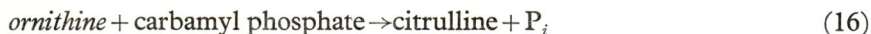

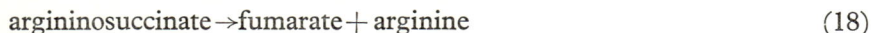

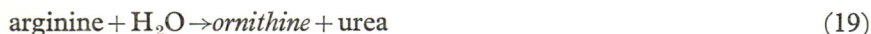

In the net process therefore one nitrogen atom from ammonia and one from aspartate are used for production of one molecule of urea. The equivalent of four molecules of ATP are hydrolyzed in this reaction.

Ammonium ion is a toxic substance, which is effectively kept at a very low concentration level by carbamyl phosphate synthesis in combination with glutamine formation. Ammonia is formed in other reactions than glutamate dehydrogenation. Some amino acids (e.g. serine, threonine, and histidine) are metabolized in special reactions which directly produce ammonia. Also amino acid oxydases, flavoproteins which transform amino acids to oxoacids and ammonia in an aerobic reaction are present in the liver. However, these reactions are believed to be of minor importance. Apart from amino acid metabolism, ammonia is also produced by deamination and oxydation of several substances belonging to other chemical groups (mono-amines, diamines and nucleotides).

Urea is not the sole waste-product of nitrogen metabolism. In man the metabolism of the purine groups in nucleic acid and nucleotides are irreversibly transformed to uric acid. Also creatine which is partially synthesized in the liver cells is irreversibly transformed to a waste-product, creatinine. This reaction occurs predominantly in muscles.

E. *Protein metabolism*

The liver liberates large amounts of protein into the blood, as it is responsible for the synthesis of nearly all plasma proteins except immuno-globulins (see Tarver, 1963). A rough estimate of the daily production may be arrived at from knowledge of the size of the protein pool, which is replenished, and from the average half-life of the proteins in question. Assuming that proteins produced in the liver constitute 4% of the plasma protein content, and that equal quantities of these proteins are found in the intra- and extravascular space, and furthermore that their average half-life is 10 days, a value of about 40 g of protein per day in a human subject is arrived at. To this must be added the turn-over of the liver proteins themselves, largely enzymes, which may easily amount to a similar figure, as the half-life of many of these proteins seems to be con-siderably shorter than that of most plasma proteins (see Tarver, 1963).

In a steady state the rate of breakdown of protein must equal the rate of synthesis. Protein breakdown is a process of which surprisingly little is known compared to the very detailed information now available on protein synthesis. The presence of proteolytic enzymes in the lysosomes has been taken as evidence that breakdown is in some way related to these cell organelles. However, detailed studies of a quantitative nature are lacking, and it is in fact not known whether the proteolytic enzymes of the lysosomes are able to hydrolyse completely (i.e. to amino acids) the proteins occurring in the cell.

VII. Specialized Metabolic Processes in Liver Cells

Several group specific chemical reactions which take place predominantly or exclusively in liver cells have been collectively labelled detoxication processes.

A number of normal intermediary metabolites are toxic to the organism. They are converted to less toxic substances or are easily eliminated. Examples are bilirubin (which is conjugated with glucuronic acid), ammonia, several hormones or transmitter substances (e.g. serotonin, epinephrine, steroids and others).

Processes similar to those involved in many physiological metabolic reactions may occur with compounds which are completely foreign to the organism. Such substances are often metabolized by reactions, which are known also to take place in normal metabolism, but it appears that generally the enzymes involved are not identical with those responsible for the normal processes. It should be mentioned that "detoxication" processes may lead to compounds, which are in fact more toxic than the parent substance (see Shuster, 1964). Only some of the characteristic types of specialized reactions will be considered here.

A. *Oxydative reactions*

Even very inert substances like hydrocarbons may be successfully attacked by liver enzymes. A very important reaction in this connection seems to be hydroxylation, which takes place in smooth endoplasmatic reticulum. This type of reaction quite generally turns out to obey the following scheme

$$RH + O_2 + NADPH + H^+ \rightarrow ROH + H_2O + NADP^+ \qquad (20)$$

Probably NADPH may be substituted by other reducing substances in certain cases. A number of apparently unrelated reactions are known to follow this scheme such as hydroxylation of aromatic rings, oxydation of side chains, sulfoxide formation, dealkylation, and others (see Brodie et al., 1958). Different enzymes are probably required for each of the different types of reaction.

Hydroxyl compounds may be further oxidized to ketones or aldehydes by means of alcohol dehydrogenases. One such enzyme is the NAD^+-requiring cytoplasmic enzyme which is responsible for the metabolism of ethanol. The metabolism of this compound serves as an example of a substance which is not normally encountered in food, yet in the case of man, it is efficiently utilized for energy production. In fact more than half the basal energy requirement of the human organism may be met through the complete oxidation of ethanol. Here ethanol is, however, unique among the known "toxic" substances.

Aldehydes are efficiently oxidized in liver. At least two enzyme systems are known to catalyse such processes. One is a NAD^+-requiring enzyme probably responsible for most physiological aldehyde oxidation reactions including that of acetaldehyde and glyceraldehyde. The products of this reaction are the corresponding carboxylic acids. Several flavoprotein enzymes are also capable of oxidizing aldehydes.

B. *Methylation and dealkylation*

Transfer of methyl groups from methionine to various acceptors with formation of *N*-methyl and *O*-methyl compounds has already been mentioned. Methylation of a large number of drugs and other foreign substances have been demonstrated to occur in liver. The reverse process, removal of methyl or other alkyl groups are also known to occur, but through an entirely different reaction mechanism, possibly involving the intermediate formation of hydroxylation products.

C. *Conjugation*

Some of the first well defined detoxication products described were the glucuronic acid conjugates and sulfate esters which are excreted in the urine after ingestion of various phenols and other substances. Again this kind of reaction also occurs with normal physiological intermediates (steroid hormones and bilirubin), although probably different enzymes are involved in most cases.

1. *Glucuronide formation*

UDPGA, the active form of glucuronic acid (see Section III. F) is used as a donor of glucuronosyl groups in the formation of glucuronides. The glucosidic linkage is established between the 1-carbon of the glucuronic acid and hydroxyl groups, amino groups (especially aromatic amines), and carboxyl groups (forming ester-type glucuronides). Substances which are lipophilic are in this way made more water soluble through introduction of the carbohydrate chain in connection with the carboxyl group.

2. *Sulfate ester formation*

The immediate donor of the acyl group in sulfate ester synthesis is also an active coenzyme compound. In this case 3'-phosphoadenosine-5'-phosphosulfate (PAPS) is the precursor of sulfate esters of alcohols and phenols, and also to a small extent, of sulfamides. PAPS is produced from inorganic sulfate through a two-step reaction requiring two molecules of ATP. The quantitative importance of sulfate ester formation appears to be much smaller than that of glucuronide conjugation.

D. Mercapturic acid formation

A remarkable reaction is utilized for the elimination of aromatic hydro-carbons and their derivatives viz., formation of mercapturic acid, aryl S-substituted N-acetyl cysteine. The mechanism of this reaction may be quite complicated, possibly involving an initial reaction with glutathione (Al-Kassab *et al.*, 1963). The glutathione compound is subsequently hydrolyzed, with formation of mercapturic acid.

The number of detoxication pathways is far from exhausted. Reduction of nitro- and azo-compounds may take place; conjugation with different amino acids, for instance, the formation of hippuric acid after administra-tion of benzoic acid, and several other reactions are known to be located in the liver cells.

VIII. Organization and Integration of Liver Cell Metabolism: Hormones

Liver cells may be considered characteristic mammalian cells on the basis of their anatomical structure. Their many metabolic potentialities are realized through a complex interplay of the various sub-cellular organelles and the *cytosol*. *The nucleus* provides the information necessary for the synthesis of enzymes. The synthesis of protein is carried out predominantly by the *endoplasmic reticulum* of the rough surface type. These membranes are characterized by the presence of ribosomes, the particles directly responsible for the synthesis of peptide chains from amino acids attached to specific, low molecular weight ribonucleic acid molecules, transfer RNA (tRNA). The sequence of amino acids in the peptide chain is deter-mined from the nucleotide sequence of another kind of nucleic acid, messenger RNA (mRNA), which functions as a connecting link between the information store of the nucleus and the synthetic machinery of the ribo-somes. The details of protein synthesis are more or less identical in all types of cells and these will not be considered here (see Chapter 8 in Vol. 1).

The *mitochondria*, which are present in abundance in liver cells, are the main source of energy utilizable in metabolic processes. These organelles carry as their most important component a highly organized multi-enzyme system, the respiratory chain, which permits the oxidation of hydrogen equivalents from various substrates by molecular oxygen. The oxidation is performed step-wise and a sizeable part of the free energy of this reaction is conserved as ATP in the process of oxidative phosphorylation.

Another organelle apparently with little internal structure are the lysosomes, which are spherical bodies containing a number of hydrolytic enzymes. The mechanism of action of lysosomes is disputed, but there is little doubt that they play a role in the degradation of cell components, which have in some way deteriorated.

Other biochemically well-defined particles include the *peroxisomes* (microbodies) which seem to be specifically equipped to perform peroxydations. They contain besides other enzymes catalase, D-amino acid oxydases, and urate oxydase (Baudhuin *et al.*, 1965).

The *endoplasmic* reticulum of the smooth surface type is the site of a large number of characteristic liver enzymes. Among these may be mentioned glucose-6-phosphatase, most of the detoxicating enzymes (hydroxylases, conjugating enzymes, and others), the enzymes responsible for sulfur metabolism, cholesterol synthesis and synthesis of a number of other lipids.

The *cytosol* contains many important enzyme systems such as those responsible for the complete glycolytic sequence from glycogen to pyruvate and all the enzymes catalyzing the reverse processes leading to glycogen. Also the enzymes of the pentose phosphate cycle are present in the cytosol and likewise a number of enzymes involved in amino acid metabolism.

Our understanding of the integration of cell metabolism, in which all of these structures play a part is far from complete. However, some features have been intensively studied in recent years (see for instance the series of volumes, *Advances in Enzyme Regulation*, started by G. Weber in 1963).

A. *Regulation of energy metabolism*

The elementary question, "Why does the metabolism of the cell not run wild when many substrates are present in abundance?", has found a preliminary answer as the result of the important discovery by Lardy and Wellman (1952) of "respiratory control". These workers observed that when mitochondria are very carefully isolated, so as to avoid damage, they respire at a very low rate, even in the presence of excess substrate if ADP is not present in the medium. As soon as ADP is added or formed through hydrolysis of ATP, respiration increases by a factor of 5–10 until the ADP is nearly completely converted to ATP. Through this mechanism the details of which are still obscure, the oxidation of reduced coenzymes and prosthetic groups keep pace with the needs of the cell. When large amounts of ATP are required, respiration increases to keep the concentration of this coenzyme constant.

In general the NADH utilized for generation of ATP is produced inside the mitochondria from the individual processes in the tricarboxylic acid cycle and from the initial steps in the oxydation of fatty acids, but NADH and some other substrates produced in the extramitochondrial compartment of the cell may also be oxidized by the mitochondria. Certain problems thus arise, as NADH does not readily penetrate the mitochondrial membrane. Presumably a cyclic carrier system is used as illustrated in Fig. 11.

Such a carrier system may also be used in the opposite direction to generate reduced coenzymes in the extramitochondrial compartment for use in synthetic processes such as the synthesis of hexoses from phosphoenol pyruvate or other precursors requiring reduction. Also in the synthesis of fatty acids, cholesterol and many other substances, a reducing substance is needed. For such reductions, however, it seems to be a rule that the co-enzyme, NADPH is used in preference to NADH. The standard redox potentials of these systems are nearly identical, but the concentration of the free (i.e. not the protein-bound) NADPH in the cytosol is very much higher than the concentration of free NADH. In this way the equilibrium of many cytoplasmic reactions which require NADPH will be in favour of reduction.

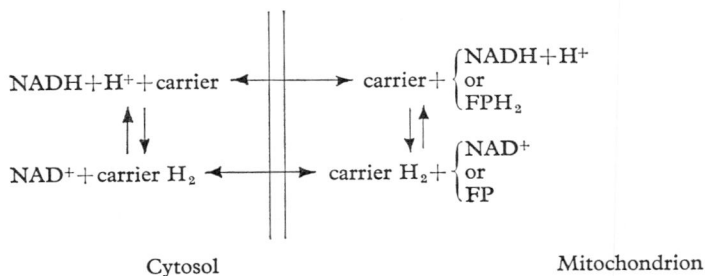

FIG. 11. The transport of hydrogen equivalents between mitochondria and the extra-mitochondrial compartments. FP denotes flavoprotein enzymes, which react directly with the carrier substance without the intervention of nicotinamide coenzymes.

It appears that the two systems, NAD/NADH and NADP/NADPH, are poised at different redox levels largely independently of each other. Trans-hydrogenation reactions realized by substrates which may react with both coenzymes (see equation 21–23) have been demonstrated, but obviously the activity of the enzymes catalysing such reactions is too low to establish equilibrium.

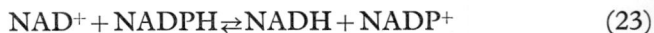

$$NAD^+ + AH_2 \rightleftharpoons NADH + H^+ + A \tag{21}$$

$$A + NADPH + H^+ \rightleftharpoons NADP^+ + AH_2 \tag{22}$$

$$NAD^+ + NADPH \rightleftharpoons NADH + NADP^+ \tag{23}$$

B. *Hormones*

Regulation of enzymatic reactions may occur at different levels ranging from simple inhibition of a reaction by the reaction product, to regulation of the rate of synthesis or breakdown of the enzyme molecule itself (see Fig. 12).

Some regulatory features regarding the feedback inhibition and activation of individual enzyme reactions by means of end-products of reaction chains have already been mentioned. Feedback to other points in the series of events leading to an active enzyme (see Fig. 12) seems to be caused largely by the action of hormones produced in other organs.

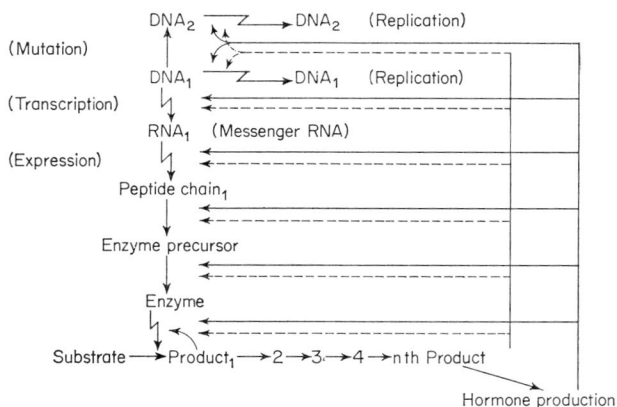

FIG. 12. Feedback regulation at various points in the production and function of an enzyme. Straight arrows represent chemical reactions and the lightning symbols represent "directing and organizing influence". (Modified after Potter, 1963.)

C. *The role of cyclic AMP*

The action of a number of hormones have been demonstrated in recent years to take place through a "second messenger" (see Sutherland *et al.*, 1967), the production or removal of which inside the target cell is influenced by the hormone in question. One such "messenger system" which has been found in a variety of organs is cyclic 3'5'-AMP. This substance is synthesized from ATP and may be inactivated by hydrolysis of the 3'-phosphate bond. Both processes seem to be influenced by hormones.

In the case of the liver, cyclic AMP production is accelerated by glucagon and epinephrine. Increased concentration of cyclic AMP triggers glycogen breakdown and inhibits glycogen synthesis through a complicated chain of reactions, resulting in the transformation of an inactive form of an enzyme into an active form, or *vice versa*. Even a tertiary messenger effect of hormone activity may be observed. The influence of increased concentration of unesterified fatty acids on a number of reactions in the carbohydrate metabolism of the liver (see Fig. 6) may be the consequence of hormones (e.g. epinephrine) increasing adipose tissue cyclic AMP concentration, which in turn causes increased lipolysis, or a similar effect of increased lipolysis in the liver itself (Bewsher and Ashmore, 1966).

Through these direct and indirect actions epinephrine and glucagon increase the glucose output of the liver. The opposite reaction, increased uptake and deposition of glucose, is caused by insulin. Some of the reactions responsible for this overall reaction may be mediated through a decrease in cyclic AMP concentration. The situation here is, however, probably more complex (Shrago *et al.*, 1967).

K

D. *Rate of enzyme production and degradation*

Some hormonal actions are undoubtedly caused by interference with the turn-over rate of enzyme protein. Thus the activating effect of gluco-corticoid hormones on some of the key enzymes in gluconeogenesis and on certain transaminases has been shown to be caused by an increased level of the enzyme protein brought about by induction (see the review by Seubert, 1967).

Treatment with insulin also causes a change in activity of certain enzymes. Glucokinase and glucose-6-phosphate dehydrogenase are thus increased in activity some time after insulin treatment, while the enzyme activities concerned with gluconeogenesis are decreased, presumably because of repression of enzyme synthesis.

Other hormones are also believed to function through an influence on protein synthesis and breakdown. This is very evident in the case of thyroxine, which has been shown to have a pronounced effect on the activity of some liver enzymes. For instance, the activity of glycerophosphate oxidase in liver mitochondria is increased by a factor of 10 or more through treatment with tri-iodo-thyronine (Lee and Lardy, 1965).

References

Al-Kassab, S., Boyland, E. and Williams, K. (1963). *Biochem. J.* **87**, 4-9.
Arion, W. J. and Nordlie, R. C. (1964). *J. biol. Chem.* **239**, 2752-2757.
Ashmore, J. and Weber, G. (1968). In *Carbohydrate Metabolism and Its Disorders* (F. Dickens, P. J. Randle and W. J. Whelan, eds), Vol. 1, pp. 336-374. Academic Press, London.
Ashwell, G., Kanfer, J., Smiley, J. D. and Burns, J. J. (1961). *Ann. N.Y. Acad. Sci.* **92**, 105-114.
Atkinson, D. E. (1965). *Science, N.Y.* **150**, 851-857.
Baudhuin, P., Beaufay, H. and deDuve, C. (1965). *J. Cell Biol.* **26**, 219-243.
Bearn, A. G., Billing, B. H. and Sherlock, S. (1952). *Clin. Sci.* **11**, 151-165.
Bergström, S. and Danielsson, H. (1963). In *The Control of Lipid Metabolism* (J. K. Grant, ed.), pp. 63-72. Academic Press, London and New York.
Bewsher, P. O. and Ashmore, J. (1966). *Biochem. biophys. Res. Comm.* **24**, 431-436.
Brodie, B. B., Gillette, J. R. and LaDu, B. N. (1958). *A. Rev. Biochem.* **27**, 427-454.
Cahill, G. F. and Owen, O. E. (1968). In *Carbohydrate Metabolism and its Disorders* (F. Dickens, P. J. Randle and W. J. Whelan, eds), Vol. 1, pp. 497-522. Academic Press, London.
Cuatrecasas, P. and Segal, S. (1965). *J. biol. Chem.* **240**, 2382-2388.
De Wulf, H. and Hers, H. G. (1967). *Europ. J. Biochem.* **2**, 50-56.
Dodgson, K. S. and Lloyd, A. G. (1968). In *Carbohydrate Metabolism and its Disorders* (F. Dickens, P. J. Randle and W. J. Whelan, eds), Vol. 1, pp. 169-207. Academic Press, London.
Eiseman, B. (1967). In *The Liver* (A. E. Read, ed.), Colsten Papers No. 19, pp. 279-285, Butterworths, London.
Ferdinand, W. (1966). *Biochem. J.* **98**, 278-283.
Friedman, D. L. and Larner, J. (1965). *Biochemistry* **4**, 2261-2264.
Friedmann, T. and Epstein, C. J. (1967). *Biochem. biophys. Acta* **138**, 622-624.
Fritz, I. B. (1961). *Physiol. Rev.* **41**, 52-114.
Gardner, D. A. and Kay, E. R. M. (1967). *Experientia* **23**, 596-597.
Green, C. and Webb, J. A. (1964). *Biochem. biophys. Acta* **84**, 404-411.

Hall, L. M. and Cohen, P. P. (1957). *J. biol. Chem.* **229**, 345-349.

Hanson, P. G., Johnson, R. E. and Zaharko, D. S. (1965). *Metabolism* **14**, 1037-1040.

Hayek, D. H. and Tipton, S. R. (1966). *J. Cell Biol.* **29**, 405-409.

Henion, W. F. and Sutherland, E. W. (1957). *J. biol. Chem.* **224**, 477-488.

Henley, K. S., Sorensen, O. and Pollard, H. M. (1959). *Nature, Lond.* **184**, 1400.

Higgins, J. A. and Green, C. (1966). *Biochem. J.* **99**, 631-639.

Horecker, B. L. (1968). In *Carbohydrate Metabolism and its Disorders* (F. Dickens, P. J. Randle and W. J. Whelan, eds), Vol. 1, pp. 139-163. Academic Press, London.

Jacob, S. T. and Bhargava, P. M. (1962). *Expl Cell Res.* **27**, 453-467.

Katz, J. and Wood, H. G. (1960). *J. biol. Chem.* **235**, 2165-2177.

Katz, J. and Wood, H. G. (1963). *J. biol. Chem.* **238**, 517-523.

Katz, J., Landau, B. R. and Bartsch, G. E. (1966). *J. biol. Chem.* **241**, 727-740.

Krebs, H. A. (1965). *Fed. Eur. Biochem. Soc. Abstr.*, pp. 351-361. Vienna.

Krebs, H. A. and Henseleit, K. (1932). *Hoppe-Seyler's Z. physiol. Chem.* **210**, 33-66.

Krebs, H. A. and Kornberg, H. L. (1957). *Ergebn. Physiol.* **49**, 212-298.

Kruhøffer, P. and Muntz, J. A. (1954). *Acta physiol. scand.* **30**, 258-274.

Landau, B. R. and Bartsch, G. E. (1966). *J. biol. Chem.* **241**, 741-749.

Lardy, H. A. and Wellman, H. (1952). *J. biol. Chem.* **195**, 215-224.

Lee, Y. P. and Lardy, H. A. (1965). *J. biol. Chem.* **240**, 1427-1436.

Leloir, L. F. and Cardini, C. E. (1957). *J. Am. chem. Soc.* **79**, 6340-6341.

Levine, R. and Fritz, I. B. (1956). *Diabetes* **5**, 209-219.

Lowry, O. H. and Passonneau, J. V. (1966). *J. biol. Chem.* **241**, 2268-2279.

Lundquist, F., Tygstrup, N., Winkler, K., Mellemgaard, K. and Munch-Petersen, S. (1962). *J. clin. Invest.* **41** , 955-961.

Meister, A. (1965). *Biochemistry of the Amino Acids*. Vols. 1 and 2, Second ed., Academic Press, New York.

Moulé, Y. and Chauveau, J. (1963). In *The Liver* (Ch. Rouiller, ed.), Vol. 1, pp. 379-427. Academic Press, New York.

Parry, M. J. and Walker, D. G. (1966). *Biochem. J.* **99**, 266-274.

Pontis, H. G. (1955). *J. biol. Chem.* **216**, 195-202.

Popják, G. and Cornforth, J. W. (1960). *Adv. Enzymol.* **22**, 281-335.

Potter, V. R. (1963). *Advances in Enzyme Regulation*, Vol. 1, 279-308.

Rall, T. W., Sutherland, E. W. and Wosilait, W. D. (1956). *J. biol. Chem.* **218**, 483-495.

Ross, B. D., Hems, R. and Krebs, A. A. (1967). *Biochem. J.* **102**, 942.

Ratner, S. (1954). *Adv. Enzymol.* **15**, 320-383.

Schimassek, H. (1968). In *Stoffwechsel der isoliert perfundierten Leber* (W. Staib and R. Scholz, eds), pp. 1-10. Springer-Verlag, Berlin.

Seubert, W. (1967). In *Wirkungsmechanismen der Hormone* (P. Karlson, ed.), pp. 158-191. Springer-Verlag, Berlin.

Shapiro, B. (1967). *A. Rev. Biochem.* **36**, 247-270.

Shepherd, D., Yates, D. W. and Garland, P. B. (1966). *Biochem. J.* **98**, 3c-4c.

Shrago, E., Young, J. W. and Lardy, H. A. (1967). *Science, N.Y.* **158**, 1572-1573.

Shuster, L. (1964). *A. Rev. Biochem.* **33**, 571-592.

Sols, A. (1968). In *Carbohydrate Metabolism and its Disorders*. (F. Dickens, P. J. Randle and W. J. Whelan, eds), Vol. 1, pp. 53-83. Academic Press, London.

Srere, P. A. (1967). *Science, N.Y.* **158**, 936.

Staib, W. and Scholz, R. (eds) (1968). *Stoffwechsel der isoliert perfundierten Leber*. Springer-Verlag, Berlin.

Sutherland, E. W. (1956). *Proc. IIIrd Int. Congr. Biochem.*, pp. 318-327.

Sutherland, E. W., Butcher, R. W., Robison, G. A. and Hardman, J. G. (1967). In *Wirkungsmechanismen der Hormone* (P. Karlson, ed.), pp. 1-29. Springer-Verlag, Berlin.

Tarver, H. (1963). In *The Liver* (Ch. Rouiller, ed.), Vol. 1, pp. 450-548. Academic Press, London.

Tygstrup, N. (1964). *Acta med. scand.* **175**, 291-300.

Tygstrup, N., Winkler, K. and Lundquist, F. (1965). *J. clin. Invest.* **44**, 817-830.

Verhue, W. and Hers, H. G. (1966). *Biochem. J.* **99**, 222-227.

Weber, G., Lea, M. A., Convery, H. J. H. and Stamm, N. B. (1967). *Adv. Enz. Regul.* **5**, 212-298.

Williamson, J. R., Kreisberg, R. A. and Felts, P. W. (1966). *Proc. natn. Acad. Sci. U.S.A.* **56**, 247-254.

Wood, J. L. and Cooley, S. L. (1954). *Proc. Soc. exp. Biol. Med.* **85**, 409-411.

CHAPTER 7

The Metabolism of Bilirubin

ROGER LESTER* and ROBERT F. TROXLER

*Department of Medicine, Boston University School of Medicine,
Boston, Massachusetts, U.S.A.*

I. Introduction

The study of bilirubin metabolism was made possible by the monumental work of Hans Fischer and his colleagues, who established the structural relationship between bilirubin and heme. The discovery that bilirubin is excreted in bile as the glucuronide conjugate provided a new impetus for research in this field. Not until the early 1960s, however, when isotopically labeled bilirubin became readily available, could many of the important problems regarding normal and aberrant bilirubin metabolism be subjected to sophisticated biochemical and physiological analysis.

The subject-matter of this chapter includes a description of the chemistry, biosynthesis and metabolism of bile pigments, and of those forms of hyperbilirubinemia produced by metabolic defects. The older literature is thoroughly covered in the monographs of Lemberg and Legge (1949), Gray (1961) and With (1967). Some of the concepts and terminology, notably those of the chemistry and biosynthesis of bile pigments, whilst

* Recipient of U.S.P.H.S. Career Development Award 12,127.

admittedly abstruse, have been simplified in the following discussion and it is hoped that the original observations have not been distorted in the process. Studies of bilirubin metabolism have so accelerated in recent years that treatment of the subject is selective rather than complete.

II. Chemistry of Bile Pigments

The bile pigments are composed of four pyrrole rings linked to one another by carbon bridges (Fig. 1). The β-carbons (i.e. the two carbons in

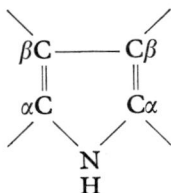

FIG. 1. Skeleton of a pyrrole ring. In both porphyrins and bile pigments the ring carbons are designated α and β.

each ring most distant from the nitrogen) have side-chain substituents, while carbonyl groups ($> C = O$) are attached to the α-carbons of the outer pyrrole rings. Bile pigments are usually referred to as "linear" open-chain tetrapyrroles. Although the linear formula is a more convenient representation, a "U" shaped configuration better represents the physical state of the molecule in non-polar organic solvents. The formulas of bilirubin and protoporphyrin (Fig. 2) illustrate the close structural relationship between the open-chain bile pigments, and their precursors, the cyclic porphyrins.

In general, bile pigments differ in the number and position of methyne ($=CH-$) and methene ($-CH_2-$) bridges connecting pyrrole rings, in the degree of oxidation or reduction of the pyrrole rings, and in the nature of side chains located on the β-carbons of the pyrrole rings. Porphyrins and bile

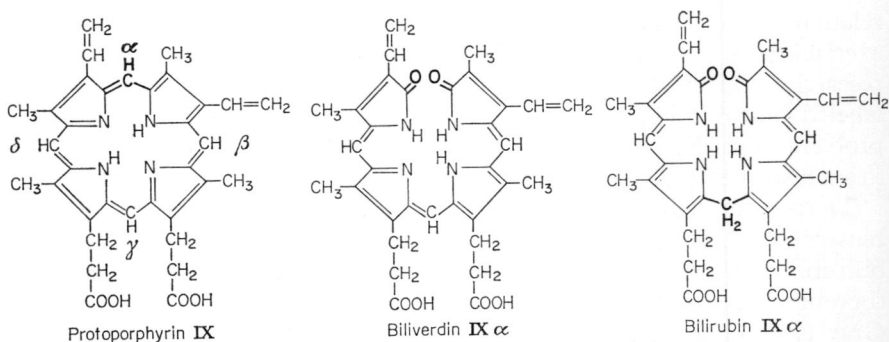

Protoporphyrin IX   Biliverdin IX α Bilirubin IX α

FIG. 2. Structural relationship between porphyrin and bile pigments. The differences between the molecules are represented in bold-faced type. The four bridge carbons of porphyrins are designated α, β, γ, and δ.

pigments are classified according to the order of their side-chains. In naturally occurring bile pigments this order is constant and has been given the designation "IXα" because the α-bridge carbon of protoporphyrin IX is eliminated during their formation. Bile pigment color is conferred by the resonance of electrons in those parts of the molecule (the "chromophore") with alternating double and single bonds (—C=C—C=C—C=). A decrease in the number of these "conjugated" double bonds in the chromophore produces a shift in the absorption maximum of pigment from longer to shorter wavelengths of visible light. For example, the conversion of biliverdin to bilirubin by reduction of a key double bond at the central methyne bridge interrupts the resonating chromophore at its midpoint and shifts the absorption maximum of pigment in chloroform from 640 mμ (green) to 450 mμ (yellow), respectively.

A. *Quantitation of bilirubin*

Bilirubin concentrations can be determined by measuring the optical density of a solution at the absorption maximum of the pigment. Plasma, bile, urine and tissues contain other substances with similar spectra, however, and so the practical applicability of this method is limited. Bilirubin can be oxidized to green or purple bile pigment derivatives for colorimetric assay (Gray, 1953). With the most widely employed techniques the bilirubin molecule is ruptured at its central bridge, and the two dipyrrolic halves are coupled with diazotized sulfanilic acid (Malloy and Evelyn, 1937). Bilirubin diglucuronide reacts rapidly and directly with diazotized sulfanilic acid, while unconjugated bilirubin (the free acid) reacts only after the addition of "accelerator" substances. A correlation, sufficiently good for most clinical purposes, exists between the "direct-reacting" bilirubin and the actual concentrations of conjugated bilirubin (Fevery et al., 1967). When necessary, improved methods for the fractional estimation of conjugated bilirubin are available (Weber and Schalm, 1962).

The mechanism of the "direct" and "indirect" reactions is uncertain. It is no longer accepted that the conjugate reacts "directly", solely because of its water solubility. Intramolecular hydrogen bonding occurs in urobilins between the carbonyl oxygens of the outer pyrrole rings and the pyrrole ring nitrogens (Moscowitz et al., 1964). One explanation for the "direct" and "indirect" diazo reaction has been based on analogous intramolecular associations in bilirubin. It has been postulated that in unconjugated bilirubin, hydrogen bonding between the carboxyl groups of the propionic acid side-chains and the pyrrole ring nitrogens interferes with reactivity of the central methene (—CH$_2$—) group, the group attacked by diazotized sulfanilic acid (Fog and Jellum, 1963). Substances which disrupt hydrogen bonds (e.g. alcohol, 6 M urea) "accelerate" the diazo reaction for unconjugated bilirubin. Esterification of the bilirubin carboxyls with glucuronic acid also would disrupt interaction between the side-chain carboxyls and the pyrrole nitrogens. It is postulated that glucuronide formation would, therefore, permit a "direct" diazo reaction without the addition of "accelerator" substances. It is of interest to note that the pyrrolic derivative, mesobilirubin, like bilirubin, reacts with diazotized sulfanilic acid only after the addition of an "accelerator". A synthetic dimethyl mesobilirubin can be prepared in which the carboxyls are esterified with methyl groups. Thus, this synthetic compound resembles the ester, bilirubin diglucuronide. Unlike the natural conjugate of bilirubin, however, dimethyl mesobilirubin is extremely insoluble in water. That it reacts *directly* with diazotized sulfanilic acid (R. Lester, unpublished results) is a finding which would be anticipated if the carboxyl groups on the side-chains of mesobilirubin were involved in intramolecular bonding with the pyrrole ring nitrogens. Esterification of the acid moiety would break intramolecular bonding, and thereby enhance the rate of reaction.

B. *Quantitation of urobilins*

A few years ago, only three urobilins and their corresponding urobilinogens were thought to occur naturally (Fig. 3). The "d-", "i-" and "l-" urobilins were known to be similar but non-isomeric, with molecular weights of 589, 591 and 595 respectively (Watson, 1963). Spectrophotometric methods were devised for the identification of individual members of this series (Watson and Weimer, 1959), and more recently chromatographic and electrophoretic methods have been applied to their isolation (Royer *et al.*, 1964; Lozzio *et al.*, 1964).

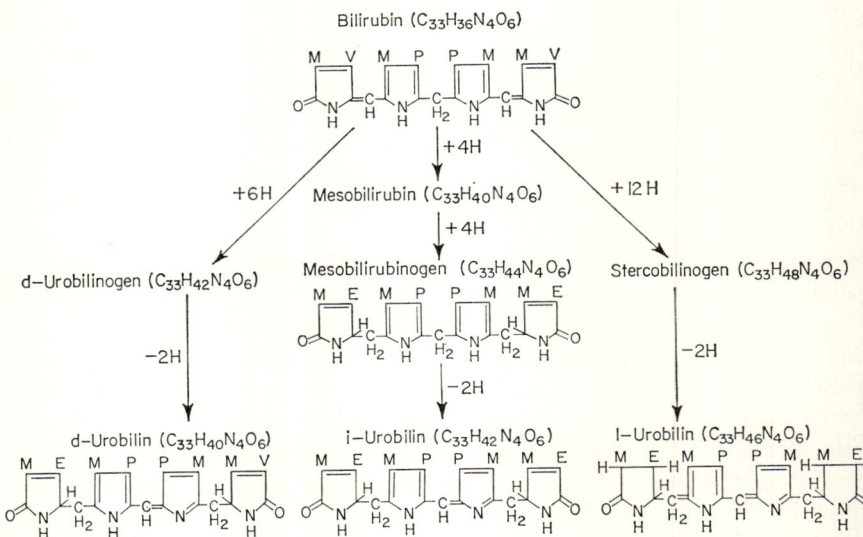

FIG. 3. Schematic representation of bile pigment derivatives according to the classical formulation. The molecular weight of bilirubin$=585$; d-urobilin$=589$; i-urobilin$=591$; $l=$urobilin$=595$. As noted in the text, recent studies indicate the existence of a host of urobilin and urobilinogen variants.

The use of modern physical-chemical techniques, however, has made it possible to identify at least ten distinct urobilins (Nicholson, 1967). The "i-urobilin" (molecular weight, 591), obtained from patients previously on broad spectrum antibiotics, has been separated into d- and l-components, that is, isomeric pigments which rotate polarized light in a dextro and laevorotatory manner; an l-form of "d-urobilin" (molecular weight, 589) and a d-form of "l-urobilin" (molecular weight, 595) have also been identified.

The optical activity of the urobilins results from the presence of centers of molecular asymmetry. Asymmetry is introduced by the geometric configuration of the pyrrole rings (the central rings lie in different planes), by asymmetric relations between the two outer rings and the two central rings, and by the presence of asymmetric carbons within the outer rings (Cole et al., 1965, 1966). The possibilities for steroisomerism are, therefore, exceedingly great. Indeed, the stereochemistry of one urobilin alone may prove to be enormously complex. The large number of asymmetric centers in stercobilin potentially permit this molecule to assume 64 isomeric forms (Nicholson, 1967). Moreover, the possibility has been raised that the three classical forms of urobilin are not homogeneous compounds, but mixtures of distinct molecules with similar properties but slightly differing molecular weight (Jackson et al., 1966; Watson et al., 1966). Part of this heterogeneity may be experimental artifact, but the conclusion is inescapable that the classification of urobilins is much more complex than had previously been conceived.

Techniques used in clinical practice do not distinguish among variants, but measure the sum of all urobilins or urobilinogens present in urine or feces. Our own experience and that of others (Henry et al., 1964) suggests that the Ehrlich reaction is at best nonspecific and semi-quantitative. An alternative method devised by Lozzio and Royer (1962) is based on the old Schlesinger reaction (see Gray, 1953, p. 23) which relies on the ability of several classes of bile pigment to form spectrally distinct complexes with divalent metal ions. The structural prerequisite for metal complex formation is the presence of (or the ability to form by isomerization or proton displacement) two free pyrrole ring nitrogens lacking protons within the tetrapyrrole (i.e. $\diagdown$N$\diagup$, as versus the protonated form, $\begin{smallmatrix} \diagdown\text{N}\diagup \\ | \\ \text{H} \end{smallmatrix}$). Bilirubin participates in weak complexes with zinc (ÓCarra, 1962), presumably because pyrrole ring nitrogen positions are freed by keto-enol shifts of protons to the outer carbonyl groups. Urobilin forms stronger zinc complexes than bilirubin, and the metal imposes a rigid configuration on the molecule (Fig. 4). These changes in the urobilin molecule are reflected in spectral shifts to longer wavelengths and a diminishing of optical rotation of polarized light (Cole et al., 1965, 1966). In addition, an intense green fluorescence is emitted by the urobilin zinc complex in methanol, which permits the measurement of extremely small concentrations of the pigment.

Lozzio has used this property for the estimation of urobilin in plasma, but the method has not yet been applied widely enough to provide a complete assessment of its accuracy.

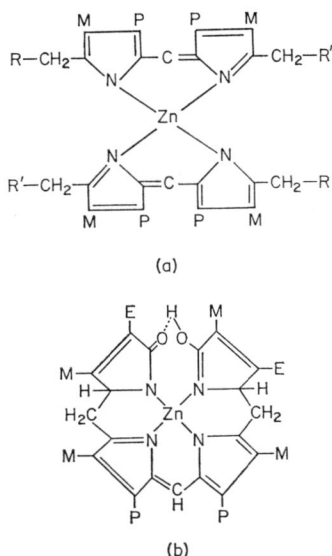

(a)

(b)

FIG. 4. Zinc complex formation with urobilin. Alternative structures are shown in (a) urobulin-Zn complex (2:1) and (b) urobilin-Zn complex (1:1). Potentially, an ion of zinc might complex with two molecules of urobilin as depicted in (a) or with one molecule as depicted in (b) (see Cole et al., 1965, 1966).

C. Bile pigment structure

Our present view of the structure of bile pigments is largely based on the ingenious but relatively crude syntheses of these pigments from simple organic constituents which were performed at the turn of the century (Fischer and Orth, 1937). Studies of the structure of certain plant and synthetic bile pigments with infrared and nuclear magnetic resonance spectroscopy, and by mass spectral analysis (Chapman et al., 1967; Cole et al., 1967), have verified most of the older postulates about structure. However, comparable studies of the common mammalian bile pigments would be desirable.

III. Biosynthesis of Bilirubin

The metallo-porphyrin (heme) moiety of hemoglobin is the major source of bile pigment. It accounts for 80–90% of the 200–250 mg of bilirubin produced per day in normal individuals (Watson, 1965). Although it is well established that senescent erythrocytes are destroyed in the reticulo-endothelial system (RES), the widely held belief that heme is degraded at this site (see Harris, 1963) is largely based on inferential evidence in the older literature (Rich, 1925), and the site of bile pigment formation has not been firmly established. Hemoglobin conversion to bilirubin begins within minutes after intravenous administration. The efficiency of conversion depends in part on the size of the hemoglobin load (Ostrow *et al.*, 1962). When large amounts of hemoglobin are administered, it is probable that part of the load is degraded by alternate metabolic pathways other than those yielding bilirubin. The kinetics of heme conversion to bilirubin are similar to those observed for hemoglobin, suggesting that binding to globin is not obligatory for porphyrin ring opening (Snyder and Schmid, 1965). On the other hand, the presence of metal bound to the porphyrin ring probably is essential for bile pigment formation. Metal-free protoporphyrin-IX administered intravenously to dogs is converted to bile pigment slowly and inefficiently (Ibrahim *et al.*, 1966). The small quantities of administered material ultimately excreted as bilirubin probably are first converted from protoporphyrin to heme.

A. *Breakdown of hemoglobin*

The metabolic steps in the conversion of hemoglobin to bilirubin are poorly understood. A number of intermediates between heme and biliverdin have been described, but none has been isolated in pure form, and many have been identified only by their characteristic spectra (Lemberg, 1956). A scheme summarizing the hypothetical intermediates of heme degradation in "model systems" is shown in Fig. 5. It should be noted, however, that

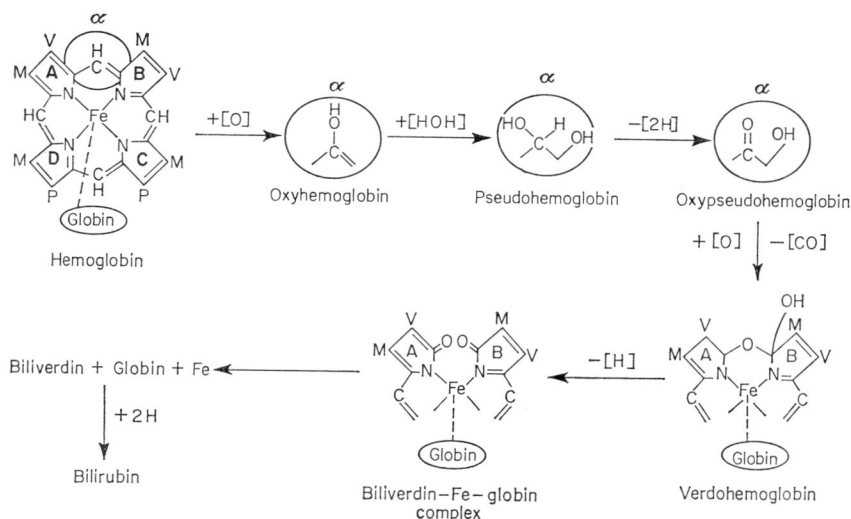

FIG. 5. Hypothetical scheme for the degradation of hemoglobin. For simplification, the bonding between iron and globin is diagrammatic and the valency of iron has been eliminated. The initial stages of hemoglobin oxidation at the α bridge carbon are represented in abbreviated form within circles. During this stage of hemoglobin breakdown the rest of the molecule remains essentially intact.

the scheme is based on *in vitro* studies of the coupled oxidation of hemo-globin (or heme bound to nitrogenous bases) with ascorbic acid (or hydra-zine) performed under aerobic conditions (Lemberg, 1956). The relation of this model system to normal heme metabolism is uncertain. Porphyrin ring opening *in vivo* is thought to proceed via a series of oxidative steps at the α-methyne ($=CH_2-$) bridge carbon. In the model system, however, oxida-tion occurs to some extent at the β, γ, and δ bridge carbons as well (Petryka, 1962). It is postulated that heme molecules at successive stages of oxidation are green and these derivatives are called choleglobins (if bound to proteins) or cholehemes (if bound to nitrogenous bases). The α-methyne bridge carbon is eventually replaced with an oxygen atom in order to form verdo-hemoglobin (or verdoheme), and with the removal of the ether ($-O-$) linkage in this intermediate, verdohemoglobin is converted to biliverdin-iron-globin complex, the unstable end-product of heme oxidation.

Nakajima *et al.* (1963a, b) described an enzyme called "heme-α-methenyl oxygenase", which catalyzed the conversion of hemoglobin-haptoglobin, myoglobin and the dipyridine complex of heme (but not protoporphyrin-IX or alkaline hemin) into a verdoheme-like biliverdin precursor (see Fig. 5). Recent investigations, however, cast doubt on the hypothesis that the reaction ascribed to "heme-α-methenyl oxygenase" is enzymatic since the preparation withstands conditions which regularly eliminate enzymatic activity (Levin, 1967; Murphy *et al.*, 1967). The heme degrading system when prepared by Nakajima's method from pigeon, rat, and beef liver homogenates is unaffected by boiling for 5–15 minutes and successive treatment of the boiled extract by acidification to pH 2·0, neutralization, and oven drying at 150°C. Comparable stability was demonstrated for the verdoheme synthesizing factors isolated from a red alga which normally synthesizes large quantities of a bilirubin-like pigment (Murphy *et al.*, 1967).

On the other hand, the nearly quantitative conversion of heme to bili-verdin precursors by "heme α-methenyl oxygenase" is not characteristic of biliverdin production in the non-enzymatic "model system" described above in which considerably lower yields are generally observed. Moreover, Nakajima and Gray (1967) reported that only the IXα isomer of biliverdin was produced by "heme α-methenyl oxygenase". It is clear from the scheme of heme degradation that this isomer could arise only by removal of the α-bridge carbon of heme. When heme is converted to biliverdin by coupled oxidation with ascorbic acid, mixtures of isomers are obtained, e.g. por-phyrin ring cleavage occurs at all of the bridge carbons (Petryka *et al.*, 1962). In biologic systems, however, oxidative attack at the α-carbon is heavily favored. The fact that biliverdin IXα is the only isomer produced by the degradation of heme with "heme α-methenyl oxygenase" might suggest the relevance of this material to physiologic heme catabolism. However, it must be borne in mind that the methods employed for the identification of biliverdin IXα are not definitive.

Wise and Drabkin (1964) described an enzyme prepared from the "hemophagous organ" of pregnant dogs (an area at the rim of the dog placenta with a heavy deposit of biliverdin) which converted heme-labeled [^{14}C]hemoglobin and [^{14}C]hematin into radiolabeled biliverdin. About 88% of the ^{14}C-labeled biliverdin was identical to the synthetic IXα isomer of this bile pigment. In addition, radioactive carbon monoxide was evolved during product formation (Wise and Drabkin, 1965). This distinguishes the enzyme in the hemophagous organ from "heme α-methenyl oxygenase" in which the α-bridge carbon is eliminated as formaldehyde (Nakajima et al., 1963a, b). It is of interest that Sjöstrand (1949) and Coburn et al. (1966) have reported that the α-bridge carbon of heme in man is liberated as carbon monoxide in vivo. These data suggest that the enzyme in the hemophagous organ of dogs may be more closely related to normal physiological phenomena than "heme α-methenyl oxygenase".

In summary, the metabolic pathways between heme and bilirubin are obscure. The postulated intermediates are based on "model systems" which may not be relevant to events in vivo. Two biologic systems which degrade heme to bilirubin precursors have been described, but the relationship of each to the normal metabolism of hemoglobin has not yet been established.

B. Alternate sources of bile pigment formation

The classic studies of Gray et al. (1950) and London et al. (1950) on bile pigment biogenesis in man demonstrated that 10–20% of the [^{15}N]glycine ultimately incorporated into fecal [^{15}N]urobilinogen appeared in an "early-labeled peak" within several days of isotope administration. It was apparent that "early-labeled" bile pigment could not derive from hemoglobin in circulating erythrocytes directly because the life span of the erythrocyte (and therefore the hemoglobin in it) is about 120 days. Moreover, much of the "early-labeled" [^{15}N]urobilinogen appeared within one week of isotope administration during which time the specific activity of heme in circulating red cell hemoglobin had not yet reached a maximum (Gray et al., 1950; London et al., 1950). In fact, much of the "early labeled" [^{15}N]urobilinogen was recovered well before the time that appreciable labeling of red cell hemoglobin was observed. The theoretical basis for subsequent research on the "early labeled peak" was provided in large part by the critical analysis of potential sources of bile pigment made initially by Gray and London and their colleagues.

The following three hypotheses were proposed:

First, early-labeled bile pigment might derive from erythroid sources. A small fraction of newly made red cells appears to be destroyed rapidly in situ, or destroyed in the spleen shortly after release from the bone marrow into the plasma. Alternatively, "early-labeled" bile pigment could arise from heme synthesized in excess of globin, from cytoplasmic hemoglobin lost during expulsion of the nucleus from developing red cells, or from red cells which synthesize and destroy hemoglobin simultaneously.

Second, early-labeled bile pigment might derive from non-erythroid sources such as the non-hemoglobin heme-containing enzymes (catalase, peroxidase, cytochromes, etc.) present in especially high concentrations in the liver and kidney. Myoglobin might be another major source of "early-labeled" bile pigment, and recent experimentation in our laboratory with heme-labeled [^{3}H]myoglobin demonstrated that it is converted to [^{3}H]bilirubin after intravenous administration. In addition, however, these studies indicated that the turnover is much slower than would be anticipated if myoglobin were a major contributor to the "early-labeled" peak (Daly et al., 1967).

Third, the term shunt bilirubin has been used ambiguously over the years, at times apparently intended to mean nothing more than bile pigment formed rapidly from sources other than hemoglobin in circulating red cells. Both London and Gray discussed the intriguing possibility that bilirubin might be formed directly, by the polymerization of monopyrroles without the intermediate formation of a porphyrin ring or of heme. However, there has never been a shred of evidence to substantiate the formation of bile pigment without prior formation of heme. Such a process would necessitate the end-to-end polymerization of porphobilinogen, the endogenous pyrrolic precursor of porphyrin and of heme. However, the bile pigment so produced could under no circumstances have the IXα arrangement of side-chains. Moreover, the side-chain substituents of the bilirubin molecule which are different from those of porphobilinogen are formed only in reactions involving porphyrin intermediates. It is highly improbable that identical transformations would occur in the non-porphyrin intermediates of the postulated shunt pathway. Since porphyrin ring formation and ring cleavage appears to be an essential step in the formation of bilirubin-like compounds even in phylogenetically primitive organisms (see Section II. C), it is possible that heme is also an obligatory intermediate for bilirubin formation in mammals.

During the past several years, largely as a result of work by Israels et al. (1963), Yamamoto et al. (1965), Ibrahim et al. (1966) and Robinson et al. (1966), this entire area has been greatly clarified. Essentially all of the work was made possible by the single observation that the porphyrin precursor, δ-aminolevulinic acid (ALA), penetrates red cells poorly and is, therefore, sparingly incorporated into hemoglobin while heavily labeling other heme-containing proteins.

It was found that the rate of production of radioactive bilirubin is maximal within one to two hours after administration of [^{14}C]ALA (Robinson et al., 1966). Thus bilirubin can be produced from ALA extremely rapidly in both laboratory animals (Robinson et al., 1966) and in humans (Robinson et al., 1967), in contrast to the somewhat slower rates that might have been inferred from earlier studies (Israels et al., 1963). The rapid appearance of the "early-labeled" peak was confirmed in kinetic studies which demonstrated that the appearance and disappearance of radioactivity in hepatic heme-containing enzymes preceded the appearance of ^{14}C-labeled bilirubin in bile (Ibrahim *et al.*, 1966). The demonstration that isolated perfused liver formed [^{14}C]bilirubin from [^{14}C]ALA provided direct evidence that bilirubin is generated by the liver in the complete absence of erythropoiesis (Robinson *et al.*, 1965). In their most recent publication, Schmid and coworkers (1966) have suggested that hepatic microsomal cytochrome P-450, a heme containing enzyme involved in drug detoxification, is at least one major source of non-erythroid "early-labeled" bile pigment. This does not rule out the possibility that there is, in addition, a significant erythropoietic contribution to "early-labeled" bile pigment. It has been shown that when large numbers of red cells are destroyed during their formation in the bone marrow, i.e. "ineffective erythropoiesis", that the "early-labeled" peak can account for up to 80% of the daily production of bile pigment (Robinson *et al.*, 1962). It appears that even under normal conditions a small portion of newly formed red cells turn over rapidly (Stohlman, 1962). Therefore, it is conceivable that both erythroid and non-erythroid components normally contribute to the "early-labeled" peak in bile pigment formation.

IV. Metabolism of Bile Pigments

A. *Metabolism of bilirubin in adults*

1. *Plasma binding*

Bilirubin is moderately soluble in protein-free aqueous solutions at physiologic pH under ideal conditions (Burnstine and Schmid, 1962). Aqueous solutions of bilirubin are unstable, however, and the solubility of the pigment is vastly increased by protein binding. After release from sites of hemoglobin breakdown, bilirubin is transported in plasma bound exclusively to albumin (Ostrow and Schmid, 1963). The binding characteristics of albumin from different species vary, but the affinity of *human* albumin for bilirubin is extremely high (Schmid *et al.*, 1965). As measured under artificial conditions by several different techniques, one mole of albumin can bind up to two moles of bilirubin (Ostrow and Schmid, 1963; Schmid *et al.*, 1965). It appears probable, however, that the first mole of bilirubin is bound more tightly than the second mole. Therefore, with a plasma albumin concentration of 4 g/100 ml. bilirubin would be tightly bound at concentrations as high as 30–35 mg/100 ml. When bilirubin concentrations exceed this level pigment might diffuse into intracellular fluid (Odell, 1959). Besides the concentration of albumin, factors such as plasma pH, ions which compete for albumin binding, and differences in tissue characteristics may influence the degree to which bilirubin enters cells (see Section IV. B). For example, the defective tubular reabsorption of sodium observed in congenitally jaundiced (Gunn) rats has been ascribed to the dissociation of albumin and bilirubin in the hypertonic environment of the renal medulla, and the entry of unbound bilirubin into renal tubular cells (Odell *et al.*, 1967).

For technical reasons, the binding of conjugated bilirubin has been more difficult to study. The best available information suggests that conjugated bilirubin is bound to albumin, but less avidly than unconjugated bilirubin (Fulop et al., 1965). In patients with jaundice due to hepatocellular or obstructive liver disease, the unbound fraction of conjugated bilirubin may be increased by the presence of ions which compete for albumin binding.

Conjugated bilirubin is excreted by the kidney primarily through glomerular filtration of the unbound fraction. Indirect evidence suggests that tubular reabsorption may occur with drastic alterations of body pH, but this process probably is of little significance under physiologic conditions (Ali and Billing, 1966). There is no evidence indicating that conjugated bilirubin is secreted by renal tubules (Schenker and McCandless, 1964; Fulop et al., 1965; Ali and Billing, 1966).

2. Hepatic uptake

Red cells and other extrahepatic tissues absorb plasma bilirubin slowly and in small quantities, presumably largely by passive non-ionic diffusion (Watson, 1962). In contrast, the hepatic uptake of bilirubin is an extremely rapid and efficient process (Hunton et al., 1961; Brown et al., 1964; Bernstein et al., 1966; Ali and Billing, 1967). Entry into the liver cell is preceded by dissociation of the bilirubin-albumin complex (Bernstein et al., 1966). Competitive inhibition of bilirubin uptake by other organic anions has been demonstrated (Hunton et al., 1961; Berthelot and Billing, 1966; Hammaker and Schmid, 1967). These characteristics make it probable that hepatic uptake is carrier-mediated. By analogy with mechanisms of bromsulfophthalein (BSP) uptake, it might be inferred that the hepatic uptake of bilirubin involves "active" transport (Goresky, 1965).

3. Intracellular transport, conjugation and excretion

Bilirubin transport within the liver cell is poorly understood. A storage space analogous to that for BSP has been described by Goresky (1965). Attempts at characterizing "acceptor sites" for intracellular bilirubin have so far not been fruitful (Grodsky, 1967). A greater proportion of hepatocyte unconjugated bilirubin is associated with the microsomal subcellular fraction than might be anticipated (Brown et al., 1964; Bernstein et al., 1966, but for different results, see Rodriguez-Garay and Dickson, 1967). The association of bilirubin with microsomes might reflect the binding of bilirubin by microsomal glucuronyl transferase (Bernstein et al., 1966).

Bilirubin is conjugated with glucuronic acid to form bilirubin glucuronide (Talafant, 1956; Billing et al., 1957; Schmid, 1957). As shown in Fig. 6, conjugating enzyme, bilirubin glucuronyl transferase, is bound to the smooth endoplasmic reticulum of liver cells; glucuronic acid is provided for the reaction by uridine diphosphoglucuronic acid (UDPGA). For technical reasons, hepatic glucuronyl transferase is frequently estimated with glucuronide acceptor molecules called "aglycones", rather than with bilirubin directly. Unfortunately, glucuronyl transferase activity measured with these aglycones may not necessarily reflect the liver's capacity to conjugate bilirubin. In fact, several or many hepatic glucuronyl transferases probably exist, and bilirubin glucuronyl transferase may be distinct from the enzymes which form other ester, ether and N-linked glucuronides (Isselbacher et al., 1962). While a mixture of glucuronyl transferases has been solubilized and partially purified, attempts to isolate bilirubin glucuronyl transferase have been discouraging (Isselbacher et al., 1962).

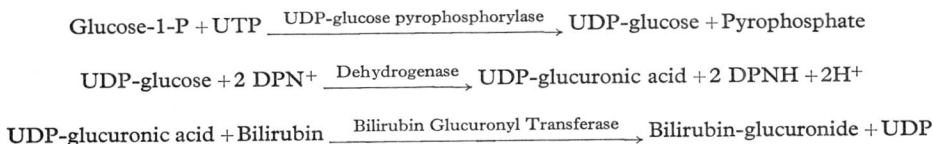

$$\text{Glucose-1-P} + \text{UTP} \xrightarrow{\text{UDP-glucose pyrophosphorylase}} \text{UDP-glucose} + \text{Pyrophosphate}$$

$$\text{UDP-glucose} + 2\,\text{DPN}^+ \xrightarrow{\text{Dehydrogenase}} \text{UDP-glucuronic acid} + 2\,\text{DPNH} + 2\text{H}^+$$

$$\text{UDP-glucuronic acid} + \text{Bilirubin} \xrightarrow{\text{Bilirubin Glucuronyl Transferase}} \text{Bilirubin-glucuronide} + \text{UDP}$$

FIG. 6. Formation of bilirubin diglucuronide.

The best evidence suggests that both carboxyl groups of bilirubin are esterified to form the diglucuronide, and that so-called "monoglucuronide" is a complex of unconjugated bilirubin and bilirubin diglucuronide (Nosslin, 1960; Gregory, 1963; Weber et al., 1963). Formation of bilirubin sulphate by the liver has been the subject of controversy (Isselbacher and McCarthy, 1959; Noir et al., 1967). More than one conjugate spot is often observed on chromatography of derivatives of bile bilirubin. Moreover, a fraction of conjugated bilirubin in bile appears to be alkali-stable (although it is thought that the ester linkage in bilirubin diglucuronide is alkali-labile) and resistant to hydrolysis with β-glucuronidase. On the other hand, perhaps because of technical limitations, the formation of bilirubin sulphate has never been demonstrated convincingly. Even if it exists, the sulphate conjugate must be of minor functional significance because its formation fails to serve as an effective alternate pathway for bilirubin excretion in rats with a congenital deficiency of glucuronyl transferase (Schmid and Hammaker, 1963).

Conjugation is virtually essential for the biliary excretion of bilirubin. Low-level transient increases in the concentration of unconjugated bilirubin in bile can be produced by injecting a load of bilirubin intravenously (Berthelot and Fauvert, 1967). Indeed, the presence of relatively insoluble unconjugated bilirubin in bile might be related to the formation of pigment stones in patients with chronic hemolysis. Under normal conditions, however, essentially all bilirubin in bile is in the form of the conjugate. When the hepatic conjugating enzyme is absent, bile bilirubin levels are extremely low (Schmid and Hammaker, 1963).

While it is clear that conjugation drastically alters the physical and chemical properties of bilirubin, the relationship between conjugation and excretion has not been fully explained. One highly speculative formulation, based on studies of the comparative excretion of bilirubin and other tetra-pyrroles, is that the glucuronide conjugation of bile pigments is governed by the presence or absence of unsaturated bonds at specific points in the molecules (Lester and Klein, 1966). These key bonds determine the steric configuration of the bile pigment, and thus they may influence the "fit" of the molecule to the conjugating enzyme, to the canalicular secretory mechanism, or to some other macromolecular component of the excretory apparatus. On the other hand, the physical-chemical characteristics of tetrapyrroles are altered by the degree of saturation of these bonds, and changes in these characteristics may be of greater significance in effecting conjugation than steric configuration *per se*.

The excretion of bilirubin is one example of the mechanism by which a diverse group of endogenous and exogenous organic anions is secreted into bile (Fig. 7). Some, but not all of these compounds are, like bilirubin, con-

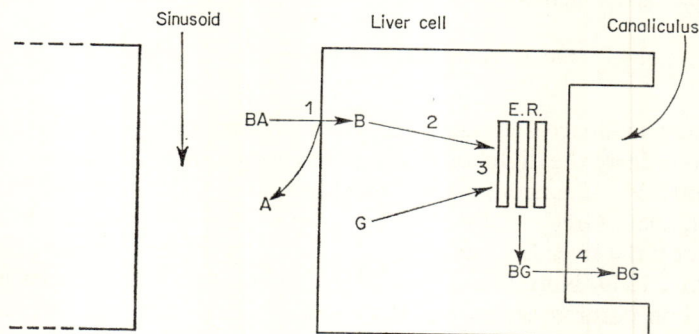

FIG. 7. Schematic representation of the hepatic excretion of bilirubin. The following symbols are used: A=albumin; B=bilirubin; BG=bilirubin glucuronide; ER=smooth endoplasmic reticulum; G=glucuronic acid (in the form of UDPGA). Stages of hepatic excretion: 1. hepatic uptake; 2. intracellular transport; 3. conjugation; 4. secretion into canaliculus.

jugated with small polar metabolites during the excretory process. Biliary secretion proceeds against large concentration gradients, competitive inhibition has been demonstrated, and the mechanism is saturable (Goresky, 1965). It is, therefore, reasonable to conclude that the biliary secretion of bilirubin glucuronide, and of other comparable organic anions, is carrier mediated, and, directly or indirectly, associated with energy-consuming processes (Shanker, 1962).

4. *Intestinal transport*

Combination with glucuronic acid increases the polarity and size of the pigment molecule. As a result, bilirubin glucuronide is not appreciably reabsorbed from the intestine (Lester and Schmid, 1963*a, b*) or gall bladder (Ostrow, 1967). Conjugation (with taurine and glycine) exerts a comparable effect in preventing absorption of bile salts from the proximal portion of the small bowel (Dietschy *et al.*, 1966). The bilirubin glucuronide ester linkage probably remains intact during transit through the small bowel in humans, although some hydrolysis may occur in rats (Lester and Schmid, 1963*a*, *b*). Bacterial β-glucuronidase present in the large bowel partially or completely hydrolyzes bilirubin glucuronide, while at the same time bilirubin is reduced to urobilinogen (see Section IV. C).

B. *Metabolism of bilirubin in the fetus and newborn*

1. *Bilirubin excretion*

Fetal bilirubin metabolism varies from one species to another. In the rat (Grodsky *et al.*, 1963) and dog (Bernstein, Novy, Jackson and Lester, unpublished observations) direct transfer of bilirubin across the placenta is minimal. Unlike most species examined, the fetal canine liver is capable of forming and excreting significant amounts of bilirubin glucuronide. There is little doubt, however, that bilirubin can diffuse across primate placenta at rates which are sufficient to assume the excretion of most, if not all, the fetal bilirubin normally produced (Lester *et al.*, 1963; Schenker *et al.*, 1967). On the other hand, hepatic excretion by the primate fetus is grossly inefficient. Responsible at least in part for this defect is the reduced level of fetal hepatic UDPGA and glucuronyl transferase, which contributes to the diminution of bilirubin conjugation, and therefore of bilirubin excretion. Again, species variation exists, but glucuronyl transferase activity in the near term primate fetus is about one-third that in adults (Lucey *et al.*, 1963). Since *in vitro* and *in vivo* estimations of glucuronyl transferase do not necessarily reflect the liver's ability to conjugate bilirubin (see Section IV. A, 3) the actual reduction in glucuronyl transferase activity may be greater than that suggested by the assay procedures.

Defective conjugation of bilirubin does not appear to be the sole cause of impaired fetal bilirubin excretion. For instance, when conjugated bilirubin was administered intravenously to viable guinea pig fetuses with intact placental circulation, little, if any, intact conjugated pigment was excreted by the placental mechanism. Of greater interest, however, was the observation that only 0·5–14% of the dose was excreted by the fetal liver in 2 hr (Schenker *et al.*, 1964). Adult guinea pigs given weight adjusted loads of conjugated bilirubin excreted essentially all of the dose during a comparable period. Failure of the fetal liver to excrete "preconjugated" bilirubin efficiently suggests that the defect in fetal hepatic excretion cannot be explained by the reduction in bilirubin diglucuronide synthesis alone. The nature of this second defect which could result from an intrinsic deficiency of the fetal hepatic excretory apparatus, or from the presence in fetal plasma of factors which inhibit hepatic uptake or block biliary secretion, is unknown. Studies of uptake and excretion of free and conjugated bilirubin by isolated, perfused fetal liver might help to pinpoint the loci of these defects in the hepatic fetal excretory apparatus.

An awareness of the differences between the fetus and the adult makes it easier to understand the changes in bilirubin metabolism which occur at birth. Defective conjugation persists through the early neonatal period, and the second fetal excretory defect, referred to in the preceding paragraph, is also evident in newborns (Schenker and Schmid, 1964). That bilirubin concentrations in cord plasma are at or near adult normal levels indicates the effectiveness of placental excretion in the fetus. During the period after the placenta is interrupted and before the neonatal hepatic excretory apparatus "matures", plasma bilirubin levels normally rise, occasionally to disturbingly high levels. The best available estimates of newborn red cell turnover indicate that pigment production from this source, on a weight for weight basis, is similar to that in adults (Vest et al., 1965). It has been proposed, but not rigorously proven, that intestinal absorption of bilirubin adds significantly to the pigment load in plasma during the early neonatal period (Ulstrom and Eisenklam, 1964). At least for the present, however, "physiologic jaundice" of the newborn is generally assumed to be due to the prolonged retention of bilirubin resulting from normal bilirubin production, but inadequate hepatic excretion. Whether the so-called "inspissated bile duct syndrome" – the development of conjugated hyperbilirubinemia late in the course of erythroblastosis fetalis – represents maturation of the hepatic conjugating apparatus with a persistent fetal excretory defect, remains an interesting but uncertain speculation.

2. *Kernicterus*

Several key aspects of the pathogenesis of kernicterus have been examined in studies completed within the past several years. The concept that bilirubin produces encephalopathy by uncoupling oxidative phosphorylation had gained wide acceptance on the basis of *in vitro* studies (Ernster et al., 1957). Furthermore, it had been shown that mitochondria obtained from brain, unlike those from other organs, were suceptible *in vitro* to the toxic effects of bilirubin, either bound to albumin or in the unbound form (Menken et al., 1966). These results seemed to have been confirmed by *in vivo* studies which suggested that the absolute concentration of ATP in the cerebellum of kernicteric Gunn rats was significantly reduced when compared with normals (Schenker et al., 1966). As originally noted by Schenker, however, the absolute concentration of ATP may not be a meaningful estimate of oxidative phosphorylation (Schenker et al., 1966). When oxygen consumption and inorganic phosphorus utilization were measured using mitochondria from brains of animals with "experimental kernicterus", no decrease in oxidative phosphorylation was observed (Diamond and Schmid, 1967; Menken and Weinbach, 1967). The bilirubin concentrations in the brains of animals with experimental kernicterus were far below those employed in most *in vitro* studies (Diamond and Schmid, 1966). When oxidative phosphorylation was estimated for normal brain mitochondria incubated with bilirubin concentrations equal to those observed in the brains of kernicteric animals, no inhibition was observed (Diamond and Schmid,

1967). Therefore, at present, there is considerable doubt about the precise biochemical mechanism of cytotoxicity produced by bilirubin in the brain.

The mode of entry of bilirubin into the brain has proven to be another controversial question. If, as had been suggested (Ernster *et al.*, 1957), bilirubin gained entry into the brain complexed with albumin, a defect in the "blood-brain barrier" – in the form of neonatal "immaturity" or as a result of anoxic or toxic damage – would be a necessary precondition for the development of kernicterus. An entirely different emphasis was advanced by Odell (Odell, 1959). On the basis of *in vitro* studies of the dissociation of bilirubin from albumin, it was proposed that kernicterus results from the diffusion of unbound bilirubin across the intact blood-brain barrier. The concentration of unbound bilirubin would be increased by hypo-albuminemia, by competition for albumin binding by endogenous meta-bolites (e.g. hematin) or drugs (e.g. sulphonamides or salicylates), and by decreases in plasma pH. Each of these factors, therefore, would permit greater permeation of the blood-brain barrier and increased risk of entry into, and toxic damage to, cells of the central nervous system.

These postulates have been fully confirmed by experiments with an animal model devised for the study of kernicterus (Diamond and Schmid, 1966). Infusion of protein-bound [^{14}C]bilirubin into newborn guinea pigs produced high plasma levels but low concentrations of radioactivity in the brain. However, when unbound [^{14}C]bilirubin was infused, or when binding was decreased by concurrent infusions of competing anions or by lowering plasma pH, diffusion into the brain increased and signs of neurotoxic damage developed. Of particular interest was the finding that entry of [^{14}C]bilirubin into the brain of *adult* animals could be demonstrated under conditions comparable to those employed for the study of newborns. This suggested that there is no fundamental difference between the adult and neonatal blood-brain barrier in so far as it influences entry of bilirubin into the brain. Indeed, although its occurrence outside the neonatal period must be rare, an instance of kernicterus developing in a 15-year-old patient with Crigler-Najjar syndrome (see Section V. A) has been reported (Gardner and Konigsmark, 1968).

Why then is the development of kernicterus almost exclusively limited to the neonatal period? Severe *unconjugated* hyperbilirubinemia, which occurs in newborns with erythroblastosis foetalis and in certain premature infants, is relatively uncommon in adults. Moreover, the levels of unbound, diffusible bilirubin must be markedly increased by the coincident presence of the severe metabolic and respiratory acidosis frequently observed in sick, jaundiced, newborn infants. The presence of low serum albumin and of materials which compete with bilirubin for binding are contributory. Whether neonatal brain cells absorb more bilirubin or are uniquely suscept-ible to the toxic effects of bilirubin remains to be demonstrated conclusively. In any event, the lines of preventive therapy are indicated by the con-siderations above. Drugs which compete with bilirubin for binding to albumin should be avoided. Infusions of albumin which provide increased binding capacity and which, therefore, "trap" bilirubin in the plasma have in some instances been successfully employed in combination with exchange transfusion (Odell *et al.*, 1962). Stringent measures should be directed to the early correction of respiratory and metabolic acidosis.

C. *Urobilinogen metabolism*

Estimations of urine and fecal urobilinogen are commonly employed as semi-quantitative measures of hepatic function and hemoglobin turnover. It is not surprising, therefore, that there has been continued interest in urobilinogen metabolism over the course of decades. The older literature is discussed in detail in the monographs of Gray (1961) and Watson (1963) and can be summarized briefly. Urobilinogen is a generic name for an entire class of colorless tetrapyrrolic metabolites (see Section II. B) found in feces, bile and urine, which form a purple association complex with *p*-dimethyl-aminobenzaldehyde (Ehrlich reagent), and which are oxidized on standing in air to pigmented urobilins. Thus the "Ehrlich reaction" and "Schlesinger reaction" for "fecal urobilinogen" measure not one compound, but the sum total of an entire series. Conversion of bilirubin to urobilinogen has been demonstrated in cultures of mixed fecal bacteria (Watson *et al.*, 1958). Urobilinogen is absent in germ-free animals (Gustafsson and Lanke, 1960), and is eliminated by broad spectrum antibiotic therapy (Watson, 1963) or by external biliary drainage (McMaster and Elman, 1925). On the basis of its chemical structure and the foregoing information, it has been concluded that urobilinogen is formed in the intestine by the bacterial reduction of bilirubin, that it is partially absorbed, and then re-excreted by the liver and kidney.

Because of intrinsic technical difficulties, a number of questions related to urobilinogen metabolism have gone unanswered until recently. How great is the intestinal absorption and hepatic return (enterohepatic circulation) of urobilinogen? What are the characteristics of hepatic excretion? What factors determine the extent of renal excretion and how does it compare with the liver's excretory capacity? How do intestinal bacteria reduce bilirubin to urobilinogen? Our interest in this area began with the realization that many of the technical problems limiting study of urobilinogen metabolism could be circumvented by preparing radiolabeled material. Initially this was accomplished by converting [^{14}C]bilirubin (Ostrow *et al.*, 1961) to [^{14}C]urobilinogen (Lester and Schmid, 1965), and more recently we have been able to produce a less expensive, heavily labeled, tritiated urobilinogen by catalytic reduction of unlabeled bilirubin in tritiated water with sodium amalgam (Lester and Klein, 1966). Using radiolabeled material, it was possible to provide the first direct demonstration that urobilinogen is absorbed from the intestine (Lester and Schmid, 1965). It was shown that absorption from the terminal ileum and large bowel, the physiologic sites of urobilinogen formation, is limited in short-term experiments to 10–20% of a physiologic dose, and that, therefore, under normal conditions the major portion of urobilinogen is probably lost directly in feces rather than reabsorbed. The normal liver has an immense reserve capacity to excrete urobilinogen, which is comparable to its ability to excrete bilirubin (Lester and Schmid, 1965; Lester and Klein, 1966). Whereas conjugation with glucuronic acid is an essential step in bilirubin excretion, urobilinogen is excreted in bile intact and unaltered (Lester and Klein, 1966) (see Section IV. A, 3).

Using the available spectrophotometric and fluorescence techniques, three studies of urine urobilinogen excretion led to three different conclusions. It was suggested that excretion is by glomerular filtration alone (Fassati et al., 1966), by both filtration and tubular secretion (Royer and Solari, 1941), or by combined filtration, secretion and tubular reabsorption (Bourke et al., 1965). The plasma clearance and renal excretion of urobilinogen was, therefore, studied using the radiolabeled preparation described above (Levy et al., 1967). In brief, it was established that, like many other weak organic acids partially bound to albumin, urobilinogen is filtered by the glomerulus, secreted by the proximal tubule, and reabsorbed. In agreement with Bourke et al. (1965), reabsorption was found to be greatest from acid urine, in which the molecules are largely un-ionized. The results indicated that renal function, urine pH, and urine volume must be considered in the clinical interpretation of measurements of urine urobilinogen (Levy et al., 1968).

As noted above, urobilinogen is produced in the intestine by the bacterial reduction of bilirubin (Watson, 1963). It is unclear which organism(s) is necessary for the reduction, and although clostridia have been implicated, most investigators have found it necessary to employ two or more organisms in order to demonstrate urobilinogen formation in bacterial cultures. In any event, the reduction probably is enzymatic, requires anaerobic conditions, and appears to be mediated by both a membrane-bound enzyme(s) and soluble cofactors (Troxler et al., 1968). Both conjugated and unconjugated bilirubin are suitable substrates for the reaction (Watson et al., 1958). While it has been suggested that conjugated urobilinogen may be formed by bacterial reduction of bilirubin glucuronide, the presence of bacterial β-glucuronidase in the intestine should prevent the accumulation of appreciable quantities of intact urobilinogen glucuronide.

The older and more recent literature on urobilinogen metabolism is summarized in Fig. 8. It is clear that the urine urobilinogen concentration is the net result of multiple variables. First, obviously changes in bilirubin formation and bile pigment output alter urobilinogen formation. Second, suppression of intestinal bacteria with broad spectrum antibiotics reduces or eliminates urobilinogen production. On the other hand, production may remain constant but absorption would increase in association with proximal intestinal invasion by colonic bacteria. Absorption of urobilinogen from the small bowel is more efficient than absorption from the colon, and the presence of urobilinogen-forming bacteria in the small bowel would, therefore, increase total absorption, and possibly thereby increase renal excretion

(Lester and Schmid, 1965). Third, hepatocellular disease and/or trans-hepatic shunting of portal blood increases the amount of urobilinogen escaping into the systemic circulation (Bernstein *et al.*, 1968), and this in turn may increase renal excretion. Finally, urine urobilinogen excretion depends in part on the patient's state of hydration, renal function, and urine pH. Each of these factors may influence urinary excretion of urobilinogen, and each should be considered in interpreting the results of urine urobilino-gen estimations. In order to improve what is at best a semi-quantitative test, it may be advisable to measure urine urobilinogen under standard conditions of hydration, and with urine pH controlled.

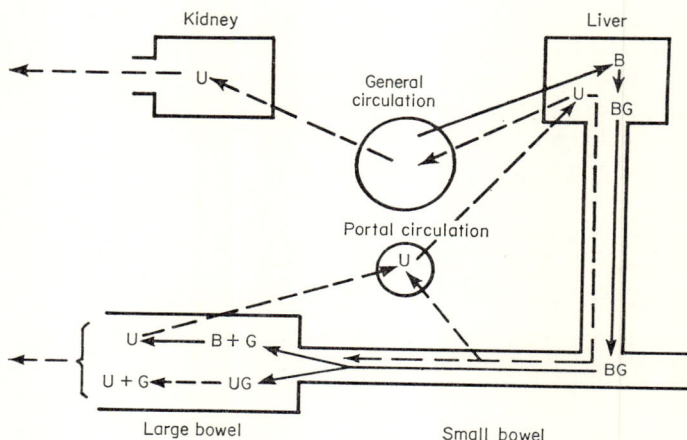

FIG. 8. Diagram of the enterohepatic circulation of urobilinogen. The following symbols are used: B = bilirubin; BG = bilirubin glucuronide, G = glucuronic acid; U = urobilinogen; UG = urobilinogen glucuronide. As indicated in the text, it is not known whether bilirubin or bilirubin glucuronide is the natural substrate for urobilinogen formation.

V. Jaundice produced by Metabolic Defects

A. *Crigler-Najjar syndrome*

The initial description of "congenital familial nonhemolytic jaundice with kernicterus", or the Crigler-Najjar syndrome, marked a new point of departure in the study of bilirubin metabolism because the entity represented the first clear-cut instance of jaundice produced by a metabolic defect in the hepatic excretory apparatus. This hereditary syndrome first described by Crigler and Najjar (1952) is characterized by a persistent "indirect" hyper-bilirubinemia despite otherwise normal liver function and histology, and without hemolysis or overproduction of bile pigment. The incidence of the syndrome is rare, and thus far only about 20–40 case reports have been documented (Kaplan *et al.*, 1966). Jaundice develops during the early neonatal period and usually results in severe neurologic damage and death.

Elaboration of the disease mechanism was facilitated by the availability of an animal model in which a disease similar to the Crigler-Najjar syndrome occurred. The defect was inherited by a mutant strain of Wistar rats described by Gunn in 1938. Heterozygotes of the strain appeared to be essentially normal while animals homozygous for the gene which caused the defect had "indirect" hyperbilirubinemia and kernicterus. As in the Crigler-Najjar syndrome, hepatic function (except for bilirubin excretion) and histology, as well as bilirubin production were normal (Schmid et al., 1958).

Following the demonstration in the mid-1950s that bilirubin is normally excreted into bile as the diglucuronide conjugate, a more enlightened approach to investigation of the mechanism of jaundice in the Gunn rat became possible. It was thus shown by in vivo and in vitro techniques that Gunn rats, that is, animals homozygous for the trait, lack the enzyme glucuronyl transferase, and, as a result, are unable to excrete bilirubin in the conventional manner (Axelrod et al., 1957; Carbone and Grodsky, 1957). The small amounts of unconjugated bilirubin present in Gunn rat bile probably reflect passive diffusion of pigment from plasma into bile. Although the activity of enzymes for the synthesis of glucuronic acid conjugates of other aglycones may be near normal or only moderately deranged, the formation of o-aminophenol glucuronide is completely abolished (Axelrod et al., 1957). While bilirubin glucuronyl transferase is completely absent in all strains, the deficiency for other glucuronyl transferases varies in Gunn rats from different scientific centers, as the strains are inbred with genetically distinct German, French, English, etc., Wistar rats (see Bouchier and Billing, 1965, p. 188). Therefore, the initial studies which demonstrated the complete or partial absence of one or more of the glucuronyl transferases may no longer be valid.

Since bilirubin glucuronide formation is completely deficient and since hepatic excretion is normally dependent on conjugate formation, bilirubin is eliminated from the Gunn rat by alternate excretory pathways (Schmid and Hammaker, 1963). After the intravenous administration of [^{14}C]bilirubin to Gunn rats, the plasma (biologic) "half-life" varied from one and a half to four days. Approximately half to two-thirds of the administered isotope label was ultimately excreted in bile, while lesser quantities appeared in bile-free feces and minute amounts were excreted in urine. The label excreted in bile and urine was largely in the form of diazo negative derivatives of bilirubin. The chemical structure of these derivatives is unknown, but on the basis of their spectral and chromatographic properties, they are thought to be mono- and dipyrrolic products of tetrapyrrole degradation. Whether they are formed enzymatically or by nonenzymatic physical processes is also unknown. In addition to this excretory route, a variable portion of [^{14}C]bilirubin administered intravenously to Gunn rats appeared in bile-free feces as intact bilirubin, transferred directly across the gut wall from plasma into the gut lumen (Schmid and Hammaker, 1963).

It is reasonable to assume that comparable phenomena occur in patients with Crigler-Najjar syndrome, and that their ability to conjugate bilirubin is either entirely lacking or severely reduced. Unlike the Gunn rat in which defective bilirubin conjugation appears to be uniform and near absolute, there are certain "Crigler-Najjar" patients who appear to have bilirubin diglucuronide in aspirated bile samples and, therefore, differ from the majority of patients considered to have the syndrome (Billing et al., 1964). Whether this divergency represents a permutation of the syndrome as described initially or whether it is a distinctive metabolic defect is unknown. Again, unlike the Gunn rat model in which the heterozygotes have normal serum bilirubin concentrations, relatives of patients with Crigler-Najjar syndrome may have low-grade icterus (Crigler and Najjar, 1952). The number of such instances is sufficient to raise the possibility that individuals who are heterozygous for the defect have a partial decrease in bilirubin conjugation sufficient to produce low-grade hyperbilirubinemia. Despite normal plasma bilirubin levels, heterozygous Gunn rats are also thought to have a partial deficiency of glucuronyl transferase (Arias, 1959). As mentioned previously, however, the enzyme which conjugates bilirubin cannot be measured adequately, so that the significance of this observation is difficult to assess.

B. Gilbert's syndrome

Mild to moderate hyperbilirubinemia occurring without liver disease has been variously designated Gilbert's disease, hereditary or familial non-hemolytic hyperbilirubinemia, and constitutional hepatic dysfunction (Foulk et al., 1959; Arias, 1962). The diagnosis is by exclusion and the patients are probably heterogeneous. Some of them have a prior history of viral hepatitis. While this association is generally accepted, it has not been definitely established that viral hepatitis can produce prolonged intermittent unconjugated hyperbilirubinemia without other evidence of hepatic dysfunction. A history of "hepatitis" may represent a misdiagnosis at the time that idiopathic unconjugated hyperbilirubinemia is first observed. Furthermore, the occasional unrelated occurrence of hepatitis in an individual with Gilbert's syndrome would be anticipated. One or two of the patients described by Arias (1962) had persistent unconjugated hyperbilirubinemia following an episode of histologically and biochemically typical viral hepatitis. In these patients at least one normal plasma bilirubin concentration had been obtained by chance well before the onset of their illness. They, in fact, provide the most convincing demonstration of Gilbert's syndrome produced by hepatitis. Each of these patients, however, had minor abnormalities of hepatic function and histology which would differentiate their condition from Gilbert's syndrome when rigorously defined.

Jaundice is associated with low-grade hemolysis in a second group of patients (Powell et al., 1967; Smith et al., 1967). The changes in red cell survival are relatively minor when measured by ^{51}Cr-labeling, and it has been questioned whether they are sufficient to produce hyperbilirubinemia without an associated hepatic defect. On the other hand, it is conceivable that hepatic function may deteriorate during prolonged overproduction of bile pigment. The relationship between jaundice and hemolysis in Gilbert's syndrome is further complicated by the observation that jaundice of almost any etiology may be associated with shortened red cell survival (Pitcher and Williams, 1963). For the present, therefore, the precise role of low-grade hemolysis in the genesis of unconjugated hyperbilirubinemia remains uncertain.

If other etiologic factors are excluded, there remains a large group of patients with unexplained chronic unconjugated hyperbilirubinemia (Foulk et al., 1959; Arias, 1962; Powell et al., 1967; Smith et al., 1967). Liver histology, hepatic function as measured by standard techniques, and bile pigment production are normal. Plasma bilirubin concentrations usually range between 1 and 7 mg/100 ml. and intermittently, normal values may be observed. When total concentrations exceed 3 mg/100 ml. the apparent "conjugated" fraction may equal 10% of the total, and, therefore, appear to be abnormal. Patients with Gilbert's syndrome may complain of fatigue, malaise or abdominal pain, but it is generally assumed that in most or all instances the symptoms are not pathogenetically related to the jaundice, but, rather, lead to the diagnosis by serendipity or result from the patient's awareness of disease. In most well-documented series, males predominate over females. Parents and siblings are frequently found to have unconjugated hyperbilirubinemia (17% of parents and 28% of siblings in one series – Powell et al., 1967), but no completely satisfactory scheme of inheritance has been established. The bimodal distribution of bilirubin values in relatives has been used as the basis of a single gene hypothesis (Powell et al., 1967). Until more specific diagnostic tests are developed, however, the possibility that more than one entity can produce the picture of Gilbert's syndrome cannot be excluded.

The etiology of jaundice in Gilbert's syndrome is not entirely clear. Glucuronide formation is normal when measured by the available in vivo and in vitro tests (Arias, 1962; Pitcher and Williams, 1963), and the bile contains abundant bilirubin glucuronide. Plasma disappearance curves have been interpreted to indicate that hepatic uptake of bilirubin is diminished (Billing et al., 1964). Indeed, low-grade unconjugated hyperbilirubinemia which is believed to result from defective hepatic uptake is inherited as an autosomal recessive in a mutant species of Southdown sheep (Cornelius and Gronwall, 1965). As in Gilbert's syndrome, the hepatic architecture appears to be undisturbed. The defect is clearly more severe and general than that underlying Gilbert's syndrome, however, and BSP, indocyanin green and cholic acid are all abnormally retained.

Finally, Arias (1962) has described a group of patients with features intermediate between Crigler-Najjar and Gilbert's syndromes. Plasma unconjugated bilirubin levels lie between 6 and 19 mg/100 ml. Specimens of bile contain predominantly conjugated bilirubin, but in vivo and in vitro tests indicate a partial deficiency of glucuronyl transferase. The disorder is postulated to be inherited as an autosomal dominant with incomplete penetrance.

C. *Neonatal unconjugated hyperbilirubinemia*

1. *Physiologic jaundice*

Unconjugated hyperbilirubinemia regularly occurs in newborn infants during the first few days of life (Weech, 1947). Marked elevations of plasma bilirubin concentration are observed occasionally, but mild to moderate increases are more common, and a return to or toward normal can be anticipated within one to two weeks after birth. For reasons that are not known, overt jaundice occurs less often in infants than in adults.

The relationship of "physiologic jaundice" to fetal bilirubin metabolism is discussed in Section IV. B, 1. In brief, the placental mechanism for fetal bilirubin excretion is interrupted (Lester *et al.*, 1963; Schenker *et al.*, 1964). Low neonatal levels of hepatic glucuronyl transferase and UDPGA limit the rate of bilirubin conjugation (Dutton, 1959; Brown and Zuelzer, 1968). Moreover, the diminished capacity to excrete conjugated bilirubin observed in the fetus persists in the newborn (Schenker and Schmid, 1964). The neonatal hepatic excretory apparatus is, therefore, inefficient, and unconjugated hyperbilirubinemia occurs without overproduction of bile pigment.

2. *Breast-milk jaundice*

A syndrome of neonatal unconjugated hyperbilirubinemia is observed in association with breast-feeding (Arias *et al.*, 1964). Jaundice becomes maximal during the first 10–20 days post-partum, and then disappears within the first one or two months of life despite continued breast-feeding. Plasma bilirubin concentrations diminish abruptly when cow's-milk feedings are substituted. A majority of breast-fed siblings exhibit a similar syndrome.

Milk from mothers of affected infants contains measurable concentrations of an unusual steroid, prenane-3 (α), 20 (β)-diol (Arias *et al.*, 1964; Gartner and Arias, 1966; Rosenfeld *et al.*, 1967), which like many other steroidal metabolites competitively inhibits glucuronyl transferase activity *in vitro* (Lathe and Walker, 1958). In order to clarify this relationship, pregnane-3 (α), 20 (β)-diol in amounts equivalent to those ingested by infants with "breast-milk jaundice" were administered to two normal, full-term newborn infants (Arias and Gartner, 1964). Within several days hyperbilirubinemia was observed, which remitted when steroid administration was discontinued. These results suggest that "breast-milk jaundice" is directly related to the presence of pregnane-3 (α), 20 (β)-diol in maternal milk, rather than to an intrinsic defect in the neonatal liver. This conclusion has been disputed, however, and the area remains controversial (Ramos *et al.*, 1966).

3. Lucey-Driscoll syndrome

Several women have been described who have given birth to more than one infant with transient neonatal hyperbilirubinemia which was not attributable to hepatic dysfunction or overproduction of pigment (Arias et al., 1965). Maximal serum bilirubin concentrations ranged from 9 to 65 mg/100 ml. and, unlike the outcome in "breast-milk jaundice" which has generally proven to be a benign disorder, four out of sixteen infants developed kernicterus. An inhibitor of in vitro assays of glucuronyl transferase was present in the serum of both the affected infants and their mothers. The inhibitor has not been isolated, but because of its occurrence in the plasma of pregnant women, it has been suggested that it may be a progestational steroid (Arias et al., 1965).

D. Other causes of unconjugated hyperbilirubinemia

Marked overproduction of bilirubin can produce unconjugated hyperbilirubinemia when the capacity for hepatic bilirubin uptake and/or conjugation is exceeded. It is generally less appreciated that plasma conjugated bilirubin concentrations can rise during hemolytic episodes in both newborns (Hsia et al., 1952) and adults (Schalm and Weber, 1964) with apparently normal hepatic function. The explanation for these phenomena will remain obscure until improved techniques are devised for studying the individual phases of hepatic bilirubin excretion.

Moderate elevations of "indirect-reacting" bilirubin, with relatively little elevation of the "direct-reacting" fraction, have been observed after portacaval anastomosis (da Silva et al., 1960). Hyperbilirubinemia, presumably due to less efficient hepatic perfusion or extraction, may persist for prolonged periods while other measures of hepatic function are relatively normal.

A variety of drugs including the antibiotics novobiocin and rifamycin, the antihelminthic, flavaspidic acid, and cholecystographic media such as bunamiodyl, can produce hyperbilirubinemia (Sutherland and Keller, 1961; Acocella et al., 1965; Berthelot and Billing, 1966; Hammaker and Schmid, 1967). While most of these agents inhibit glucuronyl transferase activity in vitro, their in vivo action is probably more complex, and may involve altered hepatic uptake and intracellular transport of bilirubin (Goresky, 1965).

E. Attempts to treat unconjugated hyperbilirubinemia

The hyperbilirubinemia associated with neonatal erythroblastosis has, in the past, been treated by exchange transfusion. This disease can now be prevented by the administration of anti-Rh-containing γ-globulin to Rh-negative mothers following childbirth. A major decline in the incidence of erythroblastosis can, therefore, be anticipated (Freda et al., 1967).

Bilirubin decomposes when exposed to intense blue (440 mμ) or ultraviolet light. Exposure of jaundiced patients to sunlight or artificial blue light can significantly reduce plasma bilirubin concentrations within 12–48 hr of the start of irradiation (Broughton et al., 1965). The derivatives of the photo-oxidation of bilirubin have not been characterized, but it is reasonable to suppose that they are more water-soluble and potentially less toxic than bilirubin itself (Ostrow et al., 1961).

Bidirectional flux of unconjugated bilirubin across the intestinal mucosa of Gunn rats has been demonstrated (Lester and Schmid, 1963a; Schmid and Hammaker, 1963). Oral administration of the resin cholestyramine, which binds bilirubin nonspecifically, produces a marked decrease in Gunn rat plasma bilirubin levels, presumably by "trapping" of the pigment in the intestine (Lester et al., 1962). The results of similar attempts at therapy in humans have been less dramatic (Schmid et al., 1963; Ulstrom and Eisenklam, 1964), perhaps because of differences in plasma bilirubin binding (Schmid et al., 1965).

The administration of barbiturates to patients with severe congenital unconjugated hyperbilirubinemia sometimes, but not invariably, results in a significant decrease in plasma bilirubin concentrations occurring gradually over days or weeks (Crigler and Gold, 1966; Yaffee et al., 1966). Formation of salicylamide glucuronide is enhanced by barbiturate, and it has been proposed that the lowering of plasma bilirubin concentrations results from the induction of glucuronyl transferase (Yaffee et al., 1966). On the other hand, barbiturates enhance the hepatic metabolism of a host of other substrates by increasing the activity of the microsomal electron transport system and the key cytochrome P450 (Coney, 1967). Rather than resulting from the specific induction of glucuronyl transferase, part of the decrease in plasma bilirubin concentrations observed with barbiturate administration may conceivably reflect increased bilirubin degradation by alternate metabolic pathways. Of interest in this connection is the preliminary observation that barbiturate therapy decreases the "direct-reacting" plasma bilirubin concentrations in patients with cholestasis (Thompson and Williams, 1967).

F. Conjugated hyperbilirubinemia

1. Acquired conjugated hyperbilirubinemia

In the overwhelming majority of patients with hepatocellular or obstructive liver disease, jaundice reflects elevation of both conjugated and unconjugated bilirubin. The precise mechanisms that lead to jaundice in these circumstances are unknown. Recent studies suggest that several forms of intrahepatic cholestasis may be explained by the physical chemical properties of bile salts, and by the interaction of bile salts with other compounds (Hoffman and Small, 1967). A discussion of cholestasis is beyond the scope of the present chapter, but a provocative review by Javitt and Arias (1967) is available.

2. Familial jaundice with conjugated hyperbilirubinemia

Chronic familial jaundice with conjugated hyperbilirubinemia (Dubin-Johnson syndrome) was described in detail by Dubin (1958). Butt *et al.* (1966) proposed that the disorder is inherited as an autosomal dominant. Jaundice, which may be noted first at almost any age, fluctuates in intensity. Vague gastrointestinal symptoms may be associated. The gall bladder often is not visualized after oral administration of cholecystographic material. Conventional liver function tests are usually normal, but BSP is retained abnormally, and estimates by Wheeler's technique indicate that the BSP transfer maximum (Tm) is severely reduced (Wheeler *et al.*, 1960). These results suggest that the secretion of bile pigment and other organic anions from the liver cell into bile is defective in the Dubin-Johnson syndrome.

Liver cells obtained from patients with the syndrome are filled with a melanin-like pigment. The concentration of pigment in some specimens is sufficiently great to make the liver appear black on gross inspection. The relationship between this finding and the secretory defect is not entirely clear. The melanin-like pigment may be absent from the hepatocytes of affected relatives, which leads one to suspect that Rotor's syndrome (familial unconjugated hyperbilirubinemia, but with normal liver histology) results from the same metabolic defect (for a contrary view, see Dubin, 1962).

A disorder remarkably similar to the Dubin-Johnson syndrome has been observed in a mutant species of Corriedale sheep (Arias *et al.*, 1964). Again, the "direct-reacting" plasma bilirubin concentrations are elevated, the gall bladder cannot be visualized radiographically, a melanin-like pigment is deposited in the hepatocytes, and the Tm for BSP is markedly diminished. As in the Dubin-Johnson syndrome, the metabolic defect appears to be a failure of the hepatic secretory apparatus to secrete organic anions. Interestingly, the hepatic secretion of at least one organic *cation* (procaine amide ethobromide), and the secretion of taurocholate are apparently unaffected (Arias, 1966).

VI. Summary

The yellow skin and sclerae of the jaundiced patient are a dramatic manifestation of disease, and a sufficient explanation for the intense interest which has been centered in this area for years. It has become increasingly clear, however, that major technologic innovations will be required to solve many of the remaining problems. Moreover, disruption of hepatic function may be better represented by abnormalities in the metabolism of substances that are quantitatively and functionally of greater significance than bilirubin. Specifically, it will frequently make greater sense to analyze problems of hepatic function by studying the metabolism of bile acids, synthetic dyes, hormones and drugs.

Nevertheless, a number of questions related to the metabolism of bilirubin remain, and deserve an answer. The assumption that bilirubin is normally made in the reticuloendothelial tissue has never been proven. The enzymatic pathways and intermediate metabolites involved in the conversion of heme to bilirubin are poorly understood. The mechanisms of hepatic pigment excretion require clarification. The characteristics of hepatic uptake are unknown; there is little information on the intracellular transport of bilirubin from the sinusoidal surface of the liver cell to the endoplasmic reticulum; there is more to be learnt about the functional relationship between the conjugating and secretory apparatus.

Bilirubin glucuronide has never been isolated or synthesized. Its structure has never been characterized fully, and questions remain about the existence of other conjugates. Since no pure preparation is available, it is hardly surprising that a number of basic questions about the plasma protein binding, the hepatic uptake, and the biliary excretion of bilirubin glucuronide remain unanswered. One would like to know more about the solubility of pure bilirubin glucuronide in bile or bile constituents in order to understand the formation of pigment stones.

The alternate pathways of heme degradation – the processes by which heme is catabolized to non-bilirubin derivatives – are virtually unexplored. The pyrrolic pigment constituents of fetal amniotic fluid, of bile from patients and animals with defective conjugation, and possibly of normal bile, have not been identified. It is not known where these compounds are made, or whether their formation is enzymatic.

Finally, the known forms of "metabolic jaundice" have not been explained fully. Gilbert's syndrome remains a poorly differentiated diagnostic wastebasket, largely because so little is known about the hepatic uptake and intracellular transport of bilirubin. Similarly, an analysis of the etiology of the Dubin-Johnson syndrome awaits the development of new experimental approaches to the study of the secretion of pigment into the canaliculus. This is not to mention that a number of additional congenital syndromes associated with jaundice await discovery by a discerning clinical eye. Thus, the fact is that the ground has been worked over, but what is needed today are new miners with fresh ideas and advanced techniques.

Acknowledgement

This work was supported in part by U.S.P.H.S. Grant AM09881.

References

Acocella, G., Nicolis, F. B. and Tenconi, L. T. (1965). *Gastroenterology* **49**, 521-525.

Ali, M. A. M. and Billing, B. H. (1966). *Clin. Sci.* **30**, 543-552.

Ali, M. A. M. and Billing, B. H. (1967). *Proc. Soc. exp. Biol. Med.* **124**, 339-342.

Arias, I. M. (1959). *J. Histochem. Cytochem.* **7**, 250-252.

Arias, I. M. (1962). *J. clin. Invest.* **41**, 2233-2245.

Arias, I. M. (1966). *Medicine* **45**, 513-515.

Arias, I. M. and Gartner, L. M. (1964). *Nature, Lond.* **203**, 1292-1293.

Arias, I. M., Bernstein, L., Toffler, R., Cornelius, C., Novikoff, A. B. and Essner, E. (1964). *J. clin. Invest.* **43**, 1249-1250.

Arias, I. M., Gartner, L. M., Seifter, S. and Furman, M. (1964). *J. clin. Invest.* **43**, 2037-2047.

Arias, I. M., Wolfson, S., Lucey, J. F. and McKay, R. J. (1965). *J. clin. Invest.* **44**, 1442-1450.

Axelrod, J., Schmid, R. and Hammaker, L. (1957). *Nature, Lond.* **180**, 1426-1427.

Bernstein, L. H., Ezzer, J. B., Gartner, L. M. and Arias, I. M. (1966). *J. clin. Invest.* **45**, 1194-1201.

Bernstein, R. B., Troxler, R. F. and Lester, R. (1968). *Gastroenterology* **54**, 150.

Berthelot, P. and Billing, B. H. (1966). *Am. J. Physiol.* **211**, 395-399.

Berthelot, P. and Fauvert, R. (1967). *Revue fr. Étud. clin. biol.* **12**, 702-710.

Billing, B. H., Cole, P. G. and Lathe, G. H. (1957). *Biochem. J.* **65**, 774-784.

Billing, B. H., Gray, C. H., Kulczycka, A., Manfield, P. and Nicholson, D. C. (1964). *Clin. Sci.* **27**, 163-170.

Billing, B. H., Williams, R. and Richards, T. G. (1964). *Clin. Sci.* **27**, 245-257.

Bouchier, I. A. D. and Billing, B. H. (1965). *Bilirubin Metabolism*, p. 188. Blackwell Scientific Publications, Oxford.

Bourke, E., Milne, M. D. and Stokes, G. S. (1965). *Br. med. J.* **2**, 1510-1514.

Broughton, P. M. G., Rossiter, E. J. R., Warren, C. B. M., Goulis, G. and Lord, P. S. (1965). *Archs Dis. Childh.* **40**, 666-671.

Brown, A. K. and Zuelzer, W. W. (1958). *J. clin. Invest.* **37**, 332-340.

Brown, W. R., Grodsky, G. M. and Carbone, J. V. (1964). *Am. J. Physiol.* **207**, 1237-1241.

Burnstine, R. C. and Schmid, R. (1962). *Proc. Soc. exp. Biol. Med.* **109**, 356-358.

Butt, H. R., Anderson, V. E., Foulk, W. T., Baggenstoss, A. H., Schoenfield, L. J. and Dickson, E. R. (1966). *Gastroenterology* **51**, 619-630.

Carbone, J. V. and Grodsky, G. M. (1957). *Proc. Soc. exp. Biol. Med.* **94**, 461-463.

Chapman, D. J., Cole, W. J. and Siegelman, H. W. (1967). *J. Am. chem. Soc.* **89**, 5976-5977.

Coburn, R. F., Williams, W. J. and Khan, S. B. (1966). *J. clin. Invest.* **45**, 460-468.

Cole, W. J., Gray, C. H. and Nicholson, D. C. (1965). *J. chem. Soc.* **754**, 4085-4091.

Cole, W. J., Gray, C. H., Nicholson, D. C. and Norman, M. (1966). *J. chem. Soc.* C, 1321-1326.

Cole, W. J., Chapman, D. J. and Siegelman, H. W. (1967). *J. Am. chem. Soc.* **89**, 3643-3645.

Conney, A. A. (1967). *Pharmac. Rev.* **19**, 317-366.

Cornelius, C. E. and Gronwall, R. R. (1965). *Fedn Proc. Fedn Am. Socs exp. Biol.* **24**, 144.

Crigler, J. F. and Gold, N. I. (1966). *J. clin. Invest.* **45**, 998-999.

Crigler, J. F. and Najjar, V. A. (1952). *Pediatrics* **10**, 169-180.

Daly, J. S. F., Little, J. M., Troxler, R. F. and Lester, R. (1967). *Nature, Lond.* **216**, 1030-1031.

Diamond, I. and Schmid, R. (1966). *J. clin. Invest.* **45**, 678-689.

Diamond, I. and Schmid, R. (1967). *Science, N.Y.* **155**, 1288-1289.

Dietschy, J. M., Salomon, H. S. and Siperstein, M. D. (1966). *J. clin. Invest.* **45**, 832-846.

Dubin, I. N. (1958). *Am. J. Med.* **24**, 268-292.

Dubin, I. N. (1962). *Archs intern. Med.* **110**, 823-824.

Dutton, G. J. (1959). *Biochem. J.* **71**, 141-148.

Ernster, L., Herlin, L. and Zetterstrom, R. (1957). *Pediatrics* **20**, 647-652.

Fassati, M., Fassati, P. and Andel, J. (1966). *Čas Lék čes* **105**, 640-645.

Fevery, J., Claes, J., Heirwegh, K. and De Groote, J. (1967). *Clin. chim. Acta* **17**, 73–79.

Fischer, H. and Orth, H. (1937). *Die Chemie des Pyrrols*. Akademische Verlagsgellschaft, Leipzig.

L

274 R. LESTER AND R. F. TROXLER

Fog, J. and Jellum, E. (1963). *Nature, Lond.* **198**, 88-89.
Foulk, W. T., Butt, H. R., Owen, C. A., Whitcomb, F. F. and Mason, H. L. (1959). *Medicine* **38**, 25-46.
Freda, V. J., Gorman, J. G. and Pollack, W. (1967). *New Engl. J. Med.* **277**, 1022-1023.
Fulop, M., Sandson, J. and Brazeau, P. (1965). *J. clin. Invest.* **44**, 666-680.
Gartner, L. M. and Arias, I. M. (1966). *J. Pediat.* **68**, 54-66.
Gardner, W. A. and Konigsmark, B. W. (1968). *J. Neuropath.* **27**, 154-155.
Goresky, C. A. (1965). *Can. med. Ass. J.* **92**, 851-857.
Gray, C. H. (1953). *The Bile Pigments.* John Wiley and Sons, New York.
Gray, C. H. (1961). *Bile Pigments in Health and Disease.* Charles C Thomas, Springfield, Illinois.
Gray, C. H., Neuberger, A. and Sneath, P. H. A. (1950). *Biochem. J.* **47**, 87-92.
Gregory, C. H. (1963). *J. Lab. clin. Med.* **61**, 917-925.
Grodsky, G. M. (1967). In *Bilirubin Metabolism* (I. A. D. Bouchier and Barbara H. Billing, eds), pp. 159-166. Blackwell Scientific Publications, Oxford.
Grodsky, G. M., Contopoulos, A. N., Fanska, R. and Carbone, J. V. (1963). *Am. J. Physiol.* **204**, 837-841.
Gustafsson, B. E. and Lanke, L. S. (1960). *J. exp. Med.* **112**, 975-981.
Hammaker, L. and Schmid, R. (1967). *Gastroenterology* **53**, 31-37.
Harris, J. W. (1963). *The Red Cell: Production, Metabolism, Destruction: Normal and Abnormal*, p. 242. Harvard University Press, Cambridge, Massachusetts.
Henry, R. J., Fernandez, A. A. and Berkman, S. (1964). *Clin. Chem.* **10**, 440-446.
Hoffman, A. H. and Small, D. M. (1967). *A. Rev. Med.* **18**, 333-376.
Hsia, D. Y., Patterson, P., Allen, F. H., Diamond, L. K. and Gellis, S. S. (1952). *Pediatrics* **10**, 243-252.
Hunton, D. B., Bollman, J. L. and Hoffman, H. N. (1961). *J. Clin. Invest.* **40**, 1648-1655.
Ibrahim, G. W., Schwartz, S. and Watson, C. J. (1966). *Metabolism* **15**, 1120-1128.
Ibrahim, G. W., Schwartz, S. and Watson, C. J. (1966). *Metabolism* **15**, 1129-1139.
Israels, L. G., Yamamoto, T., Skanderbeg, J. and Zipursky, A. (1963). *Science, N.Y.* **139**, 1054-1055.
Isselbacher, K. J. and McCarthy, E. A. (1959). *J. clin. Invest.* **38**, 645-651.
Isselbacher, K. J., Chrabas, M. F. and Quinn, R. C. (1962). *J. biol. Chem.* **237**, 3033-3036.
Jackson, A. H., Smith, K. M., Gray, C. H. and Nicholson, D. C. (1966). *Nature, Lond.* **209**, 581-583.
Javitt, N. B. and Arias, I. M. (1967). *Gastroenterology* **53**, 171-175.
Kaplan, M., Straus, P., Bijaoui, G. and Bensadoun, M. (1966). *Ann. pediat.* **40**, 583-596.
Lathe, G. H. and Walker, M. (1958). *Q. Jl exp. Physiol.* **43**, 257-265.
Lemberg, R. (1956). *Rev. pure appl. Chem.* **6**, 1-23.
Lemberg, R. and Legge, J. W. (1949). *Hematin Compounds and Bile Pigments.* Interscience Publishers, New York.
Lester, R. and Klein, P. D. (1966). *J. clin. Invest.* **45**, 1839-1846.
Lester, R. and Schmid, R. (1963a). *J. clin. Invest.* **42**, 736-746.
Lester, R. and Schmid, R. (1963b). *New Engl. J. Med.* **269**, 178-182.
Lester, R. and Schmid, R. (1965). *J. clin. Invest.* **44**, 722-730.
Lester, R., Hammaker, L. and Schmid, R. (1962). *Lancet ii*, 1257.
Lester, R., Behrman, R. E. and Lucey, J. F. (1963). *Pediatrics* **32**, 416-419.
Levin, E. Y. (1967). *Biochim. biophys. Acta* **136**, 155-158.
Levy, M., Lester, R. and Levinsky, N. G. (1968). *J. clin. Invest.* **47**, 2117-2124.
London, I. M., West, R., Shemin, D. and Rittenberg, D. (1950). *J. biol. Chem.* **184**, 351-358.

Lozzio, B. B. and Royer, M. (1962). *Revta Soc. argent. Biol.* **38**, 8-23.

Lozzio, B. B., Gorodisch, S. and Royer, M. (1964). *Clinica chim. Acta* **9**, 78-81.

Lucey, J. F., Behrman, R. E. and Warshaw, A. L. (1963). *Am. J. Dis. Child.* **106**, 350-355.

Malloy, H. T. and Evelyn, K. A. (1937). *J. biol. Chem.* **119**, 481-490.

McMaster, P. D. and Elman, R. (1925). *J. exp. Med.* **41**, 719-738.

Menken, M. and Weinbach, E. C. (1967). *J. Neurochem.* **14**, 189-193.

Menken, M., Waggoner, J. G. and Berlin, N. I. (1966). *J. Neurochem.* **13**, 1241-1248.

Moscowitz, A., Kruger, W. C., Kay, I. T., Skewes, G. and Bruckenstein, S. (1964). *Proc. natn. Acad. Sci., U.S.A.* **52**, 1190-1194.

Murphy, R. F., Ó hEocha, C. and ÓCarra, P. (1967). *Biochem. J.* **104**, 6-8C.

Nakajima, H. (1963a). *J. biol. Chem.* **238**, 3797-3801.

Nakajima, H., Takamura, T., Nakajima, O. and Yamaoka, K. (1963b). *J. biol. Chem.* **238**, 3784-3796.

Nakajima, O. and Gray, C. H. (1967). *Biochem. J.* **104**, 20-22.

Nicholson, D. C. (1967). In *Bilirubin Metabolism* (I. A. D. Bouchier and B. H. Billing, eds), pp. 75-83. Blackwell Scientific Publications, Oxford.

Noir, B. A., DeWalz, A. T. and Rodriguez-Garay, E. A. (1967). In *Bilirubin Metabolism* (I. A. D. Bouchier and B. H. Billing, eds), pp. 99-101. Blackwell Scientific Publications, Oxford.

Nosslin, B. (1960). *Scand. J. clin. Lab. Invest.* **12**, (Suppl. 49): 1-76.

ÓCarra, P. (1962). *Nature, Lond.* **195**, 899-900.

Odell, G. B. (1959). *J. clin. Invest.* **38**, 823-833.

Odell, G. B., Cohen, S. N. and Gordes, E. H. (1962). *Pediatrics* **30**, 613-621.

Odell, G. B., Natzschka, J. C. and Storey, G. N. B. (1967). *Am. J. Physiol.* **212**, 931-938.

Ostrow, J. D. (1967). *J. clin. Invest.* **46**, 2035-2052.

Ostrow, J. D. and Schmid, R. (1963). *J. clin. Invest.* **42**, 1286-1299.

Ostrow, J. D., Hammaker, L. and Schmid, R. (1961). *J. clin. Invest.* **40**, 1442-1452.

Ostrow, J. D., Jandl, J. H. and Schmid, R. (1962). *J. clin. Invest.* **41**, 1628-1637.

Petryka, Z., Nicholson, D. C. and Gray, C. H. (1962). *Nature, Lond.* **194**, 1047-1049.

Pitcher, C. S. and Williams, R. (1963). *Clin. Sci.* **24**, 239-252.

Powell, L. W., Hemingway, E., Billing, B. H., and Sherlock, S. (1967). *New Engl. J. Med.* **277**, 1108-1112.

Ramos, A., Silverberg, M. and Stein, L. (1966). *Am. J. Dis. Child.* **111**, 353-356.

Rich, A. R. (1925). *Physiol. Rev.* **5**, 182-224.

Robinson, S. H., Vanier, T., Desforges, J. F. and Schmid, R. (1962). *New Engl. J. Med.* **267**, 523-529.

Robinson, S. H., Owen, C. A., Flock, E. V. and Schmid R. (1965). *Blood* **26**, 823-829.

Robinson, S. H., Tsong, M., Brown, B. W. and Schmid, R. (1966). *J. clin. Invest.* **45**, 1569-1586.

Robinson, S. H., Lester, R., Crigler, J. F. and Tsong, M. (1967). *New Engl. J. Med.* **277**, 1323-1329.

Rodriguez-Garay, E. A. and Dickson, E. R. (1967). *Proc. Soc. exp. Biol. Med.* **125**, 1291-1293.

Rosenfeld, R. S., Arias, I. M., Gartner, L. M., Hellman, L. and Gallagher, T. F. (1967). *J. clin. Endocrin.* **27**, 1705-1710.

Royer, M. and Solari, A. V. (1941). *Revta Soc. argent. Biol.* **17**, 329-335.

Royer, M., Lozzio, B. B. and Gorodisch, S. (1964). *Acta physiol. latinoam.* **14**, 94-98.

Schalm, L. and Weber, A. Ph. (1964). *Acta med. scand.* **176**, 549-553.

Schenker, S. and McCandless, D. W. (1964). *Nature, Lond.* **202**, 1344-1345.
Schenker, S. and Schmid, R. (1964). *Proc. Soc. exp. Biol. Med.* **115**, 446-448.
Schenker, S., Dawber, N. H. and Schmid, R. (1964). *J. clin. Invest.* **43**, 32-39.
Schenker, S., McCandless, D. W. and Zollman, P. E. (1966). *J. clin. Invest.* **45**, 1213-1220.
Schenker, S., Bashore, R. A. and Smith, F. (1967). In *Bilirubin Metabolism* (I. A. D. Bouchier and B. H. Billing, eds), pp. 199-205. Blackwell Scientific Publications, Oxford.
Schmid, R. (1957). *J. Biol. Chem.* **229**, 881-888.
Schmid, R. and Hammaker, L. (1963). *J. clin. Invest.* **42**, 1720-1734.
Schmid, R., Axelrod, J., Hammaker, L. and Swarm, R. L. (1958). *J. clin. Invest.* **37**, 1123-1130.
Schmid, R., Forbes, A., Rosenthal, I. M. and Lester, R. (1963). *Lancet ii*, 938-939.
Schmid, R., Diamond, I., Hammaker, L. and Gunderson, C. (1965). *Nature, Lond.* **206**, 1041-1043.
Schmid, R., Marver, H. S. and Hammaker, L. (1966). *Biochem. biophys. Res. Comm.* **24**, 319-328.
Shanker, L. S. (1962). *Pharmac. Rev.* **14**, 501-530.
da Silva, L. C., deGodoy, A., Mendes, F. T., Leite, G. M. and Pontes, J. F. (1960). *Gastroenterology* **39**, 605-614.
Sjöstrand, T. (1949). *Scand. J. clin. Lab. Invest.* **1**, 201-214.
Smith, P. M., Middleton, J. E. and Williams, R. (1967). *Gut* **8**, 449-453.
Snyder, A. and Schmid, R. (1965). *J. Lab. clin. Med.* **65**, 817-824.
Stohlman, F. (1962). *New Engl. J. Med.* **267**, 342-348.
Sutherland, J. M. and Keller, W. H. (1961). *Am. J. Dis. Child.* **101**, 447-453.
Talafant, E. (1956). *Nature, Lond.* **178**, 312.
Thompson, R. P. H. and Williams, R. (1967). *Lancet ii*, 646-648.
Troxler, R. F., Dawber, N. H. and Lester, R. (1968). *Gastroenterology* **54**, 568-574.
Ulstrom, R. A. and Eisenklam, E. (1964). *J. Pediat.* **65**, 27-37.
Vest, M., Strebel, L. and Hauenstein, D. (1965). *Biochem. J.* **95**, 11-12C.
Watson, C. J. (1963). *J. clin. Path.* **16**, 1-11.
Watson, C. J. (1965). *Ann. intern. Med.* **63**, 931-944.
Watson, C. J. and Weimer, M. (1959). *J. Lab. clin. Med.* **54**, 1-25.
Watson, C. J., Campbell, M. and Lowry, P. T. (1958). *Proc. Soc. exp. Biol. Med.* **98**, 707-711.
Watson, C. J., Moscowitz, A., Lightmer, D., Kruger, W. C. and Weimer, M. (1966). *J. biol. Chem.* **241**, 5037-5043.
Watson, D. (1962). *Clin. chim. Acta* **7**, 733-734.
Weber, A. Ph. and Schalm, L. (1962). *Clin. chim. Acta* **7**, 805-810.
Weber, A. Ph., Schalm, L. and Witmans, J. (1963). *Acta med. scand.* **173**, 19-24.
Weech, A. A. (1947). *Adv. Pediat.* **2**, 346-366.
Wheeler, H. O., Meltzer, J. I. and Bradley, S. E. (1960). *J. clin. Invest.* **39**, 1131-1144.
Wise, C. D. and Drabkin, D. L. (1964). *Fedn Proc. Fedn Am. Socs exp. Biol.* **23**, 223.
Wise, C. D. and Drabkin, D. L. (1965). *Fedn Proc. Fedn Am. Socs exp. Biol.* **24**, 222.
With, T. K. (1967). *Bile Pigments. Chemical, Biological and Clinical Aspects.* Academic Press, New York.
Yaffee, S. J., Levy, G., Matsuzawa, T. and Baliah, T. (1966). *New Engl. J. Med.* **275**, 1461-1466.
Yamamoto, T., Skanderbeg, J., Zipursky, A. and Israels, L. G. (1965). *J. clin. Invest.* **44**, 31-41.

Note added in proof

Since the completion of this manuscript, several papers have been published which deserve mention.

The enzymatic mechanism for heme degradation (see III. A, above) has been clarified. Tenhunen *et al.* (1968) have described a microsomal enzyme, heme oxygenase, which catalyzes the formation of bilirubin from heme with the intermediate formation of biliverdin. Heme oxygenase activity is found in liver, spleen, and kidney. The enzyme is heat labile, requires NADPH and O_2, and is inhibited by CO in the presence of O_2. The characteristics of heme oxygenase resemble those of the "mixed function oxidase" normally found in liver. Microsomal cytochrome P-450 is the terminal electron acceptor for the "mixed function oxidase", and as suggested by the authors, cytochrome P-450 may perform a similar function in heme oxygenase.

It has been suggested that the "early-labeled" peak (see III. B, above) results from the breakdown of "free tissue heme" (Levitt *et al.*, 1968). Data are presented which tend to show a divergence between P-450 turnover and "early-labeled" peak formation in the presence of inhibitors of protein synthesis. The authors interpret their results as indicating that the earliest component of "early-labeled" peak formation results from the rapid turnover of hepatic heme which is *not* bound to the apoprotein of an enzyme.

Homogenates of Gunn rat liver form relatively little glucuronide conjugate of o-aminophenol (see V. A, above). The addition of diethylnitrosamine (DEN) to homogenates of normal rat liver increases their capacity to conjugate o-aminophenol three-fold. The addition of DEN to Gunn rat liver homogenates increases their limited capacity to form o-aminophenol glucuronide by 20-fold. In fact, glucuronide formation by DEN-stimulated Gunn rat liver homogenates is as great as conjugation by DEN-stimulated normal control homogenates (Stevenson *et al.*, 1968). The results raise the question whether glucuronyl transferase activity deficiency in Gunn rats is the result of an absolute deficiency of enzyme, or of the formation of an altered enzyme, or the presence of an enzyme inhibitor.

Patients with "classical" Crigler-Najjar syndrome (see V. A, above) do *not* respond to phenobarbital administration with a drop in serum bilirubin concentration (Arias *et al.*, 1968). Patients with "Crigler-Najjar syndrome" who have bilirubin diglucuronide in their bile do respond. It is proposed that the two groups have genetically distinct diseases, the former inheriting the defect as an autosomal recessive, while the latter displaying an autosomal dominant mode of inheritance.

References

Arias, I. M., Gartner, L. M., Cohen, M., Ben-Ezzer, J. and Levi, A. J. (1968). *Trans. Ass. Am. Physicians* **81**, 66-73.

Levitt, M., Schacter, B. A., Zipursky, A. and Israels, L. G. (1968). *J. clin. Invest.* **47**, 1281-1294.

Stevenson, I., Greenwood, D. and McEwen, J. (1968). *Biochem. biophys. Res. Commun.* **32**, 866-872.

Tenhunen, R., Marver, H. S. and Schmid, R. (1968). *Proc. natn. Acad. Sci., U.S.A.* **61**, 748-755.

CHAPTER 8

Formation and Metabolism of Bile Acids

HENRY DANIELSSON and KURT EINARSSON

*Department of Chemistry, Karolinska Institutet,
Stockholm, Sweden*

I. Introduction

The main bile acids in bile of most mammalian species are cholic acid (3α,7α,12α-trihydroxy-5β-cholanoic acid), chenodeoxycholic acid (3α,7α-dihydroxy-5β-cholanoic acid) and deoxycholic acid (3α,12α-dihydroxy-5β-cholanoic acid). Bile acids are formed from cholesterol in the liver and are present in bile as conjugates with taurine or glycine. Bile acids are excreted with the bile into the intestine, reabsorbed in the ileum and again excreted with the bile. During this enterohepatic circulation of bile acids, part of the bile acids is not reabsorbed and is excreted with the feces. In the intestine, the bile acids are subjected to the action of intestinal microorganisms. The conjugated bile acids are hydrolysed and the 7α-hydroxyl group is eliminated, yielding deoxycholic acid from cholic acid and litho-cholic acid (3α-hydroxy-5β-cholanoic acid) from chenodeoxycholic acid. Other structural modifications of the bile acids also occur including oxida-tion of hydroxyl groups and reduction of the keto groups formed to α- or β-hydroxyl groups. Many of these metabolites appear to be poorly reabsorbed. The bile acids excreted with the feces consist of a complex mixture of microbially formed metabolites. The bile acids reabsorbed from the intestine are conjugated with taurine or glycine in the liver. In some species, for example the rat and the mouse, the deoxycholic acid reabsorbed from the intestine is converted into cholic acid by a 7α-hydroxylase system in the liver. In other species, e.g. man and the rabbit, such a 7α-hydroxylase system is lacking and deoxycholic acid is a major bile acid in the bile.

Bile acids formed from cholesterol in the liver can be referred to as primary bile acids. Secondary bile acids are those bile acids that are formed from the primary bile acids by the action of intestinal micro-organisms.

The discussion that follows centres on recent developments and the reader is referred to other reviews for a discussion of much of the early work in this field (Bergström *et al.*, 1960; Danielsson, 1963; Haslewood, 1964).

II. Mechanisms of Formation of the Primary Bile Acids

A. *Changes of the steroid nucleus in cholic acid formation*

The conversion of cholesterol into bile acids entails saturation of the Δ^5 double bond, epimerization of the 3β-hydroxyl group, and introduction of hydroxyl groups in the 7α-position and the 12α-position (in the case of cholic acid). In addition, the side-chain is shortened by three carbon atoms, and the carbon atom in the 24-position is transformed into a carboxyl group. The detailed sequence of reactions in the conversion of cholesterol into cholic acid has been established mainly through investigations of the metabolism of cholesterol and other C_{27}-steroids *in vitro*.

The first step in the conversion of cholesterol into cholic acid is the introduction of a hydroxyl group at position C-7 yielding cholest-5-ene-3β,7α-diol, as indicated in Fig. 1. This reaction has been shown to be catalysed by enzyme(s) present in the 20 000 ×*g* supernatant fluid of rat liver homogenates (Danielsson and Einarsson, 1964; Mendelsohn *et al.* 1965*a*). The co-factor requirements for this 7α-hydroxylase system and the mechanism of the reaction are not fully known. Mitton and Boyd (1967) have reported in preliminary form that the microsomal fraction fortified with NADPH catalyses the conversion of cholesterol into cholest-5-ene-3β,7α-diol. Björkhem *et al.* (1968*b*) found that the formation of cholest-5-ene-3β,7α-diol occurred to a lesser extent in the microsomal fraction fortified with NADPH than in the 20 000 ×*g* supernatant fluid. However, in the presence of microsomal fraction fortified with NADPH, there was a marked increase in the amount of 3β-hydroxycholest-5-en-7-one formed. Since the total amount of cholest-5-ene-3β,7α-diol and 3β-hydroxycholest-5-en-7-one formed was about the same in the two enzyme preparations, it was suggested that both compounds might originate from a common intermediate, 3β-hydroxycholest-5-en-7α-hydroperoxide. In the presence of 20 000 $\times g$ supernatant fluid, 3β-hydroxycholest-5-en-7α-hydroperoxide might be preferentially converted into cholest-5-ene-3β,7α-diol,

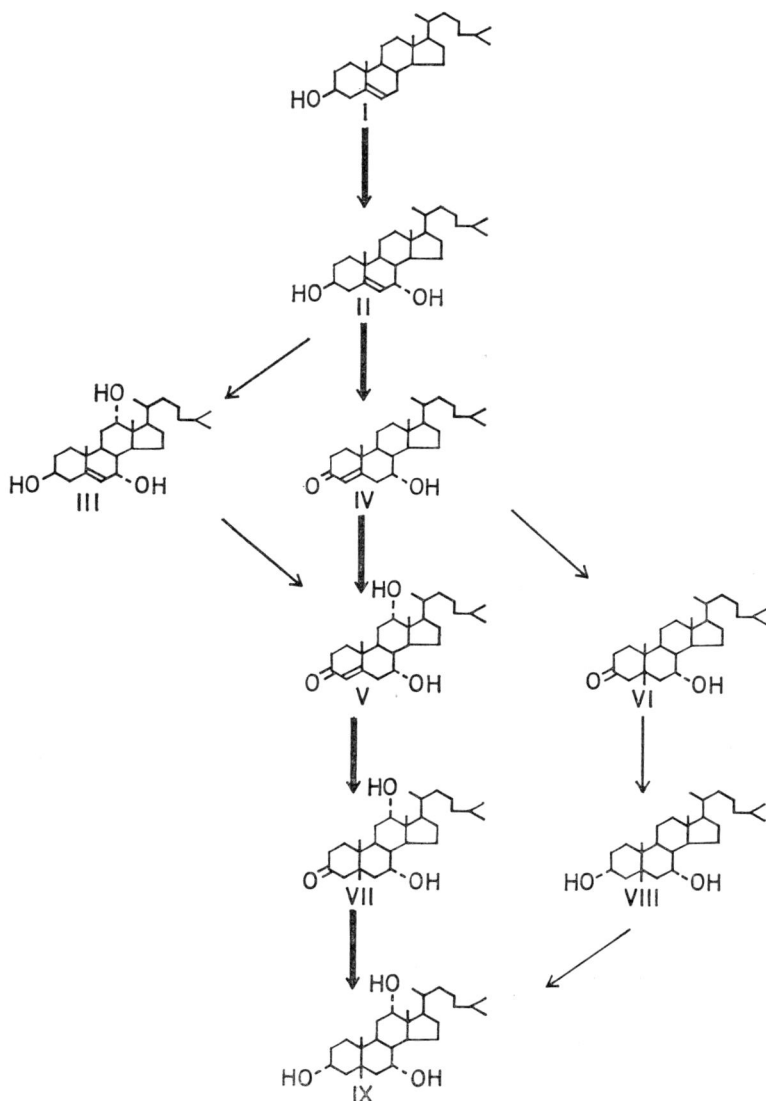

Fig. 1. Conversion of cholesterol to 5β-cholestane-3α,7α,12-triol.

I, cholesterol;
II, cholest-5-ene-3β,7α-diol;
III, cholest-5-ene-3β,7α,12α-triol;
IV, 7α-hydroxycholest-4-en-3-one;
V, 7α,12α-dihydroxycholest-4-en-3-one;

VI, 7α-hydroxy-5β-cholestan-3-one;
VII, 7α,12α-dihydroxy-5β-cholestan-3-one;
VIII, 5β-cholestane-3α,7α-diol;
IX, 5β-cholestane-3α,7α,12α-triol.

whereas in the presence of microsomal fraction fortified with NADPH it might be metabolized mainly into 3β-hydroxycholest-5-en-7-one. However, no conclusive evidence for the intermediary formation of 3β-hydroxycholest-5-en-7α-hydroperoxide was obtained.

The further metabolism of cholest-5-ene-3β,7α-diol can follow two pathways (see Fig. 1). One pathway entails hydroxylation at C-12 to yield cholest-5-ene-3β,7α,12α-triol, which in turn is converted into 7α,12α-dihydroxycholest-4-en-3-one in the presence of microsomal fraction fortified with NAD (Berséus *et al.*, 1967). The other pathway involves conversion of cholest-5-ene-3β,7α-diol into 7α-hydroxycholest-4-en-3-one, also catalysed by the microsomal fraction fortified with NAD (Hutton and Boyd, 1966a; Berséus and Einarsson, 1967). The mechanism of this reaction has been studied by Björkhem (1969a), who has shown that the isomerization of the double bond involves partial transfer of hydrogen from the 4β-position to the 6β-position. It is possible that the reaction is catalysed by a single enzyme.

The further metabolism of 7α-hydroxycholest-4-en-3-one appears to follow two pathways. Mendelsohn and Staple (1963) and Mendelsohn *et al.* (1965a, b, 1966) found that in the presence of 20 000 ×g supernatant fluid of rat liver homogenates, cholesterol was converted into 5β-cholestane-3α,7α-diol and 5β-cholestane-3α,7α,12α-triol in addition to cholest-5-ene-3β,7α-diol and 7α-hydroxycholest-4-en-3-one. Since in these experiments very small amounts of 7α-hydroxy-5β-cholestan-3-one were formed, Mendelsohn *et al.* (1966) suggested that 7α-hydroxycholest-4-en-3-one was converted into 5β-cholestane-3α,7α,12α-triol by means of the intermediary formation of cholest-4-ene-3α,7α-diol and 5β-cholestane-3α,7α-diol. According to these authors the main pathway for the conversion of cholesterol into 5β-cholestane-3α,7α,12α-triol would be: cholesterol→ cholest-5-ene-3β,7α-diol→7α-hydroxycholest-4-en-3-one→cholest-4-ene-3α,7α-diol→5β-cholestane-3α,7α-diol→5β-cholestane-3α,7α,12α-triol (pathway 1 – see Fig. 1). Danielsson and Einarsson (1966) and Berséus *et al.* (1967), on the other hand, isolated cholest-5-ene-3β,7α-diol, 7α-hydroxycholest-4-en-3-one, cholest-5-ene-3β,7α,12α-triol, and 7α,12α-dihydroxycholest-4-en-3-one as the main metabolites after incubation of cholesterol with the 20 000 ×g supernatant fluid and suggested that 7α-hydroxycholest-4-en-3-one is metabolized mainly into 7α,12α-dihydroxycholest-4-en-3-one, which in turn is transformed into 5β-cholestane-3α,7α,12α-triol by two soluble enzymes, a Δ⁴-3-ketosteroid 5β-reductase and a 3α-hydroxysteroid dehydrogenase (Berséus, 1967; and see Fig. 1). On the basis of these results two other pathways for the conversion of cholesterol into 5β-cholestane-3α,7α,12α-triol were proposed: cholesterol→cholest-5-ene-3β,7α-diol→cholest-5-ene-3β,7α,12α-triol→7α,12α-dihydroxycholest-4-en-3-one→7α,12α-dihydroxy-5β-cholestan-3-one→5β-cholestane-3α,7α,12α-triol (pathway 2) (see Fig. 1); cholesterol→cholest-5-ene-3β,7α-diol→7α-hydroxycholest-4-en-3-one →7α,12α-dihydroxycholest-4-en-3-one→7α,12α-dihydroxy-5β-cholestan-3-one→5β-cholestane-3α,7α,12αtriol (pathway 3) (see Fig. 1). The Δ^4-3-ketosteroid 5β-reductase has been purified by about a ten-fold factor from the 100 000 $\times g$ supernatant fluid obtained from rat liver homogenates (Berséus, 1967). The enzyme preparation catalysed the reduction of the double bond in a number of Δ^4-3-ketosteroids of the C_{19}, C_{21}, C_{24} and C_{27} series. NADPH is required as co-factor and it has been shown that the reduction of the Δ^4 double bond involves the transfer of a hydride ion from the A-position of NADPH to the 5β-position of the steroid and the addition of a proton to the 4α-position of the steroid (Berséus and Björkhem, 1967; Björkhem, 1969b). The 3α-hydroxysteroid dehydrogenase has been purified by about a 70-fold factor from the 100 000 $\times g$ supernatant fluid of rat liver homogenates (Berséus, 1967). This partially purified enzyme preparation catalyses the reduction of the 3-keto group in a number of 3-keto steroids of the C_{19}, C_{21}, C_{24} and C_{27} series. NADPH is the co-factor required and the reduction of the 3-keto group has been found to involve the direct transfer of hydrogen from the A-position of NADPH to the 3β-position of the steroid (Berséus and Björkhem, 1967).

It is not possible at present to fully assess the relative quantitative importance of the three pathways for the conversion of cholesterol into 5β-cholestane-3α,7α,12α-triol. Some information relevant to this question has been obtained (Hutton and Boyd, 1966b; Björkhem et al., 1967; Björkhem and Danielsson, 1967; Björkhem, 1967). It has been shown that the formation of cholest-4-ene-3α,7α-diol from 7α-hydroxycholest-4-en-3-one is a side-reaction and that direct saturation of the double bond in cholest-4-ene-3α,7α-diol does not occur to a significant extent. The rate of 12α-hydroxylation of 7α-hydroxycholest-4-en-3-one by the microsomal fraction fortified with NADPH is considerably faster than that of either 5β-cholestane-3α,7α-diol or cholest-5-ene-3β,7α-diol (Einarsson, 1968). These findings indicate that a pathway involving 7α-hydroxycholest-4-en-3-one and 7α,12α-dihydroxycholest-4-en-3-one as intermediates (pathway 3) (see Fig. 1) might be the main pathway for the formation of 5β-cholestane-3α,7α,12α-triol from cholesterol.

The formation of 5β-cholestane-3α,7α,12α-triol from cholesterol has also been studied in homogenates of human liver (Björkhem et al., 1968a). The sequence of reactions, the subcellular localization of the enzymes, and the co-factor requirements were found to be the same as those described for rat liver and discussed above.

B. Oxidation of the side-chain of cholesterol

The degradation of the side-chain of cholesterol in bile acid formation entails an ω-oxidation followed by a β-oxidation with the release of propionic acid. The first step in the oxidation of the side-chain is a 26-hydroxylation (see Fig. 2). This reaction has been shown to be stereospecific (Mitropoulos and Myant, 1965b; Berséus, 1965a) and is catalysed by the mitochondrial fraction of rat liver homogenates (Danielsson, 1960; Suld *et al.*, 1962). The substrate for the 26-hydroxylase in cholic acid formation appears to be 5β-cholestane-3α,7α,12α-triol, and the product of the reaction is thus 5β-cholestane-3α,7α,12α,26-tetrol. 5β-Cholestane-3α,7α, 12α,26-tetrol (see Fig. 2) is further transformed into 3α,7α,12α-trihydroxy-5β-cholestan-26-oic acid (Danielsson, 1960; Suld *et al.*, 1962) by means of the intermediary formation of 3α,7α,12α-trihydroxy-5β-cholestan-26-al (Okuda and Danielsson, 1965; Herman and Staple, 1965; Masui *et al.*,

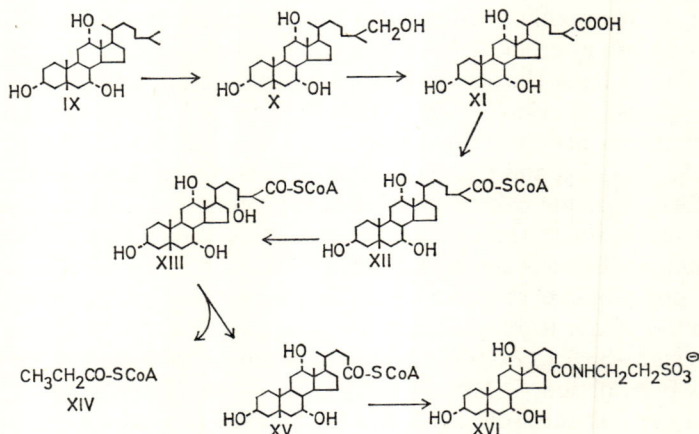

FIG. 2. Conversion of 5β-cholestane-3α,7α,12α-triol to taurocholic acid.

   IX, 5β-cholestane-3α,7α,12α-triol;
    X, 5β-cholestane-3α,7α,12α,26-tetrol;
   XI, 3α,7α,12α-trihydroxy-5β-cholestan-26-oic acid;
  XII, 3α,7α,12α-trihydroxy-5β-cholestan-26-oyl coenzyme-A;
 XIII, 3α,7α,12α,24α-tetrahydroxy-5β-cholestan-26-oyl coenzyme-A;
 XIV, propionyl coenzyme-A;
  XV, cholyl coenzyme-A;
 XVI, taurocholic acid.

1966). The formation of the aldehyde as well as the conversion of the aldehyde into the acid are catalysed by NAD-dependent enzymes present in the 100 000 ×*g* supernatant fluid of rat liver homogenate (Masui *et al.*, 1966). 3α,7α,12α-Trihydroxy-5β-cholestan-26-oic acid is present in small amounts in human bile (Carey and Haslewood, 1963) and labeled 3α,7α, 12α-trihydroxy-5β-cholestan-26-oic acid has been isolated from human bile after administration of labeled cholesterol (Staple and Rabinowitz, 1962; Carey, 1964). The conversion of 3α,7α,12α-trihydroxy-5β-cholestan-26-oic acid into cholic acid and propionic acid (likely in the form of co-enzyme-A derivatives, see Fig. 2) proceeds in the mitochondrial fraction supplemented with the 100 000 ×*g* supernatant fluid and involves the intermediary formation of 3α,7α,12α,24α-tetrahydroxy-5β-cholestan-26-oic acid (Suld *et al.*, 1962; Masui and Staple, 1965, 1966, 1967). The introduction of the hydroxyl group in the 24α-position is catalysed by the mitochondrial fraction supplemented with 100 000 ×*g* supernatant fluid, whereas subsequent reactions are catalysed by enzymes in the 100 000 ×*g* supernatant fluid.

The oxidation of the side-chain in chenodeoxycholic acid formation has not been studied in detail, but it is likely that the sequence of reactions is the same as that of cholic acid formation.

Dean and Whitehouse (1966), who studied the distribution of the enzymes catalysing β-oxidation in various tissues of the rat, found that the enzymes catalysing the β-oxidation of 3β-hydroxycholest-5-en-26-oic acid were restricted to liver tissue, whereas enzymes catalysing the β-oxidation of fatty acids were distributed also in extrahepatic tissues.

C. *Chenodeoxycholic acid formation*

Early investigations showed that C_{27}-steroids with a hydroxyl group in the C-26 position are 12α-hydroxylated only to a limited extent and are converted predominantly into chenodeoxycholic acid when administered to rats with a bile fistula. Cholest-5-ene-3β,26-diol, cholest-5-ene-3β,7α,26-triol, 7α,26-dihydroxycholest-4-en-3-one, and 5β-cholestane-3α,7α,26-triol (Fig. 3), which are *in vivo* transformed into chenodeoxycholic acid and its metabolites have been shown to be formed *in vitro* from the corresponding C_{27}-steroids lacking a 26-hydroxyl group (Danielsson, 1961*a*, *b*; Berséus and Danielsson, 1963). It is thus evident that all these compounds do not fit into a single pathway for the conversion of cholesterol into chenodeoxycholic acid. Probably the formation of these different 26-hydroxylated derivatives *in vitro* reflects the low degree of substrate specificity of the mitochondrial 26-hydroxylase system rather than a multiplicity of pathways. Evidence that 5β-cholestane-3α,7α-diol may be the main substrate for the 26-hydroxylase in chenodeoxycholic acid formation has been brought forward by Björkhem *et al.* (1967). The formation of 5β-cholestane-3α,7α-diol from cholesterol could be shown in homogenates of liver from guinea pigs having chenodeoxycholic as their main primary bile acid. The sequence of reactions and the subcellular localization of the enzymes were found to be the same as those in rat liver and it was suggested that a major pathway for chenodeoxycholic acid formation might be: cholesterol→cholest-5-ene-3β,7α-diol→7α-hydroxycholest-4-en-3-one→7α-hydroxy-5β-cholestan-3-one→5β-cholestane-3α,7α-diol→5β-cholestane-3α,7α,26-triol→chenodeoxycholic acid (see Fig. 3). It is interesting that labeled 5β-cholestane-3α,7α-diol has been isolated from human bile after administration of labeled cholesterol (Herman *et al.*, 1966).

Mitropoulos and Myant (1967*a*, *b*) described the conversion of cholesterol into chenodeoxycholic acid by means of the intermediary formation of lithocholic acid in reactions catalysed by a mitochondrial system from rat liver. The quantitative importance of this pathway has yet to be established. Lithocholic acid is metabolized to a very limited extent in some species that have chenodeoxycholic acid as a major primary bile acid (Section III. C), thus indicating that a pathway from cholesterol to chenodeoxycholic acid

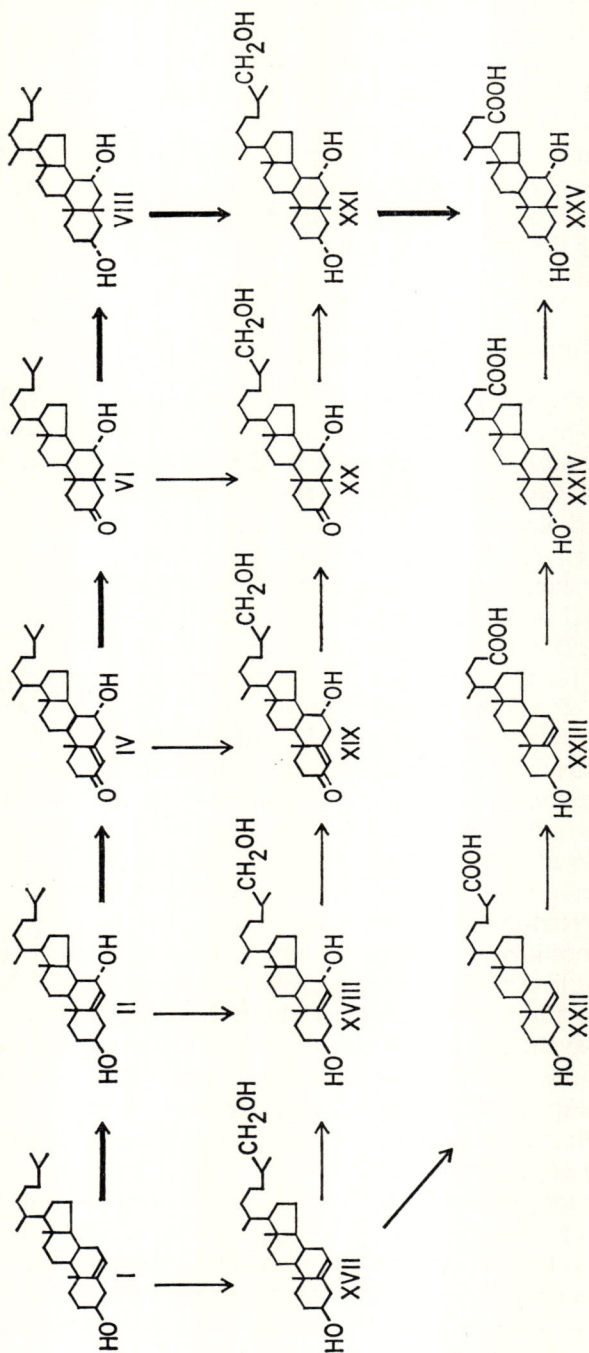

Fig. 3. Conversion of cholesterol to chenodeoxycholic acid.

I, cholesterol;
II, cholest-5-ene-3β,7α-diol;
IV, 7α-hydroxycholest-4-en-3-one;
VI, 7α-hydroxy-5β-cholestan-3-one;
VIII, 5β-cholestane-3α,7α-diol;
XVII, cholest-5-ene-3β,26-diol;
XVIII, cholest-5-ene-3β,7α,26-triol;

XIX, 7α,26-dihydroxycholest-4-en-3-one;
XX, 7α,26-dihydroxy-5β-cholestan-3-one;
XXI, 5β-cholestane-3α,7α,26-triol;
XXII, 3β-hydroxycholest-5-en-26-oic acid;
XXIII, 3β-hydroxychol-5-enoic acid;
XXIV, lithocholic acid;
XXV, chenodeoxycholic acid.

involving lithocholic acid as an intermediate is not important in these species.

D. *Conjugation of bile acids*

Bile acids occur in bile as conjugates with taurine or glycine. The ratio of glycine- to taurine-conjugated bile acids varies with the species. (For a detailed discussion of the conjugation of bile acids in different species, see Haslewood, 1964.) The ratio of glycine- to taurine-conjugated bile acids is also influenced by factors such as age, diet, hormones, and liver disease (Section V). Conjugation of bile acids with ornithine occurs in some pathological conditions (Section V), but ornithine-conjugated bile acids have also been isolated from the bile of patients with normal liver function (Gordon *et al.*, 1963). More recently, Palmer (1967) reported the isolation of labeled glycolithocholic acid sulfate and taurolithocholic acid sulfate from human bile after oral administration of labeled lithocholic acid. Cholesteryl sulfate which can be converted into steroid hormone sulfates without hydrolysis of the sulfate ester does not appear to be a precursor of bile acids (Raggatt *et al.*, 1965).

Early studies showed that the enzymes involved in the conjugation of bile acids were localized mainly in the microsomal fraction and required ATP, CoA and Mg^{2+} (Bergström *et al.*, 1960). Further investigations have shown that the activation of the bile acid is catalysed by the microsomal fraction and requires ATP, CoA and Mg^{2+}, whereas the conjugation proper is catalysed by bile-acyl transferase(s) localized in the lysosomal fraction (Scherstén, 1967a; Scherstén *et al.*, 1967).

III. Metabolism of Bile Acids

A. *Metabolism of bile acids in the intestinal tract*

Bile acids excreted with the bile into the intestine become subjected to the action of intestinal microorganisms. These reactions begin in the lower part of the ileum and continue through the large intestine. The conjugated bile acids are hydrolysed to free bile acids. Studies *in vitro* with micro-organisms normally present in human and rat intestinal contents have shown that strains of *Clostridium*, *Enterococcus*, *Bacteroides* and *Lactobacillus* are able to split off the conjugates (Norman and Grubb, 1955; Norman and Widström, 1964; Drasar *et al.*, 1966; Midtvedt and Norman, 1967, 1968b). Nair *et al.* (1965, 1967) have described the partial purification of a peptide bond hydrolase from cell-free extracts of strains of *Clostridium perfringens*. The enzyme is specific for some naturally occurring bile acid conjugates.

Another important reaction catalysed by enzymes from intestinal micro-organisms is the removal of the 7α-hydroxyl group with the formation of deoxycholic acid from cholic acid and lithocholic acid from chenodeoxycholic acid. Recent studies *in vitro* with micro-organisms isolated from rat feces and human feces have shown that the removal of the 7α-hydroxyl group is effected by anaerobic, Gram-positive rods belonging to *Lactobacilleae* (Gustafsson *et al.*, 1966; Midtvedt, 1967; Midtvedt and Norman, 1968*a*). The mechanisms of 7α-dehydroxylation have been elucidated by the use of cholic acid labeled with tritium in specific positions and have been shown to involve a *trans* elimination of the elements of water (6β-hydrogen, 7α-hydroxyl group) yielding 3α,12α-dihydroxy-5β-chol-6-enoic acid followed by a *trans* hydrogenation in the 6α- and the 7β-position (Bergström *et al.*, 1959*c*; Lindstedt and Samuelsson, 1959; Samuelsson, 1960*c*). The same reaction mechanism applies to the 7α-dehydroxylation of hyocholic acid (3α,6α,7α-trihydroxy-5β-cholanoic acid) yielding hyodeoxycholic acid (3α,6α-dihydroxy-5β-cholanoic acid) in the pig intestine (Bergström *et al.*, 1959*b*; Samuelsson, 1960*b*) and probably also to the 7α-dehydroxylation of chenodeoxycholic acid. The removal of the 7β-hydroxyl group from 3α,7β, 12α-trihydroxy-5β-cholanoic acid (Samuelsson, 1960*a*) and ursodeoxycholic acid (3α,7β-dihydroxy-5β-cholanoic acid (Matkovics and Samuelsson, 1962) as well as the removal of the 7-keto group from 3α,12α-dihydroxy-7-keto-5β-cholanoic acid (Norman and Sjövall, 1958) have been shown to occur in rat intestine but the mechanisms of these reactions are unknown.

Other reactions carried out by intestinal microorganisms include oxidation of hydroxyl groups at C-3, C-7 and C-12. These oxidative reactions have been shown to be carried out *in vitro* by different micro-organisms isolated from rat and human feces. Strains of *Alcaligenes faecalis*, *Bacteroides*, *Clostridium perfringens*, *E. coli* and *Lactobacillus* can carry out many of these reactions (Schmidt and Hughes, 1942; Schmidt *et al.*, 1942; Hoehn *et al.*, 1944; Hayakawa and Morimoto, 1950; Norman and Bergman, 1960; Gustafsson *et al.*, 1966; Midtvedt and Norman, 1967, 1968*a*, 1968*b*). The oxidation of the hydroxyl group at C-6 of 3α,6β-dihydroxy-5β-cholanoic acid has been shown to occur in rat intestine (Einarsson, 1966). The reduction of keto bile acids to both α-hydroxy and β-hydroxy epimers has also been shown to be performed *in vitro* by strains of *Bacteroides*, *Clostridium perfringens*, *E. coli* and *Lactobacillus*. The reduction of the keto group at C-6 of 3α-hydroxy-6-keto-5β-cholanoic acid to 3α,6α-dihydroxy-5β-cholanoic acid (hyodeoxycholic acid) has been shown to occur in rat intestine (Einarsson, 1966). Kallner (1967*a*) has provided evidence that there is an equilibrium between the oxidized and the reduced form with respect to the oxygen function at C-3. It is conceivable that an equilibration of oxygen functions in other positions of the steroid molecule may occur as well.

The elimination of the 7α-hydroxyl group from cholic acid and chenodeoxycholic acid is a main reaction catalysed by microbial enzymes and 3α,12α-dihydroxy-5β-cholanoic acid (Carey and Watson, 1955) and 3α-hydroxy-5β-cholanoic acid (Heftmann *et al.*, 1959) are major bile acids excreted with the feces (Fig. 4) (Rosenfeld and Hellman, 1962; Eneroth *et al.*, 1966*a*). 3β-Hydroxy-5β-cholanoic acid (Heftmann *et al.*, 1959), 3β-hydroxy-12-keto-5β-cholanoic acid (Danielsson *et al.*, 1963*a*), 3α-hydroxy-12-keto-5β-cholanoic acid (Heftmann *et al.*, 1959), and 3β,12α-

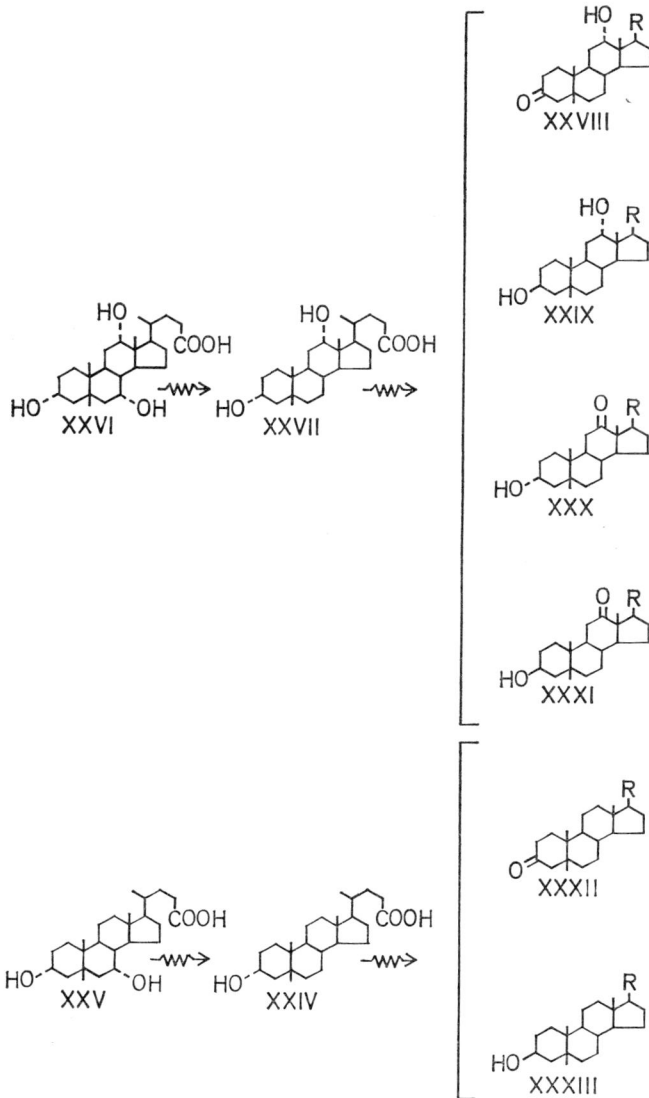

FIG. 4. The main metabolites of the primary bile acids formed by the action of intestinal micro-organisms.

XXVI, cholic acid;
XXVII, deoxycholic acid;
XXVIII, 12α-hydroxy-3-keto-5β-cholanoic acid;
XXIX, 3β,12α-dihydroxy-5β-cholanoic acid;
XXX, 3α-hydroxy-12-keto-5β-cholanoic acid;
XXXI, 3β-hydroxy-12-keto-5β-cholanoic acid;
XXV, chenodeoxycholic acid;
XXIV, lithocholic acid;
XXXII, 3-keto-5β-cholanoic acid;
XXXIII, 3β-hydroxy-5β-cholanoic acid.

dihydroxy-5β-cholanoic acid (Danielsson *et al.*, 1962) are also quantitatively important bile acids in human feces (see Fig. 4) (Danielsson *et al.*, 1963a; Norman, 1964). Other 3,12-disubstituted bile acids occurring in smaller amounts have been isolated from human feces: 3,12-diketo-, 12α-hydroxy-3-keto-, 3α,12β-dihydroxy-, and 3β,12β-dihydroxy-5β-cholanoic acids (Eneroth *et al.*, 1966a). 3,7-Disubstituted bile acids are present in human feces in smaller amounts than the 3,12-disubstituted bile acids (Eneroth *et al.*, 1966a). These acids include chenodeoxycholic acid, 7α-hydroxy-3-keto-, 3α-hydroxy-7-keto-, 3β,7α-dihydroxy-, and 3α,7β-dihydroxy-5β-cholanoic acids (Danielsson *et al.*, 1963a; Eneroth *et al.*, 1966a). Small amounts of 3-keto-5β-cholanoic acid are also present (see Fig. 4) (Danielsson *et al.*, 1963a; Norman and Palmer, 1964). 3,7,12-Trisubstituted bile acids usually account for less than 10% of the total bile acids in human feces (Eneroth *et al.*, 1966b). 3α,7α,12α-Trihydroxy-5β-cholanoic acid was identified by Jenke and Bandow (1937); and Hamilton (1963) provided evidence for the presence of 3α,12α-dihydroxy-7-keto-5β-cholanoic acid and 3α,7β,12α-trihydroxy-5β-cholanoic acid. The identification of these acids and of 3β,7α,12α-trihydroxy-, 3β,7β,12α-trihydroxy-, and 3α,7α-dihydroxy-12-keto-5β-cholanoic acids has been reported by Eneroth *et al.* (1966b).

Some of above-mentioned bile acids occur in feces partly in the form of esters, probably with long-chain fatty acids. Norman (1964) found that at least 25% of 3,12-dihydroxycholanoic acids and mainly in the form of the 3β-isomer, occurred as esters. Norman and Palmer (1964) also found that the transformation of 3α-hydroxy-5β-cholanoic acid into 3β-hydroxy-5β-cholanoic acid was to a large extent associated with the formation of esters so that almost all of the 3β-isomer in feces was esterified while almost all of the 3α-isomer was unesterified.

The presence in human feces of a bile acid having the 5α-configuration (3α,7α,12α-trihydroxy-5α-cholanoic acid, allocholic acid) was reported by Eneroth *et al.* (1966b). In an earlier communication Eneroth *et al.* (1966a) reported that they were unable to detect any mono- or disubstituted 5α-cholanoic acid in human feces. However, 3α,12α-dihydroxy-5α-cholanoic acid (allodeoxycholic acid) has been isolated from rat and rabbit feces (Danielsson *et al.*, 1963b; Kallner, 1967a). The mechanism underlying the formation of 5α-cholanoic acids has not been fully established. Karavolas *et al.* (1965) have shown that 3α,7α,12α-trihydroxy-5α-cholanoic acid is formed from 5α-cholestan-3β-ol in rat liver. Although not conclusively shown, 3α,12α-dihydroxy-5α-cholanoic acid would be expected to be formed by microbial 7α-dehydroxylation of 3α,7α,12α-trihydroxy-5α-cholanoic acid in a manner analogous to the formation of 3α,12α-dihydroxy-5β-cholanoic acid from 3α,7α,12α-trihydroxy-5β-cholanoic acid (Kallner, 1967c). In addition, 3α,12α-dihydroxy-5α-cholanoic acid can be formed from 3α,12α-dihydroxy-5β-cholanoic acid in reactions catalysed by microbial enzymes (Danielsson *et al.*, 1963b; Kallner, 1967a, b). This transformation is reversible but the nature of the mechanism is not known. The probable sequence is: 3α,12α-dihydroxy-5β-cholanoic acid→12α-hydroxy-3-keto-5β-cholanoic acid→12α-hydroxy-3-ketochol-4-enoic acid→12α-hydroxy-3-keto-5α-cholanoic acid→3α,12α-dihydroxy-5α-cholanoic acid. However, present information does not exclude direct dehydrogenation of 3α,12α-dihydroxy-5β-cholanoic acid to 3α,12α-dihydroxychol-4-enoic acid, followed by hydrogenation with the formation of 3α,12α-dihydroxy-5α-cholanoic acid (Kallner, 1967a, b).

B. *Intestinal absorption of bile acids*

The main site of absorption of bile acids is the distal part of the ileum, which has been found to be capable of moving conjugated and unconjugated bile acids against a concentration gradient (Frölicher, 1935-36; Baker and Searle, 1960; Lack and Weiner, 1961; Weiner and Lack, 1962; Holt, 1964; Playoust and Isselbacher, 1964; Glasser et al., 1965). Absorption of bile acids from the caecum has been demonstrated in the rat (Danielsson, 1963). Dietschy et al. (1966) and Dietschy (1967b) have studied the mechanisms of bile acid transport across the intestinal wall both *in vitro* and *in vivo*. They identified three transport mechanisms: passive ionic diffusion, passive nonionic diffusion, and active transport. Under physiological conditions only conjugated bile acids are present in the jejunum and since both taurine and glycine conjugates have a relatively low pK (approximately 1·5 and 3·5, respectively) and the intestinal pH is about 6·2, the conjugates are completely in the ionic form. Thus, it is inferred that conjugated bile acids are absorbed from the jejunum by passive ionic diffusion at a rate which is proportional to the activity of these substances. In the ileum, the conjugated bile acids become absorbed by the same mechanism, but in the lumen of the ileum, and especially in its distal part, deconjugation of the bile acids occurs. The pK of unconjugated bile acids is approximately 6·4 and hence they may occur in the lumen of the ileum in both the ionized and nonionized form. This implies that unconjugated bile acids are transported across the intestinal epithelium of the ileum by both passive ionic and passive non-ionic diffusion at a rate proportional to the activity of the free bile acids in the lumen. In the distal part of the ileum, both conjugated and unconjugated bile acids are also absorbed by an active transport mechanism.

Holt (1966), who has studied the absorption of bile acids in slices of ileum, has provided evidence indicating the existence of a common transport site for which dihydroxycholanoic acid derivatives have a greater affinity than trihydroxycholanoic acid derivatives. Holt (1966) observed competitive inhibition of taurocholic and cholic acid absorption in the presence of other conjugated and unconjugated bile acids. Working with everted sacs of ileum, Lack and Weiner (1966) observed decreased absorption of a given bile acid in the presence of another bile acid. Dihydroxycholanoic acids were found to be more inhibitory than trihydroxycholanoic acids. These workers also presented evidence that trihydroxycholanoic acids are absorbed better than dihydroxycholanoic acids and conjugates better than free acids by the active transport mechanism. However, Dietschy *et al.*, (1966) have provided evidence that the differences in transport of conjugated and unconjugated bile acids in everted gut sacs are artifactual and that conjugated bile acids are absorbed at the same rate by the active transport mechanism.

Recent studies on the composition of the bile acids in portal blood of the rat have shown that the chief bile acids are: cholic, hyodeoxycholic, β-muricholic ($3\alpha,6\beta,7\beta$-trihydroxy-5β-cholanoic), chenodeoxycholic, and deoxycholic acids. About 65% of these acids were in conjugated form (Okishio and Nair, 1966; Cronholm and Sjövall, 1967). The relative amounts of free bile acids and of hyodeoxycholic acid and deoxycholic acid were higher in portal blood draining the distal part of the intestine. The ratios between the different bile acids as well as between conjugated and unconjugated bile acids were about the same in the portal blood and in the intestine, indicating that bile acids are absorbed to about the same extent. According to Dietschy *et al.* (1966), cholic acid should be absorbed more readily in free form than in conjugated form. That is to say mainly by non-ionic diffusion, which would result in a higher ratio between free cholic acid and conjugated cholic acid in the portal blood than in the intestine. Similarly, according to Lack and Weiner (1966), the ratio between trihydroxycholanoic acids and dihydroxycholanoic acids would be higher in portal blood than in the intestine. According to Cronholm and Sjövall (1967), the discrepancies in results might be explained by the fact that the results of Dietschy *et al.* (1966) and Lack and Weiner (1966) were derived from experiments carried out *in vitro*.

The differences in composition of biliary bile acids and fecal bile acids may be due to many different factors. In the liver, enzymes are present that are capable of oxidizing 3α-hydroxy and 3β-hydroxy bile acids to 3-keto bile acids as well as of reducing 3-keto bile acids to 3α-hydroxy bile acids which might explain the usual absence of 3β-hydroxy and 3-keto bile acids from bile. In feces some bile acids occur in partly esterified form whereas no such bile acid esters have been detected in bile. However, no data are available concerning the absorption of bile acid esters and it is possible that they may not be absorbed at all. Norman and Shorb (1962) have shown that lithocholic acid becomes tightly bound to intestinal microorganisms, probably intracellularly. Lithocholic acid, formed *in vivo* in the intestine, might therefore be accessible for absorption only to a limited extent. It is noteworthy that lithocholic acid is present in human bile and rat bile only in very small amounts (Hellström and Sjövall, 1961a) and that only trace amounts can be detected in rat portal blood (Okishio and Nair, 1966). The low solubility of some bile acids may also influence the extent of absorption. Furthermore, many metabolites might be formed in segments of the intestine, distal to the main sites of absorption. Non-absorbable components of the diet may also influence the absorption of bile acids (Eastwood and Boyd, 1967, 1968) (Section V. B).

C. *Metabolism of reabsorbed bile acids in the liver*

Upon reaching the liver with the portal blood the free bile acids are quantitatively conjugated with taurine or glycine. As mentioned in Section II. D, Palmer (1967) showed that during enterohepatic circulation and probably in the liver, lithocholic acid is converted into glycolithocholic acid sulfate and taurolithocholic acid sulfate. In most mammalian species, including man, deoxycholic acid is not further metabolized in the liver except for being conjugated. In the rat and the mouse, taurodeoxycholic acid is 7α-hydroxylated to yield taurocholic acid (Bergström *et al.*, 1960). The metabolism of chenodeoxycholic acid (see Fig. 5) varies with the species. In

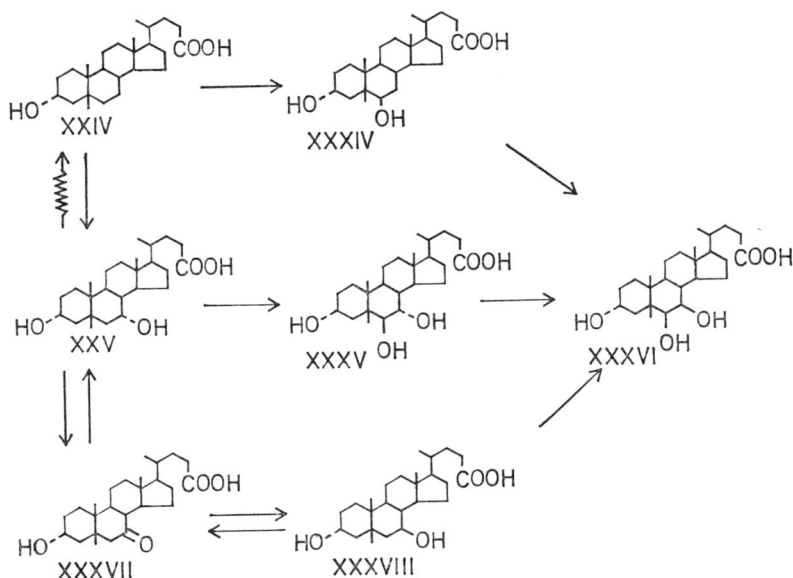

FIG. 5. Some metabolites of chenodeoxycholic acid and of lithocholic acid.

XXIV, lithocholic acid;
XXXIV, $3\alpha,6\beta$-dihydroxy-5β-cholanoic acid;
XXV, chenodeoxycholic acid;
XXXV, α-muricholic acid;
XXXVI, β-muricholic acid;
XXXVII, 3α-hydroxy-7-keto-5β-cholanoic acid;
XXXVIII, ursodeoxycholic acid. $\longrightarrow$, reaction catalysed by liver enzymes; $\wedge\wedge\rightarrow$, reaction catalysed by microbial enzymes.

the rat and the mouse chenodeoxycholic acid is transformed mainly into α-muricholic acid ($3\alpha,6\beta,7\alpha$-trihydroxy-5β-cholanoic acid) and β-muricholic acid ($3\alpha,6\beta,7\beta$-trihydroxy-5β-cholanoic acid) (Mahowald *et al.*, 1957; Hsia *et al.*, 1957, 1958a; Samuelsson, 1959c; Danielsson and Kazuno, 1959). $3\alpha,6\beta,7\beta$-Trihydroxy-5β-cholanoic acid is formed from $3\alpha,6\beta,7\alpha$-trihydroxy-5β-cholanoic acid by means of the intermediary formation of

$3\alpha,6\beta$-dihydroxy-7-keto-5β-cholanoic acid (Samuelsson, 1959c). Cheno-deoxycholic acid is converted to some extent into ursodeoxycholic acid ($3\alpha,7\beta$-dihydroxy-5β-cholanoic acid) (Samuelsson, 1959c) with 3α-hydroxy-7-keto-5β-cholanoic acid as an intermediate (Mahowald et al., 1958; Samuelsson, 1959a, c). $3\alpha,7\beta$-Dihydroxy-5β-cholanoic acid is further transformed into $3\alpha,6\beta,7\beta$-trihydroxy-5β-cholanoic acid (Samuelsson, 1959b). In the guinea pig, 3α-hydroxy-7-keto-5β-cholanoic acid, which is a major bile acid, is transformed mainly into chenodeoxycholic acid (Danielsson and Kazuno, 1959). In the pig, chenodeoxycholic acid is converted into hyocholic acid ($3\alpha,6\alpha,7\alpha$-trihydroxy-5β-cholanoic acid) (Bergström et al., 1959a). Human bile contains small amounts of $3\alpha,7\beta$-dihydroxy-5β-cholanoic acid, possibly formed by reduction of 3α-hydroxy-7-keto-5β-cholanoic acid (Sjövall, 1959; Hellström and Sjövall, 1961a). In a patient with bile fistula, about 15% of the administered chenodeoxycholic acid is transformed into more polar metabolites with the chromatographic properties of $3\alpha,6\beta,7\alpha$-trihydroxy- and $3\alpha,6\beta$-7β-trihydroxy-5β-cholanoic acids (Hellström and Sjövall, 1961a). In the rat hyodeoxycholic acid ($3\alpha,6\alpha$-dihydroxy-5β-cholanoic acid) is partly converted into ω-muricholic acid ($3\alpha,6\alpha,7\beta$-trihydroxy-5β-cholanoic acid) (Matschiner et al., 1957; Hsia et al., 1958b). Lithocholic acid is present only in small amounts in bile and in portal blood, but the metabolism of lithocholic acid in the liver is of considerable interest (see Section VII). In several mammalian species including man and the rabbit, lithocholic acid is not transformed into more polar metabolites (Carey and Williams, 1963; Norman and Palmer, 1964; Johansson, 1966). In the rat lithocholic acid is efficiently converted into $3\alpha,6\beta$-dihydroxy-5β-cholanoic acid and $3\alpha,7\alpha$-dihydroxy-5β-cholanoic acid (see Fig. 5) (Okuda and Kazuno, 1961; Thomas et al., 1964). $3\alpha,6\beta$-Dihydroxy-5β-cholanoic acid is further metabolized into $3\alpha,6\beta,7\beta$-trihydroxy-5β-cholanoic acid (see Fig. 5) (Thomas et al., 1965). In the guinea pig, $3\alpha,7\alpha$-dihydroxy-5β-cholanoic acid and one unidentified dihydroxy-cholanoic acid are formed from lithocholic acid, and in the pig, $3\alpha,6\alpha$-dihydroxy-5β-cholanoic acid and $3\alpha,7\alpha$-dihydroxy-5β-cholanoic acid are major metabolites of lithocholic acid (Kurata, 1963). The metabolism of lithocholic acid has been studied in homogenates of rat, guinea pig and pig liver and it is worth mentioning that the introduction of the hydroxyl group in the 6α-position has been reported to be NADH-dependent (Kurata, 1964).

D. *Excretion of bile acids*

Under normal conditions bile acids are excreted mainly with the feces. After administering 24-^{24}C-labeled bile acids insignificant amounts of isotope were recovered in expired carbon dioxide. The excretion of bile acids with the urine constitutes less than 1% and 4% of the total amount excreted in the rat and man, respectively. In the rabbit about 10% of the excreted bile acids have been found in the urine (Danielsson, 1963). The bile acids in feces are a complex mixture of microbially formed metabolites of the biliary bile acids. The composition and structure of the fecal bile acids in man have been studied in detail (see Section III A).

E. *Regulation of bile acid formation*

The mechanisms by which the formation of bile acids in the liver are regulated are still not known in detail. If bile is continuously drained, the synthesis of bile acids increases. This increase is several-fold in man (Ekdahl and Sjövall, 1957) and the rabbit (Gregg and Poley, 1966) and up to 10- to 15-fold in the rat (Thompson and Vars, 1953, 1954; Eriksson, 1957a). A plateau is reached after about 36–48 hr in the rat and after several days in man and the rabbit. If 5–10 mg of taurochenodeoxycholic acid per hour is continuously supplied to a rat with a biliary fistula by intraduodenal infusion, the rate of bile acid synthesis, as measured by cholic acid formation, is found to return to about the same level as in the intact rat (Bergström and Danielsson, 1958; Lee *et al.*, 1965). This finding implies the existence of a homeostatic mechanism, whereby the amount of bile acids in the portal blood influences the rate of formation of bile acids in the liver. However, under the same experimental conditions, the infusion of taurocholic acid is without effect (Lee *et al.*, 1965). The amount of taurochenodeoxycholic acid needed daily to suppress bile acid formation in a rat with a biliary fistula can be calculated to correspond to the total amount of bile acids reaching daily the liver of the intact rat. This is not true of chenodeoxycholic acid normally present in the portal blood, since its amount only corresponds to 5% of the total bile acids reaching the liver through the portal circulation (Okishio and Nair, 1966; Cronholm and Sjövall, 1967). In view of the difference in effect on bile acid synthesis between taurocholic acid and taurochenodeoxycholic acid, it is possible that taurochenodeoxycholic acid has an effect on bile acid formation which is not related to the physiological regulation of bile acid production. Beher *et al.* (1962, 1963) have examined the influence of different bile acids and cholesterol on the formation and degradation of cholesterol in different animal species. They suggested the existence of a "double feedback" mechanism by means of which bile acids suppress the degradation of cholesterol to bile acids. This would be expected to lead to an increase in liver cholesterol which in turn would suppress the synthesis of cholesterol. On the other hand, Myant and Eder (1961) showed that in a rat with a biliary fistula the increase in cholesterol synthesis precedes the increase in bile acid synthesis, indicating that the regulation of bile acid synthesis might be exerted primarily on the rate of cholesterol synthesis. Dietschy and Siperstein (1965) and Dietschy (1967a, b, 1968) reported that cholesterol synthesis in the intestinal wall is increased manyfold in the rat with a biliary fistula. This rise was suppressed by bile acids, whereas cholesterol had no effect. It was further shown that cholic acid and taurocholic acid specifically inhibited the increase in cholesterol synthesis, whereas deoxycholic acid had a nonspecific inhibitory effect. Ogilvie and Kaplan (1966) have isolated from bile a protein fraction of low molecular weight, which inhibits the incorporation of acetate into cholesterol in the liver. Several reports have appeared in which conjugated and unconjugated bile acids have been added to liver homogenates to study the inhibitory effect of these compounds on different enzymatic reactions. For example, Fimognari and Rodwell (1965) studied the synthesis of mevalonate from acetate, Dean and Whitehouse (1967) studied several steps in the conversion of cholesterol into bile acids and Lee and Whitehouse (1965) studied the effects of bile acids and their conjugates on electron transport and coupled phosphorylation in liver mitochondria. However, it is difficult to evaluate the significance of these observations because unconjugated bile acids are known to be toxic to *in vitro* preparations (Miller and Gaylor, 1967; Dietschy, 1967b), let alone the fact that commercially available conjugated bile acids commonly contain contaminants which affect enzyme reactions (Parkinson and Olson, 1963; Pope *et al.*, 1966; Dietschy, 1967b).

The site of control of cholesterol biosynthesis is the reduction of β-hydroxy-β-methylglutaryl-CoA to mevalonate (Siperstein and Guest, 1959, 1960; Bucher *et al.*, 1960). Other sites of control also exist, but these do not appear to influence significantly the over-all rate of cholesterol synthesis (Gould and Swyryd, 1966). The possible site of control in the formation of bile acids from cholesterol has been studied by Danielsson *et al.* (1967). Several steps in the conversion of cholesterol into cholic acid were studied in homogenates of liver taken from rats with a biliary fistula. It was shown that the extent of 7α-hydroxylation of cholesterol was about eight times greater than in homogenates of liver from normal rats. The conversion of cholest-5-ene-3β,7α-diol into 7α-hydroxycholest-4-en-3-one and the 12α-hydroxylation of 7α-hydroxycholest-4-en-3-one were far less influenced. These results indicate that the first step in the conversion of cholesterol into bile acids might be a rate-determining step.

IV. Quantitative Aspects of Formation and Metabolism of Bile Acids

In healthy subjects on a normal diet the half-life time of cholic acid is 2–3 days and the amount of daily synthesis of cholic acid is about 350 mg (Lindstedt, 1957). In two subjects fed a standardized diet with 40% of the calories as butter fat the half-life times of cholic acid and chenodeoxycholic acid were 2–4 days and 4–6 days, respectively, and the total daily synthesis of bile acids was 500–600 mg (Danielsson *et al.*, 1963a). The excretion of bile acids in feces has been measured by several investigators and the values reported vary within a wide range, from less than 100 mg to over 1000 mg per day. The differences between the reported values can be ascribed, in part, to differences in methodology. The possible inadequacies of many of the methods used in early studies were discussed in a review by Danielsson (1963). In more recent investigations a combination of isotopic methods and chromatographic methods, mainly gas liquid and thin-layer chromatography, has been utilized for measurements of fecal excretion of bile acids and neutral steroids. With these methods the values obtained by different groups of investigators agree fairly well.

Ever since it became clear that the serum cholesterol level is influenced by the degree of unsaturation of the dietary fat, much interest and effort have been devoted to measurements of steroids under different dietary regimens. These studies were performed with standardized diets containing saturated or unsaturated fat. Measuring isotope excretion in feces after administration of 4-[^{14}C]cholesterol, Rosenfeld and Hellman (1962) found an average excretion of 290 mg of bile acids per day. Using a steroid-free diet containing saturated fat or unsaturated fat, Grundy et al. (1965) and Spritz et al. (1965) found the daily excretion of bile acids to be 100 mg and 130 mg, respectively. When the diet contained steroids the corresponding figures were 250 and 270 mg, respectively. With a diet containing 60% of the calories as saturated and unsaturated fat, respectively, Avigan and Steinberg (1965) found the excretion of bile acids to be 800 and 500 mg, respectively. Ali et al. (1966a) studied the excretion of bile acids in three men who were kept on a fat-free diet and found that it ranged between 100 and 650 mg per day. With diets containing 35–60% of total calories as saturated or unsaturated fat, Ali et al. (1966b) could not establish any significant differences in bile acid excretion. Eneroth et al. (1964) and Eneroth et al. (1968) found values ranging between 50 and 500 mg per day in healthy subjects on a solid-food diet with 40% of the calories as fat. No significant differences were observed whether saturated or unsaturated fat was used.

In the above-mentioned studies the excretion of neutral steroids in feces was measured simultaneously, so that it became possible to obtain values for total steroid balance. The values for neutral steroid excretion obtained by different groups of investigators were 500–750 mg per day. It was thus concluded that there are no consistent differences in bile acid and neutral steroid excretion when diets with saturated fat or with unsaturated fat are involved. Lindstedt et al. (1965) measured cholic acid turnover in humans on formula diets with saturated or unsaturated fat, but these authors could not find any differences. Similar results were obtained by Hellström and Lindstedt (1966) in a study of the turnover of cholic acid in healthy subjects and hypercholesterolemic subjects fed a standardized solid-food diet containing either saturated or unsaturated fat. These investigations revealed a significant reduction in serum cholesterol level upon changing from a diet containing saturated fat to one containing unsaturated fat. Apparently, the reduction in serum cholesterol level induced by the intake of unsaturated fat is due to redistribution of cholesterol from the blood to the tissues. However, the possibility cannot be excluded that this initial redistribution of cholesterol is followed by a small increase in excretion of bile acids and neutral steroids over periods of months that may be difficult to detect with present techniques.

The half-life time of cholic acid and chenodeoxycholic acid in the rat is

2–3 days (Lindstedt and Norman, 1956). Generally, the half-life time of bile acids is longer when the animals are fed synthetic diets or diets with large amounts of sucrose, and shorter when chow diets or diets with indigestible material are given (Portman and Murphy, 1958; Gustafsson et al., 1960). In germ-free rats the half-life time of cholic acid has been found to be about seven days (Gustafsson et al., 1957), but this can be shortened by adding indigestible material to the diet (Gustafsson and Norman, 1969). The cholic acid pool in the rat is about 15 mg (Eriksson, 1960). The diet also influences the cholic acid pool, e.g. 15 mg on a standardized diet, about 20 mg on Purina chow, and about 9 mg on starch diet, sucrose diet and sucrose plus Celluflour diet (Portman and Murphy, 1958; Gustafsson et al., 1960). In germ-free rats the cholic acid pool amounts to 18–19 mg (Gustafsson et al., 1957). The daily production of cholic acid is about 4 mg and the total daily production of bile acids is about 5 mg (Eriksson, 1960). Wilson (1962a, b) has studied in the rat the effect of dietary cholesterol on the metabolism of intravenously administered 4-[^{14}C]cholesterol. When the rats were given a sterol-free diet, the isotope excreted was equally distributed between the neutral steroid fraction and the bile acid fraction in the feces. On the addition of cholesterol to the diet, the major part of the isotope was present in the bile acid fraction and the amount of bile acids formed per day was calculated to be 15–20 mg. Evidently rat liver is able to deal with excess dietary cholesterol by increasing the conversion of cholesterol into bile acids.

The turnover of deoxycholic acid has been studied in rabbits in connection with investigations of the effect of dietary fat on bile acid metabolism (Hellström and Sjövall, 1962; Hellström et al., 1962). On a chow diet with a low content of fat the half-life time of deoxycholic acid was about seven days and the daily production about 70 mg. It should be pointed out that the main bile acid synthesized in rabbit liver is cholic acid, which is rapidly dehydroxylated to deoxycholic acid by microbial enzymes. The total daily synthesis of bile acids – small amounts of chenodeoxycholic acid are formed in addition to cholic acid – was calculated to be about 80 mg. Replacement of the chow diet by a semisynthetic diet containing corn oil or hydrogenated coconut oil led to an increase in half-life time of deoxycholic acid from seven days to 24–27 days and to a decrease in daily synthesis of bile acids from about 80 mg to about 30 mg. No significant differences in bile acid metabolism were observed between a corn oil and a coconut oil diet, indicating a redistribution of cholesterol when changing from saturated to unsaturated fat. A report by Bieberdorf and Wilson (1965) lends additional support to this contention.

The concentration of bile acids in human serum was found by Sandberg et al. (1965) to be 0·03–0·23 mg per 100 ml. of serum and by Roovers et al. (1968) to be 0·1–0·4 mg per 100 ml. of serum. Deoxycholic acid, chenodeoxycholic acid and cholic acid were the major bile acids and they were present mainly as conjugates. The concentration of bile acids in rat serum was found by Grundy and Sjövall (1961) to be 0·08 mg per 100 ml. of serum and by Okishio and Nair (1966) to be 1·5 mg per 100 ml. of serum. Okishio and Nair (1966) and Cronholm and Sjövall (1967) have found the concentration of bile acids in rat portal blood to be about 8·3 and 2·6 mg per 100 ml. of serum, respectively. The concentration of bile acids in rabbit serum has been reported to be about 1·2 mg per 100 ml. of serum (Hellström, 1965).

V. Factors Influencing Bile Acid Formation and Metabolism

A. *Age*

The ability of rat embryos to synthesize bile acids was found by White-house et al. (1962) to begin to develop from the 13th day after fertilization. Danielsson and Rutter (1968), who studied the appearance in rat embryos of several enzyme systems involved in the formation of bile acids, found that embryonic liver exhibits a low and rather constant activity between the 15th and 19th day after fertilization. There is afterwards a sharp, synchronous rise in the activity of the enzyme systems, reaching a plateau three days after birth. Another rise in activity occurs between this age and adulthood.

The bile acids in human fetal gallbladder have been investigated by Poley et al. (1964) and the bile acids in the gallbladder and the duodenal contents of infants and children have been studied by several investigators (Encrantz and Sjövall, 1959; Poley et al., 1964; Bongiovanni, 1965). By the second half of the gestation period, both taurine and glycine conjugates of bile acids were present in the gallbladder. During the first days after birth the main part of the bile acids were conjugated with taurine and only at an age of 12 months did the ratio of glycine- to taurine-conjugated bile acids approach the ratio found in the adult (3·1:1·0). The main bile acids were cholic acid and chenodeoxycholic acid. Deoxycholic acid began to appear at an age of 12 months.

B. *Diet*

As pointed out in Section IV, diet has a pronounced influence on the formation and metabolism of bile acids. A more detailed review of this subject can be found elsewhere (Danielsson, 1963). The effects of feeding bile acids and cholesterol on the formation and metabolism of bile acids were discussed in Sections III. E and IV. When rats were fed a diet containing cholesterol only a slight increase in serum cholesterol occurred, whereas the fecal excretion of bile acids rose 4–5 times (Wilson, 1962a, b). In the rabbit, the addition of 1% cholesterol to a low-fat pellet diet caused a marked increase in serum cholesterol and a reduction in the turnover and fecal excretion of deoxycholic acid (Hellström, 1965). In man kept on a daily diet containing 1·4 g of cholesterol, there is a moderate increase in serum cholesterol level, but the turnover of cholic acid is unaffected (Hellström, 1965).

In general, a change from a regular diet – *ad libitum* diet in humans, commercial chow diet in rabbits and rats – to a semisynthetic diet leads to an increase in half-life time of bile acids and a decrease in bile acid production (Danielsson, 1963). Addition of indigestible material to such diets causes a more or less complete reversal of the effects (Danielsson, 1963). It is not known in detail what role the intestinal microorganisms play in connection with the changes in bile acid metabolism induced by different diets. It is conceivable that the dietary effects are mediated by changes in intestinal flora as well as by changes in the rate of passage of content through the intestinal tract.

C. *Vitamins*

Nicotinic acid in large amounts lowers the serum cholesterol level in man and in rabbits (Parsons, 1961). The mechanisms of this effect of nicotinic acid are not fully known (Altschul, 1964). Studies by Goldsmith *et al.* (1960) and Miller *et al.* (1962) indicated that in man the fecal excretion of steroids and bile acids is unchanged by nicotinic acid. Wollenweber *et al.* (1967), who studied the influence of nicotinic acid on the half-life, pool size and turnover of cholic acid and chenodeoxycholic acid in hypercholesteremic patients, found no significant differences in these parameters before and after the administration of nicotinic acid.

Pyridoxine deficiency in rats results in increased glycine conjugation (Doisy *et al.*, 1956; Bergeret and Chatagner, 1956).

D. *Hormones*

Studies of hormonal influence on the formation and metabolism of bile acids have dealt mainly with the effects of thyroid hormones (Danielsson, 1963). It has long been known that a relationship exists between the level of serum cholesterol and the degree of thyroid activity. The rate of synthesis of cholesterol in patients who are hyperthyroid is higher than normal and lower than normal in the patient with hypothyroidism (see Danielsson, 1963). It has thus been suggested that the reduction in serum cholesterol observed in the hyperthyroid state could be due to an increase in metabolism and excretion of cholesterol which is greater than the increase in cholesterol synthesis. Conversely, the decrease in degradation and elimination of cholesterol in the hypothyroid state would be expected to be more pronounced than the decrease in cholesterol synthesis (Kritchevsky, 1960).

The half-life time of cholic acid in the hypothyroid patient was longer and the daily production lower than normal, and after medical treatment there was a decrease in the half-life time of cholic acid and an increase in daily synthesis of bile acids (Hellström and Lindstedt, 1964). Hyperthyroidism was associated with an increase in bile acid production. Hellström and Sjövall (1961b) found that the pattern of conjugation of bile acids was influenced by the level of thyroid activity. For example, in hypothyroid patients, there was a preponderance of bile acids conjugated with glycine. Upon treatment the ratio of glycine- to taurine-conjugated bile acids decreased to normal values.

In rats with biliary fistulas, the excretion of bile acids was lower in the hypothyroid state than in the euthyroid state (Thompson and Vars, 1953, 1954; Eriksson, 1957b). The total excretion of bile acids in hyperthyroid rats with biliary fistulas was about the same as in euthyroid rats with biliary fistulas. However, there was a reversal of the normal ratio of 3 between cholic acid and chenodeoxycholic acid (Eriksson, 1957b). Similar effects on the pattern of bile acid excreted in rats with biliary fistulas were induced by non-calorigenic doses of D-triiodothyronine (Strand, 1962). Similar results were obtained by Lin et al. (1963). In intact rats, the hyperthyroid state was associated with the same reversal of the ratio of cholic acid to chenodeoxycholic acid and with an increase in daily production of bile acids and a decrease in half-life time (Strand, 1963). The half-life time and daily synthesis of bile acids in hypothyroid rats were about the same as in euthyroid rats (Strand, 1963; Beher et al., 1966). Non-calorigenic doses of D-triiodothyronine produced the same effects on bile acid metabolism in intact rats as those observed in the hyperthyroid state (Strand, 1963). The influence of the thyroid on bile acid formation has also been studied in vitro. Mitropoulos and Myant (1965a) found increased formation of propionic acid from cholesterol in liver homogenates from hyperthyroid rats as compared with those from euthyroid rats and a decrease in those from hypothyroid rats. The same effects were observed by Berséus (1965b) in a study of the oxidation of 5β-cholestane-$3\alpha,7\alpha,12\alpha$-triol. More recently, it has been shown that the 12α-hydroxylation of 7α-hydroxycholest-4-en-3-one is increased in homogenates from hypothyroid rats as compared with those from euthyroid rats and decreased in homogenates from hyperthyroid rats as compared with those from euthyroid rats (Mitropoulos et al., 1968). Thyroid hormones might thus exhibit specific effects on the hydroxylation reactions involved in the conversion of cholesterol into bile acids in the rat.

Little is known about the action of other hormones on bile acid metabolism. In adrenalectomized rats the ratio of glycine- to taurine-conjugated bile acids is about 1 as compared with a normal ratio of 0·1. Treatment of adrenalectomized rats with cortisone leads to a normal pattern of bile acid conjugation (Hellström and Strand, 1963).

Kritchevsky et al. (1961, 1963) and Mukherjee and Gupta (1967) found that the extent of oxidation of cholesterol is considerably greater in the presence of liver mitochondria of female rats than in the presence of mitochondria of male rats. Estrogens were shown to increase and androgens to decrease the oxidation of cholesterol (Kritchevsky et al., 1961, 1963; Mukherjee and Gupta, 1967). Estrogens reduce the serum cholesterol level (see Danielsson, 1963).

E. Obstructive jaundice and liver diseases

The presence of free bile acids was long considered a sign of liver damage. However, with the possible exception of as little as a few per cent, all bile acids occur conjugated as determined in choledochostomy drainage bile

(Ekdahl and Sjövall, 1957), gallbladder bile (Sjövall, 1960; Dam et al., 1966), duodenal contents (Sjövall, 1960), and serum (Sandberg et al., 1965) of patients suffering from various diseases. The conjugation pattern of bile acids in man has been studied in various pathological conditions. The ratios of glycine conjugated to taurine-conjugated bile acids (G/T ratio) in the gallbladder bile of patients suffering from cholelithiasis, with more or less pronounced cholecystitis but without severe disturbance in liver function are similar to those observed in healthy subjects (Sjövall, 1960; Dam et al., 1966). Patients with portal cirrhosis have no definite rise in the proportion of taurine conjugates (Sjövall, 1960), but in choledochostomy drainage bile and gallbladder bile from patients with obstructive jaundice, the G/T ratio is reduced (Ekdahl and Sjövall, 1957; Sjövall, 1960). As mentioned in Section II. D, ornithine-conjugated bile acids have been isolated from guinea pig bile and human bile (Peric-Golia and Jones, 1962, 1963). It is possible that the abnormal conjugation was the result of nonspecific hepatic injury.

Several studies have dealt with the pattern of conjugation of cholic acid in specimens of human liver biopsies. Ekdahl and Stenram (1958) and later Sunzel (1963) found that the trauma associated with the procedure gave rise to reduced conjugation with glycine. Sunzel (1963) also found that the influence of surgical trauma on the capacity of the liver to conjugate bile acids could be reduced by giving the patient glucose pre-operatively. Ekdahl and Zederfeldt (1963) have shown that the infusion of low-molecular weight dextran (Rheomacrodex) into patients pre-operatively prevents the changes in conjugation. Ekdahl (1958) has studied the influence of several diseases (with or without jaundice) on the conjugation of bile acids in the liver. Patients with malignant tumours and some of them with liver metastases but without jaundice were found to have a normal conjugation pattern. Patients without jaundice but with portal hypertension caused by extrahepatic block also showed normal conjugation capacity, whereas portal hypertension caused by cirrhosis of the liver was associated with decreased glycine conjugation. All the patients suffering from diseases associated with jaundice had decreased glycine conjugation, but not those suffering from pericholangiolitic hepatitis. Malignant tumours with liver metastases, carcinoma of the biliary tract and biliary cirrhosis were associated with decreased glycine conjugation. Common-duct stones and carcinoma of the head of the pancreas were also associated with decreased glycine conjugation that was apparent after 10 days of jaundice. This decrease was less marked in patients with carcinoma of the head of the pancreas. It was also evident that increasing jaundice was associated with decreased glycine conjugation, whereas disappearing jaundice was associated with restoration of glycine conjugation to normal levels. Hepatitis (infectious, serum and toxic types) led to reduced glycine conjugation during the first three weeks. Ekdahl et al. (1966) reported that not only glycine conjugation but also taurine conjugation was depressed in human liver homogenates obtained by biopsy from patients known to have acute cholecystitis and obstructive jaundice.

Reduced conjugation in acute cholecystitis appeared to be the consequence of insufficient amounts of glycine and taurine for conjugation. On the other hand, the decreased synthesis of glycine and taurine in obstructive jaundice was thought to depend on the catalytic activity of the enzyme system. Scherstén (1967b) studied the synthesis of taurocholic acid and glycocholic acid in homogenates of liver obtained from patients with obstructive jaundice caused by carcinoma of the pancreas or choledocholithiasis. In agreement with the results of Ekdahl (1958) and of Ekdahl et al. (1966), Scherstén found the synthesis of taurocholic acid and glycocholic acid to be depressed, the latter being more reduced than the former. Recent investigations (Scherstén et al., 1966; Scherstén, 1967b; Björkerud et al., 1967) have provided evidence that in patients suffering from obstructive jaundice for more than 14 days, the reduced capacity of the liver to conjugate bile acids may be attributed to increased concentration of bile acid conjugates in the liver which might in turn inhibit conjugation by product inhibition and which might stimulate mitochondrial ATPase activity, thus resulting in the depletion of ATP at a time when ATP is necessary for the conjugation reaction.

Sjövall (1960) has analysed the ratios of glycocholic acid, glycochenodeoxycholic acid, and glycodeoxycholic acid (GC/GCD/GD) in gallbladder bile collected from patients with a variety of diseases. The GC/GCD/GD ratios in non-jaundiced patients with gallstones, and with or without signs of cholecystitis, were similar to those obtained in healthy human subjects. Similar results have been reported by Dam et al. (1966), who also found that the ratios of dihydroxycholanoic acids to trihydroxycholanoic acids were unchanged. Obstructive jaundice was associated with a decrease in GD, an observation which correlated with the severity of the jaundice. Often an increase in the relative amount of GC was also observed. These changes in the amounts of GD and GC may be explained by the fact that GD is formed from GC in the intestine during the enterohepatic circulation of bile acids and hence is not formed when the enterohepatic circulation is interrupted. In patients with portal hypertension due to cirrhosis of the liver, GD is either present in small amounts or absent. The amount of GC in those patients is also decreased and in most of them the relative amount of GCD is increased, occasionally comprising 2–3 of the total bile acids. GD is absent in patients with hepatitis and biliary dyskinesia.

Rudman and Kendall (1957), Carey (1958), Sandberg et al. (1965) and Roovers et al. (1968) determined the ratios between cholic acid, chenodeoxycholic acid, and deoxycholic acid in serum from patients suffering from various liver diseases and found the ratios to be similar to those of biliary bile acids. The relative amount of deoxycholic acid was very low in the serum of patients with portal cirrhosis, hepatitis and obstructive jaundice. In all the patients with liver disease the concentration of serum bile acids was above normal and in some of them it was greatly elevated. Blum and Spritz (1966) studied the metabolism of intravenously injected 24-[^{14}C]-cholic acid in normal subjects and in patients with Laennec's cirrhosis.

They found the initial rate of removal of the labeled compound from plasma to be slower in those with cirrhosis. This was also true of the amount of labeled compound conjugated in one hour. The most striking finding was that in patients with cirrhosis radioactivity in plasma persisted up to 14 days, whereas in normal subjects there was no radioactivity left in the plasma after six hours.

VI. Role of Bile Acids in Absorption

Bile acids play an important role in the digestion and absorption of many nutrients, particularly lipids and lipid-soluble vitamins (vitamins A, D, E and K). This subject will be dealt with in Chapter 11.

VII. Role of Bile Acids in Different Pathological Conditions
A. *Gallstone formation*

Cholesterol is the major compound of most gallstones occurring in man. It remains in solution in bile probably because of phospholipid-bile salt-complexes. The ratios between bile acids and cholesterol and between phospholipids and cholesterol in gallbladder bile obtained from patients who had undergone surgery do not necessarily reflect the conditions existing at the time of formation of the gallstone (Isaksson, 1953-54a, b; Norman, 1965; van der Linden and Norman, 1967). But in animals with experiment-ally induced gallstones the ratios between bile acids and cholesterol and between phospholipids and cholesterol in gallbladder bile are known to be lower than in controls (Dam, 1964; Caldwell *et al.*, 1965). The solubility properties of bile acids and the ability of bile acids to solubilize cholesterol depend on the structure of the steroid nucleus and on the type of conjugate (Norman, 1960). By feeding rabbits a diet containing 1% cholestanol (5α-cholestan-3β-ol), gallstones, which were composed of sodium and cal-cium salts of glycine-conjugated bile acids (Hofmann and Mosbach, 1964), developed; the predominant bile acid was allodeoxycholic acid. In the presence of Na^+ ions the solubility of calcium glycoallodeoxycholate was lower than that of calcium glycodeoxycholate. Dam and Christensen (1962) showed that in hamsters the addition of 0·1% of hyodeoxycholic acid to a lithogenic diet largely inhibited the formation of cholesterol gallstones. The addition of other bile acids (cholic, deoxycholic or lithocholic acid) had no protective effect. However, in mice hyodeoxycholic acid had no protective effect against gallstone formation, indicating a species difference with respect to gallstone formation (Bergman and van der Linden, 1967). The oral administration of 1% lithocholic acid has been shown to induce gall-stones in rats (Carey *et al.*, 1965; Palmer, 1965b; Palmer and Hruban, 1966; Zaki *et al.*, 1966, 1967) but not in baboons (Zaki and Hoffbauer, 1967). The gallstones consisted predominantly of calcium salts of free and glycine-conjugated lithocholic acid and $3\alpha,6\beta$-dihydroxy-5β-cholanoic acid with smaller amounts of chenodeoxycholic acid, hyodeoxycholic acid, and cholic acid. Only traces of taurine-conjugated bile acids were present. The chole lithiasis could be prevented by supplementing the diet with taurine (Palmer, 1965b; Palmer and Hruban, 1966). The mechanism of this inhibitory effect on gallstone formation is not clear. The proportion of taurine-conjugated bile acids rose when the amount of taurine in the diet was increased; this is not surprising since it is known that taurolithocholic acid is more soluble than lithocholic acid and glycolithocholic acid (Norman, 1960). Schoenfield and Sjövall (1966) fed guinea pigs a lithogenic diet and then analysed the gallbladder bile. Low ratios between bile acids and cholesterol and between chenodeoxycholic acid and 3α-hydroxy-7-keto-5β-cholanoic acid were associated with gallstone formation. 3α-Hydroxy-7-keto-5β-cholanoic acid can be expected to be less effective in solubilizing cholesterol than chenodeoxycholic acid (Norman, 1960). Peric-Golia and Jones (1962, 1963) isolated bile acids conjugated with ornithine from the bile of the guinea pig and man, and found that the conditions associated with excretion of ornithine-conjugated bile acids also were associated with the presence of soft gallstones. Jones et al. (1965) suggested that free bile acids could be of importance in the formation of gallstones in man. Schoenfield et al. (1966), who studied the bile acid composition of human gallstones, found that the bile acids occurring in gallstones were also present in bile. Less deoxycholic acid and taurine-conjugated bile acids were found in the center than in the whole gallstone. If the composition of bile acids in the center of the gallstone reflects the composition of bile acids in bile at the time of gallstone formation, then these findings indicate that a disturbance of the enterohepatic circulation may have occurred at the time of gallstone formation.

B. *Liver cirrhosis*

The experimental induction of liver cirrhosis has been extensively studied in the rabbit. Holsti (1960) demonstrated that lithocholic acid, administered to rabbits by gastric tube, produced severe cirrhosis of the liver. Conjugation of lithocholic acid with glycine failed to abolish the cirrhogenic effect (Holsti, 1962). Also shown was that chenodeoxycholic acid was as effective as lithocholic acid in producing cirrhosis, whereas other bile acids (cholic, taurocholic, deoxycholic, hyodeoxycholic, 3α-hydroxy-6-keto-5β-cholanoic, and 3α-hydroxy-6-keto-5α-cholanoic acids) were inactive (Holsti, 1962). Lithocholic acid is not metabolized in rabbit liver except for conjugation (Johansson, 1966) and chenodeoxycholic acid is converted into more polar compounds only to a limited extent (Hellström and Sjövall, 1960). During the enterohepatic circulation chenodeoxycholic acid is converted mainly into lithocholic acid (Hellström and Sjövall, 1960). Thus, the cirrhogenic effect of chenodeoxycholic acid might be mediated through lithocholic acid. Also in man, lithocholic acid (Carey and Williams, 1963; Norman and Palmer, 1964) and chenodeoxycholic acid (Hellström and Sjövall, 1961a) are metabolized to more polar compounds only to a limited extent and lithocholic acid is formed from chenodeoxycholic acid in the intestine (Hellström and Sjövall, 1961a; Danielsson et al., 1963a). Further-

M

more, in patients suffering from liver cirrhosis chenodeoxycholic acid is the predominant bile acid in serum (Rudman and Kendall, 1957; Carey, 1958; Sandberg *et al.*, 1965; Roovers *et al.*, 1968). Carey and Williams (1965) reported that lithocholic acid was present in the serum of patients with cirrhosis in higher amounts than in the serum of healthy subjects. Thus, bile acids may be involved in the initiation and/or the progression of liver cirrhosis in man.

C. *Steroid fever and inflammation*

Certain steroids have been shown to have pyrogenic and inflammatory properties (Palmer and Kappas, 1963; Kappas and Palmer, 1963). Palmer *et al.* (1961, 1962) found that intramuscular injection of lithocholic acid into man produces fever and inflammation. Lithocholic acid can cause inflammatory reactions in various experimental animals, but it must be kept in mind that there is considerable variation in individual responses and sensitivity of various species (Palmer, 1965a). The fact is, however, that lithocholic acid fails to produce fever in animals. The glycine conjugate of lithocholic acid as well as its synthetic 3-acetate and 24-methylether derivatives have pyrogenic and inflammatory properties similar to those of free lithocholic acid. Taurolithocholic acid, however, does not have pyrogenic activity but retains the property of lithocholic acid to induce inflammation. Hyodeoxycholic acid and ursodeoxycholic acid have slight pyrogenic but no inflammatory activity in man. Several other bile acids which have been tested in man have been found to be nonpyrogenic. Thus, introduction of hydroxyl groups in the 7α- and 12α-positions in bile acids suppresses pyrogenicity. The mechanisms by which bile acids produce fever and inflammation are not known. The demonstration of dissociation of the pyrogenic and inflammatory activities indicates that these activities represent independent biological properties and that a nonspecific inflammation does not explain the mechanism of steroid fever.

D. *Pruritus*

In biliary obstruction, be it intra- or extrahepatic in origin, and in patients suffering from liver diseases with pruritus, the serum concentration of bile acids is raised (Rudman and Kendall, 1957; Carey, 1958; Sandberg *et al.*, 1965; Roovers *et al.*, 1968). Thus, pruritus associated with liver diseases has been thought to be related to the raised serum bile acid concentration (for a review, see van Itallie and Hashim, 1963). Early work by Varco (1947) demonstrated that biliary drainage stopped the pruritus in patients with biliary obstruction and that pruritus returned if bile salts were given orally to these patients. On the other hand, Carey (1958) fed a patient suffering from alcoholic cirrhosis, pure cholic acid for several days. The serum concentration of bile acids reached a level exceeding that which accompanies pruritus in other individuals, but no pruritus occurred. The difference between the results of Varco (1947) and those of Carey (1958) might be explained by the fact that Varco (1947) used commercial bile salt preparations containing constituents of bile other than bile acids. Not all patients with elevated levels of serum bile acids have pruritus (Carey, 1958; Osborn et al., 1959). Sjövall and Sjövall (1966) studied the serum bile acids in pregnant women who had pruritus in the last trimester of gestation. There was a 10- to 100-fold increase in concentration of bile acids compared to pregnant women without pruritus. The ratios between the bile acids were similar to those found in patients suffering from biliary obstruction (Section V. E), indicating that pregnancy with pruritus is associated with cholestasis. After delivery, the serum bile acid levels returned to normal and pruritus disappeared.

Schoenfield et al. (1967) studied the occurrence of bile acids on the skin of healthy subjects and of patients suffering from hepatic biliary diseases with and without pruritus. All of these patients were found to have high levels of serum bile acids. Patients with pruritus were found to have more total bile acids on the skin than patients without pruritus. One patient who was studied one month following cholecystojejunostomy was already free of pruritus and the amount of bile acids on the skin was equal to that found in healthy subjects. An ion exchange resin, cholestyramine, which increases the fecal excretion of bile acids and lowers the level of serum bile acids, was given to patients suffering from hepatobiliary diseases with pruritus (Carey and Williams, 1961; van Itallie et al., 1961; Datta and Sherlock, 1963; Oster et al., 1965; Schaffner et al., 1965) and to pregnant women with pruritus (Brown et al., 1963; Fast and Roulston, 1964). Patients in whom significant amounts of bile entered the intestine, as in primary biliary cirrhosis, or incomplete biliary obstruction, and in pregnant women with pruritus, the pruritus disappeared. It should be kept in mind that cholestyramine binds not only bile acids but conjugates of steroid hormones, which represent compounds that may be involved in the genesis of pruritus (Sjövall et al., 1966).

E. Hemolysis

For a more detailed discussion of the hemolytic effects of bile acids and the possible mechanisms of these effects the reader is referred to a review by Kappas and Palmer (1963). Early work by Berliner and Schoenheimer (1938) showed that the hemolytic action of bile acids depended mainly on the spatial configuration of the substituents at carbons 3 and 5. Thus 3α-hydroxy bile acids are more hemolytic than 3β-hydroxy bile acids and bile acids having a 5β-configuration are more hemolytic than those having a 5α-configuration. Furthermore, the hemolytic activity of the 3α-hydroxyl group is reduced by its oxidation to a ketone. Differences exist between the results of studies of the hemolytic activity of various bile acids: these can be explained in some cases by the presence of impurities in the bile acids used. However, there are differences between the bile acids with respect to hemolytic activity. Palmer and Kappas (1963), for example, confirmed and extended the results of Berliner and Schoenheimer (1938), by showing that lithocholic acid is an active hemolytic bile acid as are its glycine- and taurine-conjugates. The 3-acetate derivative of lithocholic acid is more potent than free lithocholic acid. Introduction of additional hydroxyl groups in various positions of the steroid nucleus diminishes the hemolytic activity. A 7α-hydroxyl group is more effective in this respect than a 12α-hydroxyl group, which in turn is more effective than hydroxyl groups in the 6α- and 7β-positions. Cholic acid is essentially inert. Inhibition of hemolysis caused by a given bile acid can be observed with bile acids and sterols whose steric configuration is opposite that of the hemolytic compound used (Kappas and Palmer, 1963).

F. *Blind loop steatorrhea*

The role of bile acids in blind loop steatorrhea has not yet been fully clarified. Dawson and Isselbacher (1960) put forward the theory that the altered bacterial flora of the small intestine accompanying the clinical condition of intestinal blind loop might serve to convert conjugated bile acids into toxic, unconjugated bile acids, which could then interfere with lipid absorption. These workers showed that free deoxycholic acid in contrast to conjugated bile acids inhibited re-esterification of fatty acids. Donaldson (1965) found both in man and in the rat that dihydroxy bile acids accumulated in the contents of the blind loop and that the steatorrhea could be reduced by giving antibiotics. Donaldson (1965) also found that the presence of deoxycholic acid resulted in greater impairment of fatty acid uptake than of esterification. He considered the possibility that the formation of micelles could be impaired. On the other hand, lipolysis in rats with steatorrhea was as effective as in control animals. Kim *et al.* (1966) studied experimentally produced blind loop steatorrhea in dogs and confirmed that the steatorrhea was lessened by antibiotics. The metabolism of bile acids was shown to be different in the small intestine, including the blind loop of dogs with steatorrhea, as compared with the control animals. Thus, the percentage of unconjugated bile acids was high and the unconjugated bile acids were converted into mono- and dihydroxy bile acids. Since feeding of taurocholic acid reduced the steatorrhea, Kim *et al.* (1966) proposed that the deficiency of conjugated bile acids rather than the abnormal accumulation of unconjugated bile acids was the critical factor. Jejunal fluid has a pH of about 6·2 so that conjugated bile acids (relatively low pK) occur mainly in ionic form, while unconjugated bile acids (relatively high pK) occur mainly in nonionic form and as a result cannot optimally participate in micelle formation. This provides an explanation as to why Kim and his co-workers found that dogs with steatorrhea had impaired micelle formation. This is that the defect in the formation of micelles, probably caused by a deficiency in the ionic species of the bile acids, could be the basis of decreased fat absorption.

References

Ali, S. S., Kuksis, A. and Beveridge, J. M. R. (1966a). *Can. J. Biochem.* **44**, 957-969.

Ali, S. S., Kuksis, A. and Beveridge, J. M. R. (1966b). *Can. J. Biochem.* **44**, 1377-1388.

Altschul, R. (1964). *Niacin in Vascular Disorders and Hyperlipemia.* Charles C Thomas, Springfield, Illinois.

Avigan, J. and Steinberg, D. (1965). *J. clin. Invest.* **44**, 1845-1856.

Baker, R. D. and Searle, G. W. (1960). *Proc. Soc. exp. Biol. Med.* **105**, 521-523.

Beher, W. T., Baker, G. D. and Anthony, W. L. (1962). *Proc. Soc. exp. Biol. Med.* **109**, 863-868.

Beher, W. T., Baker, G. D. and Penney, D. G. (1963). *J. Nutr.* **79**, 523-530.

Beher, W. T., Beher, M. E. and Semenuk, G. (1966). *Metabolism* **15**, 181-188.

Bergeret, B. and Chatagner, F. (1956). *Biochim. biophys. Acta* **22**, 273-277.

Bergman, F. and van der Linden, W. (1967). *Acta chir. scand.* **133**, 479-481.

Bergström, S. and Danielsson, H. (1958). *Acta physiol. scand.* **43**, 1-7.

Bergström, S., Danielsson, H. and Göransson, Å. (1959a). *Acta chem. scand.* **13**, 776-783.

Bergström, S., Göransson, Å. and Samuelsson, B. (1959b). *Acta chem. scand.* **13**, 1761-1766.

Bergström, S., Lindstedt, S. and Samuelsson, B. (1959c). *J. biol. Chem.* **234**, 2022-2025.

Bergström, S., Danielsson, H. and Samuelsson, B. (1960). In *Lipide Metabolism* (K. Bloch, ed.), pp. 291-336. John Wiley and Sons, New York.

Berliner, F. and Schoenheimer, R. (1938). *J. biol. Chem.* **124**, 525-541.

Berséus, O. (1965a). *Acta chem. scand.* **19**, 325-328.

Berséus, O. (1965b). *Acta chem. scand.* **19**, 2131-2135.

Berséus, O. (1967). *Europ. J. Biochem.* **2**, 493-502.

Berséus, O. and Björkhem, I. (1967). *Europ. J. Biochem.* **2**, 503-507.

Berséus, O. and Danielsson, H. (1963). *Acta chem. scand.* **17**, 1293-1298.

Berséus, O. and Einarsson, K. (1967). *Acta chem. scand.* **21**, 1105-1108.

Berséus, O., Danielsson, H. and Einarsson, K. (1967). *J. biol. Chem.* **242**, 1211-1219.

Bieberdorf, F. A. and Wilson, J. D. (1965). *J. clin. Invest.* **44**, 1834-1844.

Björkerud, S., Björntorp, P. and Schersten, T. (1967). *Scand. J. clin. Lab. Invest.* **20**, 224-230.

Björkhem, I. (1967). *Acta chem. scand.* **21**, 2561-2564.

Björkhem, I. (1969a). *Europ. J. Biochem.* (In the press.)

Björkhem, I. (1969b). *Europ. J. Biochem.* **7**, 413-417.

Björkhem, I. and Danielsson, H. (1967). *Europ. J. Biochem.* **2**, 403-413.

Björkhem, I., Danielsson, H. and Einarsson, K. (1967). *Europ. J. Biochem.* **2**, 294-302.

Björkhem, I., Danielsson, H., Einarsson, K. and Johansson, G. (1968a). *J. clin. Invest.* **47**, 1573-1582.

Björkhem, I., Einarsson, K. and Johansson, G. (1968b). *Acta chem. scand.* **22**, 1595-1605.

Blum, M. and Spritz, N. (1966). *J. clin. Invest.* **45**, 187-193.

Bongiovanni, A. M. (1965). *J. clin. Endocr. Metab.* **25**, 678-685.

Brown, D. F., Porta, E. A. and Reder, J. (1963). *Archs intern. Med.* **111**, 592-606.

Bucher, N. L. R., Overath, P. and Lynen, F. (1960). *Biochim. biophys. Acta* **40**, 491-501.

Caldwell, F. T., Jr., Levitsky, K. and Rosenberg, B. (1965). *Am. J. Physiol.* **209**, 473-478.

Carey, J. B., Jr. (1958). *J. clin. Invest.* **37**, 1494-1503.

Carey, J. B., Jr. (1964). *J. clin. Invest.* **43**, 1443-1448.
Carey, J. B., Jr. and Haslewood, G. A. D. (1963). *J. biol. Chem.* **238**, PC 855-856.
Carey, J. B., Jr. and Watson, C. J. (1955). *J. biol. Chem.* **216**, 847-850.
Carey, J. B., Jr. and Williams, G. (1961). *J. Am. med. Ass.* **176**, 432-435.
Carey, J. B., Jr. and Williams, G. (1963). *J. clin. Invest.* **42**, 450-455.
Carey, J. B., Jr. and Williams, G. (1965). *Science, N.Y.* **150**, 620-622.
Carey, J. B., Jr., Hoffbauer, F. W., Zaki, F. G. and Nwokolo, C. (1965). *Gastroenterology* **48**, 809-810.
Cronholm, T. and Sjövall, J. (1967). *Europ. J. Biochem.* **2**, 375-383.
Dam, H. (1964). *Proc. VI Int. Congr. Nutr., Edinburgh, 1963* (C. F. Mills and R. Passmore, eds), pp. 6-23. E. & S. Livingstone, Edinburgh.
Dam, H. and Christensen, F. (1962). *Z. ErnährWiss.* **2**, 154-159.
Dam, H., Kruse, I., Kallehauge, H. E., Hartkopp, O. E. and Jensen, M. K. (1966). *Scand. J. clin. Lab. Invest.* **18**, 385-404.
Danielsson, H. (1960). *Acta chem. scand.* **14**, 348-352.
Danielsson, H. (1961a). *Ark. Kemi* **17**, 363-372.
Danielsson, H. (1961b). *Ark. Kemi* **17**, 373-379.
Danielsson, H. (1963). *Adv. Lipid Res.* **1**, 335-385.
Danielsson, H. and Einarsson, K. (1964). *Acta chem. scand.* **18**, 831-832.
Danielsson, H. and Einarsson, K. (1966). *J. biol. Chem.* **241**, 1449-1454.
Danielsson, H. and Kazuno, T. (1959). *Acta chem. scand.* **13**, 1137-1140.
Danielsson, H. and Rutter, W. J. (1968). *Biochemistry* **7**, 346-352.
Danielsson, H., Eneroth, P., Hellström, K. and Sjövall, J. (1962). *J. biol. Chem.* **237**, 3657-3659.
Danielsson, H., Eneroth, P., Hellström, K., Lindstedt, S. and Sjövall, J. (1963a). *J. biol. Chem.* **238**, 2299-2304.
Danielsson, H., Kallner, A. and Sjövall, J. (1963b). *J. biol. Chem.* **238**, 3846-3852.
Danielsson, H., Einarsson, K. and Johansson, G. (1967). *Europ. J. Biochem.* **2**, 44-49.
Datta, D. V. and Sherlock, S. (1963). *Br. med. J.* **1**, 216-219.
Dawson, A. M. and Isselbacher, K. J. (1960). *J. clin. Invest.* **39**, 730-740.
Dean, P. D. G. and Whitehouse, M. W. (1966). *Biochem. J.* **101**, 632-635.
Dean, P. D. G. and Whitehouse, M. W. (1967). *Biochim. biophys. Acta* **137**, 328-334.
Dietschy, J. M. (1967a). *J. clin. Invest.* **46**, 1050.
Dietschy, J. M. (1967b). *Fedn Proc. Fedn Am. Socs exp. Biol.* **26**, 1589-1598.
Dietschy, J. M. (1968). *J. clin. Invest.* **47**, 286-300.
Dietschy, J. M. and Siperstein, M. D. (1965). *J. clin. Invest.* **44**, 1311-1327.
Dietschy, J. M., Salomon, H. S. and Siperstein, M. D. (1966). *J. clin. Invest.* **45**, 832-846.
Doisy, E. A., Jr., Daniels, M. and Zimmerman, S. M. A. (1956). *Fedn Proc. Fedn Am. Socs exp. Biol.* **15**, 243-244.
Donaldson, R. M. (1965). *J. clin. Invest.* **44**, 1815-1825.
Drasar, B. S., Hill, M. J. and Shiner, M. (1966). *Lancet i*, 1237-1238.
Eastwood, M. A. and Boyd, G. S. (1967). *Biochim. biophys. Acta* **137**, 393-396.
Eastwood, M. A. and Boyd, G. S. (1968). *Biochim. biophys. Acta* **152**, 165-173.
Einarsson, K. (1966). *J. biol. Chem.* **241**, 534-539.
Einarsson, K. (1968). *Europ. J. Biochem.* **5**, 101-108.
Ekdahl, P. H. (1958). *Acta chir. scand.* **115**, 208-226.
Ekdahl, P. H. and Sjövall, J. (1957). *Acta chir. scand.* **114**, 439-452.
Ekdahl, P. H. and Stenram, U. (1958). *Acta chir. scand.* **115**, 189-202.
Ekdahl, P. H. and Zederfeldt, B. (1963). *Acta chir. scand.* **126**, 326-328.
Ekdahl, P. H., Gottfries, A. and Scherstén, T. (1966). *Bull Soc. int. Chir.* **1**, 83-89.

Encrantz, J. C. and Sjövall, J. (1959). *Clinica chim. Acta* **4**, 793-799.

Eneroth, P., Hellström, K. and Ryhage, R. (1964). *J. Lipid Res.* **5**, 245-262.

Eneroth, P., Gordon, B., Ryhage, R. and Sjövall, J. (1966a). *J. Lipid Res.* **7**, 511-523.

Eneroth, P., Gordon, B. and Sjövall, J. (1966b). *J. Lipid Res.* **7**, 524-530.

Eneroth, P., Hellström, K. and Sjövall, J. (1968). *Acta chem. scand.* **22**, 1729-1744.

Eriksson, S. (1957a). *Proc. Soc. exp. Biol. Med.* **94**, 578-582.

Eriksson, S. (1957b). *Proc. Soc. exp. Biol. Med.* **94**, 582-584.

Eriksson, S. (1960). *Acta physiol. scand.* **48**, 439-442.

Fast, B. B. and Roulston, T. M. (1964). *Am. J. Obstet. Gynec.* **88**, 314-321.

Fimognari, G. M. and Rodwell, V. W. (1965). *Science, N.Y.* **147**, 1038.

Frölicher, E. (1935-1936). *Biochem. Z.* **283**, 273-279.

Glasser, J. E., Weiner, I. M. and Lack, L. (1965). *Am. J. Physiol.* **208**, 359-362.

Goldsmith, G. A., Hamilton, J. G. and Miller, O. N. (1960). *Arch. intern. Med.* **105**, 512-517.

Gordon, B. A., Kuksis, A. and Beveridge, J. M. R. (1963). *Can. J. Biochem. Physiol.* **41**, 77-89.

Gould, R. G. and Swyryd, E. A. (1966). *J. Lipid Res.* **7**, 698-707.

Gregg, J. A. and Poley, J. R. (1966). *Am. J. Physiol.* **211**, 1147-1151.

Grundy, S. M., Ahrens, E. H., Jr. and Miettinen, T. A. (1965). *J. Lipid Res.* **6**, 397-410.

Grundy, S. M. and Sjövall, J. (1961). *Proc. Soc. exp. Biol. Med.* **107**, 306-309.

Gustafsson, B. E. and Norman, A. (1969). *Br. J. Nutr.* (In the press.)

Gustafsson, B. E., Bergström, S., Lindstedt, S. and Norman, A. (1957). *Proc. Soc. exp. Biol. Med.* **94**, 467-471.

Gustafsson, B. E., Norman, A. and Sjövall, J. (1960). *Arch. Biochem. Biophys.* **91**, 93-100.

Gustafsson, B. E., Midtvedt, T. and Norman, A. (1966). *J. exp. Med.* **123**, 413-432.

Hamilton, J. G. (1963). *Arch. Biochem. Biophys.* **101**, 7-13.

Haslewood, G. A. D. (1964). *Biol. Rev.* **39**, 537-574.

Hayakawa, S. and Morimoto, S. (1950). *Coll. Pap. Hiroshima Med. Sch.* **2**, 9.

Heftmann, E., Weiss, E., Miller, H. K. and Mosettig, E. (1959). *Arch. Biochem. Biophys.* **84**, 324-341.

Hellström, K. (1965). *Acta physiol. scand.* **63**, 21-35.

Hellström, K. and Lindstedt, S. (1964). *J. Lab. clin. Med.* **63**, 666-679.

Hellström, K. and Lindstedt, S. (1966). *Am. J. clin. Nutr.* **18**, 46-59.

Hellström, K. and Sjövall, J. (1960). *Acta chem. scand.* **14**, 1763-1769.

Hellström, K. and Sjövall, J. (1961a). *Acta physiol. scand.* **51**, 218-223.

Hellström, K. and Sjövall, J. (1961b). *J. Atheroscler. Res.* **1**, 205-210.

Hellström, K. and Sjövall, J. (1962). *J. Lipid Res.* **3**, 397-404.

Hellström, K. and Strand, O. (1963). *Acta endocr., Copenh.* **43**, 305-310.

Hellström, K., Sjövall, J. and Wigand, G. (1962). *J. Lipid Res.* **3**, 405-412.

Herman, R. and Staple, E. (1965). *Fedn Proc. Fedn Am. Socs exp. Biol.* **24**, 661.

Herman, R. H., Weinstein, D., Staple, E. and Rabinowitz, J. L. (1966). *Arch. Biochem. Biophys.* **114**, 233-234.

Hoehn, W. M., Schmidt, L. H. and Hughes, H. B. (1944). *J. biol. Chem.* **152**, 59-66.

Hofmann, A. F. and Mosbach, E. H. (1964). *J. biol. Chem.* **239**, 2813-2821.

Holsti, P. (1960). *Nature, Lond.* **186**, 250.

Holsti, P. (1962). *Acta path. microbiol. scand.* **54**, 479.

Holt, P. R. (1964). *Am. J. Physiol.* **207**, 1-7.

Holt, P. R. (1966). *Am. J. Physiol.* **210**, 635-639.

Hsia, S. L., Matschiner, J. T., Mahowald, T. A., Elliott, W. H., Doisy, E. A., Jr., Thayer, S. A. and Doisy, E. A. (1957). *J. biol. Chem.* **226**, 667-671.

Hsia, S. L., Matschiner, J. T., Mahowald, T. A., Elliott, W. H., Doisy, E A., Jr., Thayer, S. A. and Doisy, E. A. (1958a). *J. biol. Chem.* **230**, 573-580.

Hsia, S. L., Elliott, W. H., Matschiner, J. T., Doisy, E. A., Jr., Thayer, S. A. and Doisy, E. A. (1958b). *J. biol. Chem.* **233**, 1337-1339.

Hutton, H. R. B. and Boyd, G. S. (1966a). *Biochim. biophys. Acta* **116**, 336-361.

Hutton, H. R. B. and Boyd, G. S. (1966b). *Biochim. biophys. Acta* **116**, 362-378.

Isaksson, B. (1953-1954a). *Acta Soc. Med. upsal.* **59**, 277-295.

Isaksson, B. (1953-1954b). *Acta Soc. Med. upsal.* **59**, 296-306.

Jenke, M. and Bandow, F. (1937). *Hoppe-Seyler's Z. physiol. Chem.* **249**, 16-23.

Johansson, G. (1966). *Acta chem. scand.* **20**, 240-244.

Jones, R. S., Socic, H. and Hirayama, F. (1965). *Fedn Proc. Fedn Am. Socs exp. Biol.* **24**, 167.

Kallner, A. (1967a). *Acta chem. scand.* **21**, 87-92.

Kallner, A. (1967b). *Acta chem. scand.* **21**, 315-321.

Kallner, A. (1967c). *Ark. Kemi* **26**, 567-576.

Kappas, A. and Palmer, R. H. (1963). *Pharmac. Rev.* **15**, 123-167.

Karavolas, H. J., Elliott, W. H., Hsia, S. L., Doisy, E. A., Jr., Matschiner, J. T., Thayer, S.A. and Doisy, E. A. (1965). *J. biol. Chem.* **240**, 1568-1572.

Kim, Y. S., Spritz, N., Blum, M., Terz, J. and Sherlock, P. (1966). *J. clin. Invest.* **45**, 956-962.

Kritchevsky, D. (1960). *Metabolism* **9**, 984-994.

Kritchevsky, D., Staple, E., Rabinowitz, J. L. and Whitehouse, M. W. (961). *Am. J. Physiol.* **200**, 519-526.

Kritchevsky, D., Tepper, S. A., Staple, E. and Whitehouse, M. W. (1963). *J. Lipid Res.* **4**, 188-192.

Kurata, Y. (1963). *J. Biochem., Tokyo* **53**, 295-298.

Kurata, Y. (1964). *J. Biochem., Tokyo* **55**, 415-419.

Lack, L. and Weiner, I. M. (1961). *Am. J. Physiol.* **200**, 313-317.

Lack, L. and Weiner, I. M. (1966). *Am. J. Physiol.* **210**, 1142-1152.

Lee, M. J. and Whitehouse, M. W. (1965). *Biochim. biophys. Acta* **100**, 317-328.

Lee, M. J., Parke, D. V. and Whitehouse, M. W. (1965). *Proc. Soc. exp. Biol. Med.* **120**, 6-8.

Lin, T. H., Rubinstein, R. and Holmes, W. L. (1963). *J. Lipid Res.* **4**, 63-67.

Lindstedt, S. (1957). *Acta physiol. scand.* **40**, 1-9.

Lindstedt, S. and Norman, A. (1956). *Acta physiol. scand.* **38**, 121-128.

Lindstedt, S. and Samuelsson, B. (1959). *J. biol. Chem.* **234**, 2026-2030.

Lindstedt, S., Avigan, J., Goodman, DeW. S., Sjövall, J. and Steinberg, D. (1965). *J. clin. Invest.* **44**, 1754-1765.

Mahowald, T. A., Matschiner, J. T., Hsia, S. L., Richter, R., Doisy, E. A., Jr., Elliott, W. H. and Doisy, E. A. (1957). *J. biol. Chem.* **225**, 781-793.

Mahowald, T. A., Yin, M. W., Matschiner, J. T., Hsia, S. L., Doisy, E. A., Jr., Elliott, W. H. and Doisy, E. A. (1958). *J. biol. Chem.* **230**, 581-588.

Masui, T. and Staple, E. (1965). *Biochim. biophys. Acta* **104**, 305-307.

Masui, T. and Staple, E. (1966). *J. biol. Chem.* **241**, 3889-3893.

Masui, T. and Staple, E. (1967). *Steroids* **9**, 443-450.

Masui, T., Herman, R. and Staple, E. (1966). *Biochim. biophys. Acta* **117**, 266-268.

Matkovics, B. and Samuelsson, B. (1962). *Acta chem. scand.* **16**, 673-677.

Matschiner, J. T., Mahowald, T. A., Hsia, S. L., Doisy, E. A., Jr., Elliott, W. H. and Doisy, E. A. (1957). *J. biol. Chem.* **225**, 803-810.

Mendelsohn, D. and Staple, E. (1963). *Biochemistry* **2**, 577-579.

Mendelsohn, D., Mendelsohn, L. and Staple, E. (1965a). *Biochim. biophys. Acta* **97**, 379-381.

Mendelsohn, D., Mendelsohn, L. and Staple, E. (1965b). *Biochemistry* **4**, 441-444.

Mendelsohn, D., Mendelsohn, L. and Staple, E. (1966). *Biochemistry* **5**, 1286-1290.

Midtvedt, T. (1967). *Acta pathol. microbiol. scand.* **71**, 147-160.
Midtvedt, T. and Norman, A. (1967). *Acta pathol. microbiol. scand.* **71**, 629-638.
Midtvedt, T. and Norman, A. (1968a). *Acta pathol. microbiol. scand.* **72**, 313-329.
Midtvedt, T. and Norman, A. (1968b). *Acta pathol. microbiol. scand.* **72**, 337-344.
Miller, O. N., Hamilton, J. G. and Goldsmith, G. A. (1962). *Am. J. clin. Nutr.* **10**, 285-296.
Miller, W. L. and Gaylor, J. L. (1967). *Biochim. biophys. Acta* **137**, 400-402.
Mitropoulos, K. A. and Myant, N. B. (1965a). *Biochem. J.* **94**, 594-603.
Mitropoulos, K. A. and Myant, N. B. (1965b). *Biochem. J.* **97**, 26-28C.
Mitropoulos, K. A. and Myant, N. B. (1967a). *Biochem. J.* **103**, 472-479.
Mitropoulos, K. A. and Myant, N. B. (1967b). *Biochim. biophys. Acta* **144**, 430-439.
Mitropuolos, K. A., Suzuki, M., Myant, N. B. and Danielsson, H. (1968). *FEBS Letters.* **1**, 13-15.
Mitton, J. R. and Boyd, G. S. (1967). *Biochem. J.* **103**, 17P.
Mukherjee, S. and Gupta, S. (1967). *J. Atheroscler. Res.* **7**, 435-452.
Myant, N. B. and Eder, H. A. (1961). *J. Lipid Res.* **2**, 363-368.
Nair, P. P., Gordon, M., Gordon, S., Reback, J. and Mendeloff, A. I. (1965). *Life Sci.* **4**, 1887-1892.
Nair, P. P., Gordon, M. and Reback, J. (1967). *J. biol. Chem.* **242**, 7-11.
Norman, A. (1960). *Acta chem. scand.* **14**, 1295-1299.
Norman, A. (1964). *Br. J. Nutr.* **18**, 173-186.
Norman, A. (1965). In *The Biliary System*, pp. 165-174. Blackwell Scientific Publications, Oxford.
Norman, A. and Bergman, S. (1960). *Acta chem. scand.* **14**, 1781-1789.
Norman, A. and Grubb, R. (1955). *Acta pathol. microbiol. scand.* **36**, 537-547.
Norman, A. and Palmer, R. H. (1964). *J. Lab. clin. Med.* **63**, 986-1001.
Norman, A. and Shorb, M. S. (1962). *Proc. Soc. exp. Biol. Med.* **110**, 552-555.
Norman, A. and Sjövall, J. (1958). *J. biol. Chem.* **233**, 872-885.
Norman, A. and Widström, O. A. (1964). *Proc. Soc. exp. Biol. Med.* **117**, 442-444.
Ogilvie, J. W. and Kaplan, B. H. (1966). *J. biol. Chem.* **241**, 4722-4730.
Okishio, T. and Nair, P. P. (1966). *Biochemistry* **5**, 3662-3668.
Okuda, K. and Danielsson, H. (1965). *Acta chem. scand.* **19**, 2160-2165.
Okuda, K. and Kazuno, T. (1961). *J. Biochem., Tokyo* **50**, 20-23.
Osborn, E. C., Wootton, I. D. P., La Silva, L. C. and Sherlock, S. (1959). *Lancet ii*, 1049-1053.
Oster, Z. H., Rachmilewitz, E. A., Moran, E. and Stein, Y. (1965). *Israel J. med. Sci.* **1**, 599-606.
Palmer, R. H. (1965a). *Proc. Soc. exp. Biol. Med.* **119**, 108-111.
Palmer, R. H. (1965b). *Science, N.Y.* **148**, 1339-1340.
Palmer, R. H. (1967). *Proc. natn. Acad. Sci. U.S.A.* **58**, 1047-1050.
Palmer, R. H. and Hruban, Z. (1966). *J. clin. Invest.* **45**, 1255-1267.
Palmer, R. H. and Kappas, A. (1963). *Med. Clins N. Am.* **47**, 101-112.
Palmer, R. H., Glickman, P. B. and Kappas, A. (1961). *J. clin. Invest.* **40**, 1069.
Palmer, R. H., Glickman, P. B. and Kappas, A. (1962). *J. clin. Invest.* **41**, 1573-1577.
Parkinson, T. M. and Olson, J. A. (1963). *Life Sci.* **6**, 393-398.
Parsons, W. B., Jr. (1961). *A.M.A. Archs intern. Med.* **107**, 639-652.
Peric-Golia, L. and Jones, R. S. (1962). *Proc. Soc. exp. Biol. Med.* **110**, 327-331.
Peric-Golia, L. and Jones, R. S. (1963). *Science, N.Y.* **142**, 245-246.
Playoust, M. R. and Isselbacher, K. J. (1964). *J. clin. Invest.* **43**, 467-476.
Poley, J. R., Dower, J. C., Owen, C. A., Jr. and Stickler, G. B. (1964). *J. Lab. clin. Med.* **63**, 838-846.
Pope, J. L., Parkinson, T. M. and Olson, J. A. (1966). *Biochim. biophys. Acta* **130**, 218-232.

Portman, O. W. and Murphy, P. (1958). *Arch. Biochem. Biophys.* **76**, 367-376.

Raggatt, P. R., Dean, P. D. G. and Whitehouse, M. W. (1965). *Biochem. J.* **96**, 26P.

Roovers, J., Evrard, E. and Vanderhaeghe, H. (1968). *Clin. Chim. Acta* **19**, 449-457.

Rosenfeld, R. S. and Hellman, L. (1962). *Arch. Biochem. Biophys.* **97**, 406-410.

Rudman, D. and Kendall, F. E. (1957). *J. clin. Invest.* **36**, 530-537.

Samuelsson, B. (1959*a*). *Acta chem. scand.* **13**, 236-240.

Samuelsson, B. (1959*b*). *Acta chem. scand.* **13**, 970-975.

Samuelsson, B. (1959*c*). *Acta chem. scand.* **13**, 976-983.

Samuelsson, B. (1960*a*). *Acta chem. scand.* **14**, 21-27.

Samuelsson, B. (1960*b*). *Ark. Kemi* **15**, 425-432.

Samuelsson, B. (1960*c*). *J. biol. Chem.* **235**, 361-366.

Sandberg, D. H., Sjövall, J., Sjövall, K. and Turner, D. A. (1965). *J. Lipid Res.* **6**, 182-192.

Schaffner, F., Klion, F. M. and Latuff, A. J. (1965). *Gastroenterology* **48**, 293-298.

Scherstén, T. (1967*a*). *Biochim. biophys. Acta* **141**, 144-154.

Scherstén, T. (1967*b*). *Scand. J. Gastroenterol.* **1**, 1-10.

Scherstén, T., Björkerud, S., Jakoi, L. and Björntorp, P. (1966). *Scand. J. Gastroenterol.* **1**, 284-291.

Scherstén, T., Björntorp, P., Ekdahl, P. H. and Björkerud, S. (1967). *Biochim. biophys. Acta* **141**, 155-163.

Schmidt, L. H. and Hughes, H. B. (1942). *J. biol. Chem.* **143**, 771-783.

Schmidt, L. H., Hughes, H. B., Green, M. H. and Cooper, E. (1942). *J. biol. Chem.* **145**, 229-236.

Schoenfield, L. J. and Sjövall, J. (1966). *Am. J. Physiol.* **211**, 1069-1074.

Schoenfield, L. J., Sjövall, J. and Sjövall, K. (1966). *J. Lab. clin. Med.* **68**, 186-194.

Schoenfield, L. J., Sjövall, J. and Perman, E. (1967). *Nature, Lond.* **213**, 93-94.

Siperstein, M. D. and Guest, M. J. (1959). *J. clin. Invest.* **38**, 1043.

Siperstein, M. D. and Guest, M. J. (1960). *J. clin. Invest.* **39**, 642-652.

Sjövall, K. and Sjövall, J. (1966). *Clin. Chim. Acta* **13**, 207-211.

Sjövall, K., Sjövall, J., Maddock, L. K. and Horning, E. D. (1966). *Anal. Biochem.* **14**, 337-346.

Sjövall, J. (1959). *Acta chem. scand.* **13**, 711-716.

Sjövall, J. (1960). *Clin. Chim. Acta* **5**, 33-41.

Spritz, N., Ahrens, E. H., Jr. and Grundy, S. M. (1965). *J. clin. Invest.* **44**, 1482-1493.

Staple, E. and Rabinowitz, J. L. (1962). *Biochim. biophys. Acta* **59**, 735-736.

Strand, O. (1962). *Proc. Soc. exp. Biol. Med.* **109**, 668-672.

Strand, O. (1963). *J. Lipid Res.* **4**, 305-311.

Suld, H. M., Staple, E. and Gurin, S. (1962). *J. biol. Chem.* **237**, 338-344.

Sunzel, H. (1963). *Acta chir. scand.* suppl. 304.

Thomas, P. J., Hsia, S. L., Matschiner, J. T., Doisy, E. A., Jr., Elliott, W. H., Thayer, S. A. and Doisy, E. A. (1964). *J. biol. Chem.* **239**, 102-105.

Thomas, P. J., Hsia, S. L., Matschiner, J. T., Thayer, S. A., Elliott, W. H., Doisy, E. A., Jr. and Doisy, E. A. (1965). *J. biol. Chem.* **240**, 1059-1063.

Thompson, J. C. and Vars, H. M. (1953). *Proc. Soc. exp. Biol. Med.* **83**, 246-248.

Thompson, J. C. and Vars, H. M. (1954). *Am. J. Physiol.* **179**, 405-409.

van der Linden, W. and Norman, A. (1967). *Acta chir. scand.* **133**, 307-313.

van Itallie, T. B. and Hashim, S. A. (1963). *Med. clin. N. Am.* **47**, 629-648.

van Itallie, T. B., Hashim, S. A., Crampton, R. S. and Tennent, D. M. (1961). *New Engl. J. Med.* **265**, 469-474.

Varco, R. L. (1947). *Surgery* **21**, 43-45.

Weiner, I. M. and Lack, L. (1962). *Am. J. Physiol.* **202**, 155-157.

Whitehouse, M. W., Cottrell, M. C., Briggs, T. and Staple, E. (1962). *Arch. Biochem. Biophys.* **98**, 305-311.

Wilson, J. D. (1962a). *Am. J. Physiol.* **202**, 1073-1076.

Wilson, J. D. (1962b). *Am. J. Physiol.* **203**, 1029-1032.

Wollenweber, J., Kottke, B. A. and Owen, C. A., Jr. (1967). *J. Lab. clin. Med.* **69**, 584-593.

Zaki, F. G. and Hoffbauer, F. W. (1967). In *The Baboon in Medical Research* (H. Vagtborg, ed.), Vol. II, pp. 461-466. University of Texas Press, Austin.

Zaki, F. G., Carey, J. B., Jr. and Hoffbauer, F. W. (1966). *Gastroenterology* **50**, 416.

Zaki, F. G., Carey, J. B., Jr., Hoffbauer, F. W. and Nwokolo, C. (1967). *J. Lab. clin. Med.* **69**, 737-748.

CHAPTER 9

Alcohol and the Liver

C. S. LIEBER

Section of Liver Disease and Nutrition, Bronx Veterans
Administration Hospital and Department of Medicine,
Mt. Sinai School of Medicine, New York, U.S.A.

I. Introduction

The microscopic and macroscopic features of alcoholic liver disease (fat accumulation, necrosis and cirrhosis) have been extensively described since the beginning of the century. But it is only in recent years that with the availability of the electron microscope and the development of techniques to study biochemical events at the subcellular level that there has been added a new dimension to our knowledge of alcohol* induced liver injury. Many of the metabolic disturbances directly attributable to ethanol can now be linked to these alterations in function and structure of subcellular fractions of the hepatocyte after alcohol administration. These subcellular alterations appear to be the early pathology in the chain of events which ultimately result in the gross microscopic and macroscopic changes characteristic of alcohol-induced liver disease. The present chapter will therefore begin with an assessment of the subcellular effects of ethanol.

* Alcohol and ethanol (ethyl alcohol) are used synonymously in this chapter.

II. Effect of Ethanol on Subcellular Fractions of the Hepatocyte

A. *Oxidation of ethanol and associated metabolic changes in the cell sap (cytosol)*

As shown in Fig. 1, the oxidation of ethanol results in the production of acetaldehyde and acetate, and in the generation of NADH from NAD (nicotinamide adenine dinucleotide). A number of metabolic effects of ethanol can be attributed either to one of these metabolites or to the NADH.

1. *Effect of excessive hepatic NADH generation*

Evisceration, hepatectomy or procedures that damage the liver markedly reduce the rate of disappearance of alcohol from the blood (Thompson, 1956). Several other tissues have the capacity, *in vitro*, to metabolize small amounts of alcohol, as reviewed elsewhere (Lieber, 1967) but extrahepatic metabolism of ethanol, though a definite occurrence (Larsen, 1959; Forsander *et al.*, 1960), was found to be small (Bartlett and Barnet, 1949). This *in vivo* evidence, supported by the observation, *in vitro*, of a high rate of ethanol oxidation by liver tissue, led to the concept that most of the initial oxidation of ethanol *in vivo* occurs in the liver. This predominant role of the liver was confirmed by actual measurement of splanchnic ethanol consumption in individuals undergoing hepatic vein catheterization (Tygstrup *et al.*, 1965). This "organ specificity" probably explains why, despite the existence of intracellular mechanisms responsible for the maintenance of stable redox potentials, ethanol oxidation produces a shift towards a more reduced state. As indicated in Fig. 1, the oxidation of ethanol results in the transfer of hydrogen to NAD, which is reduced to NADH. This transfer occurs during the second step of ethanol metabolism, namely the oxidation of acetaldehyde. The first step of ethanol oxidation (its conversion to acetaldehyde) may also result in NADH generation, to the extent that it is catalyzed by alcohol dehydrogenase (ADH).

ADH was found to be heterogeneous both in man (Blair and Vallee, 1966) and in animals (Papenberg *et al.*, 1965). An atypical human ADH has also been described with much higher activity (at low pH) than the commonly found variety (von Wartburg and Papenberg, 1966). Although *in vitro* atypical ADH is more active, individuals with this enzyme failed to show accelerated metabolism of ethanol *in vivo* (Edwards and Price Evans, 1967).

Besides alcohol dehydrogenase, the cytosol contains catalase, an enzyme capable of oxidizing ethanol *in vitro* but which is not considered to play a major role *in vivo* (Bartlett, 1952). However, more recently a microsomal ethanol oxidizing system has been described by Lieber and DeCarli (1968) and this will be discussed in detail later on.

NADH generation produces an increased NADH/NAD ratio (see Lieber, 1967). This type of measurement, however, does not take into account cellular compartmentalization and gives only an attenuated picture of the NADH/NAD changes in the non-mitochondrial compartment of the cell. The latter cannot be measured directly, but can be assessed indirectly by the ratio of metabolites whose oxido-reduction is coupled with the metabolism of ethanol, such as pyruvate-lactate. As emphasized before (Lieber and Davidson, 1962; Lieber, 1968), a number of metabolic effects of alcohol can be attributed to the generation of NADH; these include interference with galactose, serotonin and norepinephrine metabolism. Of special interest is the coupling of the oxidation of ethanol with the reduction of pyruvate to lactate. This leads to increased lactate levels resulting from either increased hepatic lactate production and/or, depending on the metabolic state of the liver, decreased utilization by the liver of lactate derived from extrahepatic tissues (Krebs, 1967). The hyperlactacidemia reduces urinary uric acid excretion which in turn results in alcoholic hyperuricemia, a recently recognized variety of secondary hyperuricemia (Lieber *et al.*, 1962a). Reduction of oxaloacetate could also be coupled with the oxidation of ethanol, and the cyclic oxaloacetate-malate scheme (illustrated in Fig. 1), which has been proposed by various investigators as a mechanism for lipogenesis from glucose, could also explain how ethanol oxidation may result in the production of the two building blocks needed for fatty acid synthesis, namely NADPH and acetyl-CoA. According to this scheme, pyruvate diffuses into the mitochondria to be oxidized to

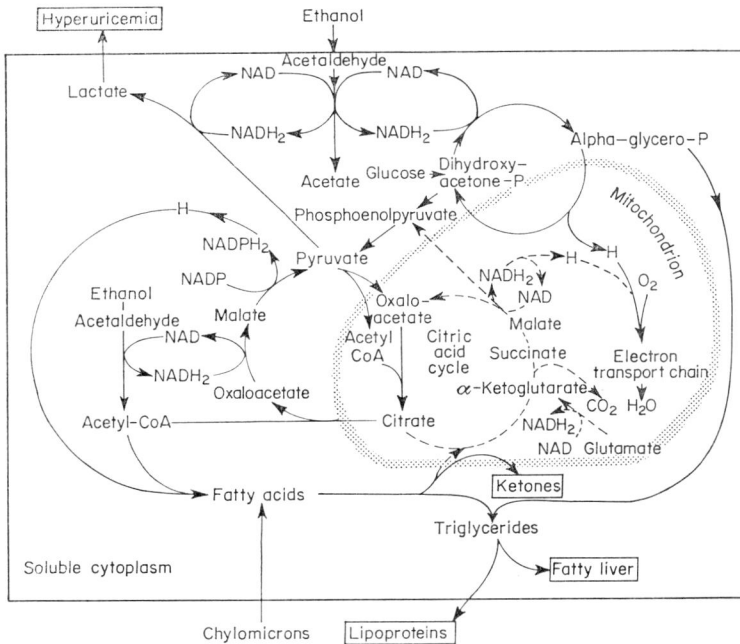

FIG. 1. Disturbances in intermediary metabolism produced by the oxidation of ethanol in the liver. Pathways which are inhibited by ethanol are represented in dotted lines.

acetyl-CoA or converted to oxaloacetate, both of which condense to form citrate. The citrate enters into the citric acid cycle (to be oxidized to CO_2), or diffuses out of the mitochondria into the extramitochondrial space, where citrate cleavage enzyme converts the citrate back to acetyl-CoA and oxaloacetate. The acetyl-CoA (together with acetyl-CoA derived directly from the ethanol) may then be utilized for fatty acid synthesis, while the oxaloacetate may be reduced to malate by malate dehydrogenase and NADH. The malate then reacts with NADP to form pyruvate, CO_2 and NADPH. The net result of these reactions is that pyruvate has been converted to acetyl-CoA and the oxidation of NADH has produced NADPH, necessary for the conversion of acetyl-CoA to fatty acids. Through the postulated coupling of the oxidation of ethanol with the reduction of oxaloacetate to malate, ethanol could accelerate these reactions which in turn could explain our initial observation that ethanol enhances the relative incorporation of [^{14}C]acetate into fatty acids in liver slices (Lieber and Schmid, 1961). As an over-all result, increased fatty acid synthesis can be considered theoretically as a means for disposing of the excess hydrogen produced upon ethanol oxidation in the liver.

The oxidation of ethanol is probably coupled, at least in part, with the reduction of hydroxyacetonephosphate to α-glycerophosphate; the latter was indeed found to be increased in rats given alcohol (Nikkila and Ojala, 1963). In addition to its contribution to the shuttle of reducing equivalents across the mitochondrial membrane (discussed later), α-glycerophosphate could favor accumulation of hepatic triglycerides through enhanced production of their glycerol moiety. Through glyceride formation, accumulation of α-glycerophosphate could be responsible for the diminution, by ethanol, of hepatic acyl-CoA concentration (Zakim, 1965); α-glycerophosphate was also found to stimulate fatty acid synthesis (Howard and Lowenstein, 1964).

2. *Metabolism and metabolic effects of acetaldehyde*

Acetaldehyde is the first and major "specific" oxidation product of ethanol, whether the latter is oxidized by the classic alcohol dehydrogenase of the cytosol or by the more recently described microsomal system. Following the ingestion of alcohol, acetaldehyde is found in both blood (Forster, 1956) and alveolar air (Freund and O'Hallaren, 1965). Except after Antabuse administration, acetaldehyde concentrations after alcohol ingestion are small, but it has long been speculated that they may contribute to the complications of alcoholism (Truitt and Duritz, 1967). The exact pathways of its metabolism remain unknown, but it is generally accepted that the oxidation of acetaldehyde results in the generation of NADH (see Lieber, 1968).

It would thus appear that the metabolism of acetaldehyde may contribute to a number of pathologic effects through the mechanism of NADH generation as pointed out earlier. Acetaldehyde could also produce its effects through the release of catecholamines (Eade, 1959); indeed catechol-amine excretion is increased after ethanol ingestion (Klingman et al., 1958; Perman, 1961). Some of the effects of ethanol upon the brain have been attributed to acetaldehyde (Ridge, 1963; Duritz and Truitt, 1966). These effects included inhibition of brain and liver monoamine oxidase (Towne, 1964), and decreased metabolism of serotonin (Lahti and Majch-rowicz, 1967) and pyruvate (Kiessling, 1962). Acetaldehyde also produced fat accumulation in the liver (Truitt and Duritz, 1966), an effect which possibly reflects the change of redox potential demonstrated in liver slices incubated with acetaldehyde (Forsander, 1966). Acetaldehyde could also be responsible for the reduction in hepatic CoA after ethanol; this has been attributed to inactivation of CoA by acetaldehyde (Ammon et al., 1967). Ethanol exerts various cardiovascular effects, including increased splanch-nic blood flow and cardiac output (Stein et al., 1963); several of these effects could be due to the action of acetaldehyde per se (James and Bear, 1967).

3. Metabolism and metabolic effects of acetate and acetyl-CoA

The fate of acetaldehyde is still the subject of debate. That acetyl-CoA is formed from ethanol is indicated by the observation that [^{14}C]ethanol can be traced to a variety of metabolites of which acetyl-CoA is a precursor, such as fatty acids and cholesterol (as reviewed elsewhere: Lieber, 1967). This includes acetylsulfanilamide (Snyder et al., 1964). The acetaldehyde which results from the oxidation of ethanol could be converted to acetyl-CoA via acetate which occurs in markedly raised concentration in the blood after ethanol administration (Lundquist et al., 1962; Crouse et al., 1968). The very opposite, namely that ethanol is converted directly to acetyl-CoA which in turn might be incorporated into various metabolites or might yield acetate, is a possibility which has yet to be excluded.

Minor metabolites such as 4-keto, 5-hydroxyhexanoic acid which derives from the condensation of acetaldehyde with α-ketoglutarate (Westerfeld and Bloom, 1966), a pathway similar to that of acetoin production, have also been described.

The acetyl-CoA which results from the metabolisn of alcohol shares the same fate as acetyl-CoA produced by various other sources. It is, to a large extent, oxidized to CO_2 through the citric acid cycle but [^{14}C]ethanol can also be traced to fatty acids, cholesterol, glycogen and amino acids (see Lieber and Davidson, 1962). Some investigators found incorporation of the label into these products to be greater from [^{14}C]ethanol than from [^{14}C]-acetate (Schulman et al., 1957; Smith and Newman, 1960; Russell and Van Bruggen, 1964; Snyder et al., 1964). This is inconsistent with the view that the pathway of ethanol requires free acetate as an intermediate. Alter-native explanations are possible: ethanol may exhibit easier penetration, activation or uptake than acetate, or there could be more than one acetate pool or the free acetate could be "enzyme-bound" in its progression course from acetaldehyde to acetyl-CoA. Furthermore, *in vitro*, if trace amounts of [14C]-labeled ethanol are used, and if isotopic dilution is taken into consideration, [14C]ethanol and [14C]acetate are incorporated similarly into lipids (Lieber *et al.*, 1959). Labeling ratios of [14C-1]ethanol and [14C-2]-ethanol (compared to [14C-2]acetate and to [14C-1]acetate) are also consistent with the view that the major pathway for ethanol metabolism proceeds via acetate (Russell and Van Bruggen, 1966).

Although, *in vitro*, the liver can readily utilize acetate, *in vivo* most of the acetate is metabolized in peripheral tissues (Katz and Chaikoff, 1955). The effects of a rise in circulating acetate on intermediary metabolism in various tissues except adipose tissue have not been defined. The rise in blood acetate after ethanol ingestion is responsible, at least in part, for the decreased release of free fatty acids (FFA) from adipose tissue and for the fall of circulating FFA (Crouse *et al.*, 1968), as discussed subsequently.

B. *Effect of ethanol on the endoplasmic reticulum (microsomes) and associated metabolic changes*

Though alcohol reduces the parallel arrays of the rough endoplasmic reticulum, it also induces proliferation of the smooth endoplasmic reticulum (SER) both in rats (Iseri *et al.*, 1964, 1966) and in man (Lane and Lieber, 1966; Rubin and Lieber, 1967; Lieber and Rubin, 1968a; Rubin and Lieber, 1968). The SER became vesicular and its proliferation after ethanol administration resembled the hypertrophy of hepatic SER produced by a wide variety of agents, including known hepatotoxins (Meldolesi, 1967), numerous therapeutic agents (Conney, 1967) and food additives (Lane and Lieber, 1967). These structural similarities between the SER response to ethanol and that following the application of a variety of drugs are paralleled by comparable functional changes (Lieber and Rubin, 1968b). Chronic administration of ethanol to rats resulted in a striking increase in the activity of a variety of microsomal drug-detoxifying enzymes (Rubin *et al.*, 1968). This may account for the clinical observation that alcoholics, when sober, are remarkably tolerant to a variety of drugs, especially sedatives (Soehring and Schuppel, 1966). Pretreatment of laboratory animals with ethanol was indeed found to decrease the sleeping time produced by several agents (Soehring and Schuppel, 1966). Ethanol thus appears to act in a way similar to drugs which produce both proliferation of SER and an increase in drug detoxifying enzymes. However, most substances which induce microsomal drug detoxifying enzymes are metabolized, at least in part, in the microsomes (which comprise the endoplasmic reticulum), whereas liver alcohol dehydrogenase, the enzyme thought to be responsible for ethanol oxidation, is not found in the microsomal fraction but in the cytosol (Nyberg *et al.*, 1953). Early attempts at demonstrating alcohol-oxidizing activity in microsomes were failures (Shull, 1959), or were limited primarily to studies of methanol (Orme-Johnson and Ziegler, 1965). More recently Lieber and DeCarli (1968) have described a microsomal ethanol oxidizing system (MEOS) which oxidizes ethanol to acetaldehyde in the liver of the rat and the human (Lieber and DeCarli, 1968). This system occurs mainly in the liver and its co-factor requirements are similar to those of drug-detoxifying enzymes, including that for NADPH. Moreover, ethanol feeding resulted in a significant adaptive increase in MEOS activity under conditions which left ADH unchanged. Whether or not ADH is capable of adaptation following ethanol ingestion is not yet known (Lieber, 1968), but failure of adaptation has been reported by von Wartburg and Rothlisberger (1961), Greenberger et al. (1965) and Lieber and DeCarli (1968). It is also significant that the optimal pH of MEOS (6·5–7·4; Lieber and DeCarli, 1968) differs strikingly from that of ADH (10·8), as reported by von Wartburg and Papenberg (1966).

It is not known how MEOS compares with ADH in the quantitative removal of ethanol *in vivo*. But even so, the mere existence of an adaptive ethanol-oxidizing system at this crucial metabolic site in the hepatocyte helps explain a number of observations on ethanol effects. These include the proliferation of SER and the increase in drug metabolizing activity secondary to the induction of drug-detoxifying enzymes. Ethanol stimulates hepatic cholesterol synthesis (Lieber and DeCarli, 1964), an effect which may be akin to the enhanced cholesterogenesis found to occur after barbiturate administration (Jones and Armstrong, 1965). Hepatic microsomes are also the site of fatty acid esterification (Kornberg and Pricer, 1953) and lipoprotein production (Stein and Stein, 1967). It is therefore tempting to speculate that the metabolism of ethanol in the microsomes plays a role in enhanced lipogenesis (*vide infra*), and in increased lipoprotein production (Baraona and Lieber, 1968), which in turn contributes to the "alcoholic hyperlipemia" (see Lieber, 1968).

The major change in hepatic lipids following ethanol ingestion occurred in the triglyceride fraction (Lieber, 1967), but hepatic phospholipids also rose significantly (Lieber et al., 1965; French, 1966). Ethanol was also found to increase the incorporation of Me[^{14}C]methionine into hepatic lecithin (Fallon et al., 1965); a similar effect has been described following phenobarbital administration (Powell et al., 1968), which suggests that the effect of ethanol on phospholipid metabolism may be partly a manifestation of its general action upon the endoplasmic reticulum.

The deleterious effects of alcohol abuse in patients suffering from porphyrias represent another type of action of ethanol which possibly can be linked to the endoplasmic reticulum. Increased urinary coproporphyrin excretion after ethanol has been observed in rats by Gajdos et al. (1967), and in man by Sutherland and Watson (1951). This could possibly be due to proliferation of the SER and to an increase in cytochrome P-450 concentration after ethanol (Rubin et al., 1968). A stimulation of the synthesis of this cytochrome has been considered among other mechanisms as a possible explanation for the adverse effect of drugs in patients with porphyrias.

Ethanol-induced changes of hepatic enzymes associated with the SER, such as glucose-6-phosphatase (Nelson *et al.*, 1967), might also be linked to the general effect of ethanol on the SER.

C. *Ethanol-induced changes in mitochondria*

Severe alcoholism results in conspicuous morphologic changes in liver mitochondria with clumping and appearance of giant forms (Schaffner *et al.*, 1963). Giant mitochondria were originally regarded as the morphologic basis of "alcoholic hyaline bodies" of Mallory (Hartroft, 1961; Schaffner *et al.*, 1963), but more recent electron microscopic studies have shown that other subcellular fractions, especially the endoplasmic reticulum, are involved (Biava, 1964; Iseri and Gottlieb, 1968). That the mitochondrial alterations observed in the livers of alcoholic patients are due, at least in part, to ethanol *per se* rather than to other associated factors such as malnutrition is suggested by the fact that mitochondrial abnormalities are readily produced by ethanol even in the presence of an adequate diet, both in rats (Keissling and Tobe, 1964; Iseri *et al.*, 1964, 1966; Porta *et al.*, 1967) and in man (Lane and Lieber, 1966; Lieber and Rubin, 1968*a*; Rubin and Lieber, 1968). The mitochondrial lesions vary greatly in size and shape and are characterized by numerous irregularities in form, including "tadpole" and circular mitochondria, and disorientation of the mitochondrial cristae. Giant forms of the mitochondria were often intimately associated with fat droplets. Intramitochondrial crystalline inclusions, rarely seen in control biopsies, were observed commonly in the volunteers given ethanol.

It is tempting to postulate that the morphologic changes just described underlie the functional changes which follow the administration of ethanol. Fatty acids are oxidized in mitochondria and ethanol decreases hepatic $^{14}CO_2$ production from [^{14}C]palmitate (Lieber and Schmid, 1961). The latter observation has been extended to include the metabolism of chylomicrons (Fig. 2) (Lieber *et al.*, 1967). Other studies showed that ethanol causes decreased oxidation of various other substrates in isolated mitochondria (Kiessling and Tilander, 1963). Reduced $^{14}CO_2$ production from [^{14}C]-palmitate was paralleled by a comparable diminution in the oxidation of [^{14}C]acetate (Lieber and Schmid, 1961). Moreover, in perfused livers, ethanol caused a reduction in total CO_2 and $^{14}CO_2$ production (with unimpaired oxygen utilization) (Forsander *et al.*, 1965; Lieber *et al.*, 1967), suggesting, as illustrated in Fig. 1, that the activity of the citric acid cycle is slowed down by ethanol. The mechanism underlying inhibition of the citric acid cycle by ethanol has not yet been elucidated. The large influx into mitochondria of hydrogen equivalents resulting from the extramitochondrial oxidation of ethanol may supplant the citric acid cycle as a source of hydrogen equivalents for the flavoprotein-cytochrome electron transport chain, possibly as a consequence of an inhibition of the normal flow of reactions of the citric acid cycle by the excess NADH (see Fig. 1). If one assumes coupling of the oxidation of ethanol to reduction of oxaloacetate to malate, there could then also be decreased citric acid cycle activity as the result of the shunting of citrate out of mitochondria into the cytosol. Thus, decreased citric acid cycle activity provides the best explanation for reduced oxidation of various substrates including lipids. And as will be discussed later it leads us to account for the deposition in the liver of lipids from various sources, especially lipids of dietary origin. Moreover, decreased citric acid cycle activity could be a likely cause of increased ketonemia and ketonuria observed in volunteers given ethanol (Lefevre and Lieber, 1967). That is to say, ketonemia and ketonuria could be the result of increased hepatic ketone production secondary to a block in citric acid cycle activity, as suggested by preliminary findings of increased ketone production in liver slices of rats pretreated with alcohol (Lefevre and Lieber, 1967).

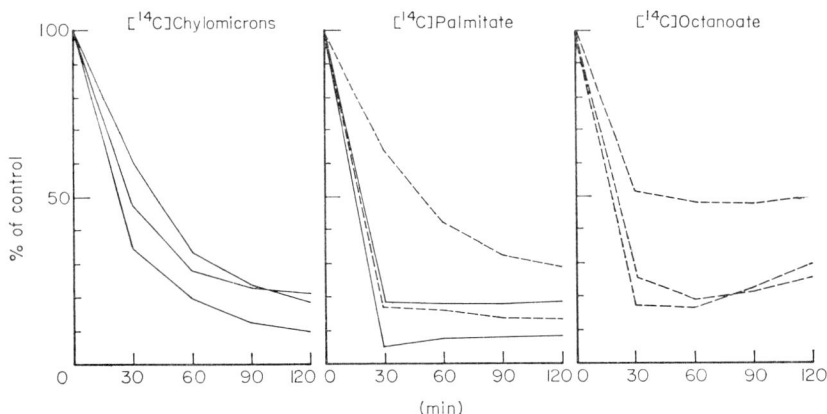

FIG. 2. Effect of ethanol on chylomicron and fatty acid oxidation in isolated perfused rat livers. The $^{14}CO_2$ production is expressed in percentages of the corresponding controls. (From Lieber et al., 1967.)

This action of ethanol on citric acid cycle activity would involve an excess of NADH. However, NADH is produced in the extramitochondrial compartment of the hepatocyte, and the mitochondrial membrane is relatively impermeable to it. One must therefore postulate that hydrogen equivalents are "shuttled" through the mitochondrial membrane by various pathways, two of which are represented, at least partially, in Fig. 1, namely the α-glycerophosphate shuttle proposed by Bücher and Klingenberg (1958) and questioned by Hassinen (1967), and the malate-oxaloacetate cycle. These (or other shuttle mechanisms) can explain how the mitochondrial flavoprotein-electron transport system reoxidizes the NADH generated by ethanol oxidation in the extramitochondrial compartment instead of the NADH which normally originates from the citric acid cycle. They also enable us to understand how, in the presence of ethanol, most of the oxygen consumed by the liver is utilized for the oxidation of ethanol to acetate (Lundquist *et al.*, 1962), instead of being utilized for the breakdown of fatty acids, as is normally the case (Fritz, 1961). Some investigators (Hyams and Isselbacher, 1964; Gajdos *et al.*, 1967) have reported hepatic adenosine triphosphate (ATP) to be decreased, while others reported it to be either unchanged (Buttner *et al.*, 1961) or increased (Oura *et al.*, 1967), suggesting that energy production must be unaltered. As indicated by Fig. 1, ethanol may actually provide the reducing equivalents which normally derive from oxidation of other substrates, primarily through the citric acid cycle. In the liver, ethanol is without effect on ATPase activity (Oura *et al.*, 1967). This contrasts with the inhibiting effect of high concentrations of ethanol on the ATPase of microsomal fractions of both rat and guinea pig brain tissues (Israel *et al.*, 1965). Inhibition of the transport enzyme might be the basis of reduced electrolyte transport across membranes (Israel-Jacard and Kalant, 1965).

D. *Multi-compartmental effects of ethanol; alcoholic hypoglycemia and hyperglycemia*

As discussed elsewhere (Freinkel and Arky, 1966), hypoglycemia has been reported in individuals with depleted hepatic glycogen stores or abnormal carbohydrate metabolism following alcohol ingestion. The hypoglycemia has been shown to be due partly to decreased gluconeogenesis (Field *et al.*, 1963; Freinkel *et al.*, 1965), which in turn might involve an increased hepatic NADH/NAD ratio in the extra- or intramitochondrial compartments of the hepatocyte. When carbohydrates are depleted, precursors of gluconeogenesis include glycerol, lactate and amino acids. Ethanol reduces the hepatic metabolism of glycerol (Lundquist *et al.*, 1965), probably because this requires the conversion of glycerol to α-glycerophosphate and subsequent oxidation to dihydroxyacetone phosphate, with reduction of NAD to NADH, whereas ethanol oxidation favors the reverse reaction. Lactate has to be converted to pyruvate before it can serve as a gluconeogenic precursor; this reaction is coupled to reduction of NAD to NADH, which is also opposed by the oxidation of ethanol.

Ethanol increases lactate production in liver slices (Krebs *et al.*, 1967) and decreases hepatic utilization of lactate of extrahepatic origin (Krebs, 1967). Some amino acids, to be utilized for gluconeogenesis, must first be converted to pyruvate; again, the diversion of pyruvate to lactate would explain the decrease in their utilization. Other amino acids enter gluconeogenic pathways after deamination to either α-ketoglutarate or succinate. These must be converted to malate or oxaloacetate via the citric acid cycle, prior to their entering gluconeogenic pathways via phosphoenolpyruvate (see Fig. 1). The decrease in citric acid cycle activity by ethanol could explain the reduction in gluconeogenesis from these precursors. Glutamate can serve as a gluconeogenic precursor, but ethanol decreases gluconeogenesis from glutamate (Madison *et al.*, 1967): conversion of glutamate to α-ketoglutarate is coupled to reduction of NAD to NADH, a reaction again opposed by the oxidation of ethanol. Furthermore, increased NADH has been shown to produce a dissociation of glutamic dehydrogenase into inactive subunits (Frieden, 1959). Similarly, decreased fatty acid oxidation (resulting from ethanol, as discussed already) would favor reduced gluconeogenesis (Eisenstein, 1967; Kreisberg, 1967).

By a combination of these various metabolic blocks (both in the extra- and intramitochondrial compartments of the hepatocyte) ethanol can contribute to a decrease in gluconeogenesis, which in turn is a probable cause of alcoholic hypoglycemia in individuals whose glycogen stores are already depleted. Ethanol itself has actually been shown to lead to glycogen depletion in rats (Mirone, 1966); the hydrocortisone-induced increase in gluconeogenesis is also inhibited by ethanol (Barboriak, 1967).

The only reaction in the gluconeogenic pathway which is NAD-dependent and which would be favored by an increase in the NADH/NAD ratio is the conversion of 1,3,phosphoglycerate to glyceraldehyde-3-phosphate. Glyceraldehyde-3-phosphate, however, is in equilibrium with dihydroxyacetonephosphate; the conversion of the latter to α-glycerophosphate is accelerated under the influence of ethanol oxidation which, depending on the metabolic state, could off-set the effect of increased NADH on 1,3, phosphoglycerate reduction. The latter is likely in view of the recent observation in liver slices incubated with [14C]alanine that ethanol stimulates the formation of glyceride [14C]glycerol more than that of [14C]glucose under conditions of enhanced gluconeogenesis, whereas ethanol failed to depress [14C]glycerol formation as much as [14C]glucose under conditions of reduced gluconeogenesis (Sandler and Freinkel, 1966). Under metabolic conditions, however, where reduction of 1,3, diphospho-d-glycerate becomes the rate-limiting reaction of gluconeogenesis, the generation of NADH from ethanol might favor gluconeogenesis, an effect shown *in vitro* by Freinkel *et al.* (1965). This could have some bearing on the hyperglycemia which, in addition to the hypoglycemia, has also been described in association with alcoholism. Thus the relationship between alcohol and carbohydrate metabolism is far from simple. The mechanism of alcoholic hyperglycemia remains obscure. In addition to the step in the Embden-Meyerhof pathway which can be affected by an increase in the NADH/NAD ratio, pancreatitis (see Lieber, 1968), which occurs rather frequently in alcoholics, could also play a role. The disturbances in catecholamine metabolism referred to earlier could also lead to hyperglycemia.

III. Pathogenesis and Prevention of the Alcoholic Fatty Liver

A. *Significance of the alcoholic fatty liver*

The association of fatty liver and alcoholism has been recognized for more than a century (Addison, 1836), but the precise nature of this relationship has remained a mystery. Though reports at the turn of this century provided evidence favoring a cause and effect relationship, the studies of Best *et al.* (1949) on animals given ethanol and diets deficient in protein and choline led to the now widely prevailing concept that alcoholic liver disease is the result of nutritional deficiencies accompanying alcoholism, rather than of ethanol itself. More recent studies (Lieber, 1968), on the other hand, indicate that, besides providing calories, alcohol has the ability to bring about a derangement in intermediary metabolism, which in turn produces a fatty liver. Now that the direct steatogenic effect of ethanol is known, the question is, what is the significance of this fat accumulation? Experimentally, the fatty liver induced by moderate amounts of alcohol administered with adequate diets is readily reversible (Lieber *et al.*, 1965; Lieber and Rubin, 1968*a*) and clinically, the alcoholic fatty liver is often a benign condition. In a number of instances, however, the alcoholic fatty liver is associated with a more severe clinical state with anorexia, nausea, vomiting, upper abdominal pain, hepatomegaly and, frequently, fever and jaundice. Biochemical tests are not characteristically altered, though they may suggest liver cell damage with sometimes a confusing obstructive element. Anemia can be present and severe leukocytosis may develop. The terms "alcoholic hepatitis" or "acute fatty metamorphosis of the liver" or "acute hepatic insufficiency of the chronic alcoholic" have been used to characterize this condition and the numerous papers describing it have been reviewed by Lieber (1967). The severity of the prognosis of this acute liver disease of the alcoholic is indicated by a mortality rate of 33% (Hardison and Lee, 1966). In addition to marked fatty changes, the histological picture is characterized by local and massive cellular degeneration and necrosis, with inflammatory reaction. On electron microscopy, the mitochondria are often enlarged and clumped, the endoplasmic reticulum appears vesiculated and the parallel arrays of rough endoplasmic reticulum are scarce; there are also extensive areas of cytoplasmic degradation (Schaffner *et al.*, 1963; Svoboda and Manning, 1964; Porta *et al.*, 1965*a*). These lesions were found in alcoholics in whom not only ethanol, but also malnutrition and possibly other factors could play a role. The etiologic role of ethanol, however, was suggested by the observation of comparable electron microscopic changes in the fatty liver produced experimentally by the administration of alcohol with adequate diets, either in rats (Iseri *et al.*, 1964, 1966; Thorpe and Shorey, 1966) or in man (Lane and Lieber, 1966; Lieber and Rubin, 1968*a*; Rubin and Lieber, 1968). Intramitochondrial crystalline inclusions, "the most conspicuous abnormality" of alcoholic hepatitis (Svoboda and Manning, 1964), was also experimentally reproduced in man (Lane and Lieber, 1966; Rubin and Lieber, 1967). Whether one dose of ethanol can produce these changes is a debatable question (Ashworth *et al.*, 1965; Stein and Stein, 1965; Nelson *et al.*, 1967). But repeated alcohol administration produces these ultrastructural lesions consistently, and therefore, the alcoholic fatty liver, with its associated electronmicroscopic alterations, could be considered as a precursor to the more severe variety of "alcoholic hepatitis".

That the ethanol-induced steatosis represents more than simple fat deposition and is accompanied by some cell "injury" is indicated not only by the striking ultrastructural changes, but also by alterations of hepatic and blood enzymes. Ethanol, for example, decreased the concentration of several enzymes in the liver, with a corresponding rise in the blood. Hepatic glutamic-pyruvic transaminase decreased in animals given ethanol (Henley et al., 1958; Estler and Ammon, 1966). In man, serum transaminases increased after ethanol administration (Bang et al., 1958; Rubin and Lieber, 1968): the increase depended on the individuals' previous ethanol consumption, the rise occurring preferentially in non-alcoholics (Mendelson et al., 1966). In patients with alcoholic liver disease, hepatic isocitric dehydrogenase (Figueroa and Klotz, 1962) was reduced, whereas serum isocitric dehydrogenase and ornithine carbamyltransferase increased after ethanol ingestion (Goldberg and Watts, 1965). In rats given ethanol, succinic dehydrogenase (demonstrated by histochemical techniques) "shifted" to the centrolobular zone, probably as a result of an ethanol induced increase in permeability of the mitochondrial membrane to the reagents used for the test rather than from an absolute increase of enzyme activity (French, 1964).

The decrease in these hepatic enzymes, possibly reflecting "injury", contrasts with the increase of other enzyme activities, especially those associated with the smooth endoplasmic reticulum (discussed elsewhere in this chapter) which more likely reflect adaptation.

The dose and duration of the alcohol abuse probably determine the type of liver response, though other factors such as toxins, congeners, nutritional deficiencies and individual susceptibility to the alcohol induced lesions may play an as yet undefined role. It is reasonable to assume that an understanding of the pathogenesis of the alcoholic fatty liver and associated ultrastructural changes may allow us eventually to develop an effective prophylactic or therapeutic approach, applicable to the prevention or treatment of the fatty liver as well as the more severe "alcoholic hepatitis".

In addition to its role as a likely precursor of the "alcoholic hepatitis", the alcoholic fatty liver may also be significant in relation to the ultimate development of cirrhosis. As pointed out by McHenry and Patterson (1944), a number of conditions which produce a fatty liver in short-term experiments lead to cirrhosis in experiments of longer duration. In experimental choline deficiency in particular, fatty liver per se has been considered to lead to the development of cirrhosis (Hartroft, 1961), but in the case of alcoholic cirrhosis, it is still not clear whether the fatty liver or some other injury must be considered as the precursor. The usual duration for the development of cirrhosis in man is 10–15 years (Lelbach, 1967a). It is conceivable that the cell damage which we observed after a few days of alcohol ingestion (Rubin and Lieber, 1967, 1968) may, if repeated over a long period of time, lead to necrosis and cirrhosis. Not all alcoholics develop cirrhosis; that is, a moderate or intermittent fatty liver need not necessarily lead to cirrhosis so that other mechanisms must play a role.

Though the relationship between fatty liver (and the associated ultra-structural and enzyme alterations) and cirrhosis is not yet clear, it is generally agreed that alcoholic cirrhosis is usually preceded by a stage of fatty liver. It is thus not unreasonable to assume that if the study of the pathogenesis of the alcoholic fatty liver ever results in the adoption of an effective pro-phylactic or therapeutic approach, any significant modification of the first stages of the disease (namely the fatty liver) may ultimately influence the incidence or the severity of cirrhosis.

B. *Role of ethanol and dietary factors in the pathogenesis of the alcoholic fatty liver*

1. *The role of ethanol as a direct etiologic factor*

a. *Studies in rats*

The traditional concept that alcoholic liver disease is a consequence of nutritional deficiencies accompanying alcoholism rather than of ethanol itself was based primarily on the studies of Best *et al.* (1949), who observed that rats given ethanol in their drinking water (in association with an adequate diet) failed to develop a fatty liver. A fatty liver was produced only when ethanol was given in combination with a deficient diet and the degree of steatosis thereby achieved was not greater than that produced by iso-caloric amounts of sucrose. From these observations it was concluded that ethanol was merely acting by providing calories and that it was not more toxic than sucrose or other carbohydrates. This concept that ethanol acts by mimicking the caloric effect of carbohydrates was challenged by Klatskin *et al.* (1954), who found that alcohol-fed rats required more choline than the rats given isocaloric amounts of sucrose. These studies of Best *et al.* (1949) and Klatskin *et al.* (1954) were done by adding ethanol to the drinking water, a technique which is known to result in low alcohol consumption and in blood alcohol levels that are far below those seen in alcoholic individuals. Thus, when the amount of ethanol was increased by gastric intubation, it was found that a larger dose of ethanol (administered either as a single or as a repeated intragastric dose) produced fat accumulation in the liver that was not duplicated by isocaloric amounts of glucose (Mallov, 1955; Mallov and Bloch, 1956). Subsequently, to avoid the need for gastric intubation, ethanol was incorporated in wholly liquid diets (Lieber *et al.*, 1963), a technique which did overcome the natural aversion of rats for alcohol and which raised the alcohol intake to a level comparable to that of moderate alcoholics. With this procedure, it became evident that even in the absence of deficiencies in protein or vitamins, isocaloric replacement of carbo-hydrate by ethanol consistently produced significant increases of hepatic triglycerides under a variety of experimental conditions involving several types of diets (Lieber *et al.*, 1963, 1965; DeCarli and Lieber, 1967). This technique was subsequently adopted by others who confirmed the fact that substitution of carbohydrate by ethanol led to a several-fold rise in hepatic triglycerides (Porta et al., 1965b). Isocaloric replacement of carbohydrate by fat (instead of ethanol) failed to produce steatosis, demonstrating that the capacity of ethanol for generating a fatty liver is greater than that of fat itself, and that steatosis can be produced by ethanol as a replacement not only of carbohydrate, but also of dietary fat (Lieber et al., 1965). As illustrated in Fig. 3, hepatic lipid accumulation developed gradually over the

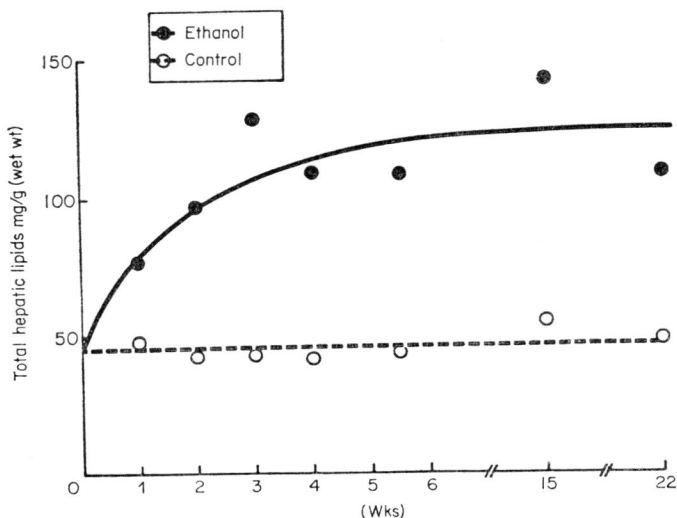

FIG. 3. Effect of prolonged ethanol feeding on hepatic lipid accumulation in rats. (From Lieber et al., 1969.)

first month of alcohol administration, and then remained stable for at least five months. With a decrease in the ethanol intake from 36% to 20% of the total calories, no fatty liver was observed, thus leading to the suggestion that there may be a "threshold" effect (Lieber et al., 1965). As pointed out earlier, the steatosis was accompanied by striking ultra-structural changes (Iseri et al., 1964, 1966), and this has been confirmed by others (Porta et al., 1965b). It was therefore concluded that in the rat, ethanol exerts a direct hepatotoxic effect, but it must be remembered that extrapolation to man from these studies can only be accepted after verification by studies in humans.

b. Studies in man

Fatty liver is a very common finding among alcoholics: for example, a liver biopsy study of chronic alcoholics showed that 90% of them had a fatty liver (Edmonson et al., 1967). In another study of 371 alcoholics, liver biopsy showed 75% of them to have varying degrees of fatty liver; among 265 heavy drinkers, only 10% had a morphologically normal liver (Lelbach, 1967a). Epidemiological studies suggested that the amount of alcohol ingested rather than the malnutrition (Lelbach, 1966) and ethanol itself rather than congeners (Lelbach, 1967b) were the primary factors. On the other hand, no deleterious effects were observed following the administration of alcohol to patients recovering from an alcoholic fatty liver (Volwiler *et al.*, 1948; Summerskill *et al.*, 1957). The amounts of alcohol given were less than the usual intake of alcoholics. With presumably larger amounts of alcohol, Menghini (1960) found that the clearing of the fat from the alcoholic fatty liver was prevented. All these studies were concerned with the effect of alcohol in subjects recovering from a fatty liver diagnosed by needle biopsy, leaving the question unanswered as to whether in individuals with a morphologically normal liver, ingestion of alcohol is capable of injuring the liver, even in the absence of dietary deficiencies. To resolve this question, volunteers (with or without a history of alcoholism) were given adequate diets under metabolic ward conditions, with alcohol either supplementing the diet (Lieber *et al.*, 1963, 1965; Rubin and Lieber, 1968) or as an isocaloric substitute of carbohydrate in a large variety of diets (Lieber *et al.*, 1963, 1965; Rubin and Lieber, 1967, 1968; Lieber and Rubin, 1968*a*). In all these individuals, ethanol administration resulted in fatty liver, this being evident on both morphologic examination and by direct measurement of the lipid content of the liver biopsies, which revealed an up to 25-fold rise in triglyceride content. This steatosis, though reversible, was accompanied by striking ultrastructural changes.

Even though these studies established a direct etiologic role of ethanol in the pathogenesis of the alcoholic fatty liver, the problem to what extent the ethanol effect could be modified by dietary factors, especially by dietary protein and fat, still remained unresolved.

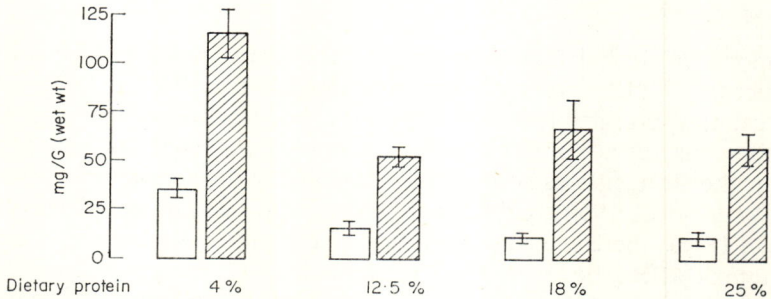

FIG. 4. Hepatic triglycerides in rats fed diets with normal fat content (35% of total calories), varying amounts of proteins and either ethanol (36% of total calories) or isocaloric carbohydrate (controls). (From Lieber *et al.*, 1969.) ☐, Control diets; ▨, Ethanol diets.

2. *Role of dietary protein and "lipotropic" factors*

As indicated by Fig. 4, the increase in hepatic triglycerides produced by ethanol and normal-protein diets (12·5–18% of total calories) was further doubled by a 3–4-fold reduction in dietary protein. The increase in steatosis was accompanied by accentuation of the ultrastructural changes (Rubin *et al.*, 1968). Protein supplements of up to 25% of the total calories were without significant effect: steatosis developed both in alcoholic

(Lieber and Rubin, 1968*a*) and non-alcoholic (Rubin and Lieber, 1968) volunteers given ethanol with a diet high in protein (25% of calories, or twice the recommended amount) and moderately low in fat (25% of calories). Thus, although protein deficiency potentiated the steatosis and ultrastructural changes produced by alcohol in the liver (at least in the rat), protein supplementation did not prevent the alcohol-induced liver injury, neither in rats nor in man.

In rats, the fatty liver produced by small amounts of alcohol in combination with diets deficient in lipotropic agents (choline and methionine) can be prevented by simply correcting the dietary deficiency (Best *et al.*, 1949; Klatskin *et al.*, 1954). By contrast, when the ethanol intake was increased either through gastric intubation (Mallov and Bloch, 1956) or by incorporation of the ethanol in entirely liquid diets (Lieber and DeCarli, 1966), massive supplementation with choline failed to prevent fully the alcohol-induced steatosis. In man, supplementation of even high protein diets, with 10 g of choline a day, failed to prevent alcohol from producing a fatty liver in alcoholic (Lieber and DeCarli, unpublished observations) or in non-alcoholic (Rubin and Lieber, 1968) volunteers. The failure of choline to exert a protective effect in man is not surprising in view of the previous observation that susceptibility to lipotrope deficiency is much less pronounced in primates than in rodents (Hoffbauer and Zaki, 1965). This is probably so because the sensitivity of different species to choline deficiency varies with the level of choline oxidase, which is much less abundant in the human than in the rodent liver (Sidransky and Farber, 1960). Even in growing rats, which are much more vulnerable to lipotrope deficiency than mature animals (Handler and Follis, 1950), there is a certain amount of fat accumulation in the liver after ethanol administration, despite the presence of large choline supplementation (Lieber and DeCarli, 1966). This indicates that ethanol must produce steatosis through effects other than, or in addition to, those related to lipotropic agents. Moreover, ethanol failed to interfere with the capacity of choline to improve the cirrhosis produced by choline deficiency in rats (Takada *et al.*, 1967); this is supporting evidence for the view that choline deficiency and alcohol induce hepatic lesions through mechanisms which are, at least in part, different. Biochemically, the two types of fatty liver are differentiated by hepatic phospholipid accumulation in the alcoholic (Lieber *et al.*, 1965), and depletion of phospholipid in the choline variety (Ashworth *et al.*, 1961). Ultrastructurally, the lesions are also different (Iseri *et al.*, 1966).

3. *Role of dietary fat*

The part played by dietary fat in the fatty liver induced by ethanol differs from that induced by choline deficiency. Whereas the degree of steatosis produced by choline deficiency does not depend on the amount of dietary fat (Iwamoto *et al.*, 1963), the degree of alcohol-induced fatty liver is strikingly influenced by the dietary fat content, as illustrated in Fig. 5. Rats fed ethanol (36% of total calories) with diets of varying fat content showed marked reduction in the steatosis accompanying a decrease in dietary fat to a level of 25% (or less) of total calories. The importance of dietary fat in man was also confirmed and as shown in Fig. 6, for a given ethanol intake, much more steatosis developed on a diet of normal fat content than on a low fat diet (Lieber and Spritz, 1966). Dietary fat, however, was not the sole factor, since some steatosis was produced in man (Lieber and Spritz, 1966) or rats fed ethanol with diets practically free of fat (Lieber et al., 1966). It appeared that the chain length of the dietary fatty acid was important in relation to the degree of fat deposition occurring in the liver after alcohol feeding:

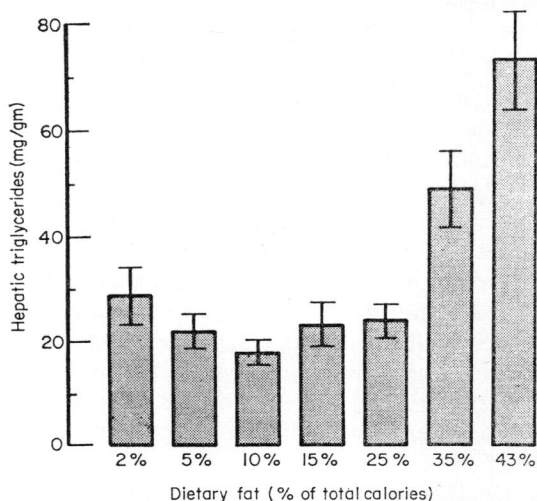

FIG. 5. Hepatic triglycerides in seven groups of rats given ethanol (36% of calories) with a diet of normal protein (18% of calories) but of varying fat content over a 24-day period. (From Lieber et al., 1969.)

replacement of dietary triglycerides containing long-chain fatty acids (LCT) by triglycerides containing medium-chain fatty acids (MCT) markedly reduced the capacity of ethanol to produce fatty liver in the rats (Lieber et al., 1967). Upon incubation with hepatic microsomes and α-glycero phosphate, octanoate (a medium-chain fatty acid) was much less esterified than palmitate (a long-chain fatty acid). This in turn probably explains the additional finding that in liver slices and isolated perfused livers, medium-chain fatty acids were not only much less esterified but also much more oxidized than long-chain fatty acids. The propensity of medium-chain fatty acids to oxidation rather than to esterification provides a likely explanation for the reduction of alcoholic steatosis upon replacement of dietary LCT by MCT.

C. Origin and mechanisms of fatty acid accumulation in the alcoholic fatty liver

As illustrated in Fig. 7, lipids which accumulate in the liver can originate from three main sources: dietary fat (which reaches the blood stream from

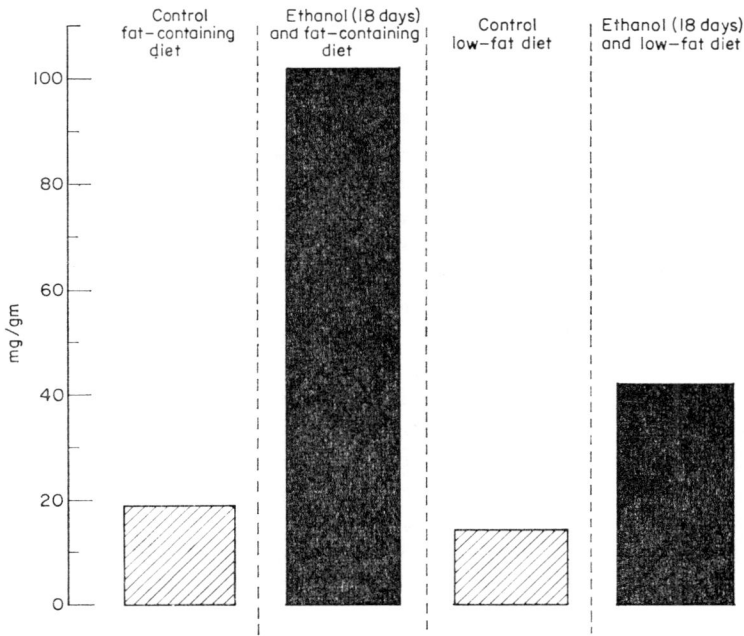

FIG. 6. Hepatic triglycerides of human liver biopsies obtained at the end of control or ethanol feeding periods, each time with either a normal fat-containing diet (35% of total calories) or a low-fat diet (5% of total calories). (From Lieber *et al.*, 1969.)

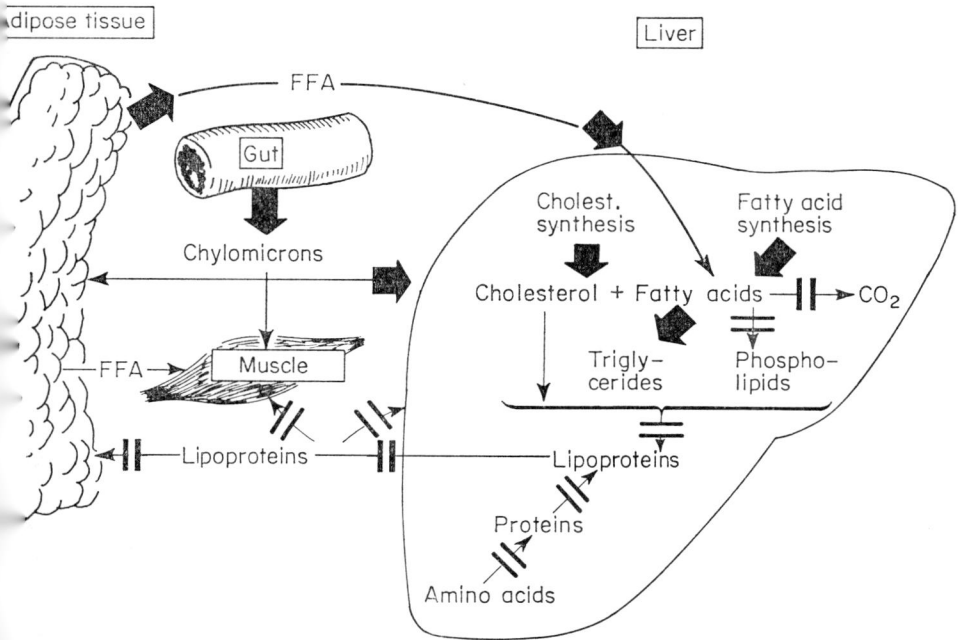

FIG. 7. Possible mechanisms of fatty liver production, through either increase (→) or decrease (⊣→) of lipid transport and metabolism. (From Lieber, 1965.)

the gut as chylomicrons), adipose tissue fatty acids (which are transported to the liver as free fatty acids) and lipid synthesized in the liver itself. A large number of metabolic disturbances can theoretically lead to excessive deposition of fat in the liver. Some of these mechanisms can produce hepatic lipid accumulation, regardless of the origin of the fat; these involve primarily decreased hepatic lipid oxidation, increased hepatic fatty acid esterification and decreased lipoprotein production and/or release. Some other more selective mechanisms involve only fatty acids of one type, either endogenously synthesized fatty acids in the case of enhanced hepatic lipogenesis or adipose tissue fatty acids in the case of increased peripheral fat mobilization.

The biochemical mechanisms linking ethanol to decreased lipid oxidation and increased lipogenesis (including increased esterification of fatty acids) have already been touched upon. In contrast with the effect of other hepatotoxins, such as carbon tetrachloride, alcohol raises the level of circulating lipoproteins (see Losowsky et al., 1963; Lieber, 1968), in part through increased lipoprotein production (Baraona and Lieber, 1968). This implies that a block in hepatic lipoprotein secretion or production does not appear to play a primary role in the pathogenesis of the alcoholic fatty liver although it has been shown that in vitro large amounts of alcohol can depress net lipoprotein release from isolated perfused livers (Schapiro et al., 1964).

The origin of the fatty acids that are deposited in the liver both in man (Lieber and Spritz, 1966) and in rats (Lieber et al., 1966) is now well established. The fatty acids which accumulate in the liver upon ingestion of ethanol and fat-containing diets are, to a large degree, of dietary origin and do not derive from adipose tissue stores. Similarly, ethanol and a low-fat diet produced a fatty liver whose triglyceride fatty acid composition was very different from that of adipose tissue, with a high percentage of endogenously synthesized fatty acids (Lieber et al., 1966; Lieber and Spritz, 1966). Adipose tissue fatty acids accumulated in the liver of rats only under one experimental condition, namely when they were given one large sublethal dose of ethanol (Brodie et al., 1961; Scheig and Isselbacher, 1965). Theoretically this lipid accumulation could have been due either to increased fat mobilization from adipose tissue (beyond the normal rate) or to decreased hepatic disposal of fatty acids coming from adipose tissue at a normal rate. Both theories have proponents and so far no general agreement has been reached. For example, an increase in circulating FFA in rats after one large dose of ethanol was interpreted as indicating increased peripheral fat mobilization (Brodie et al., 1961; Mallov, 1961). Other investigators, however, found under similar experimental conditions no rise in FFA (Elko et al., 1961). Conflicting observations on peripheral FFA mobilization have also been reported in studies of rats with pre-labelled epididymal fat pads fatty acid mobilization was either increased (Kessler and Mishkin-Yalovsky 1966) or unchanged (Poggi and DiLuzio, 1964). Experimental procedures or agents which reduce the normal rate of peripheral fat mobilization, e.g.

adrenalectomy, spinal cord transection or ganglioplegic agents (Mallov, 1957; Brodie *et al.*, 1961; Rebouças and Isselbacher, 1961) prevent or decrease the hepatic fat accumulation produced by one large sublethal dose of alcohol. However, these results should not be taken to imply that the primary mechanism responsible for the fatty liver caused by a large dose of alcohol is increased peripheral fat mobilization. A decrease in peripheral fat mobilization does indeed reduce the over-all fat load presented to the liver and may enable this organ to cope with any of the other mechanisms possibly responsible for the development of the fatty liver.

Unless very large amounts of alcohol are given (Lieber *et al.*, 1963; Schapiro *et al.*, 1965), ethanol in man produces a fall in circulating FFA (Lieber *et al.*, 1962*b*; Jones *et al.*, 1963) with a decrease in FFA turnover (Jones *et al.*, 1965) and a concomitant reduction in circulating glycerol (Feinman and Lieber, 1967). Thus, in man, ethanol administration results in reduced peripheral fatty acid mobilization. According to Crouse *et al.* (1968) the decrease in FFA release from adipose tissue is due not to ethanol itself, but to acetate, a metabolite of ethanol produced in the liver (Fig. 1) and released into the blood stream. When ethanol was given orally (Jones *et al.*, 1963; Feinman and Lieber, 1967) the fall in FFA was sustained, whereas after intravenous administration the effect was transient (Lieber *et al.*, 1962*b*), possibly because parenterally administered ethanol may elicit hormonal responses not produced by oral ethanol (Kalant *et al.*, 1963).

The major lipid fraction of the alcoholic fatty liver is triglyceride. The reason for the selective accumulation of triglycerides is not clear. It could be the result of specific stimulation of triglyceride production (Horning *et al.*, 1963; Scheig and Isselbacher, 1965), with possibly a relative block in phospholipid synthesis (Horning *et al.*, 1963). Such a block, however, cannot be considered to be the primary cause of the fatty liver, since hepatic phospholipid concentration is not reduced but slightly increased. The rise in phospholipid is much less than that of triglyceride (Lieber *et al.*, 1965; French, 1966).

D. *Prevention of the alcoholic fatty liver*

The possible roles of choline, protein and other lipotropic factors and of dietary fat in the development of alcoholic steatosis have already been emphasized in this chapter. Differences in dietary fat may explain some of the discrepancies in reports concerning the effect of antioxidants. Some investigators found that antioxidants prevented or at least partially reduced hepatic steatosis following either one large dose of ethanol or prolonged ethanol intake (Di Luzio, 1966); others found no effect (Lieber and DeCarli, 1966). These findings can be reconciled by taking into account the fat content of the diets employed. Whereas the negative results were obtained with diets containing 43% of total calories as fat (an amount comparable to that of the average U.S. diet), partial protection was observed with a relatively low-fat diet. Since dietary fat potentiates the steatogenic effect

N

of ethanol, it is quite conceivable that antioxidants may be moderately active with low fat diets but incapable of counteracting the much stronger effect of ethanol combined with dietary fat. The effect of certain chemicals upon ethanol-induced steatosis has been dwelt upon elsewhere (Lieber, 1968). These agents include ethyl chlorophenoxyisobutyrate (CPIB), a drug used to reduce hyperlipemia, which partly protects against the development in rats of an alcoholic fatty liver (Spritz and Lieber, 1966). This observation has been confirmed by Brown (1966). Anabolic steroids were reported by Jabbari and Leevy (1967) to accelerate the disappearance of fat from the alcoholic fatty liver, but Fenster (1966) has not been able to reproduce this result.

IV. Alcoholic Cirrhosis

Though cirrhosis of the liver is a very common complication of alcoholism, its pathogenesis remains obscure. Recent statistical studies (Lelbach, 1967a) carried out on a large group of alcohol addicts (with a 15-year alcoholic history) showed the development of liver damage to be dependent on the degree of alcohol abuse: 75% of those with a daily consumption in excess of 160 gm per day had severe liver damage, whereas only 17% of those who consumed less than that daily amount were affected. Besides the dose, the time factor seemed important: after 15 years of alcohol abuse, the incidence of severe liver damage was eight times greater than after five years of excessive alcohol consumption. The relationship between cirrhosis and alcoholism is further illustrated by the parallel changes in death rate from cirrhosis and in alcohol consumption: with prohibition in this country or rationing of alcoholic beverages in Europe during the world wars, the death rate from cirrhosis decreased, whereas upon repeal of prohibition in the United States or end of the wars in Europe the death rate from cirrhosis rose again (U.S. Bureau of Census, 1943; Ledermann, 1964). The public health importance of cirrhosis is also illustrated by statistics which indicate that in urban areas of the U.S., cirrhosis is the third or fourth largest cause of death in young and middle aged individuals (Summary of Vital Statistics, 1964). The majority of patients with cirrhosis in the U.S. (at least two out of three) are chronic alcoholics. Not all alcoholics, however, develop cirrhosis; it is therefore likely that, in addition to ethanol, other factors are involved. Malnutrition, commonly associated with alcoholism, has often been implicated but its exact pathogenic role is not yet known. Various clinical studies have failed to produce evidence that dietary deficiencies are significant (Steiner, 1964; Lelbach, 1966; Thaler, 1967). In alcoholics with well-established cirrhosis, it has been shown that the ingestion of alcoholic beverages in amounts less than those spontaneously consumed before hospitalization had no obvious adverse effect on the cirrhosis, provided that an adequate protein intake was maintained (Erenoglu et al., 1964). Although this study focuses our attention on the possible importance of malnutrition its significance is hard to assess in view of the difficulty in evaluating the progress of cirrhosis over a relatively short period of time in human biopsy material. The dose of alcohol may also have played a crucial role. Alcoholism and cirrhosis have been associated with color blindness (Cruz-Coke and Varela, 1966), and this raises the important but unresolved question of whether or not genetic factors play a role in the pathogenesis of cirrhosis. Fialkow *et al.* (1966), on the other hand, have questioned the validity of this observation.

Other hepatotoxins might also be involved in the pathogenesis of cirrhosis and the possible role of non-alcoholic constituents of alcoholic beverages should be considered. For instance, wines of certain vintages contain large amounts of iron (Aron *et al.*, 1961; MacDonald and Baumslag, 1964). Iron is known to accumulate in the liver and other organs of animals given these wines over a long period of time (Aron *et al.*, 1961). These observations might partly explain iron accumulation in various tissues (including the liver) of wine drinkers who have cirrhosis of the liver (Aron *et al.*, 1961; MacDonald and Baumslag, 1964). In experimental animals, iron has been shown to aggravate cirrhosis produced by other means (Kent, 1965). Moreover, alcohol can increase intestinal iron absorption (Charlton *et al.*, 1964).

It is not yet established which hepatic lesions have to be considered as precursors of the cirrhosis. None the less, the possible role of alcoholic fatty liver is specially underlined by the "injury" evidenced by both electron microscopic changes and enzymatic alterations in hepatic tissue and the blood stream. It is likely that this type of cell injury, when exaggerated, leads to necrosis which, in turn, may well be the missing link between the first signs of ethanol-induced liver injury, i.e. fatty liver (and associated electron microscopic and enzyme changes) and the ultimate stage of alcoholic liver disease, i.e. cirrhosis.

V. Conclusions

Ethanol markedly affects the structure and function of the liver. Though malnutrition is commonly associated with alcoholism and may contribute to its pathology (in part by potentiating the effects of ethanol), recent studies indicate that several of the changes occurring in the liver can be attributed directly to alterations in intermediary metabolism produced by the oxidation of ethanol itself. These effects of ethanol are either mediated by metabolites of alcohol, such as acetaldehyde or acetate, or are the result of hepatic generation of NADH, or are closely similar to processes of drug detoxification in the liver.

Acknowledgements

The author thanks Dr A. Lefevre and Miss L. M. DeCarli for their help in the preparation of this manuscript.

Original studies reported here were supported by PHS Grants MH 15558, MH 14263, AM 12511, AM 10893 and AM 09536.

References

Addison, T. (1836). *Guy's Hosp. Rep.* **1**, 476-485.

Ammon, H. P. T., Estler, C. J. and Heim, F. (1967). *Biochem. Pharmac.* **16**, 769-777.

Aron, E., Paoletti, C., Jobard, P. and Gosse, C. (1961). *Archs Mal. Appar. dig.* **50**, 745.

Ashworth, C. T., Wrightsman, F. and Buttram V. (1961). *Archs Path.* **72**, 620-624.

Ashworth, C. T., Wrightsman, F., Cooper, B. and Di Luzio, N. R. (1965). *J. Lipid Res.* **6**, 258-268.

Bang, Nils, U., Iversen, K., Jagt, T. and Madsen, S. (1958). *J. Am. med. Ass.* **168**, 156-160.

Baraona, E. and Lieber, C. S. (1968). *Clin. Res.* **16**, 279.

Barboriak, Joseph J. (1967). *Life Sci.* **6**, 445-448.

Bartlett, G. R. (1952). *Q. Jl. Stud. Alcohol* **13**, 583-589.

Bartlett, G. R. and Barnet, H. N. (1949). *Q. Jl. Stud. Alcohol* **10**, 381.

Best, C. H., Hartroft, W. S., Lucas, C. C. and Ridout, J. H. (1949). *Br. med. J. ii*, 1001-1006.

Biava, C. (1964). *Lab. Invest.* **13**, 301-320.

Blair, A. H. and Vallee, B. L. (1966). *Biochemistry* **5**, 2026.

Brodie, B. B., Butler, W. M., Horning, M. G., Maickel, R. P. and Maling, H. M. (1961). *Am. J. clin. Nutr.* **9**, 432-435.

Brown, D. F. (1966). *Metabolism* **15**, 868-873.

Bücher, T. and Klingenberg, M. (1958). *Angew. Chem.* **70**, 552-570.

Buttner, H., Portwich, F. and Engelhardt, K. (1961). *Naunyn-Schmiedebergs Arch. exp. Path. Pharmak.* **240**, 573-583.

Charlton, R. W., Jacobs, P., Seftel, H. and Bothwell, T. H. (1964). *Br. med. J.* **5422**, 1427-1429.

Conney, A. H. (1967). *Pharmac. Rev.* **19**, 317-366.

Crouse, J. R., Gerson, C. D., DeCarli, L. M. and Lieber, C. S. (1968). *J. Lipid Res.* **9**, 509-512.

Cruz-Coke, R. and Varela, A. (1966). *Lancet ii* 1282-1284.

DeCarli, L. M. and Lieber, C. S. (1967). *J. Nutr.* **91**, 331-336.

Di Luzio, N. R. (1966). *Lab. Invest.* **15**, 50-63.

Duritz, G. and Truitt, E. B., Jr. (1966). *Biochem. Pharmac.* **15**, 711-721.

Eade, N. R. (1959). *J. Pharmac. exp. Ther.* **127**, 29-34.

Edmondson, H. A., Peters, R. L., Frankel, H. H. and Borowsky, S. (1967). *Medicine* **46**, 119-129.

Edwards, J. A. and Price Evans, D. A. (1967). *Clin. Pharmac. Ther.* **8**, 824-829.

Eisenstein, A. B. (1967). *Am. J. clin. Nutr.* **20**, 282-289.

Elko, E. E., Wooles, W. R. and Di Luzio, N. R. (1961). *Am. J. Physiol.* **201**, 923-926.

Erenoglu, E., Edreira, J. G. and Patek, A. J., Jr. (1964). *Ann. intern. Med.* **60**, 814-823.

Estler, C.-J. and Ammon, H. P. T. (1966). *Med. Pharmac. exp.* **15**, 299-306.

Fallon, H. J., Pesch, L. A. and Klatskin, G. (1965). *Biochim. biophys. Acta* **98**, 470-475.

Feinman, L. and Lieber, C. S. (1967). *Am. J. clin. Nutr.* **20**, 400-403.

Fenster, L. F. (1966). *Ann. intern. Med.* **65**, 738-744.

Fialkow, P. J., Thuline, H. C. and Fenster, L. F. (1966). *New Engl. J. Med.* **275**, 584-587.

Field, J. B., Williams, H. E. and Mortimore, G. E. (1963). *J. clin. Invest.* **42**, 497-506.

Figueroa, R. B. and Klotz, A. P. (1962). *Gastroenterology* **43**, 10-12.

Forsander, O. A. (1966). *Biochem. J.* **98**, 244-247.

Forsander, O. A., Suomalainen, H. and Raiha, N. (1960). *Hoppe-Seyler's Z. Physiol. Chem.* **318**, 1-5.

Forsander, O. A., Raiha, N., Salaspuro, M. and Maenpaa, P. (1965). *Biochem. J.* **94**, 259-265.

Forster, B. (1956). *Dt. Z. ges. gericht. Med.* **45**, 221-224.

Freinkel, N. and Arky, R. A. (1966). *Psychosom. Med.* **28**, 551-563.

Freinkel, N., Cohen, A. K., Arky, R. A. and Foster, A. E. (1965). *J. clin. Endocr. Metab.* **25**, 76-94.

French, S. W. (1964). *Lab. Invest.* **13**, 1051-1056.

French, S. W. (1966). *J. Nutr.* **88**, 291-302.

Freund, G. and O'Hallaren, P. (1965). *J. Lipid Res.* **6**, 471-477.

Frieden, C. (1959). *J. biol. Chem.* **234**, 815-820.

Fritz, I. B. (1961). *Physiol. Rev.* **41**, 52-129.

Gajdos, A., Gajdos-Torok, M., Palma-Carlos, A. and Palma-Carlos, L. (1967). *Nouv. Rev. Franc. Hemat.* **7**, 15-26.

Goldberg, D. M. and Watts, C. (1965). *Gastroenterology* **49**, 256-261.

Greenberger, N. J., Cohen, R. B. and Isselbacher, K. J. (1965). *Lab. Invest.* **14**, 264-271.

Handler, P. and Follis, R. H. (1950). *Proc. Soc. exp. Biol. Med.* **75**, 567-570.

Hardison, W. G. and Lee, F. I. (1966). *New Engl. J. Med.* **275**, 61-66.

Hartroft, W. S. (1961). In *Progress in Liver Diseases* (H. Popper and F. Schaffner, eds), Vol. I, pp. 68-85, Grune and Stratton, New York.

Hassinen, I. (1967). *Annals Med. exp. Biol. Fenn.* **45**, 35-45.

Henley, K. S., Wiggins, H. S., Hirschowitz, B. I. and Pollard, H. M. (1958). *Q. Jl. Stud. Alcohol.* **19**, 54-68.

Hoffbauer, F. W. and Zaki, F. G. (1965). *Proc. Soc. exp. Biol. Med.* **118**, 1132-1165.

Horning, M. G., Wakabayashi, M. and Maling, H. M. (1963). In *Effects of Drugs on Synthesis and Mobilization of Lipids* (E. C. Horning, ed.), Vol. 2, pp. 13-27. Pergamon, Oxford.

Howard, C. F., Jr. and Lowenstein, J. M. (1964). *Biochim. biophys. Acta* **84**, 226-228.

Hyams, D. E. and Isselbacher, K. J. (1964). *Nature, Lond.* **204**, 1196-1197.

Iseri, O. A. and Gottlieb, L. S. (1968). *Fedn Proc. Fedn Am. Socs exp. Biol.* **27**, 605.

Iseri, O. A., Gottlieb, L. S. and Lieber, C. S. (1964). *Fedn Proc. Fedn Am. Socs exp. Biol.* **23**, 579.

Iseri, O. A., Lieber, C. S. and Gottlieb, L. S. (1966). *Am. J. Path.* **48**, 535-555.

Israel, Y., Kalant, H. and Laufer, I. (1965). *Biochem. Pharmacol.* **14**, 1803-1814.

Israel-Jacard, Y. and Kalant, H. (1965). *J. cell. comp. Physiol.* **65**, 127-132.

Iwamoto, A., Hellerstein, E. E. and Hegsted, D. M. (1963). *J. Nutr.* **79**, 488-492.

Jabbari, M. and Leevy, C. M. (1967). *Medicine* **46**, 131-139.

James, T. N. and Bear, E. S. (1967). *Am. Heart J.* **74**, 243-255.

Jones, A. L. and Armstrong, D. T. (1965). *Proc. Soc. exp. Biol. Med.* **119**, 1136-1139.

Jones, D. P., Losowsky, M. S., Davidson, C. S. and Lieber, C. S. (1963). *J. Lab. clin. Med.* **62**, 675-682.

Jones, D. P., Perman, E. S. and Lieber, C. S. (1965). *J. Lab. clin. Med.* **66**, 804-813.

Kalant, H., Hawkins, R. D. and Czaja, C. (1963). *Am. J. Physiol.* **204**, 849-855.

Katz, J. and Chaikoff, I. L. (1955). *Biochim. biophys. Acta* **18**, 87-101.

Kent, G. (1965). *Progress in Liver Diseases* (H. Popper and F. Schaffner eds), Vol. II, pp. 253-271. Grune and Stratton, New York.

Kessler, J. I. and Mishkin-Yalovsky, S. (1966). *J. Lipid Res.* **7**, 772-778.

Kiessling, K. H. (1962). *Expl Cell Res.* **27**, 367-368.

Kiessling, K. H. and Tilander, K. (1963). *Expl Cell Res.* **30**, 476-480.

Kiessling, K. H. and Tobe, U. (1964). *Expl Cell Res.* **33**, 350-354.
Klatskin, G., Krehl, W. A. and Conn, H. O. (1954). *J. exp. Med.* **100**, 605-614.
Klingman, G. I., Haag, H. B. and Bane, R. (1958). *Q. Jl. Stud. Alcohol* **19**, 543-552.
Kornberg, A. and Pricer, W. E. (1953). *J. biol. Chem.* **204**, 345-357.
Krebs, H. A. (1967). In *Konferenz der Gesellschaft für Biologische Chemie*, pp. 216-227. Springer-Verlag, Berlin.
Krebs, H. A., Gascoyne, T. and Notton, B. M. (1967). *Biochem. J.* **102**, 275-281.
Kreisberg, R. A. (1967). *Diabetes* **16**, 784-790.
Lahti, R. A. and Majchrowicz, E. (1967). *Life Sci.* **6**, 1399-1406.
Lane, B. P. and Lieber, C. S. (1966). *Am. J. Path.* **49**, 593-603.
Lane, B. P. and Lieber, C. S. (1967). *Lab. Invest.* **16**, 342-348.
Larsen, J. A. (1959). *Nature, Lond.* **184**, 1236.
Ledermann, S. (1964). In *Alcohol, Alcoholisme, Alcoholisation, Institut national d'etudes demographiques, Travaux et Documents, Cahier No.* 41. Presses Universitaires de France, Paris, France.
Lefevre, A. and Lieber, C. S. (1967). *Clin. Res.* **15**, 324.
Lelbach, W. K. (1966). *Acta hepatosplenol.* **13**, 321-348.
Lelbach, W. K. (1967a). *Acta hepatosplenol.* **14**, 9-39.
Lelbach, W. K. (1967b). *Dt. med. Wschr.* **92**, 1-16.
Lieber, C. S. (1965). In *Progress in Liver Diseases* (H. Popper and F. Schaffner, eds), Vol. II. Grune and Stratton, New York.
Lieber, C. S. (1967). *Ann. Rev. Med.* **18**, 35-54.
Lieber, C. S. (1968). *Adv. intern. Med.* **14**, 151-159.
Lieber, C. S. and Davidson, C. S. (1962). *Am. J. Med.* **33**, 319-327.
Lieber, C. S. and DeCarli, L. M. (1964). *Clin. Res.* **12**, 274.
Lieber, C. S. and DeCarli, L. M. (1966). *Gastroenterology* **50**, 316-322.
Lieber, C. S. and DeCarli, L. M. (1968). *Science, N.Y.* **162**, 917-918.
Lieber, C. S. and Rubin, E. (1968a). *Am. J. Med.* **44**, 200-206.
Lieber, C. S. and Rubin, E. (1968b). *Gastroenterology* **54**, 642-646.
Lieber, C. S. and Schmid, R. (1961). *J. clin. Invest.* **40**, 394-399.
Lieber, C. S. and Spritz, N. (1966). *J. clin. Invest.* **45**, 1400-1411.
Lieber, C. S., DeCarli, L. M. and Schmid, R. (1959). *Biochem. biophys. Res. Commun.* **1**, 302-306.
Lieber, C. S., Jones, D. P., Losowsky, M. S. and Davidson, C. S. (1962a). *J. clin. Invest.* **41**, 1863-1870.
Lieber, C. S., Leevy, C. M., Stein, S. W., George, W. S., Cherrick, G. R., Abelmann, W. H. and Davidson, C. S. (1962b). *J. Lab. clin. Med.* **59**, 826-832.
Lieber, C. S., Jones, D. P., Mendelson, J. and DeCarli, L. M. (1963). *Trans. Ass. Am. Physns* lxxvi, 289-299.
Lieber, C. S., Jones, D. P. and DeCarli, L. M. (1965). *J. clin. Invest.* **44**, 1009-1021.
Lieber, C. S., Spritz, N. and DeCarli, L. M. (1966). *J. Clin. Invest.* **45**, 51-62.
Lieber, C. S., Lefevre, A., Spritz, N., Feinman, L. and DeCarli, L. M. (1967). *J. clin. Invest.* **46**, 1451-1460.
Lieber, C. S., Rubin, E. and DeCarli, L. M. (1969). In *Biochemical and Clinical Aspects of Alcohol Metabolism* (V. Sardesai, ed.). Charles C Thomas, Springfield, Illinois. (In the press.)
Lind, N. and Parkes, M. W. (1967). *J. Pharm. Pharmac.* **19**, 56-57.
Losowsky, M. S., Jones, D. P., Davidson, C. S. and Lieber, C. S. (1963). *Am. J. Med.* **35**, 794-803.
Lundquist, F., Tygstrup, N., Winkler, K., Mellemgaard, K. and Munck-Peterson, S. (1962). *J. clin. Invest.* **41**, 955-961.
Lundquist, F., Tygstrup, N., Winkler, K. and Jensen, K. B. (1965). *Science, N.Y* **150**, 616-617.

MacDonald, R. A. and Baumslag, N. (1964). *Am. J. Med. Sci.* **247**, 649.
Madison, L., Lochner, A. and Wulff, J. (1967). *Diabetes* **16**, 252-258.
Mallov, S. (1955). *Proc. Soc. exp. Biol. Med.* **88**, 246-249.
Mallov, S. (1957). *Am. J. Physiol.* **189**, 428-432.
Mallov, S. (1961). *Q. Jl. Stud. Alcohol* **22**, 250-253.
Mallov, S. and Bloch, J. L. (1956). *Am. J. Physiol.* **184**, 29-34.
McHenry, E. W. and Patterson, J. M. (1944). *Physiol. Rev.* **24**, 128-167.
Meldolesi, J. (1967). *Biochem. Pharmac.* **16**, 125-131.
Mendelson, J. H., Stein, S. and McGuire, M. T. (1966). *Psychosom. Med.* **28**, 1-12.
Menghini, G. (1960). *Bull. schweiz. Akad. Med. Wiss.* **16**, 36-52.
Mirone, L. (1966). *Am. J. Physiol.* **210**, 390-394.
Nelson, P., Tan, W. C., Wagle, S. R. and Ashmore, J. (1967). *Biochem. Pharmac.* **16**, 1813-1819.
Nikkila, E. A. and Ojala, K. (1963). *Proc. Soc. exp. Biol. Med.* **113**, 814-817.
Nyberg, A., Schuberth, J. and Anggard, L. (1953). *Acta chem. scand.* **7**, 1170-1172.
Orme-Johnson, W. H. and Ziegler, D. M. (1965). *Biochem. biophys. Res. Commun.* **21**, 78-82.
Oura, E., Raiha, N. C. R. and Suomalainen, H. (1967). *Annls Med. exp. Biol. Fenn.* **45**, 57-62.
Papenberg, J., von Wartburg, J. P. and Aebi, H. (1965). *Biochem. Z.* **342**, 95-107.
Perman, E. S. (1961). *Acta Physiol. scand.* **51**, 62-67.
Poggi, M. and Di Luzio, N. R. (1964). *J. Lipid Res.* **5**, 437-441.
Porta, E., Bergman, B. J. and Stein, A. A. (1965a). *Am. J. Path.* **46**, 657-689.
Porta, E. A., Hartroft, W. S. and de la Iglesia, F. A. (1965b). *Lab. Invest.* **14**, 1437-1455.
Porta, E. A., Hartroft, W. S., Gomez-Dumm, C. L. A. and Koch, O. R. (1967). *Fedn Proc. Fedn Am. Socs exp. Biol.* **26**, 1449-1457.
Powell, G. K., McMillan, W. O. and Young, D. I. (1968). *Clin. Res.* **16**, 290.
Rebouças, G. and Isselbacher, J. J. (1961). *J. clin. Invest.* **40**, 1355-1362.
Ridge, J. W. (1963). *Biochem. J.* **88**, 95-100.
Rubin, E. and Lieber, C. S. (1967). *Gastroenterology* **52**, 1-13.
Rubin, E. and Lieber, C. S. (1968). *New Engl. J. Med.* **278**, 869-876.
Rubin, E., Hutterer, F. and Lieber, C. S. (1968). *Science, N.Y.* **159**, 1469-1470.
Russell, P. T. and Van Bruggen, J. T. (1964). *J. biol. Chem.* **239**, 719-725.
Russell, P. T. and Van Bruggen, J. T. (1966). *Psychosom. Med.* **28**, 414-423.
Sandler, R. and Freinkel, N. (1966). *Metabolism* **15**, 1020-1023.
Schaffner, F., Loebel, A., Weiner, H. A. and Barka, T. (1963). *J. Am. Med. Ass.* **183**, 343-346.
Schapiro, R. H., Drummey, G. D., Shimizu, Y. and Isselbacher, K. J. (1964). *J. clin. Invest.* **43**, 1338-1347.
Schapiro, R. H., Scheig, R. L., Drummey, G. D., Mendelson, J. H. and Isselbacher, K. J. (1965). *New Engl. J. Med.* **272**, 610-616.
Scheig, R. and Isselbacher, K. L. (1965). *J. Lipid Res.* **6**, 269-277.
Schulman, M. P., Zurek, R. and Westerfeld, W. W. (1957). In *Alcoholism.* Amer. Assoc. Advance. Sci., Publ. 47, Washington, D.C.
Shull, K. H. (1959). *Nature, Lond.* **183**, 259-260.
Sidransky, H. and Farber, E. (1960). *Archs Biochem.* **87**, 129-133.
Smith, M. E. and Newman, H. W. (1960). *Proc. Soc. exp. Biol. Med.* **104**, 282-284.
Snyder, R., Schulman, M. P. and Westerfeld, W. W. (1964). *Archs Biochem.* **108**, 215-220.
Soehring, K. and Schuppel, R. (1966). *Dt. med. Wschr.* **91**, 1892-1896.
Spritz, N. and Lieber, C. S. (1966). *Proc. Soc. exp. Biol. Med.* **121**, 147-149.

Stein, O. and Stein, Y. (1965). *Israel J. Med. Sci.* **1**, 378-388.

Stein, O. and Stein, Y. (1967). *J. Cell. Biol.* **33**, 319-399.

Stein, S., Lieber, C. S., Cherrick, G. R., Leevy, C. M. and Abelmann, W. H. (1963). *Am. J. clin. Nutr.* **13**, 68-74.

Steiner, P. E., (1964). *Path. Microbiol.* **27**, 890-924.

Summary of Vital Statistics (1964). The City of New York, Department of Health.

Summerskill, S. H. J., Wolfe, S. J. and Davidson, C. S. (1957). *Lancet i*, 335-343.

Sutherland, D. A. and Watson, C. J. (1951). *J. Lab. clin. Med.* **37**, 29-39.

Svoboda, D. J. and Manning, R. T. (1964). *Am. J. Path.* **44**, 645-662.

Takada, A., Porta, E. A. and Hartroft, W. S. (1967). *Am. J. clin. Nutr.* **20**, 213-225.

Thaler, H. (1967). *Germ. med. Mon.* **12**, 134-135.

Thompson, G. N. (1956). *Alcoholism.* Charles C Thomas, Springfield, Illinois.

Thorpe, M. E. and Shorey, C. D. (1966). *Am. J. Path.* **48**, 557-577.

Towne, J. C. (1964). *Nature, Lond.* **201**, 709-710.

Truitt, E. B., Jr. and Duritz, G. (1966). *Fedn Proc. Fedn Am. Socs exp. Biol.* **25**, 657.

Truitt, E. B., Jr. and Duritz, G. (1967). In *Biochemical Factors in Alcoholism.* Pergamon Press, Oxford.

Tygstrup, N., Windler, J. and Lundquist, F. (1965). *J. clin. Invest.* **44**, 817-830.

Vital Statistics Rates in the United States, 1900-1940, U.S. Bureau of the Census, Washington, D.C., Govt. Printing Office, 1943.

Volwiler, W., Jones, C. M. and Mallory, T. B. (1948). *Gastroenterology*, **11**, 164-182.

von Wartburg, J. P. and Papenberg, J. (1966). *Psychom. Med.* **28**, 405-413.

von Wartburg, J. P. and Rothlisberger, M. (1961). *Helv. physiol. pharmac. Acta* **19**, 30-41.

von Wartburg, J. P., Bethune, J. L. and Vallee, B. L. (1964). *Biochemistry* **3**, 1775-1782.

Westerfeld, W. W. and Bloom, R. J. (1966). *Psychom. Med.* **28**, 443-449.

Zakim, D. (1965). *Archs Biochem.* **111**, 253-256.

PART III

The Alimentary Tract

CHAPTER 10

Basic Concepts in Intestinal Absorption

H. NEWEY and D. H. SMYTH

Department of Physiology, The University of Sheffield,
Sheffield, England

I. Introduction

The food which is taken into the body is mostly in the form of large relatively inert molecules, more or less insoluble. Before these can be utilized for metabolism they must be transformed into small reactive molecules, and these transformations are carried out by the alimentary tract, so that the more reactive material is passed on to the blood stream. These processes constitute digestion and absorption. Digestion depends partly on the activity of the cells lining the alimentary tract, and also the secretions of glands outside the alimentary tract, e.g. liver, pancreas, salivary glands. Absorption can be regarded entirely as a function of the epithelial cells, and it is the function of these cells which forms the subject of the present discussion. Not all cells, however, lining the alimentary tract have this function, and many of the cells are goblet cells which secrete mucus. Intestinal absorption is of interest not only in relation to nutrition but possibly even more in relation to the transport activities of all living cells.

In the past few years, a number of useful reviews have appeared on many aspects of absorption, e.g. Crane (1960), Wilson (1962), Wiseman (1964), Newey and Smyth (1966), Smyth (1967), and these cover details of many individual substances absorbed by the intestine and the techniques for their study. The present discussion is confined to some fundamental concepts of transport activity and particularly to (*a*) the forces involved in transfer; (*b*) kinetic problems related to transfer; and (*c*) coupling of transfer processes with each other and with cellular metabolism. It is intended as an introduction to current concepts and terminology in the complex field of membrane transport. The review by Fordtran and Dietschy (1966) covers part of this field from a slightly different point of view, and will be found a useful supplement.

II. Active Transport

The term active transport has been much used in recent years in relation to activities like those of the absorbing epithelium and it is therefore necessary to attempt some definition. In general, it is applied to movement of substances in a direction and at a rate which would not be expected from the physical conditions, i.e. concentration and electric potential. The excellent discussion of this problem by Rosenberg (1954) is worth careful study and another useful discussion is that of Ussing (1954) in relation to the movement of charged particles. Many of the concepts discussed here are dealt with by Rosenberg. Rosenberg defined active transfer as transfer of substances across one or more cell membranes which is influenced not only by the force responsible for passive diffusion but also by other forces which are maintained and regulated by the metabolism of the cell. He also introduced the term uphill transfer (transfer from a lower to a higher potential) as a criterion of the participation of forces other than diffusion. Rosenberg recognized that this definition was too narrow for many biological purposes, but it had the advantage of providing a criterion based only on experimental findings and not requiring assumptions about membrane structure and mechanisms.

There are two points about active transfer which require further discussion. First, Rosenberg's concept of uphill transfer is not necessarily applicable to each individual component of a multi-component system and for this reason part of this chapter deals with coupling between different components in a multi-component system. The other point is that aspect of the definition which Rosenberg recognized as being too narrow, and in fact, if uphill transfer is regarded as the criterion of active transport, then many interesting cases of transport caused by cell metabolism would be excluded. This could happen particularly if we have two different transfer systems operating simultaneously, one for solute and one for water. In this case, uphill transport might not be demonstrable although the solute movement might qualify for inclusion as active transfer in the sense that it is regulated by metabolic activity. Thus it seems necessary to stress cell participation as distinct from the achievement of demonstrable thermodynamic work. A possible definition might be movement of substances through cells or cell membranes at rates greater than would be expected from the existing external chemical potential or osmotic, hydrostatic and electrical forces, the accelerated rate being coupled with cellular metabolism in some way other than by transport of another component in the system. The significance of this last condition is that in a multi-component system there may be coupled processes in which movement of one component supplies energy for movement of another. As will be seen from subsequent discussion, it is intended to distinguish between substances whose transport could be regarded as primarily dependent on metabolism, and substances whose transport is primarily dependent on movement of another substance. It is easy to get involved in semantic arguments in such cases, although these can be useful provided we know precisely what is meant by the expressions used. For example, it could be said that the movement of glucose by the intestine is active transfer, and yet if we accept the theories of glucose transfer discussed later, the transfer of glucose could be regarded as a process secondary to sodium transfer. There is still another complication in making involvement of metabolic energy the criterion. In any living system metabolic energy is required to maintain the system as distinct from enabling the system to carry out work, and it is not easy to distinguish between these requirements.

III. The Epithelial Cell and Intestinal Wall

Figure 1 shows a simplified diagram of the intestinal wall. The important element in the transfer process is the layer of epithelial cells which separate the intestinal lumen from the subepithelial fluid. It is these epithelial cells

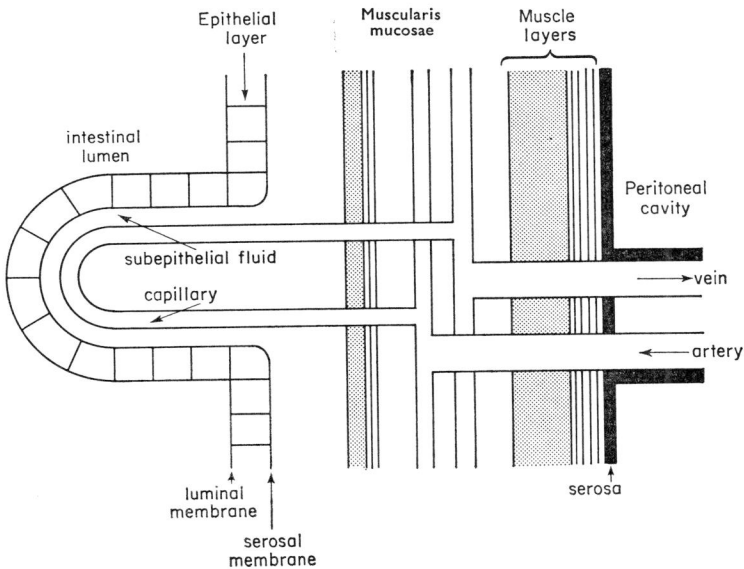

FIG. 1. Diagrammatic representation of the wall of the intestine to show the relationship of the epithelial cells to the other structures. For further discussion see text. (From *Evans' Principles of Human Physiology*, H. Davson and M. G. Eggleton, eds, p. 639, 1962, Churchill, London.)

which are actually moving substances from the lumen of the intestine into the subepithelial fluid. Having arrived in the subepithelial fluid, these substances are carried away by the blood capillaries or by the lymph capillaries. (In the diagram shown here the lymph capillaries have been omitted.) There is no reason to believe that there are special processes involved in the movement of substances from the subepithelial space through the wall of the capillary, and it is accepted that the capillary wall is permeable to small molecular weight substances.

This diagram illustrates some of the problems to be resolved in transfer, a problem discussed in more detail by Newey and Smyth (1967) and Levin (1967). It is meant to stress the fact that cellular activity results in movement of substances from the intestinal lumen into the subepithelial space. If the substance is neither metabolized nor produced by the cells, and if a steady state has been reached, then the disappearance from the lumen and appearance in the subepithelial space would be equal. Since the amount in the subepithelial space is not easily accessible to measurement, disappearance from the lumen will be the obvious measure of transfer. However, this measurement is often subject to large errors, as it will often be the difference between two larger quantities, i.e. the initial amount in the lumen and the final amount in the lumen. *In vitro* this difficulty can be overcome by measuring the total amount of substance in the gut wall and serosal fluid at the end of the experiment and if necessary subtracting from this the amount at the beginning of the experiment.

From the point of view of the animal, the important result of the absorptive process is the gain of nutrient material by the body, and the absorptive activity is probably best measured by the absolute amount of nutrients arriving in the blood stream. Attempts to measure the effectiveness of absorption in terms of unit weight or length of gut sometimes overlook this elementary consideration, as do measurements involving concentration changes. The precise measurement of the amount of substance arriving in the blood stream is very difficult in the experimental animal and human subject, and instead, the amount leaving the lumen is in practice one of the most useful measures of absorption.

Measurement of absorptive activity based on concentration changes do give useful information about uphill transfer, and are essential for some aspects of the process, although the difficulties of both measurements and interpretation must be taken into account. Some of these difficulties are well illustrated by attempts to use the concentrations in the cells themselves (Saunders and Isselbacher, 1965) as a measure of absorptive capacity. Consider first the relation between cell concentration and location of the transfer process, a matter also discussed by Parsons (1967). If the transfer process is at the luminal surface, active transfer will result in a higher concentration in the cells themselves. On the other hand, if the transfer process is at the other pole of the cell it should result in a lower concentration in the cell. The measurement of cellular concentration involves difficulties. Whatever the procedure in individual cases, the whole process must involve certain measurements, assumptions and calculations which can be discussed in general terms as follows. The basic principle is to divide the amount of substance in the epithelial cells by the volume of intracellular fluid. The epithelial cells cannot, however, readily be separated from the rest of the gut for measurement and the gut wall must be treated as a whole. The total amount of solute in the gut wall is measured and must be distributed between the intracellular fluid and the extracellular fluid. The volume of extracellular fluid is measured by means of mannitol or some other indicator, it being assumed that the indicator used penetrates fully into the extracellular space but not at all into the intracellular space. The amount of solute in the extracellular fluid is obtained by multiplying the volume of extracellular fluid by the concentration of solute on the assumption that this is the same as in the fluid bathing the gut. If the substance is being actively transferred, this assumption is likely to be wrong, as there must be a continuous gradient from the cell via the extracellular space to the surrounding fluid. The figure obtained for solute in the extracellular space is subtracted from the solute in the total gut wall, and the difference taken to be the amount in the intra-cellular space of the intestine. The intracellular fluid in the intestine is determined by the difference between total intestinal fluid and extracellular fluid. Finally the intracellular concentration is calculated by dividing the amount of intracellular solute by the volume of intracellular fluid. The whole determination is summarized by the following equation:

$$\text{Intracellular solute concentration} = \frac{\text{total amount of solute in gut} - \left(\dfrac{\text{amount of marker in gut}}{\text{concentration of marker in bathing fluid}} \times \text{solute concentration in bathing fluid}\right)}{\text{wet weight of gut} - \text{dry weight of gut} - \left(\dfrac{\text{amount of marker in gut}}{\text{concentration of marker in bathing fluid}}\right)}$$

As all the measurements are made with a certain experimental error, the final result cannot be a very precise measurement. A further unwarranted assumption is then made that the concentration so obtained gives that in the absorbing epithelial cells. The cells of the intestine include not only the epithelial cells but also those of the muscular layers of the intestine, the lymphoid tissue, connective tissue and other cells. What is measured is therefore the average concentration in all these different cells, and since the epithelial cells have a special capacity for transfer, it does not follow that the concentration in these cells is the same as in the other intestinal cells. Indeed, we know that many other cells in the body have also got a capacity for taking up substances such as glucose and amino acids, and to make the assumption that the epithelial cells which are transferring substances have the same concentration as other cells is clearly a hazardous procedure. The con-centration in the epithelial wall could in fact be either higher or lower than the average cell concentration depending on the location of the transport process. Conclusions based on measurements of concentration of substances in a mixed population of cells must thus be taken with some caution. Other parameters involving concentration have been discussed by Newey and Smyth (1967).

IV. Forces Involved in Absorption

One object of biology is to describe the changes taking place in living tissues in terms of known chemical and physical forces. This is usually possible only to a limited degree, and when this limit is reached, it is then necessary to describe events in terms of more complicated cellular activities, which are called biological processes, e.g. ion pumps, pinocytosis, etc. It is therefore convenient to divide the processes in absorption into physico-chemical processes and biological processes. It is also convenient to separate the processes involved in movement of water, and those involved in movement of other substances.

A. *Substances other than water*

These include hydrophilic substances relatively insoluble in lipids, substances with a considerable degree of both aqueous and lipid solubility and lipids with little aqueous solubility. The substances may be in the lumen of the intestine, which can be regarded as an aqueous phase, in the inside of the cell, which is presumably also a complex aqueous phase, in the cell membrane, which is partly lipid, or attached or adsorbed to cellular structures which form a solid phase. It is therefore necessary to consider movement of substances through a homogeneous (aqueous or lipid) phase, from one liquid phase to another, and movement between a liquid and solid phase (adsorption and desorption).

1. *Physico-chemical processes*

a. *Movement in a homogeneous phase*

An aqueous phase will be considered and this may be extracellular fluid, intracellular fluid or pores in a membrane. If the pores are large in relation to the molecular size of the solutes, then the same laws will apply to all the cases. In many cases the pore size will not be large in relation to the solute and these are considered later.

(i) *Thermal agitation.* The molecules or ions in a solution are in constant state of movement, a process called thermal agitation. This is a continuous bombardment of solute and solvent molecules by each other, and according to the kinetic theory explains a number of the properties of the solution. Provided the concentration of solute is uniform throughout the solution, this activity causes only random movement of solute particles, and does not lead to any measurable change of solute concentration.

(ii) *Diffusion.* Diffusion is the movement of a substance which takes place when its concentration in one part of a system is different from that in another, and this movement is such that the concentration throughout tends to become equalized. Therefore if a high concentration exists on one side of a permeable membrane and a low concentration on the other, there is no need to postulate any special force for moving substances through the membrane other than the diffusion gradient. In interpreting the results of studies down a concentration gradient, it should be remembered that this rule of movement down a concentration gradient applies only to the net movement. In the previous section it has been pointed out that there is always a random movement of particles in solution. If a membrane separates two solutes of different concentrations, there will be movement across the membrane in both directions. These movements are often referred to as fluxes, and the difference between these is called the net flux.

Quantitative aspects of interest are the rate of diffusion and the work done in particular experimental conditions, including movement through pores.

RATE. The rate of diffusion of a substance between any two points in a system depends on the difference in concentration between these two points. If the concentration at the two points are C_1 and C_2, then the rate of movement (S) of the substance will be given by the equation

$$S = K(C_1 - C_2) \tag{1}$$

where K is a constant. It is obvious that S will only have a positive value when $C_1 > C_2$ and hence net movement only takes place from the higher to the lower concentration. (It will be seen on p. 364 that the kinetic picture represented by equation 1 can be found in conditions other than simple diffusion.)

The constant K consists of two factors, the area across which diffusion is taking place and the diffusion coefficient, which is characteristic of each individual substance in the particular solvent. The diffusion coefficient is related to molecular size – small molecules diffusing more rapidly – but is also related to the chemical structure of the substance. Compounds with a capacity to form hydrogen bonds are affected by mutual forces between the solute and the solvent which can affect the diffusion rate.

In the case of diffusion through a biological membrane, it is usually assumed that the concentration on each side is uniform and the concentration gradient is across the membrane. In this case K incorporates a permeability constant characteristic of the particular membrane and particular solute.

Reference has already been made to the fluxes occurring in both directions across a membrane, the difference between these, the net flux, producing the change in concentration. This concept is implicit in equation 1, because the flux in each direction will be proportional to the concentration on the side from which the flux is taking place, i.e. it will be KC_1 and KC_2 respectively. The net flux or measurable diffusion rate is thus the difference between these.

In some cases it is desirable to know the flux in each direction, and the principle used is the following. Suppose there are two compartments A and B separated by a membrane, and a substance not present in the system is added to compartment A. Diffusion of the substance begins immediately through the membrane into compartment B, and the rate is proportional to the concentration in A. The rate, however, soon changes because of (*a*) fall of concentration in A and (*b*) back diffusion from B as the concentration there increases. It is possible to overcome these complications by using a very small time period or by having very large compartments, although the size of the compartments may be outside experimental control.

When the substance being studied is one which is already present in the system, the difficulty can be surmounted by using isotopically labelled material. The principles already discussed will then apply to the movement of the isotope. It must be stressed that the validity of this method depends on a short time-period of measurement, and the absence of any other process such as production or destruction of the substance by the membrane, or any condition in the membrane which will cause the back-diffusion into compartment A, to be influenced by some factor other than the concentration in B. For a detailed discussion of some of the problems of unidirectional flux measurements see Curran *et al.* (1967).

A more complex situation occurs when the substance is moving not only through one membrane but through a cell, and here it may be important to know the individual fluxes in each direction through the various membranes. The situation has been analysed in terms of three compartments by Ussing and Zerahn (1951). Fig. 2 shows three compartments O, C and I, divided

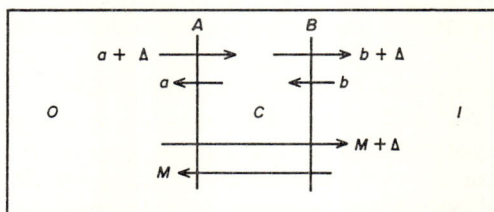

FIG. 2. Diagram of a system with two membranes, A and B, of high resistance, separating three well mixed solutions O, C, and I (see text). From Ussing and Zerahn (1951).

by two membranes A and B. Suppose the substance is being transferred from compartment O to compartment I through compartment C. There will be a flux from O to C and a back flux from C into O. There will also be a flux from C into I and a back flux from I into C. If net transfer is taking place the fluxes in the direction O to I will be greater than in the reverse direction. If the total flux from O to I is denoted as $M + \Delta$ and the total flux from I to O as M, then Δ represents the net flux from O to I. Such a system will reach a steady state when the amount of substance in C is constant, which means that the net flux across A is equal to the net flux across B. When this happens the flux from C to O is taken as a, and that from I to C as b. The corresponding fluxes in the opposite directions will be $a + \Delta$ (from O to C), and $b + \Delta$ (from C to I). The amount of substance $(a + \Delta)$ which enters C will leave either by backward movement to O or forward movement to I, and the fractions of $a + \Delta$ moving in the two directions will be proportional to the fluxes from C to O and I respectively, i.e. to a and $b + \Delta$. The amount of $a + \Delta$ which moves into I will therefore be $\dfrac{(a + \Delta)(b + \Delta)}{a + (b + \Delta)}$. It thus follows that $M + \Delta = \dfrac{(a + \Delta)(b + \Delta)}{a + b + \Delta}$.

It is evident that there are four quantities here, M, a, b, and Δ, and if three of these are known the other can be calculated. As discussed below, attempts have been made to measure M, $M+\Delta$, and $a+\Delta$ across the intestinal epithelial cell. The system could be more complicated with four or more compartments instead of three and in these conditions it would not be possible to determine all the fluxes by determination of M, a and Δ.

Schultz and Curran and their colleagues have considered three compartments, the mucosal fluid, the serosal fluid, and the gut wall, and have applied the Ussing and Zerahn analysis to determine alanine fluxes. In considering this it is useful to relate the terminologies used in the two cases; Fig. 3 shows the Schultz and Curran model of the epithelial cell; it is evident that the fluxes shown are related to those of Ussing and Zerahn as follows: $\mathcal{J}_{ms}=M+\Delta, \mathcal{J}_{sm}=M, \mathcal{J}_{mc}=a+\Delta, \mathcal{J}_{cm}=a, \mathcal{J}_{cs}=b+\Delta,$ and $\mathcal{J}_{sc}=b.$

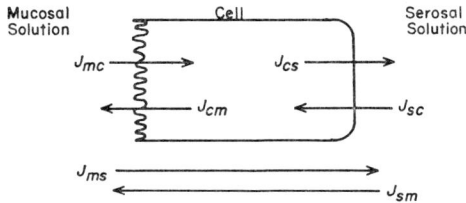

FIG. 3. Three compartment model of the intestine epithelial cell for study of fluxes. From Schultz et al. (1967).

$\mathcal{J}_{ms}$ is measured by introducing an isotope into the mucosal fluid and measuring its rate of appearance in the serosal fluid. When this reaches a constant rate, this is called the steady state unidirectional flux, and is taken as a measure of $\mathcal{J}_{ms}$. Similarly, by putting an isotope into the serosal fluid $\mathcal{J}_{sm}$ can be determined. The net flux (Δ) is $\mathcal{J}_{ms}-\mathcal{J}_{sm}$. $\mathcal{J}_{mc}$ (initial influx) is now determined before a steady state has been reached and before any back flux occurs, by choosing a short time interval. From these three experimental determinations all the steady state fluxes were then calculated from the relationships

$$\mathcal{J}_{ms}=\frac{\mathcal{J}_{mc}\mathcal{J}_{cs}}{\mathcal{J}_{cm}+\mathcal{J}_{cs}}$$

and $\mathcal{J}_{ms}-\mathcal{J}_{sm}=\mathcal{J}_{mc}-\mathcal{J}_{cm}=\mathcal{J}_{cs}-\mathcal{J}_{sc}.$

In this way a complete picture of the fluxes across the two sides of the epithelial cell was attempted. It is, however, important to examine the assumptions made in the process. (1) The gut wall is treated as one compartment by assuming that the subepithelial fluid is really an extension of the serosal fluid and that no diffusion barrier exists between the serosal pole of the epithelial cell and the serosal fluid. In fact, Schultz et al. have shown that the subepithelial layer does present an effective diffusion barrier, and hence the gut wall must be considered as consisting of two compartments, the epithelial cell and the subepithelial space. Furthermore, it is probably an unjustifiable assumption even to regard each of these two compartments as uniform. (2) The determination of steady state fluxes depends on the assumptions that the concentration in the mucosal fluid and serosal fluid does not change, the latter remaining at zero. If the amount of isotope in the mucosal fluid is large in relation to the amount entering the intestine the assumption that the concentration does not change is probably justified. In dealing with the serosal side the experimenter is faced with a dilemma. It must be assumed that the concentration remains at zero, and yet there must be enough change in successive intervals to measure accurately. (3) The value of J_{mc} used in the steady state equations is that determined in the short-period experiment without a steady state. The influx J_{mc} of amino acid is measured when the concentration in the cell is zero, and assumed to remain the same when the system reaches a steady state. This will be true if the fluxes J_{mc} and J_{cm} are not coupled in any way with each other. But since it is assumed that they are both mediated by a carrier, the value of J_{mc} is not necessarily independent of J_{cm} and thus the value of J_{mc} measured initially is not necessarily the same as in the steady state. Another possible source of error is deterioration of the tissue during the experiment with consequent changes in J_{mc} with time. All of these considerations must throw serious doubt on the validity of the analysis of fluxes across the mucosal and serosal poles of the epithelial cell.

MOVEMENT THROUGH PORES. Movement of solutes through a membrane with pores exhibits diffusion kinetics provided there is no restriction to movement by the pores either as regards to total area of pore available or the nature of the individual pores. (For the moment the effect of fluid movement is ignored.) Restriction through pores involves the size and shape of the pore and the electrical charge in the wall of the pore, and also the size, shape and electrical charge of the solute molecule. Molecular size is sometimes simplified by use of the Stokes-Einstein radius, which is the radius of a sphere with the same free diffusion properties as the molecule under consideration (see Schultz and Solomon, 1961). The size of the pore is often simplified even more by the concept of equivalent pore radius, which is the radius which would explain the experimental findings if all the pores were cylindrical with the same radius. It is evident that the relative size of the molecules and pores would be an important factor in solute diffusion through membranes, and Davson and Danielli (1943) provided quantitative evidence for this. The rate of penetration will depend on a good many factors in addition to the two simple parameters mentioned above, and the whole question has been well discussed by Pappenheimer (1953). The equivalent pore radius of the rat intestine was measured by Lindemann and Solomon (1962) who gave a value of 4 Å and has been confirmed by an independent method by Smyth and Wright (1966). This is a size of pore which prevents any significant penetration by mannitol (mol. wt = 182), but allows some penetration of erythritol (mol. wt = 122). Fordtran et al. (1965) have found values of 7·5 and 3·4 Å for the human jejunum and ileum respectively. In general it is assumed that particles move through pores independently of each other, but a special case for "in file" movement in nerve membrane has been discussed by Hodgkin and Keynes (1955). The effect of electrical charge will depend on the nature of the charge and the diameter and length of the pores. In general positively charged pores will facilitate movement of anions and restrict the movement of cations. These effects have been discussed in more detail by Bayliss (1959).

WORK. When a substance diffuses through a membrane down a concentration gradient from one compartment to another the potential energy of the concentration gradient is dissipated and work is done. While the measurements of this itself is not usually of major interest, it can become so in certain cases. Another aspect of osmotic work is the reverse process of creating a concentration gradient by means of a solute pump. In both cases the work done is given by

$$W = 2 \cdot 3 \, NRT \, \log C_1/C_2 \tag{2}$$

where W is the work done expressed in calories, $2 \cdot 3$ is the factor for conversion of natural logarithms to the base 10, N the number of molecules of solute moved, R is the gas constant ($1 \cdot 98$ cals), T the absolute temperature, and C_1 and C_2 the concentrations on the two sides of the membrane.

SOURCE OF ENERGY FOR DIFFUSION. The essential condition for diffusion is the existence of a concentration gradient across the membrane. This gradient may be created in various ways, and it is useful to think of these as processes outside the cell and independent of it, and processes inside the cell. The obvious example of an extracellular process is the creation of experimental conditions to produce a concentration gradient across a particular membrane. There are also natural physiological processes which create concentration gradients, and may do so either by accumulation of substances on one side of the membrane or removal from the other. An example of accumulation on one side of the membrane is the taking and digestion of food which results in high concentration of the products of digestion on the luminal side of the membrane of the columnar epithelial cell. An example of removal of a substance is the action of the blood flow through the mesenteric vessels in removing the products of digestion as they pass through the cells and hence maintaining a low concentration on that side of the cell.

There are also various kinds of activities inside the cell which can lead to diffusion gradients. Processes which lead to the metabolism of the nutrient materials in all living cells will create a concentration gradient for the entry of these substances into the cell, while production of excretory products will create a gradient for the removal of these from the cell. In the case of the intestine, localized digestive activity could maintain diffusion gradients which could play a role in the entry of substances into the cell. Quite a different kind of intracellular activity creating concentration gradients are solute pumps. These are discussed later (p. 369), but can be regarded as a zone in the cell (or cell membrane) which moves a solute from one side (the *cis* side) to the other (the *trans* side). The gradient of interest in this case is not the gradient created between the two sides of the pump but rather the gradient which replenishes solute removed at the cis side, and which removes that accumulated at the trans side. Solute pumps can only continue to work by diffusion processes going on at the two sides.

(iii) *Electrical forces.* When ionized substances move through a membrane, the situation is complicated by electrical forces. These may be due to electric charges in the pores of the membrane or in the surface of the membrane, already referred to, or it may be due to an electric potential between the two fluids separated by the membrane. This will either attract or repel ions depending on their charge, and the work done in moving ions will be given by

$$W = NzFE \tag{3}$$

where W is the work done in calories, N the amount of substance moved, expressed in gm ions, z the valency, F the Faraday (96 000 coulombs) and E the potential in volts.

ELECTROCHEMICAL POTENTIAL. In many cases there may exist simultaneously a concentration gradient and an electric potential, both of which have an effect on movement through the membrane. The combined effect can be expressed in terms of the electrochemical potential. This is done by calculating two fractions of work, i.e. the osmotic work and the electrical work, as described above. The total work is then given by

$$W = 2{\cdot}3 \, NRT \log \frac{C_1}{C_2} + NzFE \tag{4}$$

where the symbols have the same meaning as in equations 2 and 3.

In the case of movement through the intestine this concept of electrochemical potential is undoubtedly a useful one in deciding whether energy is required for a particular process. It is, however, seldom easy to evaluate the work done accurately, because the movement of solute is usually accompanied by movement of solvent.

It should be noted that it does not necessarily follow that because a substance is moving down an electrochemical gradient energy is not being utilized for the process.

b. Movement of solute between aqueous and lipid phases

Absorption of substances by the intestine may involve movement from an aqueous to a lipid phase, and also the reverse process. This problem has been discussed in some detail by Danielli (1949), who regards the process of penetration of a lipid layer as first a detachment of penetrating molecule from the surrounding water molecules and then movement through the lipid layer by diffusion. The energy required for the first stage will depend on the number of polar groups in the compound capable of forming attachment to the water molecules. The degree of penetration into the lipid phase can be expressed by the partition coefficient, which indicates the distribution of solute in equal volumes of the two phases in equilibrium with each other. If two aqueous phases are separated by a lipid one, it will be possible for certain substances to move by diffusion from one aqueous phase to the other through the lipid phase, provided there is a concentration difference between the two aqueous phases and a solubility in the lipid phase. There will be a concentration gradient between the two sides of the lipid phase but a sharp change in concentration at the interface at each side of the lipid phase.

(i) *Non-ionic diffusion.* The distribution of a weakly ionized substance across a membrane can be related to the hydrogen ion concentration on the two sides of the membrane. This process, which is often called non-ionic diffusion, was first quantitatively considered by Jacobs (1940). The process applies to weak acids or bases, which dissociate to different degrees according to the pH, the relationship being expressed by the equation

$$pH = pK + \log \frac{[A^-]}{[HA]}. \tag{5}$$

If a weak acid such as acetic is taken as an example, it will exist in an ionized form (CH_3COO^-), and an un-ionized form CH_3COOH. These differ in their lipid solubilities, in that the undissociated CH_3COOH is moderately lipid soluble, whereas the acetate ion is relatively insoluble. If two solutions of acetic acid are separated by a lipid barrier, it could be assumed that the undissociated acid passes through the barrier and ultimately would come into equilibrium on the two sides. If, however, the pH is different on the two sides of the membrane, the fraction dissociated would be different on the two sides, and therefore the total concentration (acetic acid and acetate together) would be different on the two sides. The actual concentrations on the two sides at equilibrium are given by the equation

$$\frac{C_1}{C_2} = \frac{1 + 10^{(pH_1 - pK)}}{1 + 10^{(pH_2 - pK)}} \tag{6}$$

where C_1 and C_2 are the total concentrations on the two sides, pH_1 and pH_2 the pH on the two sides and pK the negative logarithm of the dissociation constant.

c. Movement between liquid and solid phase: adsorption and desorption

When a solution is in contact with a surface, then part of the solute may become attached to the surface. This attachment may be of a relatively nonspecific nature, as in adsorption of gases by charcoal, more specific as in exchange resins, or highly specific as in the case of carriers to be discussed later. The graph expressing the relation between the concentration of the substance and the amount adsorbed is called the adsorption isotherm, and at least six different shapes of adsorption isotherm have been described (for details see Kippling, 1965). However, the one of interest here is that described by Langmuir (1918) in which it is envisaged that there are a limited number of sites on the solid phase for attachment of the substance adsorbed and that these sites can become saturated. The degree of saturation depends on the concentration of the solute and is expressed by the Langmuir adsorption isotherm, which has the form

$$x = \frac{abc}{1 + ac} \tag{7}$$

where a and b are constants, x is the total amount of substance adsorbed and c is the concentration or partial pressure. The equation is formally identical with the Michaelis-Menten equation for enzyme kinetics (equation 9) discussed later.

2. Biological processes

a. Facilitated diffusion

(i) *Carriers and kinetics.* A striking feature of transfer by many tissues is the selectivity exhibited. This implies that if two substances are of nearly equal molecular size and shape, one may be much more readily transported than the other. For example, glucose and galactose are very readily absorbed by the intestine whereas mannose is not. In the case of the amino acids, Gibson and Wiseman (1951) found that the L-amino acids are more easily absorbed than their D-enantiomorphs. It is difficult to explain this selectivity in terms of pore size, and the explanation which has found most favour is the concept of carriers in the cell membrane. This concept not only accounts for the selectivity but it also attempts to explain how hydrophilic substances pass through a barrier which is basically lipid. The idea of a carrier was put forward by Osterhout (1933), and it has subsequently been developed by a large number of workers. It has chiefly been studied in relation to the red cell and the kinetics of the process, usually referred to as facilitated diffusion, have largely been established with this tissue. Good reviews are available by Wilbrandt and Rosenberg (1961) and by Lefevre (1961).

The fundamental concept is that there are carrier substances in the membrane which are able to move through the material of the membrane. These carriers have specific sites for attachment of the substances carried, and as a result of diffusion these sites are brought into contact with aqueous phases on the two sides of the membrane. When in contact with one side, the substance becomes attached to the carrier, when in contact with the other side it is set free. (The carrier need not be a substance diffusing through the membrane but could be a rotating or extensile protein which is able to move so as to make contact with different phases.) Facilitated diffusion is sometimes referred to as ferry-boat transfer or shuttle transfer from the obvious analogies. The kinetics of the process depend on (1) the rate of attachment; (2) the rate of release, and (3) the speed of the intervening process, i.e. the combined carrier diffusing across the cell or the rate of the movement or rotation of the combined carrier. It is further assumed that the last is the rate-limiting step, and hence the rate of the whole process is proportional to the difference in saturation of the carrier at the two sides of the membrane.

The kinetics of facilitated diffusion are the same whether we have a diffusing carrier or an extensile or rotating carrier, and as an example the diffusing carrier may be taken. In this case the following assumptions are made: (1) the carrier can diffuse through the membrane in either the free or combined form, and the movement both of the free and combined form is due to thermal agitation, i.e. it does not require an external source of energy. (2) The attachment depends on the chemical configuration of the substance carried so that a certain specificity of transfer is given. This is not absolute but substances with a particular chemical configuration will fit better than others and therefore have a greater affinity. (3) The attachment and release of the substance follows the Langmuir adsorption isotherm. (4) The rate of transfer of substances through the membrane depends on the difference between the saturation of the carrier at the two sides of the membrane. (5) The same maximum rate of transfer is achieved for all substances which use the same carrier.

Since modern views of intestinal transfer depend on the carrier concept, it is useful to examine this in some detail. A simple mathematical approach is given here to some aspects of the problem, but for a more detailed discussion Wilbrandt and Rosenberg (1961) should be consulted.

If a substance is present in a concentration C in the aqueous phase to which the carrier site is accessible, the amount of carrier in the combined form will be given by the equation

$$s = \frac{SC}{C+K} \qquad (8)$$

where C is the concentration of substance in the aqueous phase, and S and K are constants. If arbitrary values are taken and s is plotted against C, a curve is obtained and shown in Fig. 4, in which at high values of C, s

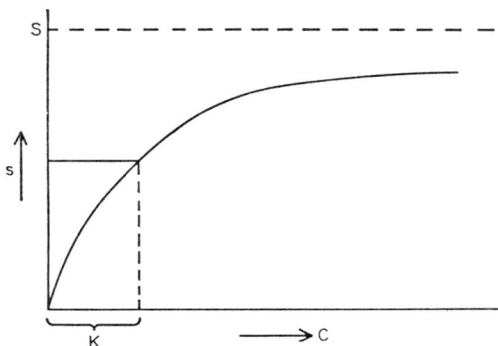

FIG. 4. Graph of Michaelis-Menten kinetics relating the concentration of a substance (abscissa) to the amount of carrier or enzyme saturated (ordinate). S is the maximum capacity of the system and K the concentration causing half-saturation of the maximum capacity.

approaches S. S is therefore a constant representing the maximum capacity of the system and is proportional to the total amount of carrier available. s/S is thus the fraction of the carrier saturated, and (8) can be rearranged as

$$\frac{s}{S} = \frac{C}{C+K}. \tag{9}$$

If C is made equal to K, s is equal to $S/2$ and hence K is the concentration of substance which causes half-saturation of the carrier. This is also explained by Fig. 4. K is therefore a measure of the affinity of the carrier for the particular substance. The relationship expressed in equations 8 and 9 is often referred to as Michaelis-Menten kinetics from the analogy with the rate of enzyme reactions worked out by Michaelis and Menten (1913). It should, however, be remembered that the analogy is a loose one, and certainly the use of these equations does not imply enzyme participation. Furthermore, K in enzyme kinetics is not necessarily a simple affinity constant and may involve other stages in the total process, as discussed by Webb (1963).

As many calculations are based on this equation it is useful to present it in the form suggested by Lineweaver and Burk (1934). By rearrangement of the terms we get

$$\frac{1}{s} = \frac{K}{S} \cdot \frac{1}{C} + \frac{1}{S}. \tag{10}$$

This is the equation of a straight line, relating the values of $\frac{1}{s}$ and $\frac{1}{C}$ (Fig. 5). The intercept on the ordinate is $\frac{1}{S}$ and the intercept on the abscissa is $-\frac{1}{K}$. This is the procedure usually employed for determining the value of K, but it is well to point out that there are pitfalls not always appreciated. The determination of K is only valid if it can be shown that there is a truly linear

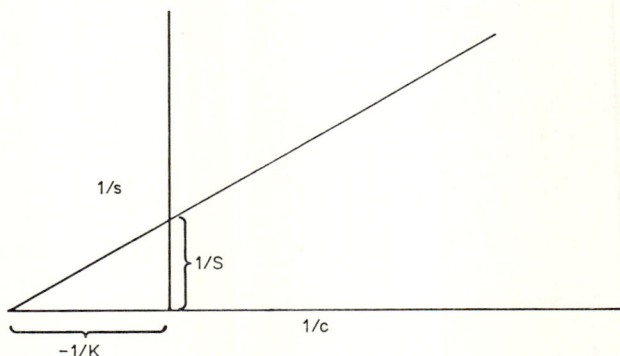

FIG. 5. Lineweaver-Burk plot of the reciprocals of concentration and amount of enzyme or carrier saturated. The intercept on the abscissa is the negative reciprocal of the affinity constant and the intercept on the ordinate the reciprocal of the maximum capacity.

relationship between $\dfrac{1}{s}$ and $\dfrac{1}{C}$. Furthermore, proper statistical procedures should be employed to show that the value of $\dfrac{1}{K}$ differs significantly from 0, and that the values of different K's differ significantly from each other. And, if the experiment is planned with concentrations evenly spaced over a linear scale, the reciprocals will not be evenly spaced, and a weighted regression analysis will be necessary. This can be avoided by suitable choice of experimental concentrations.

If the concentrations of a substance on the two sides of a membrane are C_1 and C_2, the fraction of carrier saturated on one side is $\dfrac{C_1}{C_1+K}$ while at the other side it is $\dfrac{C_2}{C_2+K}$. The net rate of transfer through the membrane, proportional to the difference in the saturation of the carrier on the two sides, is given by the equation

$$v = A\left(\frac{C_1}{C_1+K} - \frac{C_2}{C_2+K}\right) \tag{11}$$

where v is the rate of movement from side 1 to side 2, A is a constant and the other symbols are as in equation (8). This can be rearranged as

$$v = AK\left(\frac{C_1-C_2}{(C_1+K)(C_2+K)}\right). \tag{12}$$

A positive value of v means movement from side 1 to side 2, and will only be obtained when $C_1 > C_2$. Hence facilitated diffusion can only occur down a concentration gradient.

If the process followed equation 11 without any complication such as substrate inhibition (following the analogy of enzyme kinetics), the maximum rate of movement will occur when C_2 is zero and C_1 is infinitely high; and in this case $v = A$, so that A is the maximum possible rate. There is evidence in intestinal transport that complications do occur at higher concentrations (Jervis and Smyth, 1959; Matthews and Laster, 1965), but A still remains the maximum possible transfer rate.

If $C_2 = 0$, equation 11 becomes

$$v = A\left(\frac{C_1}{C_1+K}\right) \tag{13}$$

and this is identical with Michaelis-Menten kinetics.

If C_2 and C_1 are both large in relation to K, the position is approached where

$$v = AK\left(\frac{1}{C_2} - \frac{1}{C_1}\right). \tag{14}$$

In this case, if two substances with different K values are studied, the rate of transfer would be proportional to K, so that the substance with the higher value of K (i.e. low affinity) would be transferred more rapidly.

If C_1 and C_2 are both small in relation to K, the position is approached where

$$v = A\frac{(C_1 - C_2)}{K}. \tag{15}$$

In these conditions, the rate of transfer is inversely proportional to K, and if two substances with different values of K are studied, the one with the greater affinity (low value of K) would be transferred more rapidly. Wilbrandt and Rosenberg (1961), have considered that equations 14 and 15 could explain the phenomena of different relative rates of transfer of different substances at different concentrations. Newey and Smyth (1964a) have, however, pointed out that in the case of the neutral amino acids a possible alternative explanation might be the existence of more than one carrier.

A further consequence of equation 15 is that in these conditions v is proportional to $(C_1 - C_2)$ and this is the kinetics of simple diffusion. Hence, because experimentally diffusion kinetics are observed it cannot be assumed that a carrier system is not involved.

(ii) *Competition.* As much of the work on intestinal transport is concerned with competition between different substances for transport, it is useful to look at the kinetics of competitive inhibition. In enzyme kinetics if the concentration of the substrate is C and the Michaelis constant K_m, the saturation of the enzyme (s) and the maximum saturation (S) are related by the equation

$$\frac{s}{S} = \frac{1}{1 + \dfrac{K_m}{C}} \tag{16}$$

which is a rearrangement of equation 9. If another substrate is present which competes for the enzyme, and is present in concentration of i with an affinity constant of K_i, the fraction of enzyme saturated with the original substrate will be given by

$$\frac{s}{S} = \frac{1}{1 + \dfrac{K_m}{C}\left(1 + \dfrac{i}{K_i}\right)}. \tag{17}$$

For the derivation of equation 17 the reader is referred to standard textbooks on enzyme kinetics, e.g. Dixon and Webb (1964). It will be seen that this really means a different affinity constant K_p which is equal to $K_m\left(1 + \dfrac{i}{K_i}\right)$. Equation 17 may now be written

$$\frac{s}{S} = \frac{1}{1 + \dfrac{K_p}{C}} \tag{18}$$

which is identical with equation 16 but with a different affinity constant. If this equation is expressed by the Lineweaver and Burk plot $1/s$ (the intercept on the ordinate) will remain the same and therefore substances which compete for the same carrier will show a series of lines intersecting on the ordinate as in Fig. 6. This concept has been used much in intestinal transport studies, although it must be admitted the interpretation is less clear than with enzyme kinetics.

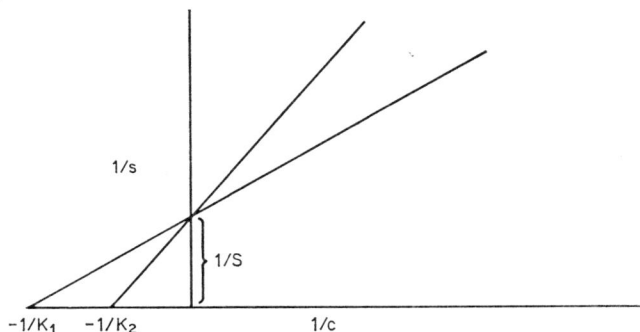

FIG. 6. Lineweaver-Burk plots for enzyme or carrier systems with the same maximum capacity but with different affinity constants.

Widdas (1963) has shown that the kinetics of competition can be handled rather more simply by expressing the concentrations of the various substances in ratios of the half saturation or affinity constant. In the above example in equation 17, let $x = \dfrac{C}{K_m}$ and $y = \dfrac{i}{K_i}$. Equation 17 then becomes

$$\frac{s}{S} = \frac{1}{1 + \dfrac{1}{x}(1+y)} \tag{19}$$

which can be rearranged as

$$\frac{s}{S} = \frac{x}{1+x+y}. \tag{20}$$

If there are two substances X and Y competing for a carrier, and the concentrations x and y are expressed in terms of the affinity constants as above, then the fraction of carrier combined with X is $\dfrac{x}{1+x+y}$, the fraction combined with Y is $\dfrac{y}{1+x+y}$ and the fraction unsaturated is $\dfrac{1}{1+x+y}$. This procedure may simplify calculations involving the kinetics of competitive inhibition.

(iii) *Uphill movement*. It follows from equation 12 that facilitated diffusion is a process in which substances move down their concentration gradient. Since active transfer involves movement against a gradient, it is pertinent to ask whether facilitated diffusion can take part. There are in fact various ways in which this is possible, which can be called (1) counterflow, (2) active transport due to differential affinities, and (3) ternary complex.

COUNTERFLOW. This is an aspect of facilitated diffusion which is observed when two substances are present which use the same carrier, and concerns the effect of one of these on transport of the other. It has been discussed in detail by Rosenberg and Wilbrandt (1963), and can be considered in an elementary way by combining the kinetics of facilitated diffusion and competitive inhibition. Consider first the situation where two substances X and Y with the same affinity are competing for one carrier. If the concentrations are x and y respectively and the affinity constant K, the saturation of the carrier with X when Y is also present can be obtained by substituting in (17) and is given by

$$\frac{s}{S} = \frac{1}{1 + \frac{K}{x}\left(1 + \frac{y}{K}\right)} \tag{21}$$

which can be written

$$\frac{s}{S} = \frac{x}{x + y + K}. \tag{22}$$

Consider now a system of facilitated diffusion separating two phases 1 and 2 containing X and Y in concentrations x_1, x_2, y_1 and y_2 respectively. The movement of X, (v_x) will be proportional to the difference in the fraction of carrier saturated with X at each side and will be given by

$$v_x = A\left(\frac{x_1}{x_1 + y_1 + K} - \frac{x_2}{x_2 + y_2 + K}\right). \tag{23}$$

If $x_1 = x_2$ and $y_1 = y_2$, the term in the brackets is zero and no movement of X occurs. But if $x_1 = x_2$ and $y_2 > y_1$ the term in the brackets is positive and movement of X takes place. This process is called counterflow, and means that X can move even against a concentration gradient. The movement of Y under these conditions, (v_y), will be given by

$$v_y = A\left(\frac{y_1}{x_1 + y_1 + K} - \frac{y_2}{x_1 + y_2 + K}\right) \tag{24}$$

and if $y_2 > y_1$, v_y will be negative. Hence X and Y are moving in opposite directions. The essential features of counterflow are (1) that there must be two substances using the same carrier; (2) one of these moves against its concentration gradient; (3) the other moves in the opposite direction down its concentration gradient; (4) there need not necessarily be any difference in the affinity of the two substances for the carrier; and (5) there must be an asymmetry of one substance which could involve either affinity, concentration or both. (In a subsequent section it will be seen that one substance, present alone, can move against a concentration gradient provided a difference of affinity exists on the two sides of the membrane, but this can be regarded as a different phenomenon, quite separate from counterflow.)

In order to appreciate the nature of this asymmetry giving rise to counterflow, it is useful to express concentrations in terms of the affinity constant, as discussed on p. 365. This makes it easier to discuss the general case of counterflow where two substances X and Y may have both different concentrations (x_1, x_2, y_1, y_2) and different affinity constants $(K_{x_1}, K_{x_2}, K_{y_1}$ and $K_{y_2})$ on two sides of the membrane. If the concentrations of X and Y (expressed as ratios of the affinity constant) are p_1, p_2, q_1 and q_2, where

$$p_1 = \frac{x_1}{K_{x_1}}, p_2 = \frac{x_2}{K_{x_2}}, q_1 = \frac{y_1}{K_{y_1}} \text{ and } q_2 = \frac{y_2}{K_{y_2}}, \text{ then the movement of } X \text{ is given}$$

by

$$V_x = A\left(\frac{p_1}{1 + p_1 + q_1} - \frac{p_2}{1 + p_2 + q_2}\right). \tag{25}$$

If X is symmetrical in that $p_1 = p_2$, then provided $q_2 > q_1$, movement of X will take place. The inequality of q_1 and q_2 could be brought about by difference in concentration, affinity or both.

Counterflow cannot exist if the carrier has an absolute specificity for one substance and its existence implies a group specificity, e.g. for hexoses or for amino acids, etc. Physiologically, intestinal absorption is likely to involve movement of all members of the group, e.g. glucose and galactose, in the same direction and counterflow is therefore unlikely to be of importance in intestinal transfer. The phenomenon of counterflow could be of interest in establishing experimentally the existence of a shuttling carrier.

Since counterflow involves movement of two substances in opposite directions, it is interesting to speculate on the possibility of a counterflow mechanism existing in a cell membrane to couple the entry of a metabolizable substance to the exit of its excretory products. Such a process has, however, not been described.

DIFFERENTIAL AFFINITIES. Equation 12 for the kinetics of facilitated diffusion shows that movement of a substance can only take place down a concentration gradient, if K has the same value on both sides of the membrane. But suppose K has different values. If the affinity constant at one side of the membrane is K_1 and at the other side K_2 and equal concentrations of the substance are present on both sides, then equation 11 becomes

$$v = A\left(\frac{C_1}{C_1 + K_1} - \frac{C_1}{C_1 + K_2}\right). \tag{26}$$

If $K_2 > K_1$, the expression in the bracket will be positive and movement will take place although no concentration gradient is available. In the equilibrium position an asymmetry of K necessitates an asymmetry of C. Such a process can cause movement of a substance against its concentration gradient and the energy for this must come from the activities which maintain a different affinity of the carrier at the two sides of the membrane.

TERNARY COMPLEX. The concept of facilitated diffusion involves only one kind of carrier site although this may have a group specificity and may be able to transfer a number of substances. A further development of facilitated diffusion is that the carrier should have two sites, and hence there could be a ternary complex of carrier and the two substances attached. It is also possible that the attachment of either substance to its own site could alter the affinity of the other site, a process analogous to allosteric effects in enzymology. Apart from the possible effects due to these allosteric changes the ternary complex could provide a means for coupling transfer of one substance to another. If there is a concentration gradient across a membrane, then one substance using one of the sites could move across the membrane down its concentration gradient. This movement could provide energy for the substance using the other site to move against its gradient. This concept of the ternary complex was developed in relation to hexose transfer and is discussed later.

b. Phagocytosis and pinocytosis

Many cells have the capacity for engulfing solids or liquids, processes known as phagocytosis (cell eating) and pinocytosis (cell drinking) respectively. Both of these processes could be involved in entry of solids into the cells but with pinocytosis the solids would be engulfed only as solutes or suspensions in the liquid taken in. Phagocytosis was originally of interest as a scavenger activity carried out by special phagocytes, but it is now regarded as a process involved in the activity of a large number of different types of cells. Further information on phagocytosis can be obtained from reviews by Gordon and King (1960), Karnovsky (1962) and Hirsch (1965).

Experimentally, the distinction between pinocytosis and phagocytosis is not very clear, and many descriptions of pinocytosis are in fact concerned with the uptake of protein rather than fluid (e.g. Clark, 1959). They are therefore discussed together here, and only a brief reference is made later to pinocytosis under the heading of biological processes in fluid transfer.

Both phagocytosis and pinocytosis are engulfing activities in which invagination of the cell surface produces a vesicle containing material originally at the outside surface of the cell. In its simplest form engulfing of fluid could not produce specificity of solute intake nor movement against a concentration gradient, since the fluid taken in is identical with that surrounding the cell. To achieve intracellular concentration of solute, water would have to be expelled from the vesicle, and to achieve transcellular concentration of solute, the water would need to be expelled on the side of the cell from which the vesicle was formed. An essential stage in the process would be separation of water from the contained solutes, as these have to be retained in the cells. A possible mechanism for this is contraction of the vesicle to expel water through pores in the wall, which are too small to allow passage of substances such as hexoses and amino acids. An alternative mechanism is some process in the wall of the vesicle for taking up the solute, as is described in other sections of this chapter in relation to the cell membrane.

Specificity of solute transfer would require specific binding sites in the wall of the vesicle. In fact some specificity of absorption of globulins has been reported in newly-born animals (Brambell, 1958; Payne and Marsh, 1962; Pierce and Smith, 1967), and since this process is thought to involve pinocytosis, such a possible complexity of the pinocytotic vesicle must be considered. Indeed, if the luminal surface of the epithelial cell membrane contains specific sites, it is easy to imagine these being retained together with bound solute in the invaginating wall of the vesicle, with consequent specificity of solute uptake. The vesicle, including the solute adsorbed to its wall, now contain solute in higher concentration than that in the fluid originally in contact with the membrane from which the vesicle was formed. The movement of this vesicle across the cell, and its disintegration and discharge at the other side of the cell would result in movement of the solute against a concentration gradient.

c. Sorption activity of protoplasm

Most of the processes described in this chapter are related to the view that the cells are bounded by a membrane with properties quite different from the cytoplasm of the cell. There is, however, another view of cellular transport, which has been called the sorption theory, according to which uptake and transfer depend on the sorption activity of the cell protoplasm as a whole. This is partly adsorption of solutes to cell protein, and partly association of solutes and water with cell colloids in the form of "coacervates". Acceptance of this theory would require major revision of many of the generally accepted ideas of cellular transfer. A detailed description is not possible here, and for a full discussion reference should be made to Troshin (1966).

d. Solute pumps

This is a term used to describe movement of solute when no explanation is available. The concept is that there is some cellular mechanism which can use metabolism to select particular constituents and move them across the cell. The term diffusion barrier is frequently used, and it implies that the pump moves solute through a zone across which backward diffusion of the transferred substance cannot occur. The existence of a diffusion barrier is essential, however, only in the sense that the pump must be able to move the substance at a faster rate than the backward diffusion occurring as a result of the local increased concentrations caused by the pump. It is not possible to discuss in detail the ingenious mechanisms proposed for solute transfer, and for references to these the monograph by Christensen (1962) should be consulted.

B. Fluid movement

1. Physico-chemical forces

There are three forces to consider in movement of water across biological membranes, hydrostatic pressure, osmotic pressure and electro-osmosis.

o

Electro-osmosis is the movement of fluid through a charged pore, when an electric potential exists between the two ends of the pore. Smyth and Wright (1966) have shown that electro-osmosis does not play a part in the intestine and only hydrostatic pressure and osmotic pressure will be considered here.

a. Hydrostatic pressure

Hydrostatic pressure is created by application of some mechanical force, and possible mechanical forces in absorption are contractions of the gut wall and of the villi. Contractions of the gut wall can create an intraluminal pressure up to 50 cm of water (Abbot *et al.*, 1943) but the average pressure must be far less, and probably only a few cm of water. Smyth and Taylor (1957) considered that luminal hydrostatic pressure did not play an important role in fluid transfer. While villous contractions might cause hydrostatic pressure changes, this pumping action has been considered by Wells and Johnson (1934) not to be significant in fluid movement. Hydrostatic pressure might also arise as a result of pinocytosis or some kind of contractile vacuole, a process discussed on p. 368.

b. Osmosis

A formal treatment of osmotic flow through membranes has been given by Dainty (1965) and the elementary account here refers only to some aspects of this. The movement of water due to osmosis depends on the concentrations of solute in different parts of the system. If two compartments separated by a permeable membrane contain fluid, the rate of movement of water between the compartments can be changed by alteration in solute content, and this can be done in two ways. One is experimentally by adding solute to the solution on one side. For example, if an unabsorbable substance is added to the lumen of the intestine the net rate of water absorption is reduced. This is due to a force which has been created outside the epithelial cells, and this process has been called exogenous osmosis (Smyth, 1965). The other way in which changes in solute concentration can be caused is by action of a "pump" in the membrane which moves solute across the membrane. In this case, the energy for the process is coming from the metabolism of the cell, and this process has been called endogenous osmosis.

Endogenous osmosis as defined in this way can cause movement of water, but in general the water is moving down its activity gradient. The only requirement for such a process is one water-permeable membrane, which is able to transport solute from one side to the other at a faster rate than it can diffuse back through the membrane. Curran (1960) has elaborated the concept of a two-membrane model which is able to move water against its activity gradient. The model consists of a compartment bounded by two membranes of different permeabilities, and this compartment separates the two fluids between which transfer is taking place (Fig. 7). In relation to the direction of transfer the bounding membranes may be called the *cis*-membrane and the *trans*-membrane. The *cis*-membrane is the site of the solute pump and is permeable to water but not to diffusing solute. The *trans*-membrane has larger pores which permit solute movement also. The action of the pump at the *cis*-membrane will build up a hydrostatic pressure in the compartment and this will preferentially force fluid through the larger pores of the *trans*-membrane.

Whatever the source of energy for solute movement, its effect in causing water movement can be considered as due to physical and biophysical components or expressed in another way, as due to properties of the solution and properties of the membrane. The former includes the osmolar concentration or number of particles in solution and the osmotic coefficient,

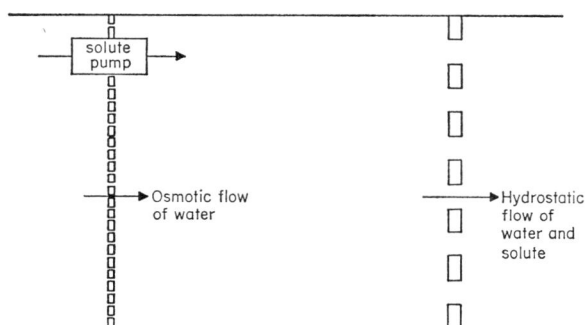

FIG. 7. Model to illustrate how a two-membrane system could result in water movement against its activity gradient. (Modified after Curran, P. F., 1960.)

which makes corrections for the degree of ionization and departure from behaviour as an ideal solution. These can be combined in the term activity of the solute. The second or biophysical component is concerned with the relative size of solute molecule and pores in the membrane. Consider first the case described as exogenous osmosis where solute is added experimentally to the solution on one side of a membrane. If the membrane is completely impermeable to the solute a maximum osmotic effect will be caused. If the membrane is partly permeable to the solute the osmotic effect will be less, and the greater the permeability the less the osmotic effect. This relation between solute size and pore size is expressed by the reflexion coefficient of Staverman (1951). A coefficient of zero means that the membrane does not distinguish between solute and solvent, a coefficient of 1 means complete impermeability to the solute.

In the case of endogenous osmosis the solute is pumped across the membrane, and the efficiency of this in causing fluid movement will again depend on the Staverman coefficient, the more effective pumping system being associated with a high Staverman coefficient. In the double membrane model of Curran, the Staverman coefficients of both membranes have to be considered and the effects of these on the osmolarity of the fluid transferred have been discussed by Durbin and Moody (1965).

2. *Biological processes*

a. *Pinocytosis*

This has been referred to on p. 369. It has been observed in the intestinal epithelial cells of the very young animal but probably does not play a part in the adult intestine. Contractile vacuoles which occur in certain types of cells could also cause movement of fluid by exertion of a hydrostatic force, but have not been described in the intestine.

C. *Interaction of fluid and solute*

The interaction of solvent and solute movement can occur in a number of ways, and formal treatment of the problem in terms of irreversible thermodynamics has been given by Kedem (1965), Katchalsky and Curran (1965), Diamond (1965) and others. The present account is in much more elementary terms and deals with the four relationships: (1) solvent drag, (2) solute drag, (3) capacity effect of solvent movement, and (4) relative independent movement of solute and solvent.

1. *Solvent drag*

Solvent drag is the effect which solvent can exert on movements of solute, e.g. the circulating blood carries with it all the substances in solution and in addition the blood cells. If the rheological complications in various parts of the circulation are ignored this could be regarded as complete solvent drag or bulk flow where the fluid carries with it all its constituents. The term solvent drag is, however, usually reserved for the solute movement caused by passage of solvent through permeable membranes. If the pores are large in relation to the solute and hydrostatic pressure moves the water through the pores, complete solvent drag or bulk flow will occur. If the pores are small and do not permit movement of larger solutes solvent drag will affect only the smaller solutes and will cause some degree of selective separation of the solutes (molecular sieving) based on molecular size. In the extreme case if the membrane is permeable to water only and not to any of the solutes, ultrafiltration occurs with no solvent drag, i.e. movement of fluid does not cause any movement at all of the contained solutes. In any particular membrane some intermediate stage is likely to exist, in which some degree of solvent drag occurs. Quantitative analysis of membrane transport therefore requires knowledge of the size of pores in relation to the solute transferred and also the rate of fluid flow. An important consideration will be the Staverman coefficient and there will also be a reciprocal effect between the solutes which are or are not dragged and the osmotic force opposing the further movement of solvent.

2. *Solute drag*

By this is meant the movement of solvent which occurs as a result of movement of solute. This is included in what has been called endogenous osmosis, and is probably the most important force in intestinal fluid transfer. A detailed discussion in relation to the gallbladder has been given by Diamond (1965), who also distinguishes a related process he calls co-diffusion.

One important feature of solute drag is that it can considerably compli-cate the assessment of active transfer if the criterion for active transfer is taken as change in concentration. It is generally accepted that movement of sodium in the intestinal epithelial cell occurs by means of an active sodium pump (see p. 374). However, movement of sodium is always accompanied by movement of water and the effect of this is that if the movement of sodium is studied in the isolated intestine only very small changes in the sodium concentration may be found. This, however, does not mean sodium is not being actively moved, since movement of water masks the movement of sodium if this is assessed by a concentration change.

3. *Capacity effect*

This effect discussed by Dawson (1965) and Barry *et al.* (1966*b*) is another means by which solvent movement can influence movement of solute. If there is a diffusion gradient or solute pump causing movement of a substance out of the epithelial cells, the effect of this will partly depend on the volume into which the substance is moving. If the volume is increased, it will be possible for a larger amount of substance to move under the same driving force. The capacity effect may well be a complicating factor in many *in vitro* experiments and should always be considered.

4. *Relative independent movement of solute and solvent*

The processes of solvent drag and solute drag involve a certain depend-ence – although a complicated one – between solute and fluid movement. If, however, two independent solute pumps were present, each of these could exert a more or less independent solute drag, and the effect of each of these fractions of fluid moved could affect the other solute both as regards the total amount moved (by means of the capacity effect) and the concentra-tions achieved.

V. Coupled Processes

Many of our ideas of transport involve a linking or coupling between movement of different substances. If such a coupling can be demonstrated then it is useful to analyse the transport mechanism to determine which component of the system is the active one. The movement of this substance must in turn be coupled to metabolism, and so the whole process can be described as a sequence of events following one after the other. In this analysis the first substance whose transfer is coupled to metabolism is said to be actively transferred and the other substances which follow from the movement of the first are said to be coupled to it. Coupling in intestinal transfer has also been discussed by Curran (1968).

The processes involved have already been discussed in earlier sections of this chapter and the object now is to classify the various forms of coupling which can take place, and to elaborate a little on the significance of these for intestinal transfer.

The various forms of coupling in intestinal transfer are: (1) solvent with transfer of solute; (2) solute with transfer of solvent; (3) solute with transfer of solute; (4) solvent with metabolism of solute, and (5) solute with metabolism of solute.

1. *Solvent transfer coupled with solute transfer*

This is the process described on p. 370 as endogenous osmosis. It implies that the intestine possesses transfer mechanisms or "pumps" for various solutes and that as a result of these fluid also moves. The main question is which solutes are linked with fluid transfer. Smyth and Taylor (1957) studied the concentration of substances in the fluid transferred by the gut and found that Na^+ occupied a special place in that it always appeared in approximately the same concentration, whereas most substances appeared in either a higher or a lower concentration. A possible explanation suggested was that movement of sodium was the fundamental process in water movement. At the same time Curran and Solomon (1957) studied ion and water fluxes in rat ileum and concluded that active Na^+ and Cl^- transport was responsible for water movement. Clarkson and Rothstein (1960) investigated in more detail a number of solutes, and found that the water movement could be accounted for by osmotic movement with the total solutes pumped. Since sodium and its accompanying anions accounted for 80–90% of total solute movement, the sodium pump played a major role in intestinal fluid transfer. It is likely that all solutes transferred by the intestine can cause fluid movement, and this includes nonelectrolytes such as hexoses and amino acids. In the case of glucose it is important to distinguish between fluid moved due to movement of glucose as distinct from metabolism of glucose. The evidence on this point is still inconclusive. McHardy and Parsons (1957) found that the volume of fluid absorbed from the intestine *in vivo* was related to the total osmoles absorbed, but left open the question whether solute movement or water movement was the primary process. Barry *et al.* (1964) showed that when hexoses were being transferred by the rat intestine *in vitro* the sodium concentration in the fluid was decreased, and considered this was because some fluid was moving with glucose in addition to that moving with sodium. Recently Newey *et al.* (1968) found that transfer of amino acids caused increased fluid movement.

While there is good reason for regarding Na^+ transfer as a prime agent in causing intestinal fluid movement, there is some doubt about the nature of this Na pump, and the relation between the Na pump, hexose transfer and metabolism. Schultz and Zalusky (1964a, b) consider that in the rabbit ileum the total sodium movement is accounted for by the short-circuit current and hence the Na pump is electrogenic. Barry *et al.* (1965) found a discrepancy between short-circuit current and net sodium transfer in rat jejunum, and postulated two pumps, an electrogenic and a nonelectrogenic, the latter being specifically related to fluid transfer. Taylor *et al.* (1968) have confirmed the inequality of short-circuit current and net Na transfer in rat jejunum, but explain this by the presence of a neutral NaCl pump in the opposite direction to that postulated by Barry *et al.* It is not possible to discuss this further here, but one of the facts to be explained by any theory is the transfer of fluid and of sodium which takes place in the presence of hexoses which are metabolized but not transferred, e.g. mannose.

2. *Solute transfer coupled with solvent transfer*

There are two ways in which solute movement can be coupled to solvent movement, i.e. solvent drag and the capacity effect. Fisher (1955) has shown that small molecules such as urea might be transported by solvent drag in the intestine. However, although solvent drag and capacity effect should always be considered, there is not much evidence that they play an important role in intestinal absorption of nutrient substances.

3. *Solute transfer coupled with solute transfer*

This includes all the effects which transfer of one solute could have in causing transfer of another and are discussed under the following headings: (*a*) the ternary complex, (*b*) facilitated diffusion with differential affinity, (*c*) counterflow, (*d*) enzyme activity, (*e*) electrical changes, (*f*) exchange diffusion, (*g*) hydrogen ion concentration changes, and (*h*) fluid movement.

a. *The ternary complex*

This concept was put forward by Crane *et al.* (1961) and Crane (1962) as a means of linking Na^+ movement and hexose movement and the modification of it put forward by Schultz and Zalusky (1964*a*, *b*) is shown in Fig. 8.

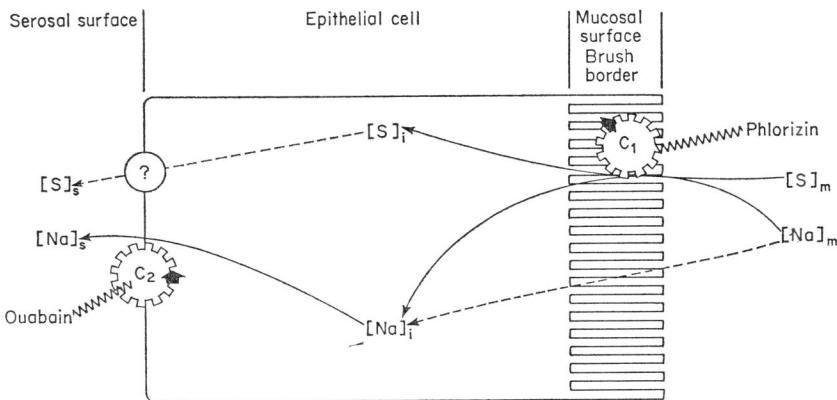

FIG. 8. Model of the Na-sugar-transfer mechanism of absorption (from Schultz and Zalusky, 1964).

It is supposed that a carrier in the membrane has sites for attachment of Na^+ and hexose and movement of the complex is only possible when both sites are occupied. If a pump is postulated which moves Na^+ out of the cell, this could cause a lowered Na^+ concentration inside the cell. As a result, a gradient is created for movement of Na^+ into the cell on the carrier, and since hexose moves on the same carrier, energy is provided for movement of hexose against its concentration gradient. Schultz and Zalusky (1965) have proposed a similar mechanism for intestinal amino acid transfer. One of the difficulties about this theory is how hexose (or amino acid) dissociates from the ternary complex inside the cell where the hexose concentration is high. This objection is removed by the further development of the theory to include different affinities of the carrier sites on the two sides of the membrane. But, as pointed out by Newey (1967), the inclusion of differential affinities makes it unnecessary to postulate a ternary complex moving across the membrane.

b. Facilitated diffusion with differential affinity

It has been shown (p. 367) that facilitated diffusion could cause movement against a gradient if the affinity on the two sides of the membrane is different. Crane *et al.* (1965) suggested that in the intestine the affinity of the carrier for hexose depends on the concentration of Na^+. The removal of Na^+ from the cell would cause different concentrations of Na^+ inside and outside the cell, and thus a Na pump in conjunction with differential affinities could cause movement of hexose against its concentration gradient. Newey *et al.* (1968) have suggested a similar process might happen with amino acids.

There is one theoretical difficulty which does not yet seem to have been considered. In demonstrating the effect of Na^+ on affinity, Crane *et al.* (1965) determined the affinities by means of the Lineweaver-Burk plot. It follows from equation 13, that the kinetics of facilitated diffusion would be equivalent to Michaelis-Menten kinetics only if the second term in the bracket was zero, as would happen if the concentration of hexose inside the cell was zero. However, this cannot be so if hexose is being moved against its concentration gradient, and the only possibility is that the value of K_2 (i.e. inside the cell) is very high. Theoretically, K_2 would have to be infinitely high but a high value of K_2 relative to K_1 might be adequate to give experimental results approximating to Michaelis-Menten kinetics.

c. Counterflow

It has been shown on p. 366 that counterflow could cause movement against a concentration gradient. This phenomenon would, however, depend on a group specificity and it has been pointed out that as different members of the group must move in the same direction in physiological absorption counterflow is not likely to be of significance in intestinal absorption.

d. Enzyme activity

It is generally believed that the energy for membrane transfer is mediated through membrane ATPases, although the coupling mechanism is still no understood. Intestinal ATPases, like those in many other tissues, are Na^+ sensitive (Taylor, 1962), and Csáky (1963) suggested that these Na^+-dependent ATPases render the chemical energy from ATP available for transfer of nonelectrolytes. This could be achieved by ATP affecting the affinity of the carrier and there would seem to be various possibilities which have not been clearly defined. Firstly a pump moving sodium from the cell might be dependent on ATP, and the resulting difference in sodium concentration across the luminal membrane might be responsible for different affinities of the carrier on the two sides of the membrane. In this case the ATPase would act at the serosal side of the cell, if this is accepted as the site of the sodium pump (see Fig. 8). A second possibility is that a critical intracellular concentration of sodium and probably also of potassium is maintained by a sodium pump. This critical concentration influences ATPases in the luminal membrane which couple ATP directly to the carrier sites and hence affect the affinity. In this case the ATPase would act near the luminal side of the cell. The major difference between these possibilities is that in the former case it is the Na^+ concentration which alters the affinity of the carrier for nonelectrolytes, whereas in the latter it is ATP which alters the affinity. Neither of these possibilities would require the participation of a ternary complex moving across the membrane.

Whittam and Ager (1965) have shown that the transfer of sodium by the red cell can exert an effect on metabolism suggesting an auto-regulatory coupling between transport and metabolic activity. As ouabain affects hexose metabolism of the intestine, it is also possible that some sort of auto-regulatory process exists in the intestinal epithelial cell, coupling metabolism with transport activity through the action of ATPases.

e. Electrical potential

The Na pump can operate in two ways in the intestine either as an electrogenic or nonelectrogenic pump. In the electrogenic pump it is assumed that Na^+ ions are pumped and this creates a potential across the cell. This potential could assist movement of anions, and hence Cl^-, HCO_3^- and lactate in the intestine could be coupled to Na^+ movement. Clarkson and Rothstein (1960) thought that this might be responsible for movement of these anions in the intestine, a problem which has also been discussed by Parsons (1967).

The nonelectrogenic Na pump transfers Na^+ without creating an electric potential, and involves movement in the same direction of cations and anions in equivalent amounts. Alternatively, there could be an equivalent exchange of cations in opposite directions. In both cases the maintenance of electric neutrality involves a tight coupling between the transfer of the different ionic species, and by this is meant simultaneous movement in equivalent amounts. It is also possible to envisage more or less independent pumps for Na^+ and anions, in which the amounts moved are not equivalent so that electrical neutrality is not obtained; e.g. the process for NaCl movement (Curran and Solomon, 1957).

f. Exchange diffusion

This is a process resembling counterflow in that the movement of one substance is linked with the movement of another in the opposite direction. The term is usually applied to cation transfer and particularly to coupled movement of sodium and potassium in red cell, muscle and nerve. The process is not necessarily electrically neutral as equal numbers of sodium and potassium ions need not be exchanged. (For further discussion see Ussing, 1960.) Exchange diffusion may well play a part in sodium and potassium movement in the intestine but this has not been investigated in any detail. Parsons (1967) has suggested that part of the chloride movement in the intestine might be an exchange for bicarbonate.

g. H^+ ion changes

The activity of the epithelial cell results in an asymmetrical movement of H^+ ions and *in vitro* experiments the luminal fluid becomes more acid than the serosal fluid. By means of non-ionic diffusion this could influence movement of weak acids or weak bases, and may play an important role in absorption of some drugs (for review see Schanker, 1962). While it is an attractive theory, few cases have been described in detail which conform quantitatively to prediction.

h. Fluid movement

From the previous discussion on solvent drag and interaction of solute and solvent, it will be evident that movement of one solute could be linked to movement of another through fluid movement. Thus if a Na pump causes fluid movement, this in turn could affect other solutes either by solvent drag or by the capacity effect.

4. Solvent transfer coupled with solute metabolism

The stimulation of fluid transfer by glucose has two components – fluid movement due to hexose transfer (already discussed) and fluid movement due to hexose metabolism. As glucose is both metabolized and transferred, it is not a suitable hexose for study of these individual effects, and the problem can be approached by using two sugars-galactose which is transferred but not metabolized and mannose which is metabolized but not transferred. Duerdoth et al. (1965) have shown that mannose which can only enter the cell with difficulty from the luminal side can readily enter from the serosal side to be metabolized and causes a movement of fluid comparable with that of glucose. While this coupling of solvent movement with solute metabolism undoubtedly exists, it is generally assumed that the coupling is an indirect one, and solvent movement follows solute movement, which in turn is linked to solute metabolism.

5. Solute transfer coupled with metabolism

In previous sections the possible dependence of various transfer processes on a Na pump has been discussed, and coupling of the Na pump to metabolism must therefore be one of the fundamental processes in intestinal transfer. It cannot, however, be assumed that the Na pump is the only solute pump linked directly to metabolism, and in spite of the theories discussed for linking Na^+ transfer to hexose and amino acid movement, the possibility of pumps for hexoses, amino acids or other solutes linked directly to metabolism must also be considered.

Intestinal metabolism has been discussed by Sherratt (1968) and only a few aspects of its relation to transfer will be discussed here. These are: (a) the sources of energy in relation to particular metabolic pathways, (b) the relation of transfer to oxygen supply, (c) possible competition between different transfer systems for available energy, and (d) the introduction of a vectorial component in energy transformation.

Since amino acids, Na^+ and nonmetabolized hexoses can be actively transferred by the intestine *in vitro*, the endogenous metabolism of the epithelial cell must be able to supply energy. This energy is unable to maintain the transfer systems at maximum rate, and the addition of metabolizable hexose can stimulate transfer of several substances, e.g. fluid (Barry et al., 1961), Na^+ (Barry et al., 1967), galactose (Newey et al., 1966), some amino acids (Dawson et al., 1965; Bingham et al., 1966a), volatile fatty acids (Barry et al., 1966a), which indicates that these transfer systems must also be linked to metabolism of hexose. Attempts to separate the contributions of endogenous metabolism (probably via the citric acid cycle) and of hexose metabolism (probably by the glycolytic pathway) have been made by using fluoride and fluoroacetate (Gilman and Koelle, 1960; Barry et al., 1961; Sanford et al., 1965; Detheridge et al., 1966). While these experiments are complicated by the lack of specificity of the inhibitors used, they suggest that both metabolic pathways supply energy for intestinal transport, but that the relative contributions of the two pathways vary in different parts of the intestine.

Since the glycolytic pathway with lactic acid as a main end-product can supply energy for transfer, it might be expected that transfer can occur anaerobically. If the generation of an electric potential is regarded as part of the transfer process, anaerobic glycolysis might supply some transfer energy, as Barry et al. (1964) found that in anoxic conditions the glucose potential only fell away slowly over 60 min whereas with galactose (which is not metabolized by the rat intestine) it fell away more quickly. There is, however, no doubt that maximum transfer activity can only be achieved in aerobic conditions, but it may be that oxygen is needed to maintain cellular structure as distinct from supplying energy to transport mechanisms. The foetal rabbit intestine appears to be less dependent on oxygen supply, as Wilson and Lin (1960) found active amino acid transfer in anaerobic conditions. Jirsova et al. (1966) have also reported transfer in foetal tissue anaerobically.

Different transfer mechanisms appear to utilize energy from a common source, since sugars (e.g. galactose), which are actively pumped but not metabolized, inhibit amino acid transfer (Newey and Smyth, 1964; Bingham *et al.*, 1966; Alvarado, 1966; Chez *et al.*, 1966). If the energy level of the intestine is increased by addition of a metabolizable hexose, e.g. glucose or mannose, the inhibition is reduced. Furthermore, concentrations of galactose which are strongly inhibitory to amino acid transfer *in vitro* are not inhibitory *in vivo*, probably because the latter preparation has its energy supply maintained by blood glucose (Bingham *et al.*, 1966). Transferred sugars utilize energy and metabolized sugars supply energy, and a sugar (glucose) which is both transferred and metabolized has effects varying from inhibitory to stimulatory, depending on the metabolic state of the tissue preparation (Hardcastle *et al.*, 1968). The concept of coupling of metabolism and transfer implies that substances dealt with by the intestine may be either energy users or energy suppliers, and the fact that glucose can act in both capacities gives it a special place in intestinal activity.

Another fundamental problem of coupling of solute transfer with solute metabolism is the fact that this particular energy transformation involves the introduction of a vectorial component. By this is meant that as a result of metabolism substances move in the cell in a particular direction, i.e. towards the serosal side of the cell. This probably depends on the spatial arrangement of enzymes and other constituents in the cell membrane, and the distribution of ATPases, sensitive to Na^+ and K^+ concentrations, which are different on both sides of the membrane, could play an important role. This aspect has been extensively studied by Mitchell (1967), whose term chemi-osmotic coupling is a useful one to describe the relation between solute metabolism and solute transfer. The nature of this chemi-osmotic coupling remains the fundamental unsolved problem of intestinal absorption; and when it is understood much will be known not only about how the epithelial cell of the intestine works, but how all living cells work.

References

Abbott, W. O., Hartline, H. K., Hervey, J. P., Ingelfinger, F. J., Rawson, A. J. and Zetzel, L. (1943). *J. clin. Invest.* **22**, 225-234.
Alvarado, F. (1966). *Science, N.Y.* **151**, 1010-1013.
Barry, B. A., Matthews, J. and Smyth, D. H. (1961). *J. Physiol., Lond.* **157**, 279-288.
Barry, R. J. C., Dikstein, S., Matthews, J., Smyth, D. H. and Wright, E. M. (1964). *J. Physiol., Lond.* **171**, 316-338.
Barry, R. J. C., Eggenton, J. and Smyth, D. H. (1967). *J. Physiol., Lond.* **191**, 72-73P.
Barry, R. J. C., Jackson, M. J. and Smyth, D. H. (1966a). *J. Physiol., Lond.* **182**, 150-163.
Barry, R. J. C., Jackson, M. J. and Smyth, D. H. (1966b). *J. Physiol., Lond.* **185**, 667-683.
Barry, R. J. C., Smyth, D. H. and Wright, E. M. (1965). *J. Physiol., Lond.* **181**, 410-431.
Bayliss, L. E. (1959). *Principles of General Physiology*, Vol. 1. Longmans, Green & Co., London.
Bingham, J. K., Newey, H. and Smyth, D. H. (1966a). *Biochim. biophys. Acta* **120**, 314-316.

Bingham, J. K., Newey, H. and Smyth, D. H. (1966b). *Biochim. biophys. Acta* **130**, 281-284.

Brambell, F. W. R. (1958). *Biol. Rev.* **33**, 488-531.

Chez, R. A., Schultz, S. G. and Curran, P. F. (1966). *Science, N.Y.* **153**, 1012-1013.

Christensen, H. N. (1962). *Biological Transport*. W. A. Benjamin, New York.

Clark, S. L. (1959). *J. biophys. biochem. Cytol.* **5**, 41-50.

Clarkson, T. W. and Rothstein, A. (1960). *Am. J. Physiol.* **199**, 898-906.

Crane, R. K. (1960). *Physiol. Rev.* **40**, 789-825.

Crane, R. K. (1962). *Fedn Proc. Fedn Am. Socs exp. Biol.* **21**, 891-895.

Crane, R. K., Forstner, G. and Eichholz, A. (1965). *Biochim. biophys. Acta* **109**, 467-477.

Crane, R. K., Miller, D. and Bihler, I. (1961). In *Membrane Transport and Metabolism* (A. Kleinzeller and A. Kotyk, eds), pp. 439-449. Publishing House of the Czechoslovak Academy of Sciences, Prague.

Csáky, T. Z. (1963). *Fedn Proc. Fedn Am. Socs exp. Biol.* **22**, 3-7.

Curran, P. F. (1960). *J. gen. Physiol.* **43**, 1137-1148.

Curran, P. F. (1968). *Physiologist*, **11**, 3-23.

Curran, P. F. and Solomon, A. K. (1957). *J. gen. Physiol.* **41**, 143-168.

Curran, P. F., Taylor, A. E. and Solomon, A. K. (1967). *Biophys. J.* **7**, 879-901.

Dainty, J. (1965). *Symp. Soc. exp. Biol.* **19**, 75-85.

Danielli, J. F. (1949). *Proc. 6th Internat. Congress Exp. Cyt.*, pp. 312-317.

Davson, H. and Danielli, J. F. (1943). *The Permeability of Natural Membranes*. Cambridge University Press, London.

Dawson, A. G. (1965). Ph.D. Thesis, Sheffield University.

Dawson, A. G., Newey, H. and Smyth, D. H. (1965). *J. Physiol., Lond.* **179**, 56-57P.

Detheridge, J. F., Matthews, J. and Smyth, D. H. (1966). *J. Physiol., Lond.* **183**, 369-377.

Diamond, J. M. (1965). *Symp. Soc. exp. Biol.* **19**, 329-347.

Dixon, M. and Webb, E. C. (1964). *Enzymes*. Longmans, Green & Co., London.

Duerdoth, J. K., Newey, H., Sanford, P. A. and Smyth, D. H. (1965). *J. Physiol., Lond.* **176**, 23-24P.

Durbin, R. P. and Moody, F. G. (1965). *Symp. Soc. exp. Biol.* **19**, 299-306.

Fisher, R. B. (1955). *J. Physiol., Lond.* **130**, 655-664.

Fordtran, J. S. and Dietschy, J. M. (1966). *Gastroenterology* **50**, 263-285.

Fordtran, J. S., Rector, F. C., Ewton, M. F., Soter, N. and Kinney, J. (1965). *J. clin. Invest.* **44**, 1935-1944.

Gibson, Q. H. and Wiseman, G. (1951). *Biochem. J.* **48**, 426-429.

Gilman, A. and Koelle, E. S. (1960). *Circulation* **21**, 948-954.

Gordon, G. B. and King, D. W. (1960). *Am. J. Path.* **37**, 279-291.

Hardcastle, P. T., Newey, H. and Smyth, D. H. (1968). *J. Physiol., Lond.* **196**, 33-34P.

Hirsch, J. G. (1965). *A. Rev. Microbiol.* **19**, 339-350.

Hodgkin, A. L. and Keynes, R. D. (1955). *J. Physiol., Lond.* **128**, 61-88.

Jacobs, M. H. (1940). *Cold Spring Harb. Symp. quant. Biol.* **8**, 30-39.

Jervis, E. L. and Smyth, D. H. (1959). *J. Physiol., Lond.* **149**, 433-441.

Jirsova, V., Koldovsky, O., Heringova, A., Hoskova, J., Jirasek, J. and Uher, J. (1966). *Biol. Neonat.* **9**, 44-49.

Karnovsky, M. L. (1962). *Physiol. Rev.* **42**, 143-168.

Katchalsky, A. and Curran, P. F. (1965). *Nonequilibrium Thermodynamics in Biophysics*. Harvard University Press, Cambridge.

Kedem, O. (1965). *Symp. Soc. exp. Biol.* **19**, 61-73.

Kipling, J. J. (1965). *Adsorption from Solutions of Non-electrolytes*. Academic Press, London.

Langmuir, I. (1918). *J. Am. Chem. Soc.* **40**, 1361-1403.
Lefevre, P. G. (1961). *Pharmacol. Rev.* **13**, 39-70.
Levin, R. J. (1967). *Br. med. Bull.* **23**, 209-212.
Lindemann, B. and Solomon, A. K. (1962). *J. gen. Physiol.* **45**, 801-810.
Lineweaver, A. and Burk, D. (1934). *J. Am. chem. Soc.* **56**, 658-666.
Matthews, D. M. and Laster, L. (1965). *Gut* **6**, 411-426.
McHardy, G. J. R. and Parsons, D. S. (1957). *Q. Jl exp. Physiol.* **42**, 33-48.
Michaelis, L. and Menten, M. L. (1913). *Biochem. Z.* **49**, 333-369.
Mitchell, P. (1967). *Adv. Enzymol.* **29**, 33-87.
Newey, H. (1967). *Br. med. Bull.* **23**, 236-240.
Newey, H., Sanford, P. A. and Smyth, D. H. (1966). *J. Physiol., Lond.* **186**, 493-502.
Newey, H., Sanford, P. A. and Smyth, D. H. (1968). *J. Physiol., Lond.* **194**, 237-248.
Newey, H. and Smyth, D. H. (1964a). *J. Physiol., Lond.* **170**, 328-343.
Newey, H. and Smyth, D. H. (1964b). *Nature, Lond.* **202**, 400-401.
Newey, H. and Smyth, D. H. (1966). *D-glucose und verwandte Verbindungen in Medizin und Biologie* (H. Bartelheimer, W. Heyde and W. Thorn, eds), pp. 277-291. Ferdinand Enke Verlag, Stuttgart.
Newey, H. and Smyth, D. H. (1967). *Proc. Nutr. Soc.* **26**, 5-12.
Osterhout, W. J. V. (1933). *Ergebn. Physiol.* **35**, 967-1021.
Pappenheimer, J. R. (1953). *Physiol. Rev.* **33**, 387-423.
Parsons, D. S. (1967). *Br. med. Bull.* **23**, 252-257.
Payne, L. C. and Marsh, C. L. (1962). *Fedn Proc. Fedn Am. Socs exp. Biol.* **21**, 909-912.
Pierce, A. E. and Smith, M. W. (1967). *J. Physiol., Lond.* **190**, 19-34.
Rosenberg, T. (1954). *Symp. Soc. exp. Biol.* **7**, 27-41.
Rosenberg, T. and Wilbrandt, W. (1963). *J. theor. Biol.* **5**, 288-305.
Sanford, P. A., Smyth, D. H. and Watling, M. (1965). *J. Physiol., Lond.* **179**, 72-73P.
Saunders, S. J. and Isselbacher, K. J. (1965). *Biochim. biophys. Acta* **102**, 397-409.
Schanker, L. S. (1962). *Pharmacol. Rev.* **14**, 501-530.
Schultz, S. G., Curran, P. F., Chez, R. A. and Fuisz, R. E. (1967). *J. gen. Physiol.* **50**, 1241-1260.
Schultz, S. G. and Solomon, A. K. (1961). *J. gen. Physiol.* **44**, 1189-1199.
Schultz, S. G. and Zalusky, R. (1964a). *J. gen. Physiol.* **47**, 567-584.
Schultz, S. G. and Zalusky, R. (1964b). *J. gen. Physiol.* **47**, 1043-1059.
Schultz, S. G. and Zalusky, R. (1965). *Nature, Lond.* **204**, 292-294.
Sherratt, H. S. A. (1968). *Comp. Biochem. Physiol.* **24**, 745-761.
Smyth, D. H. (1965). *Symp. Soc. exp. Biol.* **19**, 307-328.
Smyth, D. H. (ed.) (1967). *Br. med. Bull.* **23**, 205-290.
Smyth, D. H. and Taylor, C. B. (1957). *J. Physiol., Lond.* **136**, 632-648.
Smyth, D. H. and Wright, E. M. (1966). *J. Physiol., Lond.* **182**, 591-602.
Staverman, A. J. (1951). *Rec. trav. chim. Pays-bas* **70**, 344-352.
Taylor, A. E., Wright, E. M., Schultz, S. G. and Curran, P. F. (1968). *Am. J. Physiol.* **214**, 836-842.
Taylor, C. B. (1962). *Biochim. biophys. Acta* **60**, 437-440.
Troshin, A. S. (1966). *Problems of Cell Permeability.* Pergamon Press, London.
Ussing, H. H. (1954). *Symp. Soc. exp. Biol.* **7**, 407-422.
Ussing, H. H. (1960). *The Alkali Metal Ions in Biology.* Springer, Berlin.
Ussing, H. H. and Zerahn, K. (1951). *Acta phys. scand.* **23**, 110-127.
Webb, J. L. (1963). *Enzyme and Metabolic Inhibitors*, Vol. 1. Academic Press, New York.
Wells, H. S. and Johnson, R. G. (1934). *Am. J. Physiol.* **109**, 387-402.

Whittam, R. and Ager, M. E. (1965). *Biochem. J.* **97**, 214-227.

Widdas, W. F. (1963). *Recent Advances in Physiology*, 8th ed. (R. Creese, ed.), pp. 1-35. J. & A. Churchill Ltd., London.

Wilbrandt, W. and Rosenberg, T. (1961). *Pharmacol. Rev.* **13**, 109-183.

Wilson, T. H. (1962). *Intestinal Absorption*. Saunders, Philadelphia.

Wilson, T. H. and Lin, E. C. C. (1960). *Am. J. Physiol.* **199**, 1030-1032.

Wiseman, G. (1964). *Absorption from the Intestine*. Academic Press, London.

CHAPTER 11

The Basis of Malabsorption

B. BORGSTRÖM

Division of Physiological Chemistry, Chemical Centre,
University of Lund, Lund, Sweden

A. DAHLQVIST

Research Department, University Hospital, Lund, Sweden

T. LINDBERG

Department of Pediatrics, Malmö General Hospital, Malmö, Sweden

E. HESS THAYSEN

Gastroenterological Unit, Municipal Hospital, Aalborg, Denmark

I. Introduction

The main function of the digestive tract is to supply the body with the dietary constituents that are necessary for its metabolism and special functions.

Foodstuffs are divided into protein, carbohydrate and fat, and consequently conventional definitions are based on the nutritional properties

of these foodstuffs rather than on their chemical structure. Most of the foodstuffs occur in a chemical or physical form that cannot be utilized directly by
the intestinal mucosa. The proteins, and a large fraction of the carbohydrates, are present as macromolecules and hence have to be depolymer-
ized before absorption; the fat of the diet, even if present as triglycerides,
is in the form of an emulsion that has to undergo physico-chemical transformation to be absorbed. This change is catalysed in the intestinal tract
by enzymes, admixed to the intestinal content at different levels of the tract.
The function of these enzymes in general is to catalyse the hydrolysis of a
variety of chemical bonds; in other words, they act as hydrolases. The
digestive enzymes are secreted into the intestinal tract via the saliva and the
gastric and pancreatic juices. As for the succus entericus, it does not contain
any digestive enzymes as such and digestion occurring in the intestinal lumen
is a process which involves pancreatic enzymes only.

In order to provide appropriate conditions for the function of the various
digestive enzymes, the contents of the intestinal tract are admixed with
hydrochloric acid coming from the stomach and with bile from the gallbladder and bicarbonate from the pancreatic juice; and also admixed with
the mucoproteins present in the digestive secretions. However, the normal
function of the intestinal tract does not only depend on these chemical
factors but also on nervous and hormonal factors. That is to say, the intestinal
tract functions as an integrated unit. Moreover, normal absorption requires
the existence of intact mucosal cells and free passage of substances from
the mucosa to the blood and lymphatics draining the intestine. It should also
be borne in mind that the intestinal tract has both its surface and contents
exposed to the external environment, which means that the digestive
processes are taking place in a milieu exposed to micro-organisms.

Changes in any or a combination of these functions of the gastrointestinal
tract can result in disturbances in the supply of the body with essential foodstuffs. These disturbances have been grouped together under the general
heading of malabsorption. Though we have attempted in this chapter to
follow conventional lines, treatment of the subject is largely based on
physiologic and pathophysiologic knowledge of some of the more well-
established entities of malabsorption.

II. Physiology of the Intestinal Tract

A. *Saliva*

Saliva is a mixture of secretions produced by three pairs of large glands
viz., parotid, submaxillary and sublingual; and also by a large number of
small glands present in the oral mucosa (labial, lingual, buccal and palatal).
Secretion is controlled by nerve impulses and there does not seem to be any
evidence for a hormonal influence. In adult humans the total flow of saliva
has been estimated to be 1–1·5 litres per day.

The solutes found in saliva are inorganic salts, mucin and various
enzymes. The mucin acts as a lubricant for the swallowing of solid foods

About 30% of it is carbohydrate, mostly sialic acid. The most important enzymes in saliva are α-amylase and lysozyme. The amylase concentration is as high as that in pancreatic juice. Lysozyme may be of importance in its action as an antibacterial agent.

B. *Stomach*

The stomach is a storage and digestive organ. By virtue of its three layers of smooth muscle it is capable of mixing and of propulsive movements. In addition, the emptying of the stomach is subject to regulation at the pyloric sphincter (see below). The digestive secretions originate in the parietal and chief cells of the main gastric glands. The parietal cells are among the metabolically most active cells in the body. They elaborate a secretion in which the hydrogen ions are 4×10^6 times more concentrated than in blood. The actively secreting stomach requires more carbon dioxide than oxygen from the arterial blood and it secretes bicarbonate into the venous blood which in turn leads to a reversed chloride shift in red blood cells. The parietal cell uptake of carbon dioxide depends upon carbonic anhydrase. For the total gastric mucosa less than four hydrogen ions are secreted per mole of oxygen used. It must be emphasized, however, that both hydrogen and chloride are transported actively, and that some oxygen is used for other purposes. Production of intrinsic factor has been localized in the parietal cells in man (Hoedemacker, 1965). The secretion of this compound is stimulated by histamine, insulin, gastrin and methacholine. On the other hand, in cases of atrophic gastritis the impairment of intrinsic factor secretion tallies with the loss of parietal cells. In the small group of congenital pernicious anaemia patients with maintained acid secretion, the absence of intrinsic factor production must be due to a congenital metabolic defect (MacIntyre *et al.*, 1965).

Production of the proteolytically active pepsin depends upon the chief cells which are the predominant cell type in the depths of the gastric glands of the fundus and the proximal portion of the body of the stomach. Pepsin is secreted and stored in the cells as an inactive precursor, pepsinogen, which has a molecular weight of 42 000. At an optimal pH of 2 pepsinogen is autocatalytically activated to pepsin by the loss of a portion of its molecule whose molecular weight is 8000.

C. *Bile*

Bile is an excretory product of the liver which carries several substances of importance for the processes of digestion and absorption occurring in the intestinal tract. These include bile salts, lecithin and cholesterol. Bile also represents the main pathway for the excretion of substances such as the bile pigments, various metabolic end-products of steroid hormones, vitamin A, D and E, etc., which at the present time have no obvious role in the digestion and absorption processes as such. Several exogenous substances, e.g. bromsulphalein, p-amino hippuric acid and penicillin are also excreted with the bile.

Except for glucoproteins, bile has a low protein content and contains no digestive enzymes. The bile secreted by the liver is concentrated in the gall bladder when the digestive tract is at rest. The concentrated bile is emptied into the digestive tract during the first half-hour following a meal mainly by the action of hormonal factors. Liver bile thereafter continues to flow to the intestine for the rest of the digestive period.

The best information on the composition of bile has been obtained from gallbladder bile collected during abdominal operation. Liver bile is more difficult to obtain for analysis and it is known that fistulae bile is not representative as disruption of the entero-hepatic circulation changes the composition of the bile.

The most recent and complete analysis of human gallbladder bile is that of Dam *et al.* (1966) as summarized in Table I. As can be seen, the molar

TABLE I

Composition of "normal" gallbladder bile obtained by puncture of the vesica fellea of patients operated for duodenal or gastric ulcers (mean of analysis from 11 men and 3 women). (After Dam *et al.*, 1966.)

Dry matter (%)	14·9
cholesterol (mM)	12·8 (2·7–26·4)
(mg %)	495
lipid phosphorus as lecithin (mM)	38 (12·4–72·5)
(mg %)	2945
total bile acids (mM)	142 (44·2–252·7)
mg % as taurocholate	7635
dihydroxy/trihydroxy bile salt ratio	3·3 (0·99–12·0)
glycine/taurine conjugate ratio	1·7 (0·8–2·0)

ratio of bile salt/lecithin/cholesterol is approximately 11:3:1. Analysis of fistulae bile shows that this is 5–6 times more dilute. The most interesting constituents of bile from a medical point of view are the bile salts, lecithin and cholesterol. They are of interest because of their function in the digestion and absorption of fats and because of their role in the formation of gallstones. They occur in the bile as a solution of mixed micelles. The phase equilibria of these major constituents of bile have been studied in *in vitro* experiments and the results have a direct bearing on how gallstones are formed (Hofmann and Small, 1967).

D. *Pancreatic juice*

Pancreatic juice which is the main digestive juice of the human intestinal tract supplies enzymes for the intraluminal digestion of the foodstuffs in the small intestine. Aside from this, the pancreatic juice carries to the intestines bicarbonate in a concentration of 120–130 mEq/l. The composition of the pancreatic juice is influenced by the intestinal hormones; for example, administration of secretin leads to a bicarbonate-rich juice which is low in enzymes, while the administration of the second intestinal hormone, pancreozymin, results in the production of a more viscous and protein-rich juice.

TABLE II

Main enzymatic activities of pancreatic juice

Enzyme	Substrate specificity	End-products
mylase (diastase)	splits the 1-4 α-glucosidic bonds of glycogen and starch	di- and oligo-saccharides with minor amounts of glucose
pase	splits the primary ester bonds of dispersed glycerides and ester bonds of other water-insoluble esters such as β-naphthol and p-nitrophenyl esters	2-monoglyceride and fatty acid
arboxylic acid hydrolase	splits carboxylic esters which are water-soluble or dispersed in micellar solution of bile salts, monoglycerides, cholesterol esters, etc.	fatty acid and alcohol
ophospholipase A$_2$ activated by trypsin	splits the fatty acid ester bond in the 2-position of glycerophospholipids	fatty acid and lysophospholipid
ypsinogen activated by aterokinase and trypsin	endopeptidase that splits the bonds formed by the carboxyl groups of lysine and arginine	polypeptides
aymotrypsinogen activated y trypsin to chymotrypsin	endopeptidase that splits bonds adjacent to the aromatic amino acids, phenylalanine and tyrosine	peptides with minor amounts of amino acids
ocarboxypeptidase A and activated by trypsin	exopeptidases that splits the amino acids one at a time from the carboxyl end of the peptides	amino acids and di- and oligopeptides
onuclease	endonuclease that attacks the P-O bond attached to the 3-OH group of pyrimidine nucleotides	nucleotides

Pancreatic juice contains a large number of enzymes all of which are hydrolytic, i.e. they split covalent bonds in the presence of water. Most of the enzymes of the pancreatic juice have been prepared in pure form from different animal species, the pork pancreatic enzymes probably being the most intensively studied so far. Much of our information on the pancreatic enzymes therefore refers to enzymes from this species. Despite the limited evidence available from other sources, it is clear that a marked species difference exists in relation to the concentrations of the different enzymes in the pancreas and their chemical nature as revealed by differences in isoelectric points.

Information on human pancreatic enzymes is similarly rather limited. The substrate specificities of pancreatic enzymes from different species, however, appear to be alike. The function of the individual pancreatic enzymes will be discussed in the sections dealing with digestion and absorption of the different groups of foodstuffs. Table II gives a summary of the different enzymes (enzymatic activities) found in pancreatic juice.

It has been demonstrated that the relative concentrations of the different enzymes from different animal species are influenced by the composition of the diet. No such information is available for the human. Many of the enzymes of the pancreatic juice are in the inactive or zymogen form and only activated when entering the intestinal content. The primary activating agent is enterokinase, a proteolytic enzyme secreted into the duodenum by the glands of Brunner. Enterokinase activates trypsinogen to trypsin which then autocatalytically activates all of the trypsinogen. Trypsin, furthermore, activates chymotrypsinogen and the procarboxypeptidases. It has been reported that trypsin activates the zymogen form of phospholipase A_2 present in pancreatic juice (Arnesjö *et al.*, 1967).

Pancreatic juice from different species has been shown to contain proteins capable of inhibiting the various active forms of the proteolytic enzymes. These proteins have been named trypsin inhibitors even though some of them are not only specific for trypsin but also inhibit other proteolytic enzymes. Trasylol, which is one such nonspecific inhibitor of the proteolytic activities of pancreatic juice, has attracted interest as a possible therapeutic agent in pancreatic disease. Trasylol so far has only been found in the bovine pancreas.

E. *Small intestine*

The final digestion and absorption of the food constituents occurs in the small intestine. The small intestine in man is nearly three meters long (Hirsch *et al.*, 1956; Wilson, 1962), and its surface is increased about three times by the folds of Kerkring (Fig. 1). A further tenfold increase in surface area is provided by the finger- or tongue-shaped villi of the mucosa. Finally, the luminal surface of each epithelial cell forms a large number of microvilli, which cause a further 20-fold increase in total surface area. In this way a total digestive and absorbing area of not less than about 2 000 000 cm² is obtained (Fig. 1) (Wilson, 1962).

The small-intestinal epithelium undergoes rapid replacement by desquamation of old cells from the villous tops and regeneration from the crypts. The turnover-time has been estimated to be two days (Wilson, 1962; Wiseman, 1964).

The phase of digestion which occurs in the small intestine is mediated partly by enzymes secreted from the pancreas, and partly by enzymes formed in the small intestinal mucosa. It has been suggested that amylase, and possibly other enzymes from the pancreatic juice, are to some extent adsorbed on to the mucosal surface where they may act (Ugolev, 1965). Enzymes adsorbed in this way have been assumed to be more active than when in free solution (Ugolev, 1965). However, considerable amylase activity is also found in the intestinal content during the digestion and absorption of a test meal; this soluble amylase activity seems to be quite adequate for the rapid and complete hydrolysis of ingested starch (Dahlqvist and Borgström, 1961). Hence the physiological importance of the fraction of pancreatic amylase which is adsorbed on to the intestinal wall is not yet clear. The fraction adsorbed is greater in infancy than in adult life (de Laey, 1966).

The digestive enzymes of the mucosa in the form of disaccharidases and dipeptidases are not secreted, yet they exert their physiological action while still in contact with the mucosal cells (Borgström et al., 1957; Newey and Smyth, 1960; Dahlqvist and Borgström, 1961; Miller and Crane, 1961; Josefsson et al., 1968). It is known that the disaccharidases, and possibly

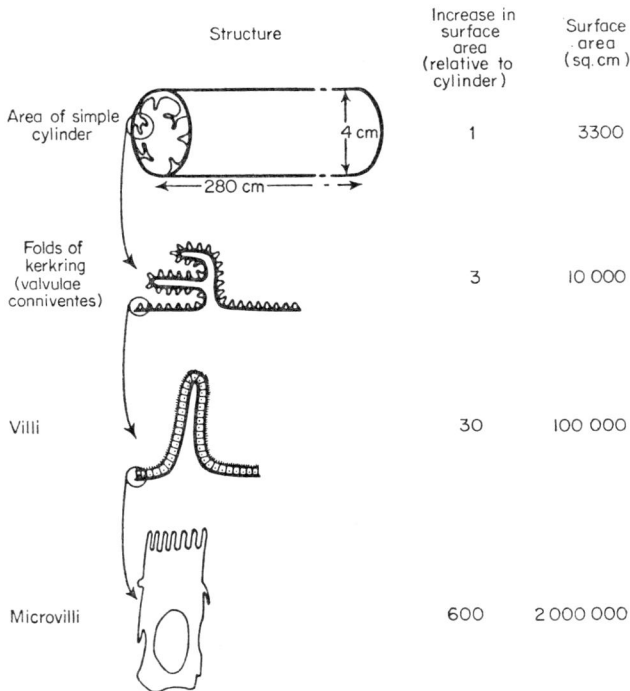

FIG. 1. The dimensions of the human small intestine, and the increase of its surface by the folds of Kerkring, the villi, and the microvilli. (From Wilson, 1962.)

also the dipeptidases, are located in the brush border (microvilli) covering the mucosal surface of the epithelial cells. It is, however, still a matter of dispute whether the disaccharidases are at least partly covered by a membrane or whether they are located outside the membrane in direct contact with the intestinal content (Dahlqvist, 1967). In electron micrographs small stalked knobs, 60 Å in diameter, have been observed on the surface of the microvilli. Experiments also show that the disaccharidase activities may be confined to these knobs (Johnson, 1967).

It has been shown both by histochemical staining (Jos et al., 1967) and by microdissection technique (Nordström et al., 1967) that the disaccharidase and dipeptidase activities are present in the villi but absent from the crypts. This localization also fits well with the concept that the small-intestinal enzymes are not secreted but act in the absorbing mucosal cells.

The small-intestinal enzymes are not uniformly distributed along the length of the small intestine. The distribution of the different disaccharidases seems to vary from species to species (Dahlqvist, 1964). In the pig the lactase and trehalase activities are highest in the proximal part of the small intestine, while the maltase, invertase and isomaltase activities are highest in its distal part. In the human the disaccharidase activity is distributed in a more parallel fashion, with low activity in the proximal part of the duodenum and maximal activity in the jejunum. When peroral biopsy preparations of the small-intestinal mucosa are used for enzyme activity assay, they are usually taken at the ligament of Treitz, where the activity is high, but not maximal. The dipeptidase activities are low in the proximal part of the duodenum but increase rapidly in its distal part to reach maximal values in the jejunum and ileum (Lindberg, 1967).

F. *Hormonal and nervous regulation of the gastrointestinal tract*

The stomach secretes its digestive juices in response to food. In man the mere thought of food, the sight, smell and above all the taste of food, will initiate gastric secretion rich in acid and pepsin. This *cephalic phase* of secretion depends on the vagus. When food enters the stomach the *gastric phase* of secretion is initiated by activation of the antral gastrin mechanism. We have some idea of the structure of this mechanism, and presumably the gastrin-producing cell has been identified recently by McGuigan (1968). The hormone, gastrin, is a strongly acid hepta-decapeptide (Gregory and Tracy, 1966), liberated into the blood upon distension of the antrum by food and upon chemical action of protein or its digestion products and ethanol. The juice produced is high in acid content, but lower in pepsin content than the secretion which results from direct vagal action (Makhlouf *et al.*, 1967).

As far as acid production is concerned there is a close interrelationship between vagal and gastrin stimulation. Under physiological conditions the direct vagal action on the parietal cells requires the presence of gastrin to produce more than negligible amounts of acid. Consequently, it is of considerable interest that vagal activation has been shown to result in direct stimulation of the parietal cells as well as in release of antral gastrin (Schofield, 1960; Olbe, 1966). This acid response to vagal activation is auto-regulated by inhibition of vagal release of gastrin at a pH below 2·5 in the antrum. Furthermore, at a low pH in the duodenal bulb, a humoral agent is liberated which counteracts gastrin at the parietal cell level (Andersson *et al.*, 1965). The existence of another duodenal inhibitory hormone, enterogastrone, has been discussed, but never proven.

There does not seem to be any synergism between gastrin and the direct vagal action on the pepsin secreting chief cells. In any case, the pepsin output resulting from gastrin stimulation is not simply the result of washing out preformed pepsin (Passaro and Grossman, 1964; Andersson and Grossman, 1964).

The physiological role of histamine in gastric secretion remains controversial (Murray, 1966). It has been proposed that under physiological conditions this potent activator of gastric secretion exerts its greatest influence on gastric motility. Gastric motility seems primarily to be stimulated by the vagus. So far there is no physiological evidence for the possible influence of gastrin. Motor activity in response to feeding is mainly limited to the distal part of the stomach which is known to be responsible for the mixing of food and for the passage of the resultant chyme. The stomach exhibits receptive relaxation, hence the intragastric pressure does not rise during eating (Grey, 1918). The pyloric sphincter constitutes an integral part of gastric peristalsis. Sphincteric contraction will last for a short time while the peristaltic wave passes along the duodenum. This prevents regurgitation. In the empty stomach without peristalsis the pyloric sphincter is open. This is also the case when cream is introduced directly into the duodenum, and indicates inhibition of gastric motility by fat via duodenal humoral agents. Fluids have been shown to leave the stomach in an exponential manner (Hunt and Spurrell, 1951). By using radioisotope-labelled food, the rate at which it leaves the stomach can be measured by external counting (Griffith et al., 1968).

In the duodenum three different gastrointestinal hormones have been recognized. These are gastrin, secretin and pancreozymin-cholecystokinin.

Gastrin is also produced in the duodenal mucosa. Presumably the content of gastrin per gram duodenal mucosa is small as compared with the gastrin content of the antrum. In view of the relatively large area of the gastrin-producing mucosa in the duodenum, however, this source may be of greater importance than is usually assumed.

Secretin is a basic heptacosapeptide that is liberated into the blood from the mucosa of the proximal small intestine on the entrance of acid chyme into duodenum. Its main effect is to stimulate the pancreas to secrete water and bicarbonate ions into the pancreatic duct. In addition, secretin seems to interfere with circulating gastrin (Gillespie and Grossman, 1964), thereby inhibiting gastric secretion.

Pancreozymin-cholecystokinin was once believed to be two hormones. It contains 33 amino acids, and it is produced by the duodenal and jejunal mucosa. As its name implies, it affects both the pancreas and the biliary system. Like vagal stimulation, the pure hormone does not produce any secretion by the pancreas when the gland is not under simultaneous stimulation by secretin. Pancreozymin-cholecystokinin influences the liberation of pancreatic enzymes by the zymogen granules of the pancreas. Pancreozymincholecystokinin affects the contraction of the gallbladder and relaxes the muscles of the sphincter of Oddi. It also affects the motility of the duodenum, and increases bile flow from the liver.

Following elucidation of the chemical structure of the gastrointestinal hormones, certain similarities between them became evident. (Jorpes, 1968;

Mutt and Jorpes, 1968). The *C*-terminal pentapeptide of pancreozymin was found to resemble that of gastrin. This is interesting because gastrin also stimulates the liberation of enzymes by the pancreas and pancreozymin stimulates the secretion of hydrochloric acid by the stomach. Furthermore, it has been found that the structures of secretin and glucagon are to some extent similar, a fact which explains why secretin, like glucagon, increases blood sugar. The quantitative aspects of this effect of the gastrointestinal hormones remain unknown.

The motility of the small intestine depends upon the auto-rhythmicity of the smooth muscle fibres, the intramural neural elements, the extrinsic nervous supply, and the humoral agents. The contractions of the smooth muscle fibres are related to changes in transmembrane potential which depend upon the movements of ions across the membrane. At least two kinds of electric activity are present: *slow waves*, or a basal electric rhythm due to periodic membrane potential variations, and *spike potentials* representing the action potentials of contracting muscle. The slow waves *per se* do not influence the intraluminal pressure. They occur at a rate of 18 per min in the duodenum, and as they are related to the frequency of the spike discharges which result in contraction, they serve as a pacemaker. The smooth muscle fibres can be activated by stretch and will conduct impulses independently of nerves at a rate of about 15 cm per sec.

The intramural neural elements including five intrinsic nerve plexuses are indispensable for normal motor function. The sensory receptors which subserve the peristaltic reflex are activated by radial stretch. Other sensory receptors are responsible for the intestinal reflexes.

The pacemaker stimulus which originates in the outer longitudinal muscle layer and the intrinsic neural elements are sufficient for the maintenance of normal motility. When gastric contents are evacuated into the duodenum, stretch receptors are triggered. The rate of contraction is controlled by the depolarization wave of the basal electric rhythm which is propagated aborally via the muscle fibres. The outer longitudinal muscle layer is connected to the circular coat via nervous pathways. The circular layer begins to contract when contraction of the longitudinal layer is half complete or complete. The contraction wave of the circular layer moves a short distance before ceasing. The mixing of intestinal contents is apparently achieved by a complex firing order of the circular muscles.

The extrinsic nerves do not seem to play any essential role in small intestinal motility. At any rate, motor activity is not influenced profoundly by vagotomy and sympathectomy in man. According to the classical concept, the parasympathetic vagal fibres are excitatory, and the sympathetic splanchnic fibres are inhibitory. The parasympathetic excitation dominates the proximal small gut. Centrally induced inhibition of this part of the intestine is completely dependent on the sympatho-adrenal hormone. Via the splanchnic fibres sympathetic inhibition dominates the distal small gut. The afferent fibres of both systems exercise some influence on the intestinal reflexes.

Some humoral agents may assist in the stimulation of motor activity. This applies to serotonin produced by the argentaffin cells, to substance P, and probably to gastrin, all of which are normally present in the gut wall.

An excellent review on small bowel motility has been written by Farrar and Zfass (1967).

III. Digestion and Absorption

A. *Carbohydrates*

Our most important dietary carbohydrates are starch, sucrose and lactose. The average daily consumption of these carbohydrates are: starch, 135 grams, sucrose, 140 grams, and lactose, 30 grams (Swedish figures). Maltose, malto-oligosaccharides and isomalto-oligosaccharides as such are present only in small amounts in our diet, but are formed during the hydrolysis of starch in the digestive tract. Glycogen, trehalose and monosaccharides are also consumed, though only in small amounts.

Dietary starch is rapidly hydrolyzed by salivary and pancreatic amylase to maltose, malto-oligosaccharides and oligosaccharides containing iso-maltose- and maltose-links. These di- and oligosaccharides, together with sucrose, lactose and other ingested disaccharides are further hydrolyzed by the small-intestinal disaccharidases to monosaccharides. As has been mentioned already, this hydrolysis takes place at the surface of the mucosal epithelial cells. The monosaccharides are then transported by active or passive transport processes through the epithelial cells to the blood.

1. *α-Amylase*

The salivary and pancreatic amylase is an α-amylase, hydrolyzing α-1,4-glucosidic bonds in the starch molecule in a random way, leaving maltose and oligosaccharides (mainly trisaccharides containing maltose- or isomaltose- plus maltose-links) as the end-product. The α-amylase is activated by chloride ions, and is dependent on calcium ions for its activity. Calcium is firmly bound to the enzyme (Fischer and Stein, 1960). α-Amylase is found not only in saliva and pancreatic juice, but also in homogenates of the small-intestinal mucosa. It is, however, not known whether this α-amylase in mucosal homogenates is formed in the epithelial cells, or is the result of contamination with pancreatic juice, or possibly adsorption of amylase on to the surface of the epithelium.

2. *γ-Amylase*

The intestinal epithelium (but not saliva or pancreatic juice) also contains a γ-amylase, which hydrolyses starch, and liberates one glucose molecule, starting from the non-reducing end of the polysaccharide molecule (Dahlqvist and Thomson, 1963). This γ-amylase together with isomaltase influences the final digestion of the dextrins formed by α-amylase. The γ-amylase activity seems to be exerted by enzymes which also account for part of the maltase activity of the mucosa.

3. *Disaccharidases*

The disaccharidases are only present in the small intestine. The specificity of the human small-intestinal disaccharidases has been studied by heat inactivation (Dahlqvist, 1962) and column chromatography (Auricchio *et al.*, 1965; Semenza *et al.*, 1965; Dahlqvist and Telenius, 1968). There exist four different maltases, which in order of increasing heat stability have been named maltase Ia, maltase Ib, maltase II and maltase III. Isomaltase is identical with maltase Ia,* and sucrase with maltase Ib. In addition there exists a specific trehalase (Table III). The lactase can be fractionated into

TABLE III

Specificity and localization of the human small-intestinal disaccharidases

Enzyme	Activity	% of total activity	Location
Maltase Ia = = isomaltase	maltase isomaltase	50 99	
Maltase Ib = = sucrase (invertase)	maltase sucrase	25 100	
Maltase II Maltase III	maltase isomaltase	25 1	brush border
Trehalase	trehalase	100	
Lactase I	lactase cellobiase hetero β-galactosidase	major fraction minor fraction	
Lactase II	lactase hetero β-galactosidase	minor fraction major fraction	lysosomes or cytoplasm

two components by gel filtration chromatography (Auricchio *et al.*, 1965 Semenza *et al.*, 1965), but only one of these components seems to be located in the brush border. The other enzyme with lactase activity is a more nonspecific β-galactosidase which is most probably located in the lysosomes of the mucosal cell, and does not take part in physiological digestion (Koldovský *et al.*, 1965, 1967). This lysosomal enzyme only accounts for a small fraction of the total lactase activity in the normal mucosa.

The sucrase (invertase) activity can under certain conditions be fractionated into two components by gel filtration chromatography (Auricchio *et al.*, 1965; Semenza *et al.*, 1965). This fractionation of the sucrase activity has, however, later turned out to be an artefact (Semenza and Kolínská, 1967; Dahlqvist and Telenius, 1969).

* Maltase II and maltase III also exert weak isomaltase activity, but this accounts for less than 1% of the total isomaltase (Dahlqvist and Telenius, 1968).

4. *Transport of monosaccharides*

There exists in the small intestine an active transport mechanism for certain monosaccharides, of which the most important ones are glucose and galactose. These monosaccharides can be transported against a chemical concentration gradient. This transport process was for a long time believed to involve phosphorylation-dephosphorylation of the monosaccharide molecule, but this theory has subsequently been contested. It is now believed that there exists in the membrane of the mucosal cells a glucose-galactose-specific carrier. This carrier can transport the monosaccharides in or out of the cells, but only if it can simultaneously transport sodium ions. There is, however, an energy-dependent sodium pump, which transports sodium ions the whole time from the inside of the cell to the outside. This sodium transport forces the monosaccharides to be transported into and accumulated in the epithelial cells (Fig. 2) (Crane, 1967).

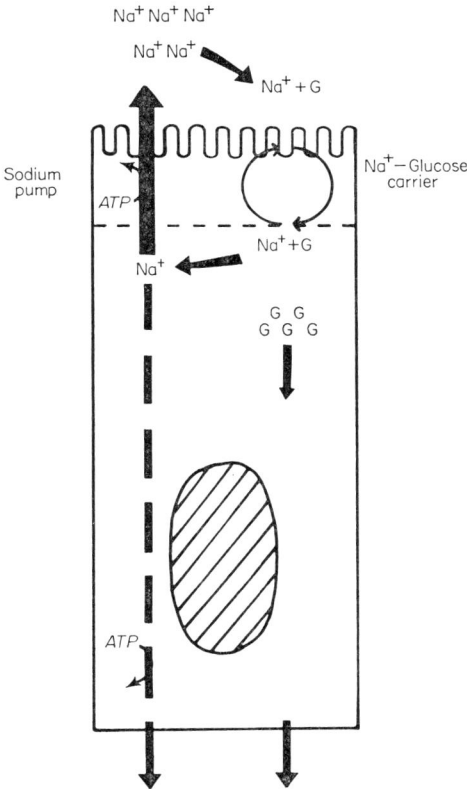

FIG. 2. Schematic representation of the glucose-galactose transport system in an epithelial cell of the small intestine. (From Dahlqvist *et al.*, 1967.)

The glucose-galactose carrier, like the disaccharidases, should be located in the brush border region of the mucosal cells. When it was found that the intestinal sucrase is activated by sodium ions, the question was raised whether the sodium activation of the sucrase and the sodium dependency of the sugar carrier might be related (Semenza, 1967). This concept is supported by the fact that the apparent K_M values for the sucrase activity and the intestinal sugar transport system for sodium ions have turned out to be similar in several of the species studied. On the other hand, the sucrase and the sugar carrier cannot be identical, since phlorizin which inhibits active sugar transport does not inhibit sucrase, and since tris which inhibits sucrase does not inhibit sugar transport (Semenza, 1967).

D-Xylose, which was earlier supposed to be transported by passive diffusion, has been found to be transported actively by the same mechanism as in glucose-galactose transport (Alvarado, 1966). The transport of xylose is, however, much less rapid than that of glucose or galactose.

Fructose is absorbed more slowly than glucose and galactose, but more rapidly than e.g. mannose. However, no active transport of fructose has been demonstrated, and fructose does not compete with the actively transported sugars.

B. *Proteins*

In the gastrointestinal tract the proteins, which are macromolecules with a complex structure, are sequentially attacked by various proteolytic enzymes in order to decompose them into products that can be absorbed and delivered to the blood. It is now widely accepted that the proteins are completely hydrolyzed to their constituent amino acids before leaving the small intestine (for ref. see Wilson, 1962; Matthews and Laster, 1965) but it has been claimed that this has still not been definitely established (Fischer, 1967).

It is known that very small amounts of whole proteins can be absorbed in man. This is, however, negligible from a nutritional point of view. In man, most of the proteins ingested are already denatured, and if not, the low pH in the stomach promotes denaturation. Thus, peptide-bonds are exposed and they become accessible to hydrolysis catalysed by various proteolytic enzymes.

1. *Stomach*

Pepsin is secreted in the inactive form, pepsinogen, by the chief cells of the gastric mucosa. At pH below 5 pepsinogen is autocatalytically converted to pepsin. The specificity of pepsin is not high, but it preferentially splits peptide-bonds formed by aromatic amino acids and by leucine (cf. Bovey and Yanari, 1960). During the last few years further proteolytic enzymes, the so-called pepsin B, C and D (Ryle, 1964), have been demonstrated in man (at least one of the three forms) and in pig (the three forms). Their specificity is about the same as that of pepsin and their biological role is still obscure.

2. *Pancreatic juice*

In the duodenum hydrolysis is continued by the action of the pancreatic enzymes, namely, trypsin, chymotrypsin, elastase and carboxypeptidase A and B. These enzymes are secreted in the form of inactive precursors (zymogens), viz., trypsinogen, chymotrypsinogen, proelastase and pro-carboxypeptidase A and B. Trypsinogen in the intestinal juice is converted to its active form by enterokinase by the splitting of a hexapeptide from the molecule. The activation can then continue autocatalytically. The other zymogens in the pancreatic juice are converted to active enzymes by the action of trypsin. Trypsin has a high specificity, splitting only bonds formed by the carboxyl groups of lysine and arginine (cf. Desnuelle, 1960*a*).

Chymotrypsin preferably attacks bonds adjacent to aromatic amino acids (cf. Desnuelle, 1960*b*). The specificity of elastase is not so well established. It has been found to attack a wide range of peptide bonds (cf. Gitler, 1964).

By the action of these so-called endopeptidases, the proteins are hydrolyzed mostly to peptides of varying lengths although free amino acids are also split off. Carboxypeptidase A and B, which belong to the group called exopeptidases, continue the digestion by splitting off amino acids from the carboxyl end of the peptides. Carboxypeptidase B attacks only bonds formed by lysine and arginine (cf. Neurath, 1960), while carboxypeptidase A hydrolyzes bonds formed by neutral, acidic or aromatic amino acids.

3. *Intestinal mucosa*

The epithelial cells of the mucosa of the small intestine probably contain a great number of peptidases associated with the final digestion of the proteins. However, our knowledge about most of them is rather limited. One of the best known is leucine aminopeptidase, which attacks peptide-bonds adjacent to amino acid residues with a free amino group. This enzyme can split some dipeptidases, but at a much lower rate than their corresponding amide compounds (Smith and Hill, 1960). Leucine amino-peptidase has been reported to be distinct from a tripeptide-splitting enzyme found in the intestinal mucosa (Smith, 1960). These enzymes have little or no activity against dipeptides, which besides amino acids are the final products of the digestion of the proteins by the above-mentioned enzymes.

In vitro dipeptides are hydrolyzed to their constituent amino acids before or during their transfer through the intestinal wall (for ref. see Matthews and Laster, 1965). This hydrolysis is catalysed by the intestinal dipeptidases: in man the activities of nine different dipeptides have been demonstrated and characterized (Lindberg, 1967; Josefsson and Lindberg, 1967). Probably the dipeptidases possess group-specificity. The precise location of their physiological action is unknown, but it would appear that the dipeptides are hydrolyzed in the immediate vicinity of the mucosal cell membrane (Ugolev and Kooshuck, 1966; Josefsson *et al.*, 1968).

4. *Absorption of amino acids*

The amino acids are absorbed by an active transport mechanism (for ref. see Wilson, 1962; Matthews and Laster, 1965; Saunders and Isselbacher, 1966). Competition, probably for one or several carriers, between the various amino acids has been demonstrated. The nature of the carrier(s) is unknown. It has been shown that the transport of the amino acids is sodium-dependent. The naturally occurring L-amino-acids are absorbed more rapidly than the corresponding D-amino acids. Active transport occurs only if the carboxyl-group and the α-amino-group of the amino acid are free and unsubstituted, and if the side-chain of the amino acid is non-polar. That the α-hydrogen be intact is important but not essential. So far four specific transport groups of amino acids have been identified: (1) for neutral amino acids, (2) for dibasic amino acids, (3) for dicarboxylic amino acids, and (4) for amino acids.

5. *Endogenous protein*

The dietary protein is mixed in the gastrointestinal tract with endogenous protein, e.g. albumin, enzymes, mucoproteins and disrupted mucosal cells. The amount of these proteins is difficult to estimate, but a figure of 40–50 g per day for man seems plausible. According to Nasset (1964) the dietary protein is diluted several times with the endogenous protein of the intestinal lumen.

6. *The rate of the digestion and absorption*

The rates of digestion and absorption of the dietary proteins vary rather widely, depending upon stomach emptying time, the nature of the protein and the other food constituents ingested. The various enzymes involved are normally present in such relatively large amounts that hydrolysis *per se* can not be considered as a rate-limiting factor. The amino acids liberated are absorbed rapidly.

Information about this question in man is rather scanty, but it has been shown that about 80% of the dietary protein (in the form of albumin) is absorbed in the upper half of the small intestine (Borgström *et al.*, 1957). Furthermore, when ^{15}N-labelled yeast protein was given to normal man maximal rate of urinary ^{15}N excretion occurred after 45 min (Crane and Neuberger, 1960).

The endogenous protein, which is native, is thought to be hydrolyzed at a lower rate and absorbed in the distal parts of the small intestine.

C. *Fats*

Most fats are insoluble in water and when present in the diet are in a physical form that cannot be utilized by the intestine. As far as is known, only three digestive enzymes participate in the digestion of the dietary fat. These enzymes are the classical lipase, a carboxylic ester hydrolase and a phospholipase A_2 (Morgan *et al.*, 1967, 1968). (In contrast to the pancreatic lipase the importance of a gastric lipase is not well established.) The action of these enzymes is to hydrolyze their substrates to products which interact with the bile salts, and which can be taken up by the intestinal cells.

Pancreatic lipase is an enzyme that attacks only substrates which are insoluble in water (Sarda and Desnuelle, 1958), and usually dispersed as an oil phase in an emulsion. The classical substrates for lipase are triglycerides with long-chain fatty acids; these are degraded to 1,2-diglycerides and 2-monoglyceride plus free fatty acid by the action of lipase. Lipase has very little or no activity against the fatty acid in the 2-position of the glyceride and hence the 2-monoglyceride is the end-product of lipolysis.

Bile salts are not obligatory for pancreatic lipase to act; on the contrary, the rate of hydrolysis of triglycerides at the pH optimum of lipase is much higher in the absence of bile salt. Under these conditions, the pH optimum of human pancreatic lipase is approximately 9·2 (Borgström, 1957), which implies that the fatty acids liberated occur in the ionized form as soaps. Addition of bile salts *in vitro* results in higher rates of hydrolysis at lower pH, and the products of lipolysis are to some extent present in solution in mixed micelles with bile salts. This latter reaction taking place in the presence of bile salt at slightly acid pH is that normally occurring in intestinal contents during the digestion of dietary fat. This involves a two-phase system: on one side an oil phase is formed mainly by the unchanged triglyceride of the dietary fat, while on the other side, a micellar phase is formed by the micelles of bile salts and the lecithin of bile (Hofmann and Borgström, 1964). The polar products of pancreatic lipolysis favour the micellar phase, while the diglycerides favour the oil phase (Borgström, 1967). The pK of long-chain fatty acids under these conditions has been shown to be nearly seven; this explains why these acids when in the proximal small intestine are mainly in the undissociated form. The chain length of the fatty acids is of importance in this respect, since the shorter the chain of the fatty acid, the less the interaction with the micellar phase, and hence the lower the pK (Borgström, 1967).

In the two-phase system just discussed, lipase is most probably located at the interphase of the emulsion droplets where it catalyses a complex reaction the equilibrium of which is quite different from that which can be expected, on *a priori* grounds, in the presence of a large excess of water. The presence of an oil phase and a very low water concentration at the site of lipase activity leads to an equilibrium with approximately equimolar concentrations of tri-, di- and monoglyceride. The overall physiological effect of these interactions is that of a system designed for the continuous generation of the end-products removed by absorption (Borgström, 1964).

Lipase not only splits triglyceride but also attacks a variety of carboxylic ester bonds, the physiological state of the substrate being of primary importance. Thus lipase splits water-insoluble esters of naphthol and *p*-nitrophenol and also the ester bonds of vitamin A esters. The nature of the alcohol moiety is, however, also of importance; cholesterol esters, for example, are not hydrolyzed by lipase (Morgan *et al.*, 1967).

The second lipolytic enzyme of pancreatic juice is a carboxylic ester

P

hydrolase, the properties of which have been less well studied. This enzyme catalyses the hydrolysis of esters which are water-soluble such as β-naphthol acetate. It also splits water-insoluble esters in the presence of bile salts; for example, monoglycerides with long-chain fatty acids (Morgan *et al.*, 1967, 1968). The role of bile salts in these latter systems might be to solubilize the substrate in the micellar form. This enzyme hydrolyzes cholesterol esters and thus is identical among other things with cholesterol esterase. This enzyme also hydrolyzes vitamin A esters. The role of the carboxylic ester hydrolase in the splitting of glyceride in intestinal contents during digestion is not known at the present time. It possibly could affect the hydrolysis of 2-monoglycerides present in the micellar form.

The third lipolytic enzyme of pancreatic juice is phospholipase A_2, which splits the ester bond in the 2-position of glycerophospholipids, thereby forming lysoglycerophospholipids. This transformation also implies a physico-chemical transformation, the water-insoluble phospholipid being transformed to water-soluble lyso-compounds which by themselves can form micellar solutions and which form mixed micelles with bile salts. The phospholipase A_2 of pancreatic juice is present in the pancreatic juice in its inactive or zymogen form. Trypsin catalyses the formation of the active enzyme (Arnesjö *et al.*, 1967).

As mentioned earlier, emulsions of dietary fat cannot be taken up by the intestinal mucosa. The chemical transformation catalysed by the pancreatic lipolytic enzymes in the presence of bile results in lipids whose physical form permits uptake by the intestinal mucosa cells. The physical form is the micelle, its chemical form the monoglyceride, fatty acid and lysolecithin. Other lipids present in minor amounts in the dietary fat are to some extent solubilized as well in the micelles and absorbed with the lipids.

The lipolytic products of most fats are absorbed by the proximal part of the jejunum, while the bile salts are absorbed by the distal part of the small intestine.

Intestinal absorption of fats seems to be non-energy dependent. Following absorption there is resynthesis of triglyceride mainly via the monoglyceride pathway. The triglycerides formed are transformed into chylomicrons, and then delivered to the lympahtic capillaries draining the mucosa cells. The formation of chylomicrons requires β-lipoprotein; however, the details of this assembly are not yet fully known. The fatty acid and monoglycerides inside the mucosa cells are probably taken up by the membranes of the smooth-surfaced vesicles where the enzymes responsible for glyceride synthesis are located (for a review see Johnston, 1968).

Most of what has so far been discussed relates to the mechanism of digestion and absorption of triglycerides with long-chain fatty acids. Short chain fatty acids which constitute a smaller fraction of the fatty acids present in normal dietary fat occur to a varying extent in some dietary fats such as butter fat or coconut fat, and the so-called medium chain triglyceride (MCT) fat that has attracted interest lately in the treatment of malabsorption. The medium chain fatty acids are characterized by diminished interaction with the micellar phase of intestinal contents and a lower pK$_a$ than the long-chain fatty acids. They are therefore absorbed as soaps and do not need bile salt for absorption. Present evidence indicates that they can also be absorbed as glycerides, even as triglycerides and hence lipase is not necessary for their absorption (Playoust et al., 1964). The MCT fat the fatty acids of which are almost 80% made up of C$_8$ fatty acid can thus be expected to be absorbed when the intestinal content is deficient in bile and/or pancreatic enzymes. Animal experiments show, however, that bile salt and/or pancreatic lipase favor the absorption of these glycerides even though they seem to be much more efficiently absorbed in their absence than the longer chain ones (Valdiviesco et al., 1965). After absorption the medium and short chain fatty acids are mainly transported from the intestine to the blood in the non-esterified form, a fact that explains their utilization in subjects with lymph stasis.

Steatorrhea which is a cardinal sign in malabsorption is accounted for by the dependence of the dietary fat on bile salt and pancreatic enzymes and also by the fact that the long-chain fatty acids are not appreciably degraded by intestinal micro-organisms. Furthermore, the relative proportions of glyceride and fatty acid in the feces are of little diagnostic importance for the elucidation of pancreatic function, since the glyceride ester bond can be split by the enzymes of the intestinal micro-organisms.

D. *Vitamins*

1. *Fat-soluble vitamins*

The absorption of the fat-soluble vitamins is intimately related to the absorption of the other fats of the diet, although they are present in solution in the normal diet as a very minor component of this fat.

There are very few studies dealing with the absorption in physiological amounts of the fat soluble vitamins in the human. With isotopically labelled vitamins (^{14}C or ^{3}H), however, it has recently been shown that these vitamins are transported from the intestine via the lymphatic pathway (Blomstrand, 1967).

Vitamin A which is absorbed with an efficiency of 40–60% appears in the thoracic duct lymph mainly as an ester with palmitic acid. Provitamin A – carotene – is absorbed less efficiently than the vitamin and is metabolized to the vitamin in the intestinal cell, with very little of the carotene itself appearing in the lymph. In the rat, oxidation products of vitamin A, retinal and retinoic acid have been shown to be excreted into the bile.

Vitamin D is also found in the thoracic duct lymph mainly in the form of free vitamin D and is reported to be absorbed with an efficiency of 60–70%. The absorption of vitamin D is highly dependent on the presence of bile in the intestine.

Vitamin E has also been found in human thoracic duct lymph and appears to circulate in the enterohepatic circulation, but the details of this are not well known.

The *vitamin K*-forms which are generally found in normal diets are fat-soluble, and bile is essential for their absorption. After absorption they are transported by the lymphatics. Though the intestinal microflora is known to produce vitamin K, the importance thereof in the human is far from clear.

Fat-soluble vitamins in "water soluble" form have been produced and generally they are vitamins in detergent solution, probably micellar. In this form their absorption has been claimed to be relatively independent of the secretion of bile and pancreatic enzymes. Most of the available evidence refers to the absorption of vitamin A as being determined by post-absorptive blood levels. Studies of the function of different parts of the gastro-intestinal tract based on the analysis of blood curves after feeding a test substance, for example, vitamin A, are open to question. After all, an atypical blood curve can be caused by several factors not directly related to the absorption process.

2. *Water-soluble vitamins*

a. *Vitamin B_{12} and folic acid*

The daily vitamin B_{12} (cyanocobalamin) requirement in man is about 1 μg. The richest dietary source of vitamin B_{12} is meat, especially offal, poultry and, to a lesser degree, fish. In food the active form of this heat-stable vitamin is complexed via peptide bonds to protein from which it must be liberated by processing or digestion before absorption. A carrier glycoprotein – intrinsic factor (IF) – is indispensable for the active absorption of vitamin B_{12} (Glass, 1963). Receptor sites for the vitamin B_{12}-IF complex are found exclusively on the brush border of the ileal mucosal cells (Rosenberg *et al.*, 1965). The attachment of the complex to the receptor requires the presence of a pH above 5·6 and ionic calcium (Okuda and Sasayama, 1965). Transit across the absorptive cell takes between one and four hours and the overall capacity for active absorption is less than 2 μg per day. The uptake of vitamin B_{12} in man is also stimulated by IF obtained from the rat and the pig but not from the dog. Vitamin B_{12} is also absorbed independently of IF (Herbert, 1968). This passive transfer occurs only in the presence of huge quantities of the vitamin, indeed far in excess of those provided by usual diet.

Malabsorption of vitamin B_{12} occurs in relation to a partial or rather a total deficiency in production of IF, as is in Addisonian pernicious anaemia and congenital pernicious anaemia (MacIntyre *et al.*, 1965). Diagnosis of the former disease depends on whether or not gastric achlorhydria is present. Further, antibody to IF is known to be present in the serum of two-thirds of all pernicious anaemia patients and parietal cell antibody can be demonstrated in 90% of these patients (Fischer *et al.*, 1966). Unquestionably, the appearance of these antibodies is secondary to the disease. Vitamin B_{12} absorption may also be hampered by ileopathy and occasionally by excessive proliferation of bacteria in the small intestine (Donaldson, 1962).

Human requirements for dietary folic acid (pteroylmonoglutamate) are approximately 50 μg daily in adults. Folate is almost ubiquitous in foodstuffs, but being very labile to heat it is easily destroyed during processing. Folate occurs in food in various reduced, coenzymatically active forms and generally as polyglutamate. Evidence suggests that all glutamate residues beyond one must be split off by intestinal conjugase prior to absorption. Folate is absorbed rapidly, but the mechanisms of uptake in man are hardly known. In the rat, absorption appears to be an active process which takes place in the proximal third of the small gut.

In contrast to vitamin B_{12}, the body stores of folate are small. Consequently, symptoms of folate deficiency develop rapidly when ingestion or absorption are curtailed. In various intestinal disorders, especially coeliac disease which involves primarily the proximal small gut, folate deficiency should always be suspected. With intestinal stasis possible bacterial overgrowth may compete with the host for the available folate. Earlier concepts of a possible connection between pregnancy *per se* and folate deficiency have not been supported by recent evidence. Structurally speaking, some anticonvulsants, e.g. diphenylhydantoin and phenobarbital, are rather closely related to folate, and it has been suggested that such agents may competitively block intestinal absorption of folate. Certain anticonvulsants act as very weak antifolic agents.

Folate deficiency is suggested by the presence of hypersegmentation of the neutrophilic leucocytes, but the diagnosis is established by determination of the serum folate level. This examination is more reliable than the figlu test (Herbert, 1967).

b. Other water-soluble vitamins

These vitamins include a heterogeneous group of compounds of widely different chemical structure. The majority of these compounds are of relatively low molecular weight and they have a weak electric charge. This applies to ascorbic acid, riboflavin, pyridoxine, nicotinamide, biotin, and pantothenic acid. Taking into account the permeability characteristics of cellular membranes, these vitamins would be expected to be absorbed with comparative ease by simple diffusion. In contrast, however, the thiamine molecule is highly basic and consequently diffusion and absorption of this vitamin would be poor. In man the maximum intestinal absorptive capacity for thiamine is about 5 mg per day, yet the normal daily requirement is approximately 1·5 mg.

In malabsorption the uptake of ascorbic acid and riboflavin is probably never appreciably curtailed. Reduced pyridoxine and thiamine absorption has been demonstrated on occasion in coeliac disease.

E. Electrolytes and water

1. Monovalent cations

Cellular membranes behave as if they were lipoidal in structure, perforated by pores of molecular size (Ussing, 1949). The rapid movement of water and electrolytes requires passage through pores or specific transport sites, as is the case with sodium. In the ordinary cell, sodium (Na^+) is transported from the cytoplasm to the extracellular fluid against an electrochemical gradient. Present evidence indicates coupling between the outward transport of Na^+ and the inward transport of K^+.

In the case of the absorptive cell of the gut, there is evidence which indicates two separate Na^+ pumps (Crane, 1962) that involve the movement of Na^+ from the intestinal lumen to the blood stream (Fig. 2). The mucosal carrier depends upon the concomitant active transport of sugar and amino acids (Schultz and Zalusky, 1965), while presumably the serosal carrier is capable of moving Na^+ alone. Aldosterone enhances active Na^+ transport in the colon (Levitan and Ingelfinger, 1965). Cardiac glycosides inhibit the activity of the Na^+-K^+-ATPase and consequently decrease Na^+ transport (Skou, 1965).

The absorption of potassium (K^+) has yet to be studied extensively. So far there is no experimental support for the concept of active K^+ transport (Code *et al.*, 1960). K^+ disappears much faster from isotonic mixtures of simple potassium salts in the gut than does Na^+ from isotonic mixtures of sodium salts. Knowing the concentrations of these two alkali ions in the blood, it is obvious that the passive transfer of K^+ is favoured by a much steeper gradient in the direction of gut to blood than is Na^+. With the active absorption of Na^+, there is created a transmembrane potential difference, whereby the mucosa is negative to the serosa. In the small intestine the potential difference is 4–8 mV (Clarkson *et al.*, 1961), and in the colon where there is additional active secretion of HCO_3^- (or OH^-) it is 20–60 mV (Ussing, 1960). Mainly in the colon, the potential difference results in net K^+ movement down the electrical gradient. This explains why the daily faecal K^+ loss is 10–15 mEq and that of Na^+ is less than 5 mEq.

For all practical purposes, chloride (Cl^-) uptake is due to passive diffusion in response to the existing electrochemical gradient just mentioned (Schultz *et al.*, 1964). In so far as the small intestine is concerned, the same applies to the transport of bicarbonate (HCO_3^-) (Clarkson *et al.*, 1961). There is, however, some evidence that in the colon there is movement of HCO_3^- into the gut lumen against an electrochemical gradient (Cooperstein and Brockman, 1959).

Cellular uptake of weak electrolytes is due to passive non-ionic diffusion. The rate of penetration of weak acids and weak bases is enormously increased by altering the pH in the direction of the pK of the compound. This is explained by the fact that cellular membranes are much more permeable to the undissociated molecule than to the ionized form (Wilson, 1962). Accordingly, it has been shown that weak acidic or basic electrolytes whose pK values are between 2·9 and 8·0 are far more rapidly absorbed from the gut than those whose pK values lie outside this range. Highly ionized compounds are poorly absorbed. This applies to most salts of strong acids and bases, especially polyvalent compounds and those of high molecular weight.

2. *Water*

Since net water movement across the pores of the absorptive cell membrane cannot occur in the absence of solute movement, it is concluded that the movement of water is a passive process dependent entirely on the active transport of dissolved substances.

Water movement involves an interplay of diffusion and osmotic filtration (bulk water flow) (Ussing and Andersen, 1955). The driving force for diffusion is related to the concentration (activity) of water molecules on the two sides of the membrane, and it is proportional to the square of the pore radius. The driving force for bulk water flow is determined by the osmotic and hydrostatic pressure difference across the membrane. Here the cylindrical shape of the pore is important. That is, the transport of water is proportional to the fourth power of the pore radius, this being in agreement with Poiseuillé's law of fluid flow through narrow tubes. This implies that by far the largest fraction of water movement is contributed by bulk water flow. Under certain conditions bulk water flow will "drag" small solute molecules through the pores in the relatively fast-moving stream. This solvent drag may be exerted on ions as well as non-electrolytes and may cause measurable electrical potentials.

The total exchange of water and electrolytes in the gastrointestinal tract by far exceeds intake. The one and one-half litres of fluid ingested are mixed with seven litres or more of isotonic secretions. At the ileocecal junction this amount is reduced to 500 ml. of isotonic fluid containing 50–60 mEq of sodium and 4–6 mEq of potassium. The maximum absorptive capacity of the colon is estimated at two litres. The daily faecal output of water is roughly 100 ml. and of sodium and potassium less than 5 mEq and 10–15 mEq, respectively.

The problems of water and electrolyte movement in the intestine have been ably reviewed by Fordtran and Dietschy (1966).

3. *Bivalent cations*

The cellular membranes are relatively impermeable to polyvalent ions. Some of these ions, e.g. Ca^{2+}, Mg^{2+} and Fe^{2+}, are indispensable for survival, and special mechanisms are responsible for their absorption.

a. *Calcium*

In the adult the average daily dietary intake of calcium is approximately one gram, chiefly derived from milk. According to conventional balance techniques about 25%, or 250 mg are absorbed (Nordin and Smith, 1965). In the gastrointestinal tract the dietary calcium is mixed with about 200 mg of endogenous calcium derived from the gastric, pancreatic and biliary secretions (Heaney and Skillmann, 1964; Briscoe and Ragan, 1965). Provided that the endogenous calcium is not treated differently from the exogenous calcium, the daily faecal loss of endogenous calcium amounts to 150 mg regardless of calcium intake. When calcium intake is increased to approximately three grams, absorption approaches a maximum of perhaps 800 mg per day. However, some studies suggest that animals fed a calcium deficient diet absorb more calcium than their normal controls.

Presumably calcium exists in the ionized form before it is absorbed (Schachter *et al.*, 1960). A large proportion of dietary calcium forms complexes with for example casein in milk, or is precipitated as relatively insoluble salts, carbonate or phosphate (Smith and McAllan, 1966). Dissociation of the complexes and dissolution of the precipitates appear to depend upon a pH between 5 and 7. Some substances such as sodium phytate and sodium oxalate act as calcium-binding agents that are able to block calcium absorption.

Animal experiments have demonstrated an active energy-dependent intestinal mechanism for Ca^{2+} transport (Schachter *et al.*, 1960). By analogy, a similar mechanism has been postulated for man. Calcium uptake is localized mainly to the proximal segments of the small gut. The active transfer can be divided into two steps: uptake by the mucosal cell, and transport across the cell (Nordin, 1968). The first step is probably a movement along a downhill concentration gradient since the concentration of "free" calcium in the cell is very low. The carrier of the second step is reported to be a protein, the synthesis of which requires vitamin D (Taylor and Wasserman, 1967), and active transport fails to occur in the absence of this vitamin. In addition, parathyroid hormone seems to be essential for optimum function of the transport mechanism.

Vitamin D deficiency is the main cause of calcium malabsorption. It should be remembered that the malabsorption of calcium in coeliac disease can be reversed by parenteral administration of vitamin D (Nordin and Smith, 1967). It is thus unlikely that the formation of calcium soaps is a significant factor in the production of calcium deficiency in this disease.

An intriguing observation is the excessive absorption of calcium in some patients with sarcoidosis. These patients have an increased sensitivity to vitamin D which is prevented by the administration of cortisone.

Nordin has published an excellent survey of intestinal calcium absorption (Nordin, 1968).

b. Magnesium

Magnesium occurs in small amounts in all foods. The average dietary intake is about 350 mg per day of which approximately 10% is absorbed (Aikawa *et al.*, 1958). Presumably, the bulk of the absorption occurs in the proximal portion of the small gut. Although magnesium is essential for nutrition, its absorption has not been investigated in any detail. Magnesium reduces the movement of calcium against a concentration gradient in sacs of everted small intestine of the rat, the guinea pig, and the rabbit (Schachter and Rosen, 1959; Alcock and MacIntyre, 1960). Such results have been thought to indicate a common active transport mechanism for the two cations (MacIntyre, 1963). Moreover, some data suggest that vitamin D increases intestinal uptake of magnesium (Meintzer and Steenbock, 1955).

In the field of gastroenterology magnesium metabolism has hitherto no attracted much interest. Magnesium depletion has been reported as a complication of intestinal resection, coeliac disease, ulcerative colitis, prolonged gastrointestinal suction and protracted parenteral alimentation with magnesium-free solutions (Fletcher et al., 1960; Booth, 1961; MacIntyre et al., 1961, Balint and Hirschowitz, 1961). Magnesium deficiency may occasionally result in watery diarrhoea which is only controlled by magnesium repletion. Hypomagnesaemia is accompanied by deficiencies in potassium, calcium and phosphorus. Reversal of the imbalance can be achieved only by magnesium administration (Petersen, 1963). It is tempting to hypothesize that some of these effects of magnesium depletion might be related to the function of this ion as an essential activator of the Na^+-K^+-ATPase. This transport enzyme is considered to play a key role in the linked transport of sodium and potassium. Thus if the ATPase is not adequately activated, intestinal absorption of sodium, potassium and water will be reduced. Furthermore, ATPase deficiency will influence the potassium content of all body cells. A consequent fall in the intracellular concentration of potassium with no change in external concentration will tend to bring the resting membrane potential of the intestinal muscle fibres closer to the threshold of excitation and thereby possibly lead to an increase in intestinal motor activity (Burnstock et al., 1963).

4. Iron

The body's daily requirement of iron is less than 1 mg in man. Healthy subjects probably absorb some 10% of the 15 mg of total daily dietary iron. According to the permeability characteristics of cellular membranes, the simple iron salts are probably absorbed almost exclusively in the ferrous state. Further, iron oxidized to the ferric state complexes readily with many substances and thus becomes less available for absorption. The uptake of the simple iron salts is not enhanced by gastric acid, but is augmented by the presence of substantial amounts of an organic acid or an organic reducing agent such as ascorbic acid or succinic acid. On the other hand, the uptake of dietary iron seems to be facilitated by gastric acid, but not by organic reducing agents (Cook et al., 1964). Haemoglobin iron is absorbed more efficiently from food than inorganic iron (Turnbull et al., 1962; Conrad et al., 1967).

The absorptive mechanism for elemental iron involves at least three steps: mucosal uptake, mucosal transfer to plasma, and mucosal storage of iron (Hallberg and Sölvell, 1960; Manis and Schachter, 1964; Wheby et al., 1964; Charlton et al., 1965). The uptake and transfer represent distinct steps of the active iron transport system that is perhaps mainly found in the duodenum (Dowdle et al., 1960). Iron which is probably stored in the ferric state is released slowly, if at all. The role of ferritin as the storage form of iron is controversial.

Our understanding of the mechanisms that regulate iron absorption is still incomplete. The concept of a "mucosal block" related to saturation of a mucosal cell receptor (apoferritin) (Granick, 1946) has been abandoned since "saturation" of the postulated carrier could not be confirmed (Smith and Pannacciulli, 1958). More recently, it has been suggested that the iron content of the mucosal cell might be important in regulating absorption (Wheby, 1966). From radioautographs prepared after parenteral injection of ^{59}Fe, it has been inferred that the iron content mainly depends upon iron incorporated into the cell during its formation in the intestinal crypt (Conrad *et al.*, 1964). Furthermore, it is supposed that the amount of iron stored in each newly formed cell reflects the simultaneous iron requirements of the body or rather the plasma iron concentration. This might explain the increased intestinal absorptive capacity for iron during accelerated erythro-poiesis when plasma iron is preferably diverted to the bone marrow. Usually there is a lag period between the time of a haemorrhage and the sub-sequent response of the absorptive mechanism. This might be due to the fact that plasma iron kinetics are unchanged until 4–5 days after an acute episode of bleeding. In addition the cells involved require 1–2 days to move from the crypts to the absorptive portion of the villus. The amount of iron incorporated by the newly formed cells is thought to represent the base-line of inhibition or regulation of the absorptive mechanism. During the short life of the cell, varying amounts of iron are stored in the cell, thus adding to the inhibition of the mucosal cell transport system. The term "self inhibition" has been proposed in preference to the older term "mucosal block". Up to a certain point the amount of iron absorbed is regulated by the transport and storage capacity of the mucosal cells. In the event of iron overload, these mechanisms may be overwhelmed, as is probably the case in haemochromatosis.

IV. Role of Bacteria in Digestion and Absorption

In health the stomach when empty is almost sterile in man. Numerous bacteria are ingested with the food, but apart from acid-fast bacilli and spore-forming organisms they appear to be killed off rapidly. In normochylic subjects who have no detectable gastrointestinal disorder, the jejunum and the proximal ileum appear to be only sparsely and transiently populated with oral-type bacteria, enterobacteriaceae and enterococci (Kalser *et al.*, 1966; Bruusgaard *et al.*, 1968), while anaerobic micro-organisms are absent. In man, the terminal ileum represents a transitional zone that is often contaminated by back-wash from the ileum (Cregan and Hayword, 1953; Gorbach *et al.*, 1967).

Earlier studies of viable bacteria in the feces have chiefly dealt with the common Gram-negative enterobacteriaceae, the Gram-positive enterococci, aerobic spore-formers, and clostridia. After introduction of improved bacteriological techniques including anaerobic incubation it was shown that anaerobic lactobacilli of different species, and Gram-negative non-sporulating anaerobic *Bacteroides* constitute the major species of colonic ecology in man (Dubos *et al.*, 1967). Numerous observations indicate that the gastrointestinal bacterial flora generally remains fairly constant. Occasionally, however, this flora may be altered rapidly by environmental influences.

After Pasteur's demonstration of the microbial nature of fermentation it became widely accepted that the indigenous intestinal flora was essential for digestion and consequently for the life of the host. On the contrary, Metchnikoff suspected the intestinal flora of being noxious for the host. Based upon assumptions which were largely unconfirmed, he came to believe that many geriatric ailments were caused by toxic products arising from intestinal fermentation. Present-day interest in the flora of the gastrointestinal tract has developed partly from observations made with broad-spectrum antibiotics and partly from investigations of germ-free animals.

Under certain conditions, the administration of antibiotics promotes growth of domestic animals and occasionally of man (Donaldson, 1964). It is well established that various nutrients can be destroyed (ascorbic acid, folic acid), metabolized (choline) or consumed (vitamin B_{12}) by many intestinal microorganisms. On the other hand, a number of intestinal bacteria are able to synthetize, for example, most vitamins of the B-complex, folic acid and vitamin K. In ruminants and in rats (in association with reinfection), nutrients synthetized by gastric and intestinal bacteria are unquestionably of importance. In such animals it is conceivable that antibiotics may influence favourably nutrition and growth. In man, however, there is little evidence of a significant bacterial flora in the small intestine and in all probability he will never benefit nutritionally from bacterially produced materials. Accordingly, a possible growth-promoting effect of antibiotics in man may rather be attributed to a reduced incidence of "sub-clinical" infections.

In the colon of man the bacteria metabolize a wide range of substances. Nitrogenous compounds are degraded into ammonia, some amino acids are decarboxylated to form biologically active amines such as tryptamine and histamine, and indole is produced by cleavage of the tryptophan side-chain. But none of these products are harmful to the intact host. In recent years interest has focused on the relationship between bacterial flora and bile acid metabolism (Donaldson, 1965). The ability to deconjugate bile salts is a property widely distributed amongst intestinal bacteria. Through bacterial action the unconjugated bile salts are further metabolically transformed into several compounds, and chiefly into deoxycholate. The physiological significance of bile salt deconjugation is still unsettled. It is possible that deconjugation facilitates bile salt reabsorption and so aids the important enterohepatic circulation of these compounds.

Studies of germ-free animals have provided striking results. Several independent lines of evidence indicate that the indigenous bacterial population exerts morphogenic effects that are essential for adequate histologic development of the gastrointestinal tract (Dubos et al., 1967). Conspicuous is the caecal enlargement in germ-free rats and mice. Simultaneously the small intestinal wall tends to remain almost in its prenatal state. The villi are thin, slender and relatively scarce, thus reducing the absorptive surface of the gut. The crypt glands are lined by a high proportion of markedly distended goblet cells, and the mucosa is characterized by an almost complete lack of inflammatory cells including the usual plasma cells which produce γ_1A-immunoglobulin. Of particular interest is the fact that germ-free animals are extremely susceptible to infection. In contrast, it is difficult and often almost impossible to establish new bacterial species in the gastrointestinal tract of normal adult animals. Also the intestinal flora in man appears to be an important link between natural resistance and intestinal pathogens.

One of the more intriguing features of the small intestine is its ability to limit bacterial invasion. At present there is no known substance originating in the intestinal mucosa that has unequivocally been shown to be a potent bacterial inhibitor. The possibility of bacteriophagic activity has been dismissed. From an investigation of 103 subjects it was concluded that normal gastric acid production is the major factor preventing unlimited bacterial growth in the small intestine (Bruusgaard *et al.*, 1968). Besides, it is quite possible that the normal small gut motor activity may be of significance. At any rate, humans with diseases of the small intestine in which hypomotility is likely may sometimes benefit from antibiotic therapy, suggesting that an abnormal bacterial flora contributes to the illness.

V. Patho-physiology of Digestion and Absorption

A. *Postgastrectomy malabsorption*

Metabolic and nutritional disorders may follow gastric surgery because of poor dietary habits which are usually combined with a reduced intake of food, and because of malabsorption. A large proportion of these patients are not given adequate dietary advice post-operatively. Often the instructions are limited to such terms as: "eat what you like", "eat as usual", or "eat the food that agrees with you". Many peptic ulcer patients may be inclined post-operatively to adhere to their previous diets. Frequently these diets are too rich in fat and consequently rather poor in essential elements such as protein and iron. Furthermore, even a diet normally considered sufficient may prove inadequate if the food intake is too small because of a reduced gastric reservoir or different types of postprandial dyspepsia. Possible malabsorption will, of course, accentuate the ill-effects of malnutrition.

Total gastrectomy is usually followed by severe steatorrhoea (Roth *et al.*, 1956). However, this view has not been substantiated. Some workers think that there is virtually no correlation between the extent of gastric resection and the degree of steatorrhoea. It is the authors' personal experience that there is no significant difference in the degree of malabsorption seen in these patients regardless of whether they were subjected to total or to partial gastrectomy (Thaysen, 1967). Patients with normal faecal fat output on a fat intake of 80–100 g per day could be found in both groups. These findings seem to indicate that neither the possible emulsifying motor activity nor the reservoir function of the stomach are vital to normal intestinal fat uptake. Upon gastric resection the control of gastric emptying is often remarkably well maintained by the formation of some sort of "neopylorus" at the site of anastomosis as evidenced cinematoradiographically (Rasmussen, 1966).

Several mechanisms may either separately or jointly be responsible for the frequent occurrence of steatorrhoea after gastric surgery. *Gastro-colic fistula* has become a relatively rare condition with the introduction of surgical procedures which reduce the risk of stomal ulceration. *Rapid small intestinal transit* is commonly seen following any type of anastomotic operation. This phenomenon may result in poor mixing of chyme and digestive juices, but generally it does not interfere with intestinal absorptive capacity. As a rule the *exocrine secretory capacity of the pancreas* is maintained to a degree sufficient for adequate digestion even if for example peptic ulcers or abdominal surgery should cause injury to this organ. Gastric surgery may cause a *reduced activation of pancreatic exocrine secretion*. This could be the result of a decrease in gastric acid production, a loss of normal gastric distention, a loss of nervous secretory control after vagotomy, or gastrojejunostomy with by-pass of the duodenum with its high content of pancreatic prophormones. Nevertheless, a significant decrease in pancreatic response to food is rare. *Defective coordination of stimuli to secretion of bile and pancreatic juice* is a common sequel to gastrojejunal anastomosis. Only if there is a pronounced delay in duodenal transit will the consequent inadequate mixing of chyme and digestive juices cause significant maldigestion (Lundh, 1958). Last, but not least, steatorrhoea may be induced by *abnormal bacterial growth in the proximal small gut* and especially in the afferent duodenal loop (Goldstein *et al.*, 1961; Thaysen, 1963). It is quite possible that this phenomenon represents the primary cause of steatorrhoea in patients subjected to gastric surgery, and in particular, gastrojejunostomy (Thaysen, 1966).

Usually the loss of calories by steatorrhoea is insignificant and to most patients this symptom does not present any major inconvenience. As appears from the survey, steatorrhoea is chiefly a complication following gastrojejunostomy and after such intervention fat malabsorption may occasionally be severe.

An abnormal faecal loss of protein is quantitatively small in the comparatively few patients in whom it is detected. Should hypoproteinemia develop, it then usually reflects inadequate dietary intake. As a rule, intestinal uptake of carbohydrates is not significantly reduced.

After gastric surgery a progressive fall in haemoglobin and serum iron is observed in many of these patients and especially in fertile women (Baird *et al.*, 1959). This is particularly true of patients with a duodenal by-pass, who show impaired utilization of iron derived from food, and who often have below average dietary intake of iron. Their anaemia responds adequately to iron-containing haematinics.

Megaloblastic anaemia may sometimes follow partial gastrectomy, and in particular, after a Billroth II-type of operation. As a rule, the anaemia is due to deficiency of vitamin B_{12} and not folic acid (Lous and Schwartz, 1959). Recent studies have disclosed that vitamin B_{12} absorption was impaired in 14–40% of patients with a Billroth II-type operation (Deller and Witts, 1962; Thaysen, 1966). This disturbance is due to loss of intrinsic factor activity or to abnormal bacterial growth in the proximal part of the small gut. The atrophic gastritis responsible for inadequate production of intrinsic factor is in all probability usually secondary to gastric surgery. That is, it is brought about by abnormal reflux of intestinal contents into the stomach, and by the frequent occurrence of sideropenia.

It has been proposed that gastric resection is the most frequent cause of osteomalacia in Europe. The statistics, however, are conflicting, and variations in technique and in selection of patients may explain the apparently variable results (Deller *et al.*, 1964; Morgan *et al.*, 1965; Deller, 1966).

Finally, the possibility should be borne in mind that gastrectomy may unmask a latent absorptive defect such as coeliac disease or lactase deficiency.

B. *Malabsorption based on pancreatic dysfunction*

From what has already been said it is evident that the various pancreatic enzymes play an important role in the digestion of carbohydrate, protein and fat. Hence the absence or presence of low amounts of these enzymes may greatly impair the utilization of food constituents. However, because of the great reserve capacity of the pancreas, malabsorption as measured in terms of fat excretion in the stool does not appear until these enzymes are reduced to 10–15% of control levels.

Pancreatic malfunction is found in various clinical entities such as protein malnutrition, mucoviscidosis (cystic fibrosis of the pancreas), congenital defect of enzyme formation, pancreatitis and cancer of the pancreas.

1. *Protein malabsorption*

Since normally the pancreas has a very high protein turnover, its normal function depends upon the adequate supply of exogenous protein. It has consistently been found that patients with protein-caloric deficiency (kwashiorkor) have pancreatic atrophy and low amounts of pancreatic enzymes (for ref. see Viteri *et al.*, 1964). Similarly, patients with enterogenic malabsorption may have more or less impaired function of the pancreas.

2. *Mucoviscidosis (cystic fibrosis of the pancreas)*

This disease is one of the most common inborn errors of metabolism and is an inherited generalized disease starting in infancy or childhood. The nature of the basic defect in this disorder is unknown. Most of the exocrine glands are affected and about 85–90% of the patients have pancreatic malfunction. In the pancreas the viscid secretion obstructs the ducts, thereby giving pancreatic fibrosis and achylia with resulting malabsorption. However, the chief complication is pulmonary involvement which accounts for the high rate of mortality of these patients (for ref. see Rossi and Stoll, 1967).

3. *Congenital defect in enzyme formation*

In pancreatic deficiency all the enzymes appear to be decreased in parallel fashion. In recent years, however, a few patients with congenital selective lipase deficiency (Rey *et al.*, 1966) and trypsinogen deficiency (Townes *et al.*, 1967) have been reported.

4. *Pancreatitis*

Acute pancreatitis often results in impairment of the pancreatic exocrine and endocrine functions. Usually the dysfunction is temporary, but it may also become permanent. Malabsorption is rare, and at all events this feature is trifling in comparison with the usual dramatic features of acute pancreatitis.

Irrespective of the many different clinical patterns of behaviour, chronic pancreatitis is usually accompanied by malabsorption and diabetes. Steatorrhoea occurs when less than 15% of the pancreatic exocrine function is maintained. Generally, the diabetes is mild, but owing to simultaneous reduction in glucagon production these patients are very sensitive to insulin.

Although the role of the pancreas in the regulation of iron absorption has been investigated rather extensively, it has been pointed out that the evidence for this in both health and disease is inadequate (Murray and Stein, 1966).

5. *Cancer of the pancreas*

Decreased pancreatic function in cancer of the pancreas probably implies obstruction of the secretory ducts. Nevertheless, 25% of patients with cancer of the head of the pancreas show normal pancreatic secretory response (Thaysen *et al.*, 1964; Worning *et al.*, 1968). Malabsorption probably occurs in about 50% of these patients, but steatorrhoea is not an important feature in the diagnosis of the tumour.

Gregory *et al.* (1967) have shown that the Zollinger-Ellison-Ström syndrome is the result of an abnormal production of gastrin by the pancreatic islet cell tissue. Besides severe ulcer disease, this syndrome is commonly associated with steatorrhoea and diarrhoea. The pancreatic exocrine function is maintained, but owing to excessive hyperchlorhydria the duodenal pH is low. This increases the partition coefficient of fatty acids in favour of the oil phase. Simultaneously, the activity of the pancreatic enzymes is abolished. It should be emphasized that the diarrhoea may cease temporarily if the gastric contents are withdrawn continuously for 12 to 24 hr. Hence, the abnormal production of gastrin cannot be regarded as chiefly responsible for this symptom.

C. *Malabsorption based on bile salt deficiency*

The malabsorption caused by a shortage of bile salts is limited strictly to a deficient uptake of lipid material. Simultaneously, however, some of the disorders responsible for this shortage may independently curtail the uptake of other materials as well.

Many patients with acute and especially chronic hepatocellular damage excrete large amounts of fat in their faeces. Generally this symptom, which is overshadowed by the other features of hepatic injury, has not hitherto been the object of many investigations. Some studies have revealed an isolated disturbance in fat uptake, suggesting a deficiency in bile salts (Oberhausen *et al.*, 1962; Summerskill and Moertel, 1962; Talley *et al.*, 1964). This shortage has been ascribed to failure in hepatic re-excretion of bile salts (Hofmann, 1966). Another possibility is reduced hepatic capacity for cholesterol conversion into bile acids. Both of these suggestions, however, have yet to be verified.

In patients with biliary obstruction the diversion of bile salts from the intestinal lumen results in marked steatorrhoea. The same applies of course to patients who have biliary fistulas. Usually, the bile salt diversion does not last long enough to create serious nutritional disturbances. But a deficiency of vitamin K which may rapidly lead to a haemorrhagic state is corrected by parenteral administration of the vitamin.

In recent years attention has been drawn to the syndrome of interrupted enterohepatic bile salt circulation which has been largely demonstrated in patients with ileal resections (Hofmann, 1967). The fully developed syndrome is characterized by ileal pathology, steatorrhoea, diarrhoea and an excessive loss of bile salts.

Ileal reabsorption of bile salts (in the dog) was first demonstrated 90 years ago (von Tappeiner, 1878). In 1936 the biological significance of this phenomenon which allows bile salts to remain in the proximal portion of the small gut where fat absorption is maximal became self-evident (Frölicher, 1936). As pointed out earlier, the total body bile salt pool in man is about three grams, the daily intestinal turnover 18 g, and the intestinal reabsorption 97%. Normally faecal excretion equals hepatic synthesis which is approximately 200–300 mg per day. Since the human liver can increase its rate of synthesis only four- to six-fold, it cannot compensate for faecal bile salt losses in excess of 2–3 g per day (Lack and Weiner, 1967).

Tracer studies have shown a greatly shortened half-life of radioactive bile salts administered to ileectomized patients (Austad *et al.*, 1967). Furthermore, upon cholecystokinin stimulation of the gallbladder, deoxycholate concentration was found to be very low in the jejunum of patients with ileal resections (Thaysen *et al.*, 1968). The same applies, but to a smaller degree, in patients with terminal ileitis. By inference these findings possibly suggest that the concentration of all bile salts is very low in the proximal part of the small bowel of these patients. This agrees well with present knowledge of bile salt kinetics which suggests that even a partial block of the entero-hepatic circuit leads to a decrease in luminal bile salt concentration below that critical for micelle formation.

It has been proposed that inefficient ileal bile salt reabsorption permits greater quantities of these substances to enter the colon where they could act as cathartics (Hofmann, 1967). This risk has probably been somewhat over-estimated. In a state of equilibrium faecal bile salt excretion will at most equal maximum hepatic synthesis which is of the order of 3 g per day as opposed to 0·3 g normally. In ileectomized patients a possible severe diarrhoea is more likely to be due to steatorrhoea or occasionally to magnesium deficiency.

A special type of bile salt deficiency is probably related to bacterial over-growth in the proximal part of the small gut. As emphasized elsewhere, abundant bacterial growth in this part of the gut may prematurely convert the usual conjugated bile salts into compounds that assist fat absorption less efficiently. Furthermore, deconjugation may result in premature reabsorp-tion of free bile salts from the jejunum.

For therapeutic use different preparations of ox bile extracts are com-mercially available. Several samples are less satisfactory since they are decomposed through bacterial action during collection. The usual dose recommended of 0·5 g three times a day is no doubt insufficient to ensure adequate micelle formation. Whenever bile shortage is pronounced, a daily dose of about 10 g would probably be more reasonable.

In patients with chronic parenchymatous disorders of the liver and with biliary obstruction, orally administered bile salts may increase the blood level of these salts. This treatment is therefore inadvisable. If necessary, the fat-soluble vitamins can be administered parenterally. It is still doubtful whether such patients benefit from a medium chain triglyceride-(MCT)-diet. In patients with external biliary fistulas it is easy to readminister the bile excreted via oral tube feeding.

In the syndrome of interrupted enterohepatic circuit, oral replacement therapy with bile salts further increases the amount of these salts in the colon. In spite of the obvious risk of aggravating the diarrhoea, this treatment has now and then been helpful. Usually, however, therapeutic trials with an MCT-diet are far more successful (Thaysen et al., 1968), but to many patients the diarrhoea and steatorrhoea do not represent any major incon-venience. It is also important to bear in mind that most of these patients require parenteral administration of vitamin B_{12}.

D. *Malabsorption based on dysfunction of the small intestine*

Broadly speaking, absorption is related to: (1) intestinal motility, (2) area of absorptive surface, (3) activity of the absorptive cells, and (4) vascular drainage of the intestine.

1. *Intestinal motility*

In animals with intestinal paralysis produced by anticholinergic drugs and in man with adynamic ileus, absorption is seriously impaired. An outstanding feature of this disturbance is the accumulation of water and electrolytes in the gut. This is probably due to decreased absorption (outflux), and also to increased secretion (influx). Moreover, several lines of evidence indicate that an atonic gut may promote rapid propulsion of intestinal contents, thereby reducing the time available for digestion and absorption (Ingelfinger and Abbott, 1940; Gregory, 1950; Dillard *et al.*, 1965).

In some malabsorption syndromes disturbances in small bowel motility may result in intestinal stasis. This may probably interfere with absorption. Intestinal stasis also promotes secondary proliferation of bacteria that may cause malabsorption. In coeliac disease the dilated atonic loops of small intestine and the relatively slow basic electric rhythm (Christensen *et al.*, 1966) indicate deranged intestinal motility that is perhaps gluten-induced. Severe diabetes is occasionally associated with chronic diarrhoea and steatorrhoea. Typically there is gastric dilatation with delayed emptying and prolonged transit through the small gut (Katz and Spiro, 1966). Mucosal biopsies have shown no abnormalities, but the impaired motility is probably somehow related to a deficient microcirculation. Intestinal scleroderma is often accompanied by marked malabsorption that is likely to be due to altered motility (Horswell *et al.*, 1961). In this disorder the patchy depositions of collagenous fibrous tissue involve all layers of the intestinal wall except the mucosa. The muscular layers also show variable atrophy. Severe starvation may result in hunger diarrhoea and probably in malabsorption as well. All layers of the intestinal wall are atrophic and transit through the small bowel is prolonged (Thaysen and Thaysen, 1949*a, b*). It is likely that the diarrhoea and malabsorption are related to alterations in small intestinal motility, although other factors such as decreased activity of the absorptive cells and pancreatic insufficiency should be considered. Severe malnutrition due to malabsorption may of course aggravate digestive and absorptive functions.

It has been repeatedly suggested that digestion and absorption may be impaired as a result of intestinal hypermotility with hasty propulsion of chyme. This view does not apply to an intact gastrointestinal tract. For instance, the functional diarrhoeas are never associated with malabsorption, even if radiological studies often reveal extreme hypermotility and very rapid transit of barium (Kalser *et al.*, 1956). Provided, however, that digestion or absorption is already impaired, a reduced transit time will frequently cause an additional aggravation of malabsorption.

2. *Area of absorptive surface*

The severity of malabsorption after small bowel resection (or by-pass) correlates roughly with the extent and site of resection, and with the state of health of the remaining intestine. Furthermore, the ileocaecal valve is an important factor in determining prognosis of the patient following massive resection (Kalser *et al.*, 1960). Loss of the valve leads to marked acceleration in the transit time.

Resection of half of the proximal or middle part of the small gut does not interfere in a significant way with nutrition. Removal of the distal ileum requires parenteral substitution therapy with vitamin B_{12}. Massive small gut resection, i.e. removal of more than two-thirds of the small intestine, can impair the absorption of virtually all food constituents, thus leading to widespread metabolic disturbances. Factors causing steatorrhoea after extensive resection include decreased absorptive surface area and decreased transit time; and after distal resection, deficient bile salt recirculation. Gradual failure of pancreatic function, possibly due to protein depletion, may contribute to the steatorrhoea. As a rule, sugar malabsorption does not cause diarrhoea in adult man since the carbohydrates are consumed by bacteria in the colon. Concomitant protein depletion is the result not only of impaired absorption, but also of increased catabolism due to caloric deficiency. Occasionally there is delayed diuresis, even after the intravenous administration of fluids. This and nocturia have been attributed to undernutrition (Thaysen and Thaysen, 1949a, b; Jackson, 1958). Potassium malabsorption with hypokalaemic nephropathy could account for this phenomenon. Since magnesium is a necessary activator of the Na^+-K^+-ATPase, depletion of this cation may impair the uptake of many actively absorbed substances including calcium and probably potassium. Magnesium depletion may aggravate the steatorrhoea (Fletcher *et al.*, 1960) and may also lead to fatal epileptiform seizures. It should be emphasized that a normal serum magnesium does not necessarily exclude magnesium deficiency (Opie *et al.*, 1964). Striking improvement of the patient's condition may accompany magnesium repletion, and it is perhaps advisable to administer magnesium to all patients with extensive small gut resection.

After extensive small gut resection compensatory changes may occur in the remaining intestine (Porus, 1965). An intriguing problem is the increased gastric acid production occasionally demonstrated after such resections (Frederik *et al.*, 1965).

3. *Activity of the absorptive cells*

Impaired activity of the intestinal absorptive cells occurs in a wide variety of diseases the majority of which are hereditary in origin. Some of the disorders are characterized by a general decrease in the absorptive capacity whereas in others the absorptive defect is limited to either a specific group of substances or to single substances.

a. *General defects*

Coeliac disease or gluten-induced enteropathy appears to be genetically determined (Thaysen, 1935; MacDonald *et al.*, 1965). It occurs in infantile and adult forms that seem identical (Thaysen, 1932). The typical histopathological changes (Rubin and Dobbins, 1965) involve predominantly the proximal portion of the small intestine. These changes are apparently due to a direct noxious effect of gluten since they may be reversed by a strict gluten-free diet. Though a relationship between gluten and an immunological mechanism has been suspected (Malik *et al.*, 1964), neither immunoglobulins reacting with gliadin nor complement-fixing immune complexes have so far been identified in the jejunal mucosa (Rubin *et al.*, 1965). The noxious factor present in gluten resists digestion with pepsin and trypsin, and may therefore be a peptide. Upon further hydrolysis into amino acids, gluten becomes inactive.

In the affected absorptive cells all biochemical functions are probably seriously impaired. This presumption is mainly based upon indirect evidence. Decreased production of dipeptidases and disaccharidases has been shown to occur in the affected cells. The usual site of pathological changes in coeliac disease generally resembles that accompanying resection of the proximal part of the small gut. This defect may in particular affect the transport of substances such as folate, vitamin D, and iron all of which are absorbed with some difficulty by the intact gut. However, the uptake of low molecular weight substances that diffuse readily may remain normal. Together with steatorrhoea, a flat glucose tolerance curve and delayed water diuresis may be characteristic features in coeliac disease. Hypoproteinaemia, which is rare, may occur in association with a secondary protein-losing enteropathy.

The distal part of the small intestine is seldom affected. Customarily, the function of this part of the intestine is determined by measuring the absorption of vitamin B_{12}, but in coeliac disease the results of this assay can be misleading on account of bacterial overgrowth in the small bowel. On a gluten-free diet all biochemical abnormalities seem to disappear long before there is any improvement in the histopathological changes.

Presumably, intestinal suction biopsy is the most sensitive method in the diagnosis of coeliac disease (Rubin and Dobbins, 1965). The claim that typical lesions may appear in patients who fail to respond to a gluten-free diet requires more extensive documentation. Some of these patients may, however, suffer from various dysgammaglubulinaemias. This is true when there is "villous atrophy" and a "sprue-like syndrome" in adult patients with acquired hypo-γ-globulinaemia (McCarthy *et al.*, 1965), and in patients with IgA deficiency due to a lack of IgA-producing cells in the lamina propria of the gut (Crabbé and Heremans, 1966). Diarrhoea and occasional steatorrhoea may also accompany nodular lymphoid hyperplasia of the small intestine (Hermans *et al.*, 1966). This syndrome is further characterized by virtual absence of IgA and IgM immunoglobulins. The histopathology of the small bowel mucosa is, however, distinct from that observed in coeliac disease. In the dysgammaglobulinaemias the malabsorption is perhaps related to chronic enteric infection with secondary damage to the absorptive cells. *Giardia lamblia* is seen rather frequently and eradication of this parasite has often led to control of the diarrhoea and steatorrhoea (James, 1968). In this context it should be mentioned that the immunoglobulin-producing cells develop poorly in the intestinal mucosa of germ-free animals.

In severe starvation the function of the absorptive cells may be impaired, as indicated by decreased absorption of D-xylose, and low disaccharidase activities (Thaysen and Thaysen, 1952).

b. Specific defects

In *a-β-lipoproteinaemia* (acanthocytosis) the lack of β-lipoproteins leads to a standstill in the formation of chylomicrons (Isselbacher *et al.*, 1964). Indeed, electron microscopic studies show no chylomicrons beyond the basement membrane (Dobbins, 1966). This disorder not only results in accumulation of triglycerides in the absorptive cells, but also in steatorrhoea.

An isolated deficiency of the enzymes that promote re-esterification of absorbed fatty acids has not been described, but some evidence suggests that this process is somehow stimulated by bile salts (Dawson and Isselbacher, 1960).

In recent years there has been an increasing interest in the study of *deranged absorption of amino acids*. A general decrease in amino acid uptake has been found in coeliac disease and Whipple's disease (Brice *et al.*, 1965). The defect is probably secondary to damage of the absorptive cells affected by these diseases.

In some inborn errors of metabolism the uptake of various amino acids is specifically impaired. Cystinuria is the only one of these disorders that is not so rare. It is characterized by renal tubular and intestinal defects in the transport of dibasic amino acids and the neutral amino acid, cystine (Milne, 1964). Cystine is transported by a specific mechanism that requires a disulphide grouping (Spencer *et al.*, 1965). The disorder may result in formation of urinary cystine stones. Patients with cystinuria are generally of shorter stature than normal. This feature may depend upon the extent of the malabsorption of the amino acids, notably arginine.

In Hartnup's disease the renal tubular and intestinal transport of many neutral amino acids is impaired (Milne, 1964). Malabsorption of tryptophane leading to decreased formation of nicotinamide, is probably responsible for the pellagra-like rash found in this disorder.

Isolated tryptophane malabsorption and hypercalcemia are not associated with amino-aciduria (Drummond *et al.*, 1964). Some evidence indicates a causal relationship between the defect in tryptophane transport and the disturbances in calcium and phosphate metabolism (Drummond and Michael, 1964).

The occurrence of isolated methionine malabsorption (Hooft *et al.*, 1964) suggests that this compound may under certain circumstances utilize a transport mechanism that is separate from that of the other neutral amino acids.

Disaccharide intolerance

When one or more of the small-intestinal disaccharidases are missing, the ingestion of moderate or large amounts of the corresponding disaccharide leads to abdominal pain and diarrhoea. In infants with such defects, the stools contain large amounts of malabsorbed sugars, but in adults the sugars are consumed by the bacteria of the large intestine. The diagnosis is established by oral tolerance tests with disaccharide solutions (giving a flat blood glucose curve and provoking abdominal symptoms) and by enzyme activity analysis of small intestinal mucosa obtained by peroral biopsy. (For references see Dahlqvist, 1966, 1967.)

The enzyme deficiency can be either congenital or acquired. The following forms of disaccharide intolerance have been described.

Lactose intolerance

The brush border lactase is missing. This causes abdominal pain and diarrhoea with failure of the infant to gain weight properly. The symptoms start shortly after birth when milk feeding is introduced and disappear when milk is omitted from the diet (Holzel *et al.*, 1959).

Another form of lactose intolerance, "severe lactose intolerance", with lactosuria and general toxic effects of dietary lactose has been described (Holzel *et al.*, 1962). These patients have symptoms even after being given small doses of lactose. The biochemical background of "severe lactose intolerance" remains unknown.

Sucrose-isomaltose intolerance

In this disease two enzymes, namely sucrase (= maltase Ib) and iso-maltase (= maltase Ia) are missing (Auricchio *et al.*, 1963; Dahlqvist *et al.*, 1963). The symptoms do not appear until the infant receives a mixed diet containing sucrose and starch.

Maltose-sucrose-isomaltose intolerance

Thus far this defect has been described on a presumed congenital basis only in one patient (Weijers *et al.*, 1961).

Acquired non-specific disaccharide intolerance

In the acquired non-specific disaccharide intolerance all the small-intestinal disaccharidase activities are found to be low. This condition is seen secondarily in patients with small intestinal or generalized diseases, such as coeliac disease, enteritis, tropical sprue, severe protein deficiency (kwashiorkor), and others. Usually several other functions of the small intestine, for example monosaccharide absorption, are also impaired.

Acquired specific lactose intolerance

The most common form of disaccharide intolerance is the acquired specific lactose intolerance (Dahlqvist *et al.*, 1963; Haemmerli *et al.*, 1963; Dunphy *et al.*, 1965; Haemmerli *et al.*, 1965). The genesis of this disease is obscure. These patients have a history of normal feeding during infancy, but at some time in their adult life they lost their ability to tolerate milk. Analysis of the small intestinal mucosa of these patients reveals low lactase activity but normal activity of the other disaccharidases. Probably only lactase I is missing, and it is possible that in many of these patients all of the residual lactase activity in the mucosa is exerted by lactase II.

Glucose-galactose malabsorption

There also exists an inherited disease in which the glucose-galactose transport system of the small intestinal mucosa is malfunctioning (Lindquist and Meeuwisse, 1962; Laplane et al., 1962). These patients have diarrhoea, which fails to stop on the omission of all polysaccharides and disaccharides from the diet unless glucose and galactose are omitted and replaced by fructose. Most probably it is the glucose-galactose specific carrier in the mucosa which is affected in this disturbance (Meeuwisse and Dahlqvist, 1966; Eggermont and Loeb, 1966). The other functions of the mucosa are normal.

4. Vascular drainage of the intestine

Malabsorption is not a feature of portal hypertension per se. Mesenteric artery occlusion results almost invariably in extensive intestinal infarction, but it has almost never been established that "milder degrees" of vascular occlusive disease impair absorption. This is in accord with the fact that the superior mesenteric artery is not an end-artery but that it may behave as such when suddenly occluded.

The malabsorption following lymphatic obstruction is characterized by an impaired uptake of fat and frequently by a simultaneous intestinal loss of protein due to leakage of chyle into the gut. Generally, lymphatic obstruction is the result of either intestinal lymphangiectasia, Whipple's disease, or lymphomatous involvement of the gut (Jarnum, 1963).

Complete recovery from Whipple's disease may be achieved with tetracycline therapy (Trier et al., 1965). Some relief may be obtained from an MCT-diet in the other disorders just mentioned.

Protein-losing gastro-enteropathy may be associated with giant rugal hypertrophy of the stomach, and a wide variety of gastro-intestinal neoplastic diseases; and occasionally with coeliac disease.

E. Malabsorption following bacterial overgrowth in the small intestine

Excessive proliferation of bacteria within the small intestine may be the consequence of abnormalities which are known to be conducive to localized stasis, such as surgical blind loops, fistulas, strictures, enterostomies and diverticula of the small gut. Moreover, bacterial overgrowth is frequently associated with gastric achlorhydria or hypochlorhydria (Bruusgaard et al.,

1967), and it mainly consists of micro-organisms which can be classified under the genus *Enterobacteriaceae*. Less abundant are the enterococci whereas anaerobic bacteria are the exception.

The occurrence of a significant number of bacteria in the proximal gut may result in macrocytic anaemia due to vitamin B_{12} deficiency and in steatorrhoea. The modern concept is that vitamin B_{12} is unavailable for absorption because it is utilized by the micro-organisms contaminating the small bowel (Doig and Girdwood, 1960; Donaldson, 1962). And when adequate antibacterial therapy is instituted, normal absorption of B_{12} is restored.

Clinically, significant steatorrhoea occurs in approximately a third of patients with pathological proliferation of bacteria in the small gut (Badenoch, 1958). The steatorrhoea is corrected by antibiotics, but the exact relationship between the bacterial overgrowth and steatorrhoea has not yet been elucidated. Orally administered radioactive fats are absorbed poorly (Donaldson, 1963) and gas-chromatographic studies show that the fatty acids excreted are practically identical to those ingested (Thaysen, 1967). The intestinal absorptive capacity seems to be maintained, and there is experimental evidence to show that bacterial destruction of lipase is unlikely. Interest has thus centred on the conjugated bile salts, and it has been proposed that the abnormal bacterial population of the proximal part of the small intestine may prematurely de-conjugate these conjugates. Since free bile salts are less efficient at forming micelles, there is an obvious possibility that fat malabsorption may be the result of bacterial action on bile salts (Hofmann and Borgström, 1962). This is all the more interesting because bacteria are in a position to transform cholate into deoxycholate which *in vitro* inhibits intestinal re-esterification of fatty acids (Dawson and Isselbacher, 1960). In addition, free bile salts may be reabsorbed prematurely from the proximal small gut. Finally, there is some indication that fatty acids which are not absorbed may be hydroxylated by bacterial enzymes. These hydroxylated fatty acids are similar to the active principle of castor oil and may cause diarrhoea because of their irritative property.

References

Aikawa, J. K., Rhoades, E. L. and Gordon, G. S. (1958). *Proc. Soc. exp. Biol. Med.* **98**, 29-31.

Alcock, N. and McIntyre, J. (1960). *Biochem. J.* **76**, 19-20.

Alvarado, F. (1966). *Biochim. biophys. Acta* **112**, 292-306.

Andersson, S. and Grossman, M. I. (1964). *Gastroenterology* **48**, 449-462.

Andersson, S., Nilsson, G. and Uvnäs, B. (1965). *Acta physiol. scand.* **65**, 191-192.

Arnesjö, B., Barrowman, J. and Borgström, B. (1967). *Acta chem. scand.* **21**, 2897-2900.

Auricchio, S., Semenza, G. and Rubino, A. (1965). *Biochim. biophys. Acta* **96**, 498-507.

Auricchio, S., Dahlqvist, A., Mürset, G. and Prader, A. (1963). *J. Pediat.* **62**, 165-176.

Austad, W. J., Lack, L. and Tyor, M. P. (1967). *Gastroenterology* **52**, 638-646.
Badenoch, J. (1958). In *Modern Trends in Gastroenterology* (F. A. Jones, ed.), pp. 231-242. Hoeber, New York.
Baird, I. M., Blackburn, E. K. and Wilson, G. M. (1959). *Q. Jl Med.* **28**, 21-41.
Balint, J. A. and Hirschowitz, B. I. (1961). *New Engl. J. Med.* (1967). **265**, 631-633.
Blomstrand, R. (1967). U.S. Dept. of Health, Education and Welfare, P.H.S. publication No. 1742, pp. 99-123.
Booth, C. C. (1961). *Post-grad. med. J.* **37**, 725-739.
Borgström, B. (1957). *Scand. J. clin. Lab. Invest.* **9**, 226-228.
Borgström, B. (1964). *J. Lipid Res.* **5**, 522-531.
Borgström, B. (1967). *J. Lipid Res.* **8**, 598-608.
Borgström, B., Dahlqvist, A., Lundh, G. and Sjövall, J. (1957). *J. clin. Invest.* **36**, 1521-1536.
Bovey, F. A. and Yanari, S. S. (1960). In *The Enzymes* (P. D. Boyer, H. Lardy and K. Myrbäck, eds), Vol. 4, pp. 63-92. Academic Press, New York.
Brice, R. S., Owen, E. E. and Tyor, M. P. (1965). *Gastroenterology* **48**, 584-592.
Briscoe, A. M. and Ragan, C. (1965). *Am. J. clin. Nutr.* **16**, 281-286.
Bruusgaard, A., Thaysen, E. Hess and Bang, H. O. (1967). *Scand. J. clin. Lab. Invest.* **19** suppl. 100, 99.
Bruusgaard, A., Frederiksen, W. and Thaysen, E. Hess (1968). VIIIth International Congress of Gastroenterology, Prague, Czechoslovakia. (In the press.)
Burnstock, G., Holman, M. E. and Prosser, C. L. (1963). *Physiol. Rev.* **43**, 482-527.
Charlton, R. W., Jacobs, P., Torrance, J. D. and Bothwell, T. H. (1965). *J. clin. Invest.* **44**, 543-554.
Christensen, J., Clifton, J. A. and Schedl, H. P. (1966). *Gastroenterology* **51**, 200-206.
Clarkson, T. W., Cross, A. C. and Toole, S. R. (1961). *Am. J. Physiol.* **200**, 1233-1235.
Clarkson, T. W., Rothstein, A. and Cross, A. C. (1961). *Am. J. Physiol.* **200**, 781-788.
Code, C. F., Bass, P., McClary, G. B., Jr., Newnum, R. L. and Orvis, A. L. (1960). *Am. J. Physiol.* **199**, 281-288.
Conrad, M. E., Weintraub, L. R. and Crosby, W. H. (1964). *J. clin. Invest.* **43**, 963-974.
Conrad, M. E., Benjamin, B. J., Williams, H. L. and Foy, A. L. (1967). *Gastroenterology* **53**, 5-10.
Cook, J. D., Brown, G. M. and Valberg, L. S. (1964). *J. clin. Invest.* **43**, 1185-1191.
Cooperstein, I. L. and Brockman, S. K. (1959). *J. clin. Invest.* **38**, 435-442.
Crabbé, P. A. and Heremans, J. F. (1966). *Gut* **7**, 119-127.
Crane, R. K. (1962). *Fedn Proc. Fedn Am. Socs exp. Biol.* **21**, 891-895.
Crane, R. K. (1967). *Protoplasma* **63**, 36-40.
Crane, C. W. and Neuberger, A. (1960). *Biochem. J.* **74**, 313-323.
Cregan, J. and Hayword, N. J. (1953). *Br. med. J.* **1**, 1356-1359.
Dahlqvist, A. (1962). *J. clin. Invest.* **41**, 463-470.
Dahlqvist, A. (1964). In *Disorders due to Intestinal Defective Carbohydrate Digestion and Absorption* (P. Durand, ed.). Il Pensiero Scientifico, Rome.
Dahlqvist, A. (1966). *J. Am. med. Ass.* **195**, 225-227.
Dahlqvist, A. (1967a). *Am. J. clin. Nutr.* **20**, 81-88.
Dahlqvist, A. (1967b). *Bull. Soc. Chim. biol.* **49**, 1635-1646.
Dahlqvist, A. and Borgström, B. (1961). *Biochem. J.* **81**, 411-418.
Dahlqvist, A. and Telenius, U. (1969). *Biochem. J.* (In the press.)

Dahlqvist, A. and Thomson, D. L. (1963). *Biochem. J.* **89**, 272-277.
Dahlqvist, A., Auricchio, S., Semenza, G. and Prader, A. (1963). *J. clin. Invest.* **42**, 446-562.
Dahlqvist, A., Hammond, J. B., Crane, R. K., Dunphy, J. V. and Littman, A. (1963). *Gastroenterology* **45**, 488-491.
Dahlqvist, A., Lindquist, B. and Meeuwisse, G. (1967). *Nährung* **11**, 541-549.
Dam, H., Kruse, I., Kallehauge, H. E., Hartkopp, O. E. and M. Krogh Jensen (1966). *Scand. J. clin. Lab. Invest.* **18**, 385-404.
Dawson, A. M. and Isselbacher, K. J. (1960). *J. clin. Invest.* **39**, 730-740.
Deller, D. J. (1966). *Am. J. dig. Dis.* **11**, 10-19.
Deller, D. J. and Witts, L. J. (1962). *Q. Jl Med.* **31**, 71-88.
Deller, D. J., Begley, M. D., Edwards, R. G. and Addison, M. (1964). *Gut* **5**, 218-225.
Desnuelle, P. (1960*a*). In *The Enyzmes* (P. D. Boyer, H. Lardy and K. Myrbäck, eds), Vol. 4, pp. 119-132. Academic Press, New York.
Desnuelle, P. (1960*b*). In *The Enzymes* (P. D. Boyer, H. Lardy and K. Myrbäck, eds), Vol. **4**, pp. 93-118. Academic Press, New York.
Dillard, R. L., Eastman, H. and Fordtran, J. S. (1965). *Gastroenterology* **49**, 58-66.
Dobbins, W. O. (1966). *Gastroenterology* **50**, 195-210.
Doig, A. and Girdwood, R H. (1960). *Q. Jl Med.* **29**, 333-374.
Donaldson, R. M. Jr. (1962). *Gastroenterology* **43**, 271-281.
Donaldson, R. M. Jr. (1963). *Clin. Res.* **11**, 291.
Donaldson, R. M. Jr. (1964). *New Engl. J. Med.* **270**, 994-1001.
Donaldson, R. M. Jr. (1965). *J. clin. Invest.* **44**, 1815-1825.
Dowdle, E. B., Schachter, D. and Schenker, H. (1960). *Am. J. Physiol.* **198**, 609-613.
Drummond, K. N. and Michael, A. F. (1964). *Nature, Lond.* **201**, 1333-1334.
Drummond, K. N., Michael, A. F., Ulstrom, R. A. and Good, R. A. (1964). *Am. J. Med.* **37**, 920-948.
Dubos, R. J., Savage, D. C. and Schaedler, R. W. (1967). *Dis. Colon Rectum* **10**, 23-34.
Dunphy, J. V., Littman, A., Hammond, J. B., Forstner, G., Dahlqvist, A. and Crane, R. K. (1965). *Gastroenterology* **49**, 12-21.
Eggermont, E. and Loeb, H. (1966). *Lancet ii*, 343.
Farrar, J. T. and Zfass, A. M. (1967). *Gastroenterology* **52**, 1019-1037.
Fischer, R. B. (1967). *Br. med. Bull.* **23**, 241-246.
Fischer, J. M., Reis, C. and Taylor, K. B. (1966). *Lancet ii*, 88-89.
Fischer, E. H. and Stein, E. A. (1960). In *The Enzymes* (P. D. Boyer, H. Lardy and K. Myrbäck, eds), Vol. 4, 2nd ed., Academic Press, New York.
Fletcher, R. F., Henley, A. A., Sammons, H. G. and Squire, J. R. (1960). *Lancet i*, 522-525.
Fordtran, J. S. and Dietschy, J. M. (1966). *Gastroenterology* **50**, 263-285.
Frederik, P. L., Sizer, J. S. and Osborne, M. P. (1965). *New Engl. J. Med.* **272**, 509-514.
Frölicher, E. (1936). *Biochem. Z.* **283**, 273-279.
Gillespie, I. E. and Grossman, M. I. (1964). *Gut* **5**, 342-345.
Gitler, C. (1964). In *Mammalian Protein Metabolism* (H. N. Munro and J. B. Allison, eds), Vol. 1, pp. 35-69. Academic Press, New York.
Glass, G. B. J. (1963). *Physiol. Rev.* **43**, 529-549.
Goldstein, F., Wirts, C. W. and Kramer, S. (1961). *Gastroenterology* **40**, 47-54.
Gorbach, S. L., Plaut, A. G., Nahas, L., Weinstein, L., Spanknebel, G. and Levitan, R. (1967). *Gastroenterology* **53**, 856-867.
Granick, S. (1946). *J. biol. Chem.* **164**, 737-746.
Gregory, R. A. (1950). *J. Physiol., Lond.* **111**, 119-137.

Gregory, R. A. and Tracy, H. J. (1966). In *Gastrin Proceedings of a Conference* (M. J. Grossman, ed.), pp. 9-26. University of California Press, Los Angeles, San Francisco.

Gregory, R. A., Grossman, M. J., Tracy, H. J. and Bentley, P. H. (1967). *Lancet ii*, 543-544.

Grey, E. G. (1918). *Am. J. Physiol.* 45, 272-285.

Griffith, G. H., Owen, G. M., Campbell, P. H. and Schields, T. R. (1968). *Gastroenterology* 54, 1-7.

Haemmerli, U. P., Kistler, H. J., Ammann, R., Auricchio, S. and Prader, A. (1963). *Helv. med. Acta* 30, 693-705.

Haemmerli, U. P., Kistler, H., Ammann, R., Marthaler, T., Semenza, G., Auricchio, S. and Prader, A. (1965). *Am. J. Med.* 38, 7-30.

Hallberg, L. and Sölvell, L. (1960). *Acta med. Scand.* Suppl. 358, 19-42.

Heaney, R. P. and Skillmann, T. G. (1964). *J. Lab. clin. Med.* 64, 29-41.

Herbert, V. (1967). *Am. J. clin. Nutr.* 20, 562-569.

Herbert, V. (1968). *Gastroenterology* 54, 110-115.

Hermans, P. E., Huizenga, K. A., Hoffman, H. N., Brown, A. L. and Markowitz, H. (1966). *Am. J. Med.* 40, 78-89.

Hirsch, J., Ahrens, E. J., Jr. and Blankenhorn, D. H. (1956). *Gastroenterology* 31, 274-284.

Hoedemacker, P. J. (1965). Doctoral Thesis, University of Groningen, The Netherlands.

Hofmann, A. F. (1966). *Gastroenterology* 50, 56-64.

Hofmann, A. F. (1967). *Gastroenterology* 52, 752-757.

Hofmann, A. F. and Borgström, B. (1962). *Fedn Proc. Fedn Am. Socs exp. Biol.* 21, 43-50.

Hofmann, A. F. and Borgström, B. (1964). *J. clin. Invest.* 43, 247-257.

Hofmann, A. H. and Small, D. M. (1967). *A. Rev. Med.* 18, 333-376.

Holzel, A., Mereu, T. and Thomson, M. L. (1962). *Lancet ii*, 1346-1348.

Holzel, A., Schwarz, V. and Sutcliffe, K. W. (1959). *Lancet i*, 1126-1129.

Hooft, C., Timmermans, J., Snoeck, J., Antener, I., Qyaert, W. and Van den Hende, C. H. (1964). *Lancet ii*, 20.

Horswell, R. R., Hargrove, M. D., Jr., Peete, W. P. and Ruffin, J. M. (1961). *Gastroenterology* 40, 580-582.

Hunt, J. N. and Spurrell, W. R. (1951). *J. Physiol., Lond.* 113, 157-168.

Ingelfinger, F. J. and Abbott, W. O. (1940). *Am. J. dig. Dis.* 7, 468-474.

Isselbacher, K. J., Scheig, R., Plotkin, G. R. and Caulfield, J. B. (1964). *Medicine* 43, 347-361.

Jackson, W. P. N. (1958). In *Modern Trends in Gastroenterology* (F. Very Jones, ed.), p. 243. Butterworth & Co. Ltd., London.

James, W. P. T. (1968). *Lancet i*, 333-335.

Jarnum, S. (1963). In *Protein-losing Gastroenteropathy*, pp. 162-176. Blackwell, Oxford.

Johnson, C. F. (1967). *Science, N.Y.* 155, 1670-1672.

Johnston, J. M. (1968). In *Handbook of Physiology* (C. F. Code, ed.), Vol. III, Section 6: Alimentary Canal, pp. 1353-1375. American Physiological Society, Washington, D.C.

Jorpes, J. E. (1968). *Gastroenterology* 55, 157-167.

Jos, J., Frezal, J., Rey, J. and Lamy, M. (1967). *Nature, Lond.* 213, 516-518.

Josefsson, L. and Lindberg, T. (1967). *Acta chem. scand.* 21, 1965-1966.

Josefsson, L., Lindberg, T. and Öjesjö, L. (1968). *Scand. J. Gastroent.* 3, 207-210.

Kalser, M. H., Cohen, R., Arteaga, I., Yawn, E., Mayoral, L., Hoffert, W. R. and Frazier, D. (1966). *New Engl. J. Med.* 274, 500-505.

Kalser, M. H., Roth, J. L. A., Tumen, H. and Johnson, T. A. (1960). *Gastroenterology* 38, 605-615.

Kalser, M. H., Zion, D. E. and Bockus, H. L. (1956). *Gastroenterology* **31**, 629-646.

Katz, L. A. and Spiro, H. M. (1966). *New Engl. J. Med.* **275**, 1350-1361.

Koldovský, O., Heringová, A. and Jirsová, V. (1967). *Biologia Neonat.* **10**, 241-253.

Koldovský, O., Noack, R., Schenk, G., Jirsová, V., Heringová, A., Branã, H., Chytil, F. and Fridrich, M. (1965). *Biochem. J.* **96**, 492-494.

Lack, L. and Weiner, I. M. (1967). *Gastroenterology* **52**, 282-287.

de Laey, P. (1966). *Nature, Lond.* **212**, 78-79.

Laplane, R., Polonovski, C., Etienne, M., Debray, P., Lods, J.-C. and Pissarro, B. (1962). *Archs fr. Pédiat.* **19**, 895-944.

Levitan, R. and Ingelfinger, F. J. (1965). *J. clin. Invest.* **44**, 801-808.

Lindberg, T. (1967). *Acta physiol. scand.* **69**, Suppl. 285, pp. 1-38.

Lindquist, B. and Meeuwisse, G. (1962). *Acta paediat., Stockh.* **51**, 674-685.

Lous, P. and Schwartz, M. (1959). *Acta med. scand.* **164**, 407-417.

Lundh, G. (1958). *Acta chir. scand.* Suppl. **231**.

MacDonald, W. C., Dobbins, W. O. and Rubin, C. E. (1965). *New Engl. J. Med.* **272**, 448-456.

MacIntyre, J. (1963). *J. chron. Dis.* **16**, 201-214.

MacIntyre, I., Hanna, S., Booth, C. C. and Read, A. E. (1961). *Clin. Sci.* **20**, 297-305.

MacIntyre, D. R., Sullivan, L. W., Jeffries, G. H. and Silver, R. H. (1965). *New Engl. J. Med.* **272**, 981-986.

Makhlouf, G. M., McManus, J. P. A. and Card, W. J. (1967). In *Gastric Secretion, Mechanisms and Control* (T. K. Shnitka, J. A. L. Gilbert, R. C. Harrison, eds), pp. 329-345. Pergamon Press, Oxford.

Malik, G. B., Watson, W. C., Murray, D. and Cruikshank, B. (1964). *Lancet i*, 1127-1129.

Manis, J. and Schachter, D. (1964). *Am. J. Physiol.* **207**, 893-900.

Matthews, D. M. and Laster, L. (1965). *Gut* **6**, 411-426.

McCarthy, C. F., Austad, W. J. and Read, A. E. (1965). *Am. J. dig. Dis.* **10**, 945-957.

McGuigan, J. E. (1968). *Gastroenterology* **55**, 315-327.

Meeuwisse, G. and Dahlqvist, A. (1966). *Lancet ii*, 858.

Meintzer, R. B. and Steenbock, H. (1955). *J. Nutr.* **56**, 285-294.

Miller, D. and Crane, R. K. (1961). *Biochim. biophys. Acta* **52**, 281-293.

Milne, M. D. (1964). *Br. med. J.* **32**, 327-336.

Morgan, D. B., Paterson, C. R., Woods, C. G., Pulvertaft, C. N. and Fourman, P. (1965). *Lancet ii*, 1085-1088.

Morgan, R. G. H., Barrowman, J., Filipek-Wender, H. and Borgström, B. (1967). *Biochim. biophys. Acta* **146**, 314-316.

Morgan *et al.* (1968). *Biochim. biophys. Acta* **167**, 355-366.

Murray, J. G. (1966). In *Gastric Secretion, Mechanisms and Control* (T. K. Shnitka, J. A. L. Gilbert and R. C. Harrison, eds), pp. 78-81. Pergamon Press, Oxford.

Murray, M. J. and Stein, N. (1966). *Gastroenterology* **51**, 694-700.

Mutt, V. and Jorpes, E. (1968). *Europ. J. Biochem.* **6**, 156-162.

Nasset, E. S. (1964). In *The Role of the Gastrointestinal Tract in Protein Metabolism* (H. N. Munro, ed.), pp. 83-96. Blackwell, Oxford.

Neurath, H. (1960). In *The Enzymes* (P. D. Boyer, H. Lardy and K. Myrbäck, eds), Vol. 4, pp. 11-36. Academic Press, New York.

Newey, H. and Smyth, D. H. (1960). *J. Physiol., Lond.* **152**, 70P-71P.

Nordin, B. E. C. (1968). *Gastroenterology* **54**, 294-301.

Nordin, B. E. C. and Smith, D. A. (1965). *Diagnostic Procedures in Disorders of Calcium Metabolism.* J. & A. Churchill Ltd., London.

Nordström, C., Dahlqvist, A. and Josefsson, L. (1967). *J. Histochem. Cytochem.* **15**, 713-721.

Oberhausen, E., Mate, H. O., Salinas, A. and Baraona, E. (1962). *Am. J. dig. Dis.* **7**, 699-711.

Okuda, K. and Sasayama, K. (1965). *Proc. Soc. exp. Biol. Med.* **120**, 17-20.

Olbe, L. (1966). In *Gastric Secretion, Mechanisms and Control* (T. K. Shnitka, J. A. L. Gilbert and R. C. Harrison, eds), pp. 83-90. Pergamon Press, Oxford.

Opie, L. H., Hunt, Barbara G. and Finlay, J. M. (1964). *Gastroenterology* **47**, 415-420.

Passaro, E. P., Jr. and Grossman, M. J. (1964). *Am. J. Physiol.* **206**, 1068-1076.

Petersen, V. P. (1963). *Acta med. scand.* **174**, 595-604.

Playoust, M. R. and Isselbacher, K. J. (1964). *J. clin. Invest.* **43**, 878-885.

Porus, R. L. (1965). *Gastroenterology* **48**, 753-757.

Rasmussen, Th. (1966). Personal communication.

Rey, J., Frezal, J., Royer, P. and Lamy, M. (1966). *Archs fr. Pèdiat.* **23**, 5-14.

Rosenberg, A. H., Lau, K-S. and Herbert, V. (1965). *Clin. Res.* **13**, 281.

Rossi, E. and Stoll, E. (eds). *Cystic fibrosis.* Proc. IVth International Conference on Cystic Fibrosis of the Pancreas (Mucoviscidosis). Part I. (1967.) S. Karger, Basel.

Roth, J. L. A., Becker, I. M., Vine, S. and Bockus, H. L. (1956). *J. Am. med. Ass.* **161**, 794-800.

Rubin, C. E. and Dobbins, W. O. (1965). *Gastroenterology* **49**, 676-697.

Rubin, W., Fauci, A. S., Sleisenger, M. H. and Jeffries, G. H. (1965). *J. clin. Invest.* **44**, 475-485.

Ryle, A. P. (1964). In *The Role of the Gastrointestinal Tract in Protein Metabolism* (H. N. Munro, ed.), pp. 25-40. Blackwell, Oxford.

Sarda, L. and Desnuelle, P. (1958). *Biochim. biophys. Acta* **30**, 513-521.

Saunders, S. J. and Isselbacher, K. J. (1966). *Gastroenterology* **50**, 586-595.

Schachter, D. and Rosen, S. M. (1959). *Am. J. Physiol.* **196**, 357-362.

Schachter, D., Dowdle, E. B. and Schenker, H. (1960). *Am. J. Physiol.* **198**, 263-268.

Schofield, B. (1960). *Gastroenterology* **39**, 511-513.

Schultz, S. G. and Zalusky, R. (1965). *Nature, Lond.* **205**, 292-294.

Schultz, S. G., Zalusky, R. and Gass, A. E., Jr. (1964). *J. gen. Physiol.* **48**, 375-378.

Semenza, G. (1967). *Protides biol. Fluids.* **15**, 201-208.

Semenza, G. and Kolínská, J. (1967). *Protides biol. Fluids* **15**, 581-583.

Semenza, G., Auricchio, S. and Rubino, A. (1965). *Biochim. biophys. Acta* **96**, 487-497.

Skou, J. C. (1965). *Physiol. Rev.* **45**, 596-617.

Smith, E. L. (1960). In *The Enzymes* (P. D. Boyer, H. Lardy and K. Myrbäck, eds), Vol. 4, pp. 1-10. Academic Press, New York.

Smith, E. L. and Hill, R. L. (1960). In *The Enzymes* (P. D. Boyer, H. Lardy and K. Myrbäck, eds), Vol. 4, pp. 37-62. Academic Press, New York.

Smith, R. H. and McAllan, A. B. (1966). *Br. J. Nutr.* **20**, 703-718.

Smith, M. D. and Pannacciulli, I. M. (1958). *Br. J. Haemat.* **4**, 428-434.

Spencer, R. P., Brody, K. R. and Mautner, H. G. (1965). *Nature, Lond.* **207**, 418-419.

Summerskill, W. H. J. and Moertel, C. G. (1962). *Gastroenterology* **42**, 380-392.

Talley, R. B., Schedl, H. P. and Clifton, J. A. (1964). *Gastroenterology* **47**, 382-387.

von Tappeiner, H. E. (1878). *Wien. Sitz. Ber.* **77**, 281.

Taylor, A. N. and Wasserman, R. H. (1967). *Archs Biochem.* **119**, 536-540.

Thaysen, T. E. Hess (1932). In *Non-tropical Sprue. A study in Idiopathic Steatorrhoea.* Oxford University Press, London.

Thaysen, T. E. Hess (1935). *Q. Jl Med.* **4**, 359-395.

Thaysen, E. H. (1963). *Ugeskr. Læg.* **125**, 973-980.

Thaysen, E. H. (1966). In *Ulcussjukdomen* (L. Hallberg, ed.), pp. 220-225. Göteborg.

Thaysen, E. H. (1967). (Unpublished observations.)

Thaysen, E. H., Bruusgaard, A. and Eriksen, B. (1968). VIIIth International Congress of Gastroenterology, Prague, Czechoslovakia. (In the press.)

Thaysen, E. H., Müllertz, S., Worning. H. and Bang, H. O. (1964). *Gastroenterology* **46**, 23-31.

Thaysen, E. H. and Thaysen, J. H. (1949a). *Acta med. scand.* Suppl. 234, 317-325.

Thaysen, E. H. and Thaysen, J. H. (1949b). *Acta path. microbiol. scand.* **26**, 370-380.

Thaysen, E. H. and Thaysen, J. H. (1952). *Acta med. scand.* Suppl. 274, 124-157.

Townes, P. L., Bryson, M. F. and Miller, G. (1967). *J. Pediat.* **71**, 220-224.

Trier, J. S., Phelps, P. C., Eidelman, S. and Rubin, C. E. (1965). *Gastroenterology* **48**, 684-707.

Turnbull, A., Cleton, F. and Finch, C. A. (1962). *J. clin. Invest.* **41**, 1897-1907.

Ugolev, A. M. (1965). *Physiol. Rev.* **45**, 555-595.

Ugolev, A. M. and Kooshuck, R. J. (1966). *Nature, Lond.* **212**, 859-860.

Ussing, H. H. (1949). *Physiol. Rev.* **29**, 127-155.

Ussing, H. H. (1960). In *The Alkali Metal Ions in Biology* p. 137. Springer-Verlag, Berlin.

Ussing, H. H. and Andersen, B. (1955). 3rd Internat. Cong. Biochem. Brussels, p. 434 (abstract).

Valdiviesco, V. D. and Schwabe, A. D. (1965). *Gastroenterology*, **48**, 336-341.

Viteri, F., Behar, M., Arroyave, G. and Scrimshaw, N. S. (1964). In *Mammalian Protein Metabolism* (H. N. Munro and J. B. Allison, eds), Vol. 2, pp. 523-568. Academic Press, New York.

Weijers, H. A., van de Kamer, J. H., Dickie, W. K. and Ijsseling, J. (1961). *Acta paediat., Stockh.* **50**, 55-71.

Wheby, M. S. (1966). *Gastroenterology* **50**, 888-892.

Wheby, M. S., Jones, L. G. and Crosby, W. H. (1964). *J. clin. Invest.* **43**, 1433-1442.

Wilson, T. H. (1962). In *Intestinal Absorption*, pp. 45-46. Saunders Co., Philadelphia.

Wiseman, G. (1964). *Absorption From the Intestine*. Academic Press, New York.

Worning, H., Müllertz, S., Thaysen, E. H. and Bang, H. O. (1968). *Scand. J. Gastroenterology* **3**, 83-90.

PART IV

The Cancer Cell

CHAPTER 12

Ultrastructure of the Cancer Cell

FRANÇOISE HAGUENAU

Laboratoire de Médecine Expérimentale du Collège de France, Paris, France

I. Introduction

A decade ago several authors writing on this subject came to the conclusion that an ultrastructural disturbance pathognomic of cell malignancy had not yet been established. Since then various techniques such as cytochemistry, autoradiography and those involving ferritin or enzyme conjugated antigens and antibodies have been adapted to the electron microscope. Yet, despite the discovery of several subcellular structures and changes, evidence that malignant cells are morphologically different from normal cells has not been forthcoming. Many types of cancer cells resemble normal cells, and it is more difficult at times to recognize malignant cells with the electron microscope than with the ordinary light microscope.

The malignant character residing in an ensemble of traits is often better

Q

discernible in a general view at low power than at high magnification. Indeed, as structures are being more magnified and as their constituents are being revealed, the unity prevailing in biological matter is also becoming manifest and consequently differences at the molecular level will not be perceived. Thus for example a ribosome from a cancer cell will look like a ribosome from a normal cell.

With these considerations in mind, the fact still remains that in some special instances the malignant nature of cells may be evident under the electron microscope and this is mainly because of the rarefaction and paucity of cell organelles, i.e. poor differentiation (anaplasia) or because of their unusual development, the hypertrophy being indicative of exaggerated growth rate. This may be so striking a feature that some structures were in fact first described in cancer cells. Thus a general account of these hypertrophied structures appearing in a variety of cancer cells will first be given and this description will also include anaplastic cancers. We will then turn to the main types of experimental cancers which have hitherto been studied with the electron microscope: essentially cancers induced by carcinogens and those induced by viruses. And finally there will be a brief review of human cancer.

II. General Description of the Ultrastructure of the Malignant Cell

A. *The nucleus*

As in the case of the light microscope, one of the most striking ultra-structural features of cancer cells is *hypertrophy of the nucleus*. However, this feature may at times be entirely lacking. Besides an increase in size, *an alteration in shape* of the nuclei is a feature well known from light microscopy. In the electron microscope this often is indicated by deep invaginations of the hypertrophied nuclear membrane. These fold in deeply, and when sections of the tissue are cut tangentially, the folds appear as membranes enclosing areas of cytoplasm (Figs 1 and 2). A typical example of this has been provided by studies on experimental hepatomas by Leduc and Wilson (1959) and is observed in many tumours and in rapidly growing tissues. Often the segregated cytoplasm is so modified that it is not recognizable, whence the numerous "nuclear inclusions" that were described were in fact not nuclear in origin.

Besides these "pseudo-inclusions" representing nuclear membrane invaginations (and except viral inclusion bodies), inclusions of the most diverse nature are sometimes observed in cancer cell nuclei. These include glycogen bodies (Friedlander-Binggeli, 1959; Gusek, 1962), lipid and myelin figures, or protein crystals (Fruhling and Porte, 1958; Haguenau 1959b; Maldonado *et al.*, 1966), filamentous or periodically arrayed structures and vacuoles of unidentified types, etc. These inclusions are no characteristic of cancer cells.

Increase of nuclear surface favours the technical achievement of tangentia sections. In such sections, the *nuclear pores* are remarkably conspicuous as annular structures. Thus the striking abundance of nuclear pores observed in some cancers is explained both by the increase in the nuclear surface and by its infolding. When the section involves only the most superficial layer of the nuclear convexity, the annulae may appear to be embedded in the cytoplasmic matrix at a distance from the nucleus, resulting in a loss of their relationship with the nucleus. In these instances, the nuclear pores have not infrequently been mistaken for viruses (Fig. 3).

One of the first examples of the abundance of nuclear pores in cancer cells was given by Haguenau *et al.* (1955). Any type of cancer cells may show this, but it occurs with remarkable frequence in some mesenchymal tumours and in hepatomas (Haguenau and Bernhard, 1955). It is of course also observed in embryonic tissues in which nuclear cytoplasmic interchanges are augmented.

If one now abandons the outer envelope of the malignant nucleus and considers the filamentous chromatin network which constitutes the *nuclear ground substance* (nucleoplasm), there emerges a wide variety of findings.

The classical description of dark nuclei with a coarse network of chromatin, clumped into patches and disposed along the nuclear membrane is essentially that of virus-induced tumours where margination of chromatin is a typical cytopathological change produced by viruses. However, this occurrence is far from being the rule and cancer nuclei often appear with a clear, light chromatin network against which the nucleolus, also hypertrophied, appears very dense. This striking looseness of the chromatin reticular meshwork in cancer cells is a finding which agrees with the interpretation of [³H]thymidine incorporation as studied with the electron microscope. For example, it was first shown by Hay and Revel (1963) and confirmed since by many others, that the finding of dispersed chromatin (euchromatin) in synthetic nuclei meant the existence of highly active metabolic sites, whereas condensed chromatin (heterochromatin or chromosomes) meant a metabolically inert nucleo-protein gel. It is, therefore, not surprising that in rapidly reproducing neoplastic cells the nuclei consist often of highly dispersed chromatin strands and do not appear laden with heavily clumped chromatin.

In the nucleoplasm of cancer cells a group of morphologically well-defined structures may undergo hypertrophy, the significance of which remains hitherto unknown. These structures are (*a*) the *interchromatin granules*, (b) the *perichromatin granules*, (c) the *dense bodies* and (*d*) the *nuclear bodies*.

(*a*) *Interchromatin granules*. First so-named by Swift (1959, 1962), these granules are sometimes definitely increased in number in cancer cells. They are found to occur in patches formed by a network of granular elements of 200–250 Å in diameter. Such clusters localized within inter-chromatinic areas are particularly conspicuous against the clear background of the dispersed, rarefied chromatin network (Fig. 4). They may be observed in any type of experimental cancer and are often found in human cancer cells (Haguenau, 1960*b*). The significance of interchromatin granules is unknown and no definite information has yet been obtained from ultrastructural chemistry, although the information available indicates that they contain both RNA and DNA (Swift, 1962). Smetana *et al.* (1963) have suggested that they may represent nucleolar RNA which migrates to the cytoplasm and is then surrounded by a protein shell.

(*b*) *Perichromatin granules* (Swift, 1962; Watson, 1962). As the term implies, they are always found within chromatinic areas and are morphologically different from the interchromatin granules in that they are larger (300–350 Å), denser, and they occur in definitely separate units and are always surrounded by a clear halo. Though rare in normal nuclei, they occur in increased number in cancer cells (Murad and Scarpelli, 1967; Sykes *et al.*, 1968). Again, their significance is unknown, even though RNA and DNA are both known to be present in them (Bernhard and Granboulan, 1963; Monneron, 1967).

(*c*) The possible relationship of perichromatin granules to the *dense bodies***** (Fig. 4) which are so frequently found in the nuclei and in the nucleoli of virus-induced tumours (Dourmashkin and Bernhard, 1959; Haguenau, 1960*a*; Bernhard, 1963) and in human malignancies (Haguenau, 1960*b*; Leplus *et al.*, 1961) has been touched upon by Sankaranarayanan and Hyde (1965). These multiple, small (0·15–0·3 *μ*) and highly osmiophilic, coarsely fibrillar structures confer upon the nuclei, and especially the nucleoli of some tumour cells, a very remarkable appearance described by Bernhard (1963) and Bernhard and Granboulan (1968) as "spotted nucleoli" (Fig. 7). The granules, however, are not specific for tumour cells, since they are observed in diverse virus infections, oncogenic or not, and also following actinomycin treatment or ultraviolet irradiation (see review by Bernhard and Granboulan, 1968). Their significance remains unknown. That they may represent synthetic activity related to chromatin or represent an accumulation of products of genetic activity are two plausible explanations.

(*d*) Another type of change described recently consists of the occurrence of *nuclear bodies*. They are characteristic and appear generally as round or oval structures of variable size (from 0·5 *μ* to 1·8 *μ*), which always seem to consist of coiled filaments, either totally made up of them in a sort of onion-like structure, or showing a filamentous cortex only, the centre of which is empty or occupied by granules (Fig. 4). It is thought that the large complex types represent an evolutionary stage of earlier filamentous forms; thus far five sequential types have been described (Bouteille *et al.*, 1967).

Like other structures described here, the nuclear bodies may be found in normal tissues, especially in the adrenal cortex of the pig (Weber *et al.*, 1964) or in hamsters (Jones and Fawcett, 1966; Krishan *et al.*, 1967).

---

* The term "dense bodies" was used by Dourmashkin, Bernhard and ourselves (*op. cit.*) when these structures were first described. Other terms include "dense granules" and "dense spots". None of them, however, is satisfactory.

However, nuclear bodies may be so markedly hypertrophied in some cancers that their presence was noticed there for the first time (De Thé *et al.*, 1960; Hinglais-Guillaud *et al.*, 1961). In two recent studies (Bouteille *et al.*, 1967; Krishan *et al.*, 1967) their predominance in cancer cells, particularly in human tumours of the nervous system, was clearly shown. We have found them in tumours induced by Rous sarcoma in the rat (Febvre *et al.*, 1964) and in great abundance in tumours induced by the same virus in hamsters (personal observation) (see Fig. 4).

The significance of nuclear bodies is not yet known. The filamentous component corresponds most probably to protein since it is digested by trypsin and contains seemingly no nucleic acid (Krishan *et al.*, 1967). It has been suggested that the granular component may correspond to either interchromatin or perichromatin granules. Whatever their significance is, it is obvious that the structures in question become gigantic in hyperactive cells.

B. *The nucleolus*

Although this organelle may be normal in size and in appearance, its *hypertrophy* in cancer cells, in which multiple nucleoli are often observed, is a feature with which all pathologists are familiar. Besides hypertrophy, the electron microscope shows in a striking manner the frequent localization of the cancer nucleoli against the nuclear membrane, as illustrated in Fig. 5. Ultrastructural studies have shown, as might be expected, that the molecular organization of the cancer nucleoli is either unchanged and entirely comparable to that of a normal nucleolus, or that it might present variation in the relative proportions of its diverse constituents. Thus hyperplasia of the nucleolus may involve both its granular and filamentous constituents, thereby affording a particularly favourable material for nucleolar study. The chromatin associated with the nucleolus may also be decreased or increased.

The vacuoles often described to be present in nucleoli of malignant cells correspond sometimes only to a circular arrangement of the dense "nucleonema filaments" around an area of light chromatin network. There are times when the vacuoles appear empty or filled with a precipitate of proteins or lipids (Fig. 6).

Accumulation of multiple "dense granules" already mentioned on p. 436 ("spotted nucleoli") is a relatively frequent finding in malignant nucleoli, especially in tumours induced by viruses (see Bernhard and Granboulan, 1963, 1968).

All the features of nucleoli just described are manifestations of hyperactivity and not of malignancy *per se*. In other words, they may be observed, as well, in any cells whose metabolic activity is quite intense.

C. *Mitotic apparatus*

Electron microscopic studies of chromosomes have been less revealing than those carried out with the light microscope, since thin sections are not readily amenable to three-dimensional studies. Differences at the molecular level between chromosomes from normal and cancer cells have not been observed and no peculiar anomaly of mitosis has yet been shown. Mitosis, however, has not been systematically studied in cancer cells with the electron microscope.

D. *Centrioles*

Centrioles may be abnormally numerous and their classical orientation, viz., perpendicular to one another, may be lost. This is best observed in lymphoid cells in which centrioles can be readily seen. Disturbed centrioles have thus been observed in myeloma (Bessis *et al.*, 1958; Maldonado *et al.*, 1966) and in experimental thymoma of the mouse (unpublished observations).

E. *The cytoplasm*

The cytoplasm shows an increase in number and *hypertrophy* of some organelles, although *rarefaction* of these same organelles may also be a striking finding. Quite often there is no change whatsoever (see Sections F–K).

F. *Mitochondria*

Mitochondria represent a particularly good example, since they may appear quite unaltered in morphology or amount. They are also reported to be decreased (Howatson and Ham, 1955; De Man, 1960; De Man and Van Rijssel, 1961; Toker and Trevino, 1966; Murad and Scarpelli, 1967) and equally often increased in number (Hinglais-Guillaud *et al.*, 1961; Brandes *et al.*, 1964; Mao *et al.*, 1966; Lynn *et al.*, 1967). Sometimes in the same cancer they are increased in some cells while in others they are decreased (Creemers and Jadin, 1968). It seems probable, as will be seen in the section dealing with cancers of specific organs, that their number is related to the original richness in mitochondria of the normal tissue. Thus renal clear-cell carcinomas arising from mitochondria-rich tubular renal epithelium are packed with them (Oberling *et al.*, 1959; Seljelid and Ericsson, 1965a; Ericsson *et al.*, 1966). This applies also, for instance, to onkocytomas (Tandler and Shipkey, 1964a; Becker, 1964; McGavran, 1965; Hübner *et al.*, 1967).

The pathological change most frequently observed in cancer cells is "cloudy swelling" (Figs 8 and 9). But although mitochondria from cancer cells are known to differ from normal cell mitochondria in their swelling response to detergents and trypsin (Mutolo and Abrignani, 1957), one also knows that they are the most sensitive organelles in the cytoplasm and they react nonspecifically to varied types of stress, in particular, to fixation. The fact remains, however, that one should expect certain changes in mitochondria of some types of cancer, as has been shown biochemically by Warburg. To demonstrate this with the electron microscope is obviously very difficult and lack of comparison with normal *homologous* tissues is a criticism applicable to almost all observations of tumours *in vivo*. *In vitro*, where comparison is quite feasible with certain experimental systems, only a few studies have so far been concerned with this problem.

In *Rous sarcoma* although glycolysis is strikingly increased, and an increase in the number of mitochondria is substantiated cytochemically (Francois, 1968), hypertrophy has been reported on the basis of electron microscopic studies by some workers only (Di Stefano and Dougherty, 1965) and not by others (Courington and Vogt, 1967; Haguenau, unpublished observations). No constant morphological alterations have been described, however.

Bernhard and Tournier (1966) and Leduc *et al.* (1966) found gigantic, irregularly-shaped and swollen mitochondria, which contained increased amounts of DNA in hamster tumour cells induced by *Adeno 12 virus*. The changes persisted through many tissue culture passages. These workers failed to observe similar changes in controls of hamster cells transformed by the Polyoma or SV40 virus. What they did observe was that the morphology of the mitochondria was influenced by the age of the culture, being more pronounced during experimental growth and tending to return to normal when stationary in a culture.

Besides changes in size and the characteristic yet nonspecific "cloudy swelling", various *deposits* may be found in the mitochondria of cancer cells. These include lipids, DNA (Thomas, 1965; Bernhard and Tournier, 1966), glycogen (Tandler and Shipkey, 1964a, b), protein crystals (Hruban *et al.*, 1966) and other unidentified inclusions (see Oberling and Bernhard, 1961; Bernhard, 1963). However, none is specific.

A good example of this is the finding of striking mitochondrial inclusions, the "corpus intra-cristae" (Frei and Sheldon, 1961), reported by Setälä *et al.* (1960, 1961) to occur specifically in precancerous and cancerous lesions of mouse skin after treatment with dimethylbenzanthracene (DMBA) and by Burt *et al.* (1961) in the small intestine of animals treated with methylcholanthrene. But these large dense bodies, usually encircled by a distinct membrane, are also observed after the administration of non-carcinogenic drugs (Mylius, 1962) and in normal tissues (Nilsson, 1958; Hollmann, 1962).

Myelin and paracrystalline intramitochondrial figures are found with relative frequency in some tissues such as liver under diverse pathological (Jezequel, 1959; Lafontaine and Allard, 1964) and also under normal conditions (Mugnaini, 1964). The role played by fixatives appears of great importance here, where glutaraldehyde is capable of inducing intramitochondrial fibrillar (Behnke, 1964) or myelinic structures (Curgy, 1968).

On the whole, it is likely that the occurrence of mitochondrial inclusions in cancer cells is linked to a basic metabolic disturbance and that it represents an unspecific reaction to injury.

G. *The Golgi apparatus*

As with all the organelles considered here, the Golgi apparatus may appear quite normal in cancer cells. But in very anaplastic cells it is usually reduced and often consists only of a few vesicles.

In cancers in which differentiation is preserved, the Golgi apparatus is often hypertrophied (Fig. 14). Hypertrophy may involve any of the three basic components of the Golgi apparatus, namely, the flat cisternae, the vacuoles and the vesicles. The fact is that no qualitative structural alteration has hitherto been reported, and although ultrastructural chemistry has been very revealing in the case of the normal Golgi apparatus there is no evidence of any constant enzymic abnormality in cancer cells.

Whatever the extent of the hyperplasia, it seems to represent more a stimulation of cellular function of the tissue being considered than the malignant state *per se*. Thus, hypertrophy of the Golgi apparatus is particularly pronounced in *tumours of glandular organs,* as in the case of the pituitary gland in the rat (Haguenau and Lacour, 1955), the islet cells of the pancreas (Lazarus and Volk, 1962; Bencosme *et al.*, 1963) and the thyroid gland (Lupulescou and Petrovici, 1963). In human mammary tumours, the Golgi apparatus shows frequent hyperplasia in those cells that are not anaplastic (Gros and Girardie, 1967). In mouse mammary tumours, where a virus is involved (*vide infra*), hypertrophy of the Golgi apparatus is remarkable and almost always present. The hypertrophy of the Golgi apparatus observed in all these cases is very likely related to the stimulation of secretion.

Hypertrophy of the Golgi apparatus in cancer cells is not restricted to epithelial cells, since it may also be observed in *mesenchymal tumours*, whether of the experimental type, e.g. Rous sarcoma (Haguenau and Beard, 1962; Di Stefano and Dougherty, 1965; Courington and Vogt, 1967) or of the human type as noted, for instance, in fibrosarcomas (Leak *et al.*, 1967) or in myeloma (Maldonado *et al.*, 1966). Here also the same remarks are pertinent: hypertrophy of the Golgi apparatus observed in Rous sarcoma may be the result of stimulation of collagen or mucopolysaccharide – the characteristic secretions of fibroblasts. At any rate, the hypertrophy even if extremely striking in some instances, may be lacking in others.

The Golgi apparatus has been associated with certain characteristic vacuoles termed *multivesicular bodies*. These may be quite increased in number or size. They had been described in human mammary tumours (Haguenau, 1959*a*) at a time when they had not yet been recognized as an entity and their significance was unknown (Fig. 11). In mice mammary tumours the increase in multivesicular bodies can be striking, as shown in Fig. 10. These bodies are frequently observed in cells of the lymphoid system (unpublished observations) and they have been reported in reticulum cell sarcomas (Vasquez *et al.*, 1963) and in myelomas (Sörenson, 1964).

The size and regularity of the vesicles found in these vacuoles may mislead the electron microscopist unfamiliar with these structures to envisage their possible viral origin (Dolowy, 1966). This pitfall has already been pointed out by Haguenau and Hollmann (1963). One should thus be acquainted with their appearance.

Multivesicular bodies have now been unequivocally demonstrated to be linked to pinocytosis. Pinocytosis is indeed often greatly increased in cancer cells, but no relation to malignant transformation has so far been demonstrated.

H. *The ergastoplasm*

The most striking difference in the appearance of the ergastoplasm in cancer cells – when it is possible to compare these with their normal homologous counterpart – concerns the *organizational pattern of the ribosomes*. These have a tendency to be diffusely dispersed throughout the cytoplasm rather than be orderly arranged along the surface of the endoplasmic reticulum (Figs 12 and 13).

While "organized ergastoplasm" is characteristic of protein synthesis in highly differentiated cells where the secretion product is exported, dispersed ribosomes are essentially found in cells where accumulation of secretion product does not occur (synthesis of structural protein) and is an attribute of rapidly growing and embryonic cells. Examination with the electron microscope of one type of cell throughout the different stages of its differentiation illustrates this point quite clearly and is a constant finding *in vivo*. The phenomenon may also be followed experimentally as in collagen synthesizing fibroblasts grown *in vitro*, where ribosomes are dispersed during the log phase of growth and organized ergastoplasm appears only later during the stationary phase together with secretion (Goldberg and Green, 1964). It is then logical to interpret the diffuse distribution of ribosomes in cancer cells as a manifestation of de-differentiation and return from specific protein synthesis to synthesis of those proteins which are necessary for rapid reproduction. A good example of this is provided by the fibroblastic cell when it becomes cancerous under the influence of Rous sarcoma virus. Whereas the normal elongated fibroblast shows a typical "organized ergastoplasm", the malignant cell, aside from a change in size and form, has little or no "organized ergastoplasm". This has been replaced by dispersed ribosomes (Figs 12 and 13).

This absence of organized ergastoplasm, though typical of some cancer cells and of some types of cancer, is far from a constant finding. In non-anaplastic cancers, the organization of ergastoplasm is maintained and it may resemble that of normal cells, as in some types of hepatomas* (Dalton, 1959; Hruban *et al.*, 1965), some secreting human and mouse mammary cancers (Oberling and Bernhard, 1961; Haguenau *et al.*, 1965), thyroid cancers (Lupulescou and Petrovici, 1963), myeloma (Bessis *et al.*, 1963; Maldonado *et al.*, 1966), to cite only a few examples (see Fig. 14).

Another frequent feature of the ergastoplasm in cancer cells is its marked variation in pattern from cell to cell. Caspersson and Santesson's classical

* See also Section III page 448 for other modifications of ergastoplasm in hepatomas.

studies with the spectrophotometer showed that in some cancers a type of cell described by them as the "A" type is much more active in terms of protein synthesis and contains a higher amount of RNA in its cytoplasm than the less basophilic cells, i.e. the B type of cells (Caspersson, 1950).

In some cancers, human (mammary gland, Haguenau, 1959b; rectal cancer, Haguenau et al., 1964; fibromyxosarcoma, Leak et al., 1967) and experimental (Rous sarcoma virus-induced tumours in mammals), electron microscopic studies have shown that some clear and dark cells co-exist. Their ergastoplasm is either extremely substantial and organized, or quite reduced and dispersed (Fig. 15). Whether they are the real counterparts of the metabolically active (A) and less active (B) cells has not yet been established.

The significance of the presence of such mixed cell populations (as far as ergastoplasm is concerned) in some cancers is unknown. It could indicate extreme stimulation of protein synthesis in some cells, thus leading to early degeneration of these cells (A cells), or it may represent different stages of differentiation or even reflect the existence originally of a mixed population in the normal tissue. Indeed, "light" and "clear" cells have been described in normal tissues, especially epithelial mucosae.

Focal changes in the ergastoplasm have also been observed, one of the most frequent being extreme and irregular dilatation of cisternae with invagination of their lining into their own lumen. This gives rise to images of "islands" of cytoplasm found in the midst of dilated ergastoplasmic cavities. Good examples of this phenomenon have been provided by the work of Smetana and Busch (1963) on Walker carcinoma.

In conclusion, then, although distinct general patterns of distribution of the ergastoplasm may be found in some cancer cells, these seem related to modes of growth rather than to malignancy.

I. *Miscellaneous cellular "inclusions"*

Other cytoplasmic structures may show changes in cancer cells. Increase in microfibrils, in tonofilaments (Sykes et al., 1968; Fiske and Haguenau, 1968), in desmosomes (Chambers and Weiser, 1964), in microbodies and in lysosomes, has been reported.

It is interesting to point out that among these, *annulate lamellae* may be extraordinarily hypertrophied in virus-infected cells (Smith, 1967; Kim and Boatman, 1967). As these structures participate in nucleo-cytoplasmic exchanges (Hsu, 1967) it is not unreasonable to consider the mechanism of hypertrophy in this light.

Remarkable profusion of *tonofilaments* (Fig. 16) has been observed in mammary gland tumour cells maintained in organ cultures (Fiske-Michelson and Haguenau, 1969) and manifest probably an embryonic potentiality of these originally ectodermic cells when they are grown *in vitro*. The same phenomenon may also occur *in vivo* (see p. 461) (Sykes et al., 1968).

One may possibly put forward a similar interpretation of the striking increase in *desmosomes* which has sometimes been observed in malpighian types of growths both *in vivo* (Haguenau *et al.*, 1964) and *in vitro* (Halpern *et al.*, 1968).

Though not a frequent occurrence, hypertrophy of *lysosomes* has been considered by Allison (1966) as so important in carcinogenesis that a theory of malignancy has been advanced by him (see also Chapter 6, Volume 1). Lysosomes tend to accumulate whenever proteolytic enzymes are needed for the elimination of undesirable cellular products. They are thus extremely abundant during certain end-stages of secretory cycles and also during viral infection since they probably represent a defence mechanism of the cell against the virus itself. That their number should be augmented in some cancer cells might thus be readily explainable.

Besides organelles, *"inclusions" of a diverse nature* are also often found in cancer cells. When large in size they can be observed with the light microscope and their occurrence had been described long ago as characteristic of some types of cancers. It is with the electron microscope that their diversity and real nature has been revealed. They generally represent the accumulation of the cell's normal secretion products or else, of local degenerative processes. Belonging to the former are the milk droplets or colostrum found in mammary tumours, the colloid globules in the thyroid gland, secretion granules in diverse endocrine gland tumours, e.g. insulinomas (Thiery and Bader, 1962; Lazarus and Volk, 1962; Bencosme *et al.*, 1963; Greider *et al.*, 1963; Greider and Elliott, 1964; Toker, 1967), pheochromocytomas (Bässler and Habighorst, 1964) and tumours of the bronchial (Bouteille *et al.*, 1964; Verley, 1965) and intestinal mucosae (Luse and Lacy, 1960; Schumacher and Schultz, 1963).

Melanin granules are observed in melanomas (Rappaport *et al.*, 1963); mast cell granules in mastocytomas (Mengel and Trier, 1961; Christensen *et al.*, 1963); lipids and glycogen in clear cell renal carcinomas (Oberling *et al.*, 1959); mucopolysaccharides in fibromyxosarcomas (Leak *et al.*, 1967).

Inclusions that represent degenerative processes are giant lysosomes, microbodies, autophagic vacuoles (Novikoff and Biempica, 1966; Mao and Molnar, 1967), as well as cytoplasmic or nuclear debris engulfed by cancer cells under circumstances where it is known that erythrophagocytosis and empiropolesis are particularly active. The electron microscope, for instance, has shown that Feulgen positive "inclusions" – considered as of great importance by light microscopists because of the possibility of their viral nature[*] – were in many cases only nuclear remnants (see pp. 462-463). There are yet other inclusions which are of unknown origin (Shipkey *et al.*, 1964; Koinov, 1967).

J. *Basal membranes*

It is most important before completing this section to state that changes in basal membrane have been noticed. The fact that basal membranes so

---

[*] True viral inclusions are not considered here.

often appear intact, and that the question of a possible artefact is always raised when they appear disrupted, has discouraged workers from attaching weight to these pathological changes. Thus research in this area has been relatively sparse (Ashworth *et al.*, 1961; Frei, 1962; Birbeck and Wheatley, 1965; Schrodt and Foreman, 1965; Fasske and Morgenroth, 1966; Tarin, 1967, 1968; Sugar, 1968). These studies have mostly dealt with skin cancers or epithelial carcinomas of the mammary gland and digestive tract and have shown the underlying pathology to be one of plain disruption and/or hyperplasia and branching of the basal membrane. Besides membrane thickening, patchy foci of membrane accumulation, often leading to the formation of an intricate membranous meshwork have also been observed (Tarin, 1967, 1968) (Fig. 17).

That increased production of basement membrane may occur contrarily to the expected rarefaction is probably not surprising since cancer cells can show any sort of metabolic impairment. Of particular significance is the observation not only of membrane disruption but also of protrusion through these gaps of cytoplasmic processes with the result that cytoplasmic material reaches the stroma. The studies of Frei (1962) on epidermal tumours induced by dimethylbenzanthracene, or those of Sugar (1968) on precancerous and cancerous lesions of human skin and larynx illustrate these points well. It is in some of these instances that the electron microscope has allowed a prompt diagnosis of malignancy to be made. Even so, it must be constantly borne in mind that migration of cytoplasmic elements across the basal membrane occurs in non-malignant conditions as well, for example, in regenerating tissues (Salpeter and Singer, 1960).

K. *Cell surfaces*

Studies of changes in the surfaces of cancer cells have progressed only recently and these have been in parallel with the discoveries that have been made in the fields of immunology and cytochemistry. It now represents one of the most active and dynamic fields of research in modern oncology. From the ultrastructural standpoint, it may be hoped that it will become possible in the near future to detect changes in the plasma membrane which would correspond to either loss of tissue-specific antigenic sites (which in normal cells might play a role in growth control) or to minute qualitative changes in the composition of immunologically expressive surface coats. The finding by Emmelot and Benedetti (1967) of a change of the normal geometrical pattern of the globular subunits of the plasma membrane in carcinogen-induced hepatoma represents perhaps the first significant observation in this direction. However, the existence of surface antigens that are specific for cancer cells, well established in the case of a series of virus-induced tumours (Sjögren *et al.*, 1961; Habel, 1962) and believed to be localized at or on the cell surfaces, has not yet been shown with the electron microscope.

The information available concerns mainly the attachment of cancerous cells to one another and the quantitative modification of the cell coat (mucopolysaccharides).

It is well known from classical studies that cancer cells are more loosely attached to one another than their normal counterparts. It is partly on this basis that metastasis has been supposed to occur (Coman, 1953). Measurements of cell to cell adhesion have indeed shown an initial decrease in adhesiveness (Coman, 1944, 1960), which in turn has been linked to an increase in negative charges of the plasma membrane (Purdom et al., 1958). In the electron microscope this would correspond to a widening of the spaces between cells which, in solid tissues, should not be more distant than 200 Å (Lesseps, 1963). This is not frequently seen except where there is a change in morphology of the cell surface, characterized by remarkable *hyper-villosity*, and where there is frequently increased spacing. This occurs particularly in human endometrial carcinoma (Nilsson, 1962) and human mammary tumours (Haguenau, 1959a); also in mammary tumours of mice (see Figs 18 and 19).

Distances between cells are of course also dependent on modifications occurring at the level of intercellular attachment, namely, *desmosomes* and *tight junctions*. *Tight junctions* appear reduced in cancer cells (Emmelot and Benedetti, 1967; Martinez-Palomo et al., 1968).

Besides their physical role in attachment, *desmosomes* are the site of intense ion exchanges from one cell to another (Loewenstein, 1966) and they are functionally disrupted in cancer where it seems, at least in hepatomas, that there is no communication at all (Loewenstein and Kanno, 1967). On the other hand, the evidence coming from electron microscopic studies is contradictory. The observation by Easty and Mercer (1960) and by others, showing a decrease in desmosomes, is in keeping with the notion of the "looseness" of cancer cells. But in other cases attachment of cells to each other does not seem to be impaired, and in other cases yet, desmosomes are markedly increased in number and hypertrophied, as shown by Fasske and Themann (1960), Hinglais-Guillaud et al. (1961), Schultz (1961) and Haguenau et al. (1964) (see also Fig. 16, and p. 461).

It is in such cases that the new techniques of cytochemistry when applied at the ultrastructural level, promise to be extremely useful. Thus, even if some desmosomes in rat hepatoma appear structurally normal, they are actually different from the desmosomes of normal liver in the light of ultracytochemical studies of mucopolysaccharides (sialic acid). Benedetti and Emmelot (1967), and Emmelot and Benedetti (1967), working with isolated membranes of liver and hepatomas, were able to show that desmosomes, which could not be stained with colloidal iron in normal cells could be stained so in some hepatomas. It could be demonstrated that the capacity to fix the iron acquired by the cancer cell was due to the presence of carboxyl groups which were not blocked by the Ca^{2+} ions present in normal cell desmosome coats (Benedetti and Emmelot, 1968). It is too early to interpret these results, partly because the situation is very complex and partly because, as shown by the authors themselves, results obtained with mice hepatomas cannot be readily extrapolated to rat hepatomas.

Information derived from ultracytochemistry is beginning to accumulate quite rapidly now that techniques for the study of mucopolysaccharides with the electron microscope have been perfected. This leads us to the second point, which is about *surface coats*.

Present studies of the surface coats of cancer cells are concerned with cells that have been infected with, and transformed by, oncogenic viruses. Modification of the surface manifests itself *in vitro* mainly by the loss of contact inhibition, thus leading to the piling up of transformed cells which focally assume the appearance of *in vitro* micro-tumours. No explanation has been given, though at present such remarkable behaviour appears to be a characteristic feature of malignant cells (see Abercrombie and Ambrose, 1962). One hypothesis put forward suggests as a cause the excessive accumulation of surface coat material, known to occur in some of these virus-induced transformed cells. Defendi and Gasic (1963), for example, have clearly shown, with classical cytochemical methods, increased mucopolysaccharides at the surface of *polyoma-transformed cells*.

It is only recently that at the ultrastructural level a great difference in the amount of mucopolysaccharides between a normal chicken fibroblast surface and that of an RSV-transformed one has been demonstrated (Bonneau and Cesarini, 1968; Morgan, 1968; Lardemer and Haguenau, 1969) (see Figs 20 and 21). Another example is that provided by the work of Martinez-Palomo and Brailowsky (1968) and Martinez-Palomo et al. (1968) with *Adeno 12- and SV40-infected hamster cells*. In none of these instances, however, is it known whether an increase in surface coat mucopolysaccharides is really responsible for reducing inhibition contact and whether it represents an antigenic qualitative modification of the cell surface.

Lastly, an increased phagocytotic activity and pinocytosis are, as mentioned already, marked in some cancer cells and represent a phenomenon which occurs at first at the cell surface. We have personally observed this in many types of cancers, especially in Rous sarcoma virus-induced hamster tumours (meningiosarcomas, fibrosarcomas and rhabdomyosarcomas). There is no reason, however, to relate this increased pinocytosis to malignant transformation *per se*, while it is reasonable to link it to modified metabolism. It might correspond to the stimulation of information transfer occurring in-between cancer cells.

We have at this point completed our prospective general "tour" of the malignant cell. Depending on the type of cancer under consideration some or all of the changes reviewed seem to be absent or predominating.

If cancer is of an *anaplastic* type, it will then tend to lose its specialized features and resemble other anaplastic cancers, regardless of its origin. This is a familiar observation based on experience with the light microscope and upon which Greenstein (1954) founded his theory.

The tendency of cells to take on a homogeneous character is peculiarly striking under the electron microscope. This is when the "pale" or "B" type of cells form a monotonous tissue in which there are few observable organelles and in which ribosomes lie scattered (Fig. 15). Mitochondria are rare and small and the Golgi apparatus is reduced to few lamellae or vesicles. The nucleus is usually very large and indented with conspicuous nucleoli.

At the other extreme, these are cells which to a more or less important degree have retained their original features (Fig. 14). In these cases different varieties of cancers can be described, which in fact correspond to the type of cell of origin. This is a well-known fact borrowed from classical pathology, and especially observable in some endocrine gland carcinomas. The term "typical" cancer in French nomenclature, as opposed to "atypical", is a reflection of this situation. The electron microscope, however, permits a much deeper analysis of the structure of such types of cancer and emphasizes in some instances the apparent morphological similarity of cancerous and normal cells. This will be made quite clear in the section dealing with human cancer.

III. Ultrastructure of Experimental Cancers

A. *Cancers induced by carcinogenic drugs*

Relatively few cancers induced by carcinogens have so far been studied with the electron microscope. This is because until the introduction of the most recent methods of embedding and fixation it has been difficult to distinguish between necrosis caused by toxic drugs, artifacts occurring in particularly fragile tissues, and "specific" changes.

The effect of only one carcinogenic hydrocarbon, methylcholanthrene (Pillai and Gautier, 1960; Setälä *et al.*, 1960; Setälä *et al.*, 1961; Nakai *et al.*, 1962; Tarin, 1967, 1968*a*, *b*; Schrodt and Foreman, 1965), and that of only a few azo-dyes, including aminofluorene (Gustafsson and Afzelius, 1963; Kobayashi, 1963; Hartmann, 1965), butter yellow (DAB) (Porter and Bruni, 1959; Svoboda, 1964; Pinchouk *et al.*, 1966) and dimethylnitrosamine (DMNA) (Emmelot and Benedetti, 1960; Mölbert *et al.*, 1962; Geil *et al.*, 1968) have been extensively studied. To this list one may add others belonging to various chemical groups among which are the compounds thioacetamide (Kleinfeld and von Haam, 1959; Salomon *et al.*, 1962), aflatoxin (Bernhard *et al.*, 1965*a*, *b*) and 4-nitroquinolyne-*N*-oxide (Reynolds *et al.*, 1963). Not only are the compounds that have been studied few, but also their action has been examined only in a restricted group of tissues, mainly those that are known to be especially affected *in vivo*. Thus, ultrastructural research has essentially been concerned with cancers arising in the *liver*, the *digestive tract* and the *skin*.

At the very outset it should be stated that although the changes described may be drastic and characteristic, they are, except perhaps for nucleolar segregation, not specific (Simard and Bernhard, 1966). For instance, the effects of very closely related compounds, one carcinogenic (3 Me-DAB), and the other non-carcinogenic (2-Me-DAB), or of drugs having the opposite effects, viz. alkylating agents, and antimetabolites, may appear to be similar at the electron microscopical level.

Another observation which may be extended to all the examples thus far mentioned is that the response of the cancer cell corresponds to the usual "answer" given by the particular type of cell studied. For example, the remarkable increase in smooth endoplasmic reticulum observed in liver cells is not necessarily observed in other tissues. Conversely, mitochondria are more universally affected, since they occur in all cells. Lastly, mammary cancers in mice induced by carcinogens have the same features as tumours induced by viruses or those occurring spontaneously (Tarin, 1968a, b).

Hepatomas have, as already noted, been more extensively studied than other types of carcinogen-induced cancers. In all cases whether the compound used was *butter yellow* (Porter and Bruni, 1959; Pinchouk *et al.*, 1966) or *dimethylnitrosamine* (Emmelot and Benedetti, 1960; Mölbert *et al.*, 1962; Mukherjee *et al.*, 1963; Geil *et al.*, 1968) or *aminofluorene* (Kobayashi, 1963; Hartmann, 1965), the lesions have turned out to be comparable (Dalton, 1964). During the initial phase the granular endoplasmic reticulum (ergastoplasm) loses its ribosomes, and striking hypertrophy of the "smooth" endoplasmic reticulum paralleling glycogen depletion is observed. The resulting excessive smooth membranes aggregate in the cytoplasm to form myelin figures, thereby corresponding to hyaline inclusions visible with the light microscope. It was also found that with these morphological changes there was inhibition of amino-acid incorporation in the microsome fraction. Changes in mitochondria, including cloudy swelling and especially changes in array of the cristae, were also observed as a rule (Lafontaine and Allard, 1964).

Besides producing similar lesions, other types of drugs, e.g. thioacetamide induces in the very early stages a giant nucleolar hypertrophy, or e.g. aflatoxin, induces nucleolar segregation. In the former case, however, the reaction occurs earliest when it is not known whether evolution into a cancer will indeed occur (only a small percentage of tumours arise with this drug). And in the latter case, as stated by the authors themselves (Bernhard *et al.*, 1965), observations were recorded at an early stage, and the doses used were very much higher than those employed for tumour induction.

It is thus likely that the lesions observed are superimposed and that the main morphological features here are represented by degranulation of ergastoplasm and hypertrophy of smooth endoplasmic reticulum. These are by no means specific, since they are features which are induced in quite as spectacular a fashion by non-carcinogenic hydrocarbons (Lafontaine and Allard, 1964), and are produced by hepatoxins such as carbon tetrachloride (Oberling and Rouiller, 1956; Stenger, 1963). Moreover, phenobarbital (Remmer and Merker, 1963a; Herdson *et al.*, 1964; Jones and Fawcett, 1966), a quite unrelated drug, is capable of producing a comparable ultrastructural entity characterized by high production of agranular reticulum and glycogen depletion. Other drugs, for example tolbutamide or nikethamide, also produce similar effects (Remmer and Merker, 1963b). Striking augmentation of smooth endoplasmic reticulum accompanied by glycogen depletion has been observed also in regenerating liver tissue following the administration of protein-deficient diet or partial hepatectomy.

A recent study by Geil *et al.* (1968) using low doses of DMNA strongly suggests that the observed cytoplasmic alterations are indeed a toxic rather than a carcinogenic reaction. Thus, although they increased in frequency and intensity up to the 289th day, they subsequently regressed. These authors hold that nucleolar changes (focal condensation of the fibrillar component of the nucleolonema) which appeared after 170 days and became permanent were more likely related to DMNA hepatocarcinogenesis than were the cytoplasmic alterations.

In *cancers of the skin* or in pre-cancerous states induced by benzanthracene or methylcholanthrene (Setälä *et al.*, 1960; Pillai and Gautier, 1960; Mylius, 1962; Nakai *et al.*, 1962; Tarin, 1968*a*), lesions are observed in *mitochondria* where changes are found more or less constantly. Special attention has been drawn to the occurrence of "corpus-intra-cristae" (Setälä *et al.*, 1960) but it has already been stated that these are not specific changes (see p. 439 and below).

Tarin (1967) states that the only characteristic lesion observed in skin tumour produced with methylcholanthrene concerns the epithelial mesenchymal junction where there is increased reduplication in basement membrane material and eventually disruption of this membrane but only with carcinogenic drugs (Tarin, 1967), and not with non-carcinogenic drugs (Tarin, 1968). An identical impairment of the basal membrane has also been observed in methylcholanthrene-induced mammary tumours of the mouse. Since it is also provoked by other carcinogenic factors, the author believes these lesions of the basal membrane to be "specific" of the malignant state and the basis of its cause.

In the *small intestine* of the mouse "corpus intra-cristae" have also been claimed to be specifically related to the carcinogenic action of methylcholanthrene (Burt *et al.*, 1961). However, it has been shown by Mylius (1962) and by Hollmann (1962) in our laboratory that they occur as well in controls.

In summary, then, one might say that on the whole the cancerous lesions induced by carcinogens reflect changes in metabolic activity, viz. impairment of the mechanisms of nucleic acid and protein synthesis (giant nucleoli, nucleolar segregation, degranulation of ergastoplasm), changes in polysaccharide and lipid metabolism (a striking increase in "smooth" endoplasmic reticulum, lipid bodies, etc.). These changes often lead to necrotic lesions, but none of them can be considered specific, although some are quite characteristic in their appearance.

B. *Cancers induced by viruses*

For a long time certain virus-induced cancers were regarded by workers studying the ultrastructure of cancer cells as a most satisfactory material because in many instances, at least, one could describe a feature that appeared to be characteristic of the tumour. This feature was the virus particle. In this respect a great difference exists between tumours induced by DNA viruses and tumours induced by RNA viruses.

Most cancers induced by DNA viruses develop by "progression". After an initial phase of inflammation (*polyoma*, *SV40*), or of benign growth (*papillomas*), during which the virus is present, the malignant tumour goes on to develop without the virus being detectable.* This implies that as far as tumours induced by DNA viruses are concerned, the continued presence of the virus is not a feature of the malignant cell. Paradoxically, one may even consider that the presence of the virus is rather indicative of a non-malignant state.

In the case of tumours induced by RNA oncogenic viruses which comprise *murine leukaemias*, *avian leucosis* and *sarcomas* and *murine mammary tumours*, it can be said that on the contrary the virus as a rule is always present if properly searched for.†

In the light of recent data, however, even the presence of virus in these tumours and leukaemias cannot be accepted in itself as a distinctive sign of malignancy. For it is now well established that virus particles similar in morphology to those responsible for the disease may be found in apparently healthy animals. They represent either a "latent" state of the same virus or are different pseudotypes of viruses belonging to the same group. In murine lymphoid tissues, for example, "C" types of particles (see later) which have been proven to be responsible for leukaemia in mice may be found, though in small numbers, to be latent in probably all murine lymphoid tissues. Likewise the virus particles responsible for fowl lymphomatosis are latent in approximately 10% of birds from flocks not deliberately bred to be free of the disease. A comparable situation exists in the case of different pseudotypes of viruses belonging to the same group.

The presence of the virus as being indicative of malignancy is also a questionable concept in the case of the mouse mammary tumour. This is simply because the virus particle, a "B" type, occurs not only in mammary cancers but also in mammary *nodules*. A great percentage of these never evolve into a cancer. The trend in thought today is to consider the particle found in benign nodules as corresponding to another agent, the Mammary Nodule inciter virus (NIV). However, the morphology is similar, and in the electron microscope there often is no way of distinguishing between a cancer and a benign nodule, if cell differentiation is well preserved (see the Proceedings of the Conference on the Mammary Tumor Virus, Inverness, 1964).

It can be seen, from this too brief analysis of an extremely complex situation, that the interpretation of the ultrastructure of the malignant cell in virus-induced tumours often rests on the appreciation of the sum of

* At least in a recognizable morphological form.
† One exception is that of mammalian tumours induced by an avian virus (RSV) but this is a very special case that is not discussed here.

different nonspecific signs and not necessarily on the morphological presence of virus.

It is with these notions in mind that the ultrastructure of the various tumours produced by oncogenic viruses will now be described. This will be done rather succinctly because a number of reviews or books on this subject have already been published (Bernhard, 1960, 1963; Dalton and Haguenau, 1962; Howatson, 1964; Haguenau, 1966-67; Bernhard, 1969; Gross, 1968). No attempt will be made to describe in detail the appearance of virus particles, as studied with the technique of negative staining and for a description of which the reader is referred to the reviews just quoted.

We are actually concerned here with the appearance of the cancer cell and with the nature of the virus-host relationship. This problem is at present best approached by studies involving thin section techniques. If one adopts the classification of viruses as proposed by Lwoff et al. (see Table I) it is then convenient to discuss the morphology of tumours induced by DNA and RNA viruses separately.

TABLE I

After the proposals of the P.C.N.V. (*Ann. Inst. Pasteur* 1965, **109**, 625.) and the New York Group (*Natn. Cancer Inst.* 1966, **37**, 395.) Virus families with oncogenic properties have been *italicized* by us.

'hylum	Subphyla	Classes	Orders	Sub-orders	Families
	Type of genetic material	Symmetry of the nucleocapsid H: helical C: cubical B: binal	Nucleocapsid naked (N) or enveloped (E)	Nucleocapsid rigid (R) or flexible (F)	For helical viruses: diameter of the nucleo-capsid For cubical viruses: number of triangulation and number of capsomeres
	DNA Deoxyvira	H Deoxyhelica	N — / E Chitovirales		100 Å *Poxviridae*
		C Deoxycubica	N Haplovirales		1–12 Microviridae / 3–32 Parvoviridae / 7–72 *Papilloviridae* / 25–252 *Adenoviridae* / 81–812 Iridoviridae / ? Inoviridae
			E Peplovirales		16–162 *Herpesviridae*
		B Deoxybinala	N Urovirales / E —		? Phagoviridae
IRA			N Rhabdovirales	R Rigidoviridales	120–130 Å Dolichoviridae / 150 Å Protoviridae / 200 Å Pachyviridae
	RNA Ribovira	H Ribohelica		F Flexiviridales	100–110 Å Leptoviridae / 120–130 Å Mesoviridae / 150 Å Adroviridae
			E Sagovirales		90 Å Myxoviridae / 180 Å Paramyxoviridae / Stomatoviridae / *Thylaxoviridae*
		C Ribocubica	N Gymnovirales / E Togavirales		3–32 Napoviridae / 9–92 Reoviridae / Arboviridae

Tumours of the *first group* are induced by four different families of viruses: the poxviridae, the papilloviridae, the adenoviridae and the herpes viridae.

Tumours of the *second group* are essentially induced by viruses belonging to one family of viruses, the "thylaxoviridae".*

1. *DNA virus-induced tumours*

a. *Poxviridae* (Figs 22 and 23)

The first of the DNA virus-induced tumours to be discussed are those caused by poxviruses. They represent an exceptional group, particularly because they are spontaneously benign, and because malignant evolution has to be induced (infection of newborn or cortisone-treated rabbits). One may therefore ask whether the malignant "quality" is linked to the cell and whether one is justified in considering some poxviruses as true oncogenic agents, the more so, since it is now known that cells in which poxvirus replicate cease to multiply through inhibition of DNA synthesis. It is customary, however, to include these poxviruses among the oncogenic viruses. They are the *Shope fibroma* of the rabbit (and various other similar fibromas of diverse animals), *molluscum contagiosum* of man and the more recently discovered *Yaba tumour* of the monkey.

Tumours in this category provide also a specific feature when studied with the electron microscope on account of the permanent presence of viral elements which are detectable morphologically. All tumour cells contain the viruses and when some cells appear devoid of them it is generally because the section was cut too thin. Since viral material is visible at all stages, the development of the virus may be followed step by step from penetration to maturation. Spectacular evidence of uncoating, release of nucleic acid core, and its assembly with membrane material has been marshalled through studies with the electron microscope. The ultrastructure of the cells of any one of these tumours is characterized by large patches of finely granular material (released DNA) described in Shope fibroma by Bernhard *et al.* (1955) as "viroplasm", or as "factory sites" (in vaccinia) by Dales (1963). These correspond to the Feulgen-positive inclusion bodies observed with the light microscope. Immature viruses appear in the midst of the "viroplasm" and consist at first of a round or ellipsoid particle bound by a simple membrane. Progressive modelling of the particle then occurs; another envelope surrounds the first, while the core undergoes a series of deep changes until the highly complex and unique structure of the mature virion is formed. This is "huge" in terms of viral dimensions and measures between 220 mμ and 350 mμ.

Aside from the virus in the tumour, there are ultrastructural abnormalities induced by its presence and these particularly concern the nuclei in which margination of chromatin and increase in nucleolar "dense granules" are

* See "Suggestions for the classification of RNA oncogenic viruses", New York, 1966.

frequent occurrences. Differences in detail exist, yet very similar observations have been made of molluscum contagiosum (Dourmashkin and Bernhard, 1959) and the Yaba tumour of the monkey (De Harven and Yohn, 1966).

Details of the remarkable structure and cycle of the poxvirus should be sought in the review by Joklik (1966), in the various general reviews mentioned above and in the very recent ultrastructural study by Scherrer (1968) of Shope fibroma virus in tissue cultures.

To sum up, the ultrastructural data on poxviruses-induced growths indicate the presence of the virus itself and the lesions it causes. However, there are no fundamental differences between the appearance of these cells and those infected with a non-oncogenic poxvirus.

b. *Papilloviridae* (Fig. 25)

Tumours induced by this family of oncogenic viruses are the diverse *papillomas*, *polyoma* and the *simian virus 40* (SV40) tumour. In striking contrast to the preceding family of viruses, the papilloviridae are small in size (around 30 mμ) and some of them induce highly malignant growths. Typically they replicate in the nucleus. The baffling fact is that these viruses are as a rule observed in the electron microscope or recovered only in benign growths. When malignant transformation occurs, they are no longer found; that is, the virus is "masked". Thus cancerous cells derived from papillomas of the rabbit (VX carcinomas), or from polyomas of mice and SV40-induced tumour in hamsters, may present no special ultrastructural feature nor offer any clue as to their viral origin (Howatson and Almeida, 1960; De Thé *et al.*, 1960; Duffel *et al.*, 1964). It should therefore be kept in mind that the description of these viruses as they appear in the cells is either gathered from *in vitro* experiments or from studies of benign growths (warts in the human, papilloma in the rabbit, etc.), or lytic lesions preceding growth, as in polyoma.

Viruses of the papilloviridae family, when observed in benign tumours, are usually extremely numerous. They begin to appear in the nuclear sap and to be associated with the nucleolus in Shope papilloma (Stone *et al.*, 1959; Bernhard *et al.*, 1959) or with the chromatin network in the case of polyoma. This organelle may be strikingly increased in size and its varied components may be changed in distribution, as is very obvious in SV40 infection (Granboulan *et al.*, 1963; Granboulan and Tournier, 1965). At a later stage the viruses destroy the karyoplasm and they replace it. The nucleus then appears like a bag filled with spherical particles of 28–32 mμ in diameter bounded by one membrane around a center which shows little detail in thin section. The overall picture is that of nuclear and cytoplasmic lysis with remnants of cell structure amidst randomly scattered virus particles.

The remarkable structure of the viral nucleocapsid discovered after the advent of the phosphotungstic acid technique is one of a polyhedron with cubic symmetry and 20 faces (icosahedron). The number of capsomeres is 72. For details on virus architecture see the reviews already quoted.

c. Adenoviridae (Fig. 24)

These viruses are not known to be oncogenic in their natural hosts, particularly in man, but they do induce cancer in heterologous hosts. Not all human adenoviruses are oncogenic and the degree of oncogenicity varies. At present oncogenic human adenoviruses include types *3, 5, 7, 12, 18* and *21*.

In the cell *in vitro* and in non-transformed cells, the virus, which is larger than the papilloviridae (65 mμ), accumulates in the nucleus where it tends to form beautiful crystalline arrays. It later erupts into the cytoplasm (Levinthal *et al.*, 1967; Martinez-Palomo, 1968). Here again no virus particle can be observed *in vivo* in the tumour with the electron microscope (Salomon, 1967) and the ultrastructural aspects of malignant cells resemble those of tumours described already.

However, the ultrastructural pathologist who is in search of some evidence of the viral origin of tumours is probably in a better research position here than when studying other types of tumours* in view of the new information acquired about "tumour" antigen. Kalnins *et al.* (1967) and Levinthal *et al.* (1967) showed that the characteristic fibres present in the nucleus (in a classical lytic cycle) could be stained with ferritin-conjugated antibodies prepared against the tumour. These fibres have been observed only during a lytic cycle. If malignant transformation in tumours induced by viruses reflected both an early event and an abortive cycle of the virus, then the presence of such fibres in malignant cells would provide a clue to its viral origin.

It is obvious that a search for antigens that are visible in the electron microscope should be made, even if only based on a hypothesis. The problem of finding traces of a "masked" virus is of so great importance, particularly in relation to human cancer, that it seems worth while to draw attention to it here.

d. Herpes-viridae (Figs 26 and 27)

These viruses occur in completely different groups of species, since they are found in cells of *amphibian tumours* (frog adenocarcinoma), and in *human tissue cultures* derived from lymphosarcomas or leukaemias.

In contrast to the papilloviridae and the adenoviridae, these viruses have an envelope, and their cycle occurs both in the nucleus and in the cytoplasm of the tumour cells. Were they to be shown to be responsible for malignant transformation, then the mechanism involved would necessarily be different from that involved in the last two families, since they are present in morphologically complete form in cancer cells, as is the case with RNA oncogenic viruses, also enveloped viruses. In neither frog adenocarcinoma nor human tissue culture, has the aetiological role of the herpes-like virus particle been definitely proven. Arguments in favour of it, however, can be brought forward. Although purified preparations of the virus have not

---

* This is also true of SV40-induced tumours (Oshiro *et al.*, 1967).

yet been tested, cell-free filtrates from amphibian tumour tissues are capable of inducing tumours (Lunger, 1964; Lunger *et al.*, 1965). In the case of human cultures, one of the major objections, that of the virus being merely a herpes simplex contaminant, has been excluded. Indeed, it has been shown that herpes virus particles observed in these human tissues are antigenically different from other known herpes viruses (see references in Conference on Acute Leukemia and Burkitt's Tumour, Rye, 1967).

For these various reasons, a description of these viruses is of primary importance to those who are concerned with the ultrastructure of cancer cells.

The virion itself measures approximately 180 mμ; it has an external envelope surrounding a protein nucleocapsid with the same icosahedral cubic symmetry as that of all other DNA viruses discussed here. The structure of herpes viruses has been largely studied by Wildy and Horne (Wildy *et al.*, 1960), and the reader is referred to their papers for details.

In frog adenocarcinoma cells and in cultures bearing the herpes type of virus (see the Proceedings of the Symposium held at Rye, 1967), the particle is found first in the nucleus where it consists of a double shell which takes on the form of a double ring in section, or as a single shell containing a variably-shaped electron dense nucleoid core (Dalton and Manaker, 1967). In the case of Lucké's carcinoma, the "core" is often found to be free in the karyoplasm and it is thought (Fawcett, 1956) that assembly of the nucleic acids and of the membrane components takes place at this site. The particle is often seen to be passing through the nuclear membrane by means of a "budding" process, which endows it with a second envelope. This double-membrane cytoplasmic particle acquires through budding at the plasma surface a third envelope which is characteristic of the complete mature virion (100–140 mμ) found in the intracellular spaces.

Save for minute details, there are no fundamental differences between a *tumour cell* containing a virus of the type described here and a cell infected by herpes simplex. In other words, as in the case of poxviridae, the characteristic lesion of these malignant cells consists solely (in the present stage of our knowledge) of the presence of the virus itself and of accompanying cellular modifications. The latter correspond to phagocytic activities (lysosomes) and to diverse manifestations of necrosis.

2. RNA virus-induced tumours

As already pointed out, the RNA viruses which induce tumours have been recently classified in the same family for which the name "thylaxoviridae" has been tentatively proposed (see footnote p. 452).

They include the *sarcoma-leukaemia viruses* of various mammals and fowl and the *mammary tumour-agent* of mice. All of them possess an envelope and are more or less comparable in structure. They all form by "budding" of the cell surface, and hence resemble in many ways myxovirus, although no helicoidal symmetry of the capsid nor any specific enzyme has so far been demonstrated. In contrast to non-enveloped DNA oncogenic viruses, they are as a rule always found in cancer cells, although, from the electron microscopic point of view, they are often scarce.

Ultrastructurally speaking, cells of tumours in this group show the involved virus particle provided it is present in great abundance, thereby acquiring a characteristic feature, or if the particle is rare, then the cells appear as the normal cells of origin. Indeed, in sharp contrast to the DNA virus-infected cells in which the accompanying lesions are especially frequent in the nucleus, cellular changes are not always detectable, since lysis is relatively rare (Fig. 29).

With these general remarks concerning tumours induced by RNA oncogenic viruses, the characteristics of each of these will now be very briefly reviewed. Further details should be sought in reviews already referred to.

a. The murine leukaemias and sarcomas (Figs 28 and 29)

Cells involved in the now classical virus-induced *leukaemias* of Gross, Moloney, Rauscher, Friend, Graffi etc., may belong to any of the lymphoid categories, viz. myeloblasts, lymphoblasts and rather surprisingly, megakaryocytes (DeHarven and Friend, 1960a, b; Dalton et al., 1961).

As just mentioned, these cells have a normal appearance, and only appear abnormal when the virus is visible (Fig. 28). When examined in thin sections, the particle belongs to the "C" type,* and presents two different aspects in terms of its stage of development. During an early stage it is spherical with an electron-lucent centre surrounded by two envelopes. During a second stage the virus appears to have lost its roundness and is slightly irregular in outline. Its centre is dense and only the external envelope is visible. Its overall size is 80–100 mμ. These particles are present in the extracellular space or in intracellular vacuoles which represent invaginations of the cell surface. Development of the particles occurs through "budding" at the surface membrane and all stages from early and progressive changes of the cell surfaces to pediculated particle formation and pedicle rupture can be followed (for details see in particular DeHarven and Friend, 1960a).

The same morphological description is true of the virus-induced murine *sarcomas*. In the case of Moloney sarcoma, however, striated muscle is also involved (rhabdomyosarcoma?) which under the electron microscope has a strikingly specific structure on account of the presence of myofibrils (Dalton, 1966).

No ultrastructural difference can be made out in the case of lymphoid tissues from non-leukaemic mice where the "C" particle is present as a latent agent, although particles in these cases are usually more rare.

The structure of the leukaemia particle as revealed by the negative staining technique has been described by De Thé and O'Connor (1966) for the Rauscher virus.

* See the recommendations of the New York Group (1967) on the classification of the A type of particle.

b. The fowl leukaemias and sarcomas

The same general remarks apply here, too. There are no specific changes in the cells and they may be altogether lacking, so that these cells often appear normal. However, in a few cases, nonspecific reactions have been found. Hypertrophy of nucleoli, an increase in "dense granules" and in inter-chromatinic granules, an increase in the number of mitochondria and loss of organized ergastoplasm have all been described to occur in Rous sarcoma (Haguenau and Beard, 1962; Di Stefano and Dougherty, 1965; Courington and Vogt, 1967).

Virus particles containing lysosomes (grey bodies) have been described to occur in myeloblastosis (Bonar *et al.*, 1959; De Thé *et al.*, 1964).

On the whole, here again, the virus represents the major observable abnormality.

The leuco-sarcomatosis particle of the fowl is somewhat different from the C murine particle in that the mature virus is able to retain better its spherical appearance and does not usually assume an irregularly shaped external envelope. The internal membrane in the complete virion remains visible. But in other respects they are alike and like the C murine particle they are extracellular or present in vacuoles that still represent the extra-cellular space. For details about the development of fowl particles, the reader is referred to Haguenau and Beard (1962), Heine *et al.* (1962), Beard (1963) and De Thé (1964); and for studies of these particles with the phosphotungstic acid technique, to Dourmashkin and Simons (1961), and Bonar *et al.* (1963).

Whilst the presence of the virus particle is in most instances a feature of leukaemic and sarcoma cells, its absence in other situations might be accounted for in two or more ways. First, it might not occur in sufficient number; second, it might be defective. As demonstrated by Bryan *et al.* (1955), the amount of virus in Rous sarcoma depends on the initial dose of virus employed to induce the tumour in the animal. Rous sarcoma induced initially with a low dose of the virus contains only a few or even no virus particles when studied with the electron microscope, while tumours induced with high doses may be laden with particles (Haguenau *et al.*, 1958). Similarly, *in vitro* studies show that when "defective" strains of Rous sarcoma are used to induce cellular transformation (the so-called "non-producing" (NP) cells), the number of particles detectable with the electron microscope is strikingly reduced (Dougherty and Di Stefano, 1965; Courington and Vogt, 1967; Robinson, 1967), to the extent of creating the impression of there being a total absence of particles in some samples (Haguenau and Hanafusa, 1968).

There are no typical avian particles in Rous sarcoma induced in *mammals* other than the dog (see below), when this tissue is studied under the electron microscope (Febvre *et al.*, 1964; Bucciarelli *et al.*, 1967*b*). Nor has any bio-logical activity been demonstrated. It is thought that in this particular case, the virus (the genome of which is known to be present because it may be reactivated by back-passage to the fowl, or by association with chicken cells) is incomplete, and incapable of achieving maturation. From a morphological standpoint one does not know with which structure this "masked" virus is identifiable and these sarcomas will present no characteristics. However, one exception exists in cerebral Rous sarcoma induced in the dog (Bucciarelli *et al.*, 1967*a*) in which particles bearing the morphology of avian particles were found (Rabotti *et al.*, 1966). If these results are substantiated and biological activity is demonstrated, then their importance in establishing a link between an avian virus and a mammalian sarcoma hardly needs stressing.

c. *Mammary cancer of mice* (Figs 10, 14, 18 and 19)

Mice adenocarcinomas characteristically contain the Mammary Tumour Agent which has been shewn to be the so-called B type of particle (see reviews by Moore, 1963; Lasfargues, 1964). Another particle, the A type of particle,⋆ is almost always present in this tissue and is probably the precursor of the B type of particle. This particle is also found in several other tumours including lymphoid and plasma cell tumours of mice. Hence it is possible that this particle at times has nothing to do with the B type of particle. Furthermore, though it does contain RNA, as demonstrated by Smith (1967) with an ultrastructural cytochemical technique, the A type of particle has never been shown to be infective.

Recent work on mammary cancer indicates the presence of characteristic lesions of the basal membrane but no specific changes in the cells. In those instances where the virus particles were found to be rare, the cells resembled normal alveolar cells lining a lumen, or cells densely packed into lobules. They appeared differentiated to the point of being functional, or, on the contrary, appeared anaplastic with very few organelles in them (Figs 14 and 18).

IV. Ultrastructure of Human Cancer

It was shown in Section II how very unspecific are the changes found in malignant cells. Indeed when no hypertrophy or hypotrophy (anaplasia) of subcellular organelles is found, malignant cells may be said to resemble normal cells. In this case some cancers may present a characteristic feature due to the particular tissue from which they derive and many studies are ultimately concerned more with the cellular histogenesis of the cancer than with unusual traits that would be related to the malignant state.

Only certain categories of cancer can be reviewed here; for example, those cancers that have already been studied sufficiently to be dealt with as a group. And even among these several have received little attention; other studies involve only one or two types of a given variety and so they will not be mentioned.

Lymphosarcomas, leukaemias, cancers of the breast and genital organs,

⋆ See the recommendations of the New York Group (1967) on the classification of the A type of particle.

hepatomas, tumours of the digestive tract, tumours of the endocrine glands, brain and skin, and renal tumours, are the principal categories considered here. The problem of identifying virus particles, which are known to be present in some of these tissues, will be touched upon because in certain cases the demonstration of particles constitutes the only evidence of any abnormality, and because the implications of such evidence are far-reaching.

A. *Lymphosarcoma and leukaemia*

Ultrastructural research in human malignancies of the lymphohemato-poietic system have been mainly directed at demonstrating virus particles. This is of course not surprising, since in most experimental lympho-sarcomas and leukaemias the available evidence has shown that the causative agent is a virus, and since the pathological findings and the evolution of the disease in man are in many respects similar to those in the animal. This explains why the bulk of the descriptions that have been published, have very little to do with the fine structure of cells *per se*.

It is difficult to distinguish *in vivo* between neoplastic cells of the lymphopoietic system and normal cells. Thus, for example, *myeloma* cells have the typical features of a plasma cell (Fruhling and Porte, 1958; Sörenson, 1964), although there are some differences relating to cell size, pleomorphism of the ergastoplasmic sacs and a tendency to forming Russell bodies. But rarely do such cells resemble lymphoblasts (Salomon *et al.*, 1963; Maldonado *et al.*, 1966).

Except for the occurrence of nine cases of Hodgkin's disease and one case of *lymphosarcoma* containing nuclear "dense granules", Leplus *et al.* (1961) were unable to find any special features in cells from 69 specimens of human *lymphosarcomas, reticulosarcomas* and *Hodgkin's disease*.

Biopsy specimens of *African lymphosarcomas* (*Burkitt's tumour*) have been studied by several workers, including Dourmashkin (1965), Achong and Epstein (1966) and Bernhard (1966). Some cells of this tumour were found to be peculiar: there were nuclear projections, numerous annulate lamellae, yet on the whole they had the appearance of typical lympho-blasts. Virus particles were never reported except by Griffin *et al.* (1966), who recognized reo- and herpes-like virus particles. These results await confirmation.

Virtually all the known varieties of *leukaemia* have been studied under the electron microscope. The granulocytic, myeloblastic and lymphocytic types have been investigated by Akasaka (1959), by Bessis and Thiery (1961, 1962a, b), by Anderson (1966) and McDuffie (1967) and here again, except for invagination of the nuclear membrane, some changes in the mitochondria, and an increase in Auer bodies, the cells were regarded as being normal in morphology (Chandra *et al.*, 1968). One team of workers, that of Dmochowski *et al.* (1967), were able to find virus particles in lymph nodes or spleen specimens from patients with lymphosarcoma or leukaemia. By closely examining their micrographs, one can recognize particles that are identical to murine leukaemia particles (Bernhard's type C). This type of particle was reported in 11 out of 35 lymph node biopsy specimens from patients with acute lymphocytic leukaemia, and in 11 out of 38 patients with malignant lymphoma. Seman (1968) has also found this type (?) of particle in recently examined leukaemic buffer-coats. No other laboratory has so far been able to confirm these findings (Bernhard and Leplus, 1964). This applies to studies of platelets and megakaryocytes as well; platelets from leukaemic patients showed no virus particles and only hypertrophy of the endoplasmic reticulum (Haguenau *et al.*, 1963; Arnoult and Haguenau, 1966), while megakaryocytes appeared relatively immature.

Thus *in vivo*, virus particles have been observed only exceptionally.

The particles reported to be present in one case of myeloma (Sörenson, 1964) may well be microvesicular bodies, and those described by Ota *et al.* (1963) in human chloroleukaemia seem to correspond to nuclear bodies and pores of the nuclear membrane. Arnoult and Haguenau (1966) and others (Anderson, 1965; De Harven, 1965) have discussed at length why some other reports of virus particles occurring in leukaemic tissues failed to provide convincing evidence and so this subject will not be dealt with here.

The situation is quite different when tissue cultures, and not the original cells or tumours, are investigated. Though cells grown *in vitro* resemble morphologically the cells of origin, they have a tendency to de-differentiate, so that they assume the appearance of blast or stem cells (Epstein and Achong, 1965; De Harven *et al.*, 1967; Uzman *et al.*, 1966; see the proceedings of the Conference on Acute Leukaemia and Burkitt's Tumour, Rye, 1967). Virus particles are definitely present in some of these cultures, but except in rare cases they are found to belong to the C type of particle causing murine leukaemia (Stewart *et al.*, 1963; Trujillo *et al.*, 1967). In most of the cases studied, the virus resembles herpes virus, the material from leukaemic patients or Burkitt's tumours. According to Dalton and Zeve (1967), 21 out of 69 tissue cultures prepared from leukaemia, lymphoma and other neoplastic specimens, and 12 out of 16 cultures from African Burkitt's tumour, were positive. However, since this finding of a virus in human malignancy is of great theoretical importance, it should be mentioned in passing that this particle has immunological characteristics of its own and is distinct from other known herpes viruses, and that the chances of contamination of the tissue specimens seem rather remote, particularly in view of the fact that the virus particle was found in cultures from many widely separated laboratories. The aetiological relationship of the particle to these diseases, nevertheless, remains far from clear.

B. *Mammary cancers*

These were among the first to be studied systematically with the electron microscope (Haguenau, 1959a, b) and this was made possible by access to a rich source of clinical material at the Cancer Institute of Villejuif. Ninety-one cancers with different histological patterns were examined and it was found that there were no special cytological changes. Inconstant but striking findings involved the nucleus where "spotted nucleoli" could be observed and where alterations in the mitochondria varied from "cloudy swelling" to "myelin degeneration". Augmentation of the Golgi apparatus so characteristic a finding in mice mammary cancer was sometimes not present. The membrane surfaces of the cells were altered: interdigitations between adjacent cells were increased, while at the apical pole microvilli were either considerably augmented or reduced. A special feature of some cancers of the mammary gland was the presence in the cytoplasm of many cells of fine *fibrils* and *intracytoplasmic ducts*. Fine fibrils were subsequently reported by many workers (Wellings and Roberts, 1963; Gros and Girardie, 1967; Sykes *et al.*, 1968). Sykes and colleagues showed that some of these fibrils represented tonofilaments, which is not surprising, since this gland is of ectodermal origin. However, evidence for the myoepithelial nature of some of these fibrils has been brought forward by Haguenau (1959*a*, *b*). As to the intracytoplasmic ducts, they may correspond to the lumen of a diverticulum (Murad and Scarpelli, 1967; Gonzales Licea *et al.*, 1967) or represent abortive canaliculi (Sykes *et al.*, 1968).

Interest in mammary gland cancer has centred on three other facets: first, the observation that *desmosomes* can be quite normal (Murad and Scarpelli, 1967; Gonzales-Licea *et al.*, 1967) and even well developed (Tellem *et al.*, 1966; Gros and Girardie, 1967). This contradicts the familiar notion of cellular looseness in cancer tissue. Second, paradoxical findings have been reported about the development of *basement membranes*. Although they were ruptured (as expected in some cases—Wellings and Roberts, 1963; Sykes *et al.*, 1968), they were thickened and consistently present in the ducts of malignant scirrhous carcinomas, as described by Murad and Scarpelli (1967). Such a finding was all the more unexpected because medullary carcinomas, supposedly of low malignancy, turned out to be free of any basal membrane.

Both of these findings, however, may be accounted for: first in the case of the desmosome, it is not evident that the laxity is augmented between all cells and metastasis may and does occur for groups of cells as well as for individual elements. The ability of highly malignant cells to form desmosomes in tissue cultures may be retained, as has been shown by studies on aggregation of cells derived from highly malignant clones (Halpern *et al.*, 1968). Finally, as mentioned already on p. 445, desmosomes, though normal in appearance in cancers, may be modified cytochemically, and may thus acquire the faculty of binding colloidal iron, a property not shared by normal desmosomes.

As for the observation of thickening of the basal membrane, both Murad and Scarpelli (1967) and Gonzales-Licea *et al.* (1967) are aware of the possibility of there being anomalous hypersecretion in cancer cells.

The third facet is concerned with the origin and variety of the pro-liferating cells. Murad and Scarpelli (1967) suggested that medullary carcinoma might originate from the cuboidal epithelium of the ducts, and scirrhous carcinoma from the myoepithelial cells. Sykes *et al.* (1968) are of the opinion that malignant cells from duct-cell cancer originate from alveolar cells. The ducts might be secondarily infiltrated. Other authors confess to being unable to classify the anaplastic tumours in terms of their epithelial or mesenchymal origin. The problem in this area of research is far from settled.

C. *Cancers of the genital glands*

Studies of *carcinoma of the prostate* (Takayasu and Yamaguchi, 1962; Brandes *et al.*, 1964; Fisher and Jeffrey, 1965; Mao *et al.*, 1966) have so far failed to produce any evidence that this cancer has any unique features. Those tumours that appear well-differentiated resemble benign tumours, or the normal gland. But the degree of differentiation may vary greatly even in neighbouring cells. Mitochondria show diverse yet nonspecific changes, they are increased in number, which in the case of cancer cells is not always the rule. Measurements of the serum level of acid phos-phatase in patients with prostatic carcinoma correlate with the degree of differentiation of the cancer cells of this gland.

The resemblance cancer cells bear to normal cells is perhaps best illustrated in *tumours of the ovary*, as has been shown by Lynn *et al.* (1967). The malignant cells of a *dysgerminoma* have the morphology of the ovum and of the thecal cell, while the cell of a *seminoma* (Pierce, 1966) has the appearance of a primitive or blast-like cell of the testis. In similar fashion, the nine *carcinomas of the uterine cervix*, studied by Hinglais-Guillaud *et al.* (1961) indicated that despite the presence of much cellular pleomorphism associated with varied degrees of differentiation, the typical features of normal Malpighian stratified epithelium could be readily recognized: tonofibrils were present and the characteristic desmosomal attachment of ectodermal cells were quite prominent. Mitochondria, however, were increased in number and the basal membrane was frequently non-existent, or else ruptured.

D. *Cancers of the digestive tract*

These cancers also exhibit the pattern shown by original epithelial cells, though in a more or less varying degree. Cancers arising in the colon or rectum (Imaï and Stein, 1963; Birbeck and Dukes, 1963; Holl-mann, 1964; Spjut and Smith, 1967) are composed of many mucous and columnar cells, not to mention the non-differentiated cells. Thus they offer material for detailed study of mucous secretion. Studies of *rectal polyps* have raised a further point of interest, this being the presence in the cytoplasm of some cells of Feulgen-positive "inclusion bodies", which Leuchtenberger (1954) suggested were of viral origin. These inclusions were in fact shown to be the nuclei of wandering blood cells (Fisher and Sharkey, 1962; Hollmann and Staubli, 1962).

In Malpighian types of cancer, the cells appear to have lost their glandular features, and instead have the character of typical epidermal tissue layers. Tonofibrils may be considerably increased and desmosomes markedly hypertrophied (Haguenau et al., 1964). As in other types of cancer, mitochondria are found to be greatly increased in number, and to be altered in morphology. Interdigitations between adjacent cells may be considerably augmented, leading to a widening of intercellular spaces, especially at the basal part of these cells and facing the basal membrane. Some workers have found basal widening to be disrupted (Imaï and Stein, 1963). At the luminal surfaces the development of microvilli may be extremely marked or reduced. Among these microvilli small vesicles, possibly of pinocytic origin, may occur on occasion in great abundance (Haguenau et al., 1964; Hollmann, 1964).

E. Human hepatomas

Though little studied hitherto (Theron et al., 1962; Yasutake et al., 1962; Theron and Mekel, 1964; Toker and Trevino, 1966; Geil et al., 1968), it is clear that these tumours do not have any of the characteristics specific of malignancy. Indeed, they resemble normal hepatic cells, but there exist certain deviations so far as the abundance of the endoplasmic reticulum and amount of glucogen are concerned. Mitochondria are also reduced in number, but this may vary from cell to cell, and their morphology may not be altered at all. The Golgi apparatus has been described as being normal (Toker and Trevino, 1966) or hypertrophied (Yasutake et al., 1962). It is interesting to compare these hepatomas with those that are induced experimentally and to observe that the dramatic changes described on p. 448 are not so marked here. This is in keeping with the idea that the majority of these changes are related to toxicity rather than to the carcinogenicity of the drugs used.

F. Tumours of the endocrine glands

Those that have been examined under the electron microscope are, by and large, benign in appearance. This includes *pheochromocytomas*, *onkocytomas* and *insulinomas*. Most workers have been concerned primarily with the problem of pathogenesis of these proliferating cells, as mentioned earlier.

G. Tumours of the nervous system

These, too, fall mostly into the benign category, so far as fine structure is concerned. The tumours studied include *meningiomas* (Kepes, 1961; Gusek, 1962; Gonatas and Besen, 1962; Napolitano et al., 1963; Robertson, 1964), peripheral *nerve sheath tumours* (Waggener, 1966) and *astrocytomas*

(Duffel *et al.*, 1963, Raimondi *et al.*, 1962). Malignant tumours, e.g. *ganglioneuromas* (ganglioneuroblastomas), are similar in morphology to the normal ganglion cell of the autonomic nervous system. At present, investigators are mainly concerned with correlating both the clinical findings and catecholamine metabolism with the pathological findings (Staley *et al.*, 1967).

H. *Skin tumours*

The above remarks apply to these tumours as well. Benign tumours such as *molluscum contagiosum*, or *warts*, have been extensively investigated but they never become malignant. A generalized malignant verrucal disease, however, has been described by Ruiter and Van Mullem (1966). A virus of the papilloviridae family similar to that found in warts is present in this human malignant affection.

Rhabdomyosarcomas (Friedman *et al.*, 1965; Toker, 1968) are formed from undifferentiated cells, but in certain instances the cells retain in their cytoplasm characteristic striated fibrils. *Fibromyxosarcomas* (Leak *et al.*, 1967) comprise two types of cells, one dark, and the other pale and less well-differentiated. Both cells are probably of fibroblastic origin, as suggested by the presence of a mucopolysaccharide coating.

I. *Tumours of the kidney*

These include *hypernephromas*, which show a striking increase in the number of mitochondria and villi of the surface membrane, and accumulation of large lipid bodies in the cytoplasm. The electron microscope made it possible to establish the origin of the tumour cells at the expense of the proximal convoluted tubule epithelium (Oberling *et al.*, 1959). These observations have been confirmed by Seljelid and Ericsson (1965*a*, *b*) and by Ericsson *et al.* (1966).

V. General Conclusions

The findings reported in this chapter indicate that even at the ultrastructural level none of the morphological changes may be considered as specific of the cancer cell. An ensemble of features of the cancer cell, in place of unique characteristics, implies that there does exist rapid and excessive growth, yet in certain types of cancer these very features may be lacking. This is true not only of cancers that occur spontaneously, but of those that are induced experimentally, where the rapid onset or the intensity of the agent provoking abnormal growth might have helped to reveal "specific" changes.

Carcinogenic drugs have been found to produce changes that are more likely to be related to toxic actions than to carcinogenicity *per se*.

In the case of virus-induced tumours, changes likewise appear related to the viral cytopathic effect, and not necessarily to the malignant condition. These comments are not meant to create a negative impression, and in fact a better understanding of cancer has already been arrived at. For example, electron microscopic studies of tumours induced by viruses have provided some fundamentally new concepts, particularly the concept that in some instances (papilloviridae, adenoviridae) the causal virus is not morphologically detectable. This has far-reaching implications in terms of our search for virus-particles in human malignancies. On the other hand, the electron microscope has also revealed that a virus particle is in fact present in tissue cultures of human lymphosarcomas and leukaemias. This virus unexpectedly belongs to a group (*Herpes viridae*) which differs from the type of particle (C type) known to induce murine leukaemias and sarcomas. Thus, the import of the electron microscope in the study of the cancer cell is more than self-evident.

References

Abercrombie, M. and Ambrose, E. J. (1962). *Cancer Res.* **22**, 525-548.

Achong, B. G. and Epstein, M. A. (1966). *J. natn. Cancer Inst.* **36**, 877-897.

Akasaka, K. (1959). *Acta haemat. jap.* **22**, 41-57.

Allison, A. C. (1966). *Proc. R. Soc. Med.* **59**, 868-871.

Anderson, D. R. (1965). In *Methodological Approaches to the Study of Leukemias* (V. Defendi, ed.), No. 4, pp. 113-146. The Wistar Institute Symposium Monograph.

Anderson, D. R. (1966). *J. Ultrastruct. Res.* **9**, 1-42.

Arnoult, J. and Haguenau, Fr. (1966). *J. natn. Cancer Inst.* **36**, 1089-1109.

Ashworth, C. T., Sternbridge, V. A. and Lurbel, F. J. (1961). *Acta cytol.* **6**, 368.

Bässler, R. and Habighorst, L. V. (1964). *Beitr. path. Anat.* **130**, 446-488.

Beard, J. W. (1963). In *Advances in Cancer Research* (A. Haddow and S. Weinhouse, eds), Vol. 7, pp. 1-127. Academic Press, New York.

Becker, M. (1964). *Acta biol. med. germ.* **13**, 615-623.

Behnke, O. (1964). *Expl Cell Res.* **37**, 687-689.

Bencosme, S. A., Allen, R. A. and Latta, H. (1963). *Am. J. Path.* **42**, 1-21.

Benedetti, E. L. and Emmelot, P. (1967). *J. Cell Sci.* **2**, 499-512.

Benedetti, E. L. and Emmelot, P. (1968). In *Ultrastructure in Biological Systems* (A. J. Dalton and Fr. Haguenau, eds), Vol. 4, pp. 33-120. Academic Press, London.

Bernhard, W. (1960). *Cancer Res.* **20**, 712-727.

Bernhard, W. (1963). *Progr. exp. Tumor. Res.* **3**, 1-34.

Bernhard, W. (1966). In *The Nucleolus, its Structure and Function.* Natn. Cancer Inst. Monogr. No. 23, pp. 13-38.

Bernhard, W. (1969). In *Handbook of Molecular Cytology* (Lima de Faria, ed.), chap. 20. North Holland, Amsterdam.

Bernhard, W. and Granboulan, N. (1963). *Expl Cell. Res.* Suppl. 9, 19-53.

Bernhard, W. and Granboulan, N. (1968). In *Ultrastructure in Biological Systems* (A. J. Dalton and Fr. Haguenau, eds), Vol. 3, pp. 81-139. Academic Press, London.

Bernhard, W. and Leplus, R. (1964). In *Fine Structure of the Normal and Malignant Human Lymph Node* (G-V. McMillan, ed.), pp. 1-101. Pergamon Press, New York.

Bernhard, W. and Tournier, P. (1966). *Int. J. Cancer* **1**, 61-80.

Bernhard, W., Bauer, A., Harel, J. and Oberling, Ch. (1955). *Bull Cancer* **41**, 423-444.

R

Bernhard, W., Febvre, H. and Cramer, R. (1959). *C. r. hebd. Séanc. Acad. Sci.,* Paris, **249**, 483-485.

Bernhard, W., Tournier, P. and Lorans, G. (1965a). *C. r hebd. Séanc. Acad. Sci.,* Paris, **261**, 2137-2140.

Bernhard, W., Frayssinet, Ch., Lafarge, Ch. and Lebreton, E. (1965b). *C. r. hebd. Séanc. Acad. Sci.,* Paris, **261**, 1785-1788.

Bessis, M. and Thiery, J. P. (1961). *Nouv. Revue fr. Hémat.* **1**, 703-728.

Bessis, M. and Thiery, J. P. (1962a). *Nouv. Revue fr. Hémat.* **2**, 387-414.

Bessis, M. and Thiery, J. P. (1962b). *Nouv. Revue fr. Hémat.* **2**, 577-601.

Bessis, M., Breton-Gorius, J. and Thiery, J. P. (1958). *Revue Hémat.* **13**, 363-386.

Bessis, M., Breton-Gorius, J. and Binet, J. L. (1963). *Nouv. revue fr. Hémat.* **3**, 159-183.

Birbeck, M. C. S. and Dukes, C. E. (1963). *Proc. R. Soc. Med.* **56**, 793-797.

Birbeck, M. S. C. and Wheatley, D. N. (1965). *Cancer Res.* **25**, 490-498.

Bonar, R. A., Heine, U., Beard, D. and Beard, J. W. (1963). *J. natn. Cancer Inst.* **30**, 949-997.

Bonar, R. A., Parsons, D. F., Beaudreau, G. S., Becker, C. and Beard, J. W. (1959). *J. natn. Cancer Inst.* **23**, 199-225.

Bonneau, H. and Cesarini, J. P. (1968). Fourth European Regional Conference Rome. Vol. II, p. 577.

Bouteille, M., Abelanet, R. and Delarue, J. (1964). *Annls Anat. path.* **9**, 389-410.

Bouteille, M., Kalifat, S. R. and Delarue, J. (1967). *J. Ultrastruct. Res.* **19**, 474-486.

Brandes, D., Kirchheim, D. and Scott, W. W. (1964). *Lab. Invest.* **13**, 1541-1560.

Bryan, W. R., Calnan, D. and Moloney, J. B. (1955). *J. natn. Cancer Inst.* **16**, 317-335.

Bucciarelli, E., Rabotti, G. F. and Dalton, A. J. (1967a). *J. natn. Cancer Inst.* **38**, 359-381.

Bucciarelli, E., Rabotti, G. F. and Dalton, A. J. (1967b). *J. natn. Cancer Inst.* **38**, 865-889.

Burt, R. C., Killmeyer, L. A., Thomson, L. R. and Grauer, R. C. (1961). *Cancer Res.* **21**, 1427-1429.

Caspersson, T. O. (1950). In *Cell Growth and Cell Function—A Cytochemical Study.* W. J. Norton, New York.

Chambers, V. C. and Weiser, R. S. (1964). *J. Cell Biol.* **21**, 133-139.

Chandra, S., Moore, G. E. and Brandt, P. M. (1968). *Cancer Res.* **28**, 1982-1989.

Christensen, H. E., Iversen, O. H. and Rask-Nielsen, R. (1963). *J. natn. Cancer Inst.* **30**, 763-781.

Coman, D. R. (1944). *Cancer Res.* **4**, 625-629.

Coman, D. R. (1953). *Cancer Res.* **13**, 397-404.

Coman, D. R. (1960). *Cancer Res.* **20**, 1202-1204.

Conference on the Mammary Tumor Virus. Inverness, California. October 1964.

Conference on Acute Leukemia and Burkitt's Tumor, Rye, New York (1967). *Cancer Res.* **26**, 2419-2660.

Courington, D. and Vogt, P. K. (1967). *J. Virology* **1**, 400-414.

Creemers, J. and Jadin, J. M. (1968). *J. de Microscopie* **7**, 257-263.

Curgy, J. J. (1968). *J. Microsc.* **7**, 63-80.

Dales, S. (1963). *J. Cell Biol.* **18**, 51-72.

Dalton, A. J. (1959). *Lab. Invest.* **8**, 514-537.

Dalton, A. J. (1964). In *Cellular Control Mechanism and Cancer* (P. Emmelot and O. Mühlbock, eds), pp. 211-225. Elsevier, Amsterdam.

Dalton, A. J. (1966). *Natn. Cancer Inst. Monogr.* **22**, 143-168.

Dalton, A. J. and Haguenau Fr. (eds) (1962). In *Ultrastructure in Biological Systems,* Vol. 1, pp. 1-229. Academic Press, London.

Dalton, A. J. and Manaker, R. A. (1967). In *Carcinogenesis: A Broad Critique*, pp. 59-90. The Williams and Wilkins Company, Baltimore.

Dalton, A. J. and Zeve, V. H. (1967). *Cancer Res.* **27**, 2465-2470.

Dalton, A. J., Law, L. W., Moloney, J. B. and Manaker, R. A. (1961). *J. natn. Cancer Inst.* **27**, 747-791.

Defendi, V. and Gasic, G. (1963). *J. comp. cell Physiol.* **62**, 23-31.

De Harven, E. (1965). In *Methodological Approaches to the Study of Leukemias* (V. Defendi, ed.), No. 4, pp. 147-156. The Wistar Institute Symposium Monograph.

De Harven, E. and Friend, Ch. (1960a). *J. biophys. biochem. Cytol.* **7**, 747-752.

De Harven, E. and Friend, Ch. (1960b). *Natn. Cancer Inst. Monogr.* **4**, 291-311.

De Harven, E. and Yohn, D. S. (1966). *Cancer Res.* **26**, 995-1008.

De Harven, E., Clarkson, B. and Strife, A. (1967). *Cancer* **20**, 911-925.

De Man, J. C. H. (1960). *J. natn. Cancer Inst.* **24**, 795-819.

De Man, J. C. H. and Van Rijssel, Th. G. (1961). *J. natn. Cancer Inst.* **26**, 919-947.

De Thé, G. (1964). *Natn. Cancer Inst. Monogr.* **17**, 652-671.

De Thé, G. and O'Connor, T. E. (1966). *Virology* **28**, 713-728.

De Thé, G., Rivière, M. and Bernhard, W. (1960). *Bull. Cancer* **47**, 569-584.

De Thé, G., Becker, C. and Beard, J. W. (1964). *J. natn. Cancer Inst.* **32**, 201-235.

Di Stefano, H. S. and Dougherty, R. M. (1965). *Virology* **27**, 360-377.

Dmochowski, L. (1968). In *Perspectives in Leukemia* (W. Dameshek and P. M. Dutcher, eds), pp. 34-63. Grune and Stratton, Inc., New York.

Dmochowski, L., Yumoto, T., Grey, C. E., Hales, R. L., Langford, P. L., Taylor, H. G., Freireich, E. J., Schullenberger, C. C., Shively, J. A. and Howe, C. D. (1967). *Cancer* **20**, 760-777.

Dolowy, W. C. (1966). *Nature, Lond.* **210**, 110-111.

Dougherty, R. M. and Di Stefano, H. S. (1965). *Virology* **27**, 351-359.

Dourmashkin, R. (1965). *Eur. J. Cancer* **1**, 309-312.

Dourmashkin, R. and Bernhard, W. (1959). *J. Ultrastruct. Res.* **3**, 11-38.

Dourmashkin, R. and Simons, P. J. (1961). *J. Ultrastruct. Res.* **5**, 505-522.

Duffel, D., Farber, L., Shelley, C., Hartmann, J. F. and Nelson, E. (1963). *Am. J. Path.* **43**, 539-554.

Duffel, D., Hinz, R. and Nelson, E. (1964). *Am. J. Path.* **45**, 59-73.

Easty, G. C. and Mercer, E. H. (1960). *Cancer Res.* **20**, 1608-1613.

Emmelot, P. and Benedetti, E. L. (1960). *J. biophys. biochem. Cytol.* **7**, 393-396.

Emmelot, P. and Benedetti, E. L. (1967). In *20th Symposium on Fundamental Cancer Research 1966*. Carcinogenesis: a broad critique. pp. 471-533. The Williams and Wilkins Company, Baltimore.

Epstein, M. A. and Achong, B. G. (1965). *J. natn. Cancer Inst.* **34**, 241-253.

Ericsson, J. L. E., Seljelid, R. and Orrenius, S. (1966). *Virchows Arch. path. Anat. Physiol.* **341**, 204-223.

Fasske, E. and Themann, H. (1960). *Beitr. path. Anat.* **122**, 313-344.

Fasske, E. and Morgenroth, K. Jr. (1966). *Oncologia, Roma* **20**, 113-128.

Fawcett, D W. (1956). *J. biophys. biochem. Cytol.* **2**, 725-742.

Febvre, H., Rothschild, L., Arnoult, J. and Haguenau, Fr. (1964). *Natn. Cancer Inst. Monogr. No.* 17, pp. 459-477.

Fisher, E. R. and Sharkey, D. A. (1962). *Cancer* **15**, 160-170.

Fisher, E. R. and Jeffrey, W. (1965). *Am. J. clin. Path.* **44**, 119-134.

Fiske-Michelson, S. and Haguenau, F. (1969). *J. natn. Cancer Inst.* **42**, 545-558.

François, D. (1968). Thèse, Faculté des Sciences, Paris.

Frei, J. V. (1962). *J. Cell Biol.* **15**, 335-341.

Frei, J. V. and Sheldon, H. (1961). *J. biochem. biophys. Cytol.* **11**, 724-729.

Friedlander-Binggeli, M. (1959). *J. biochem. biophys. Cytol.* **5**, 143-152.

Friedmann, I., Harrison, D. F. N., Tucker, W. N. and Bird, E. S. (1965). *J. clin. Path.* **18**, 63-68.

Fruhling, L. and Porte, A. (1958). *Annls. Anat. Path.* **3**, 538-557.

Geil, J. H., Stenger, R. J., Behki, R. M. and Morgan, W. S. (1968). *J. natn. Cancer Inst.* **40**, 713-730.

Goldberg, B. and Green, H. (1964). *J. Cell Biol.* **22**, 227-258.

Gonatas, N. V. and Besen, M. (1962). *J. Neuropathol. exp. Neurol.* **22**, 263-273.

Gonzales-Licea, A., Yardley, J. H. and Hartmann, W. H. (1967). *Cancer* **20**, 1234-1247.

Granboulan, N. and Tournier, P. (1965). *Annls Inst. Pasteur, Paris* **109**, 837-854.

Granboulan, N., Tournier, P., Wicker, R. and Bernhard, W. (1963). *J. Cell Biol.* **17**, 423-440.

Greenstein, J. P. (1954). *Biochemistry of Cancer*, 2nd ed. Academic Press, New York.

Greider, M. H. and Elliott, D. W. (1964). *Am. J. Path.* **44**, 663-678.

Greider, M. H., Elliott, D. W. and Zollinger, R. M. (1963). *J. Am. med. Ass.* **186**, 566-569.

Griffin, E. R., Wright, D. H., Bell, T. M. and Ross, M. G. R. (1966). *Eur. J. Cancer* **2**, 353-358.

Gros, C. M. and Girardie, J. (1967). *Bull. Cancer* **54**, 225-246.

Gross, L. (1968). *Oncogenic Viruses*, 2nd ed. Pergamon Press, New York and Oxford.

Gusek, W. (1962). *Beitr. path. Anat.* **127**, 274-326.

Gustafsson, R. G. and Afzelius, B. A. (1963). *J. natn. Cancer Inst.* **30**, 1045-1075.

Habel, K. (1962). *J. exp. Med.* **115**, 181-193.

Haguenau, Fr. (1959a). *Path. Biol.* **7**, 989-1015.

Haguenau, Fr. (1959b). *Bull. Ass. fr. Étude Cancer* **46**, 177-211.

Haguenau, Fr. (1960a). In *The Gustav Stern Symposium on Perspectives in Virology*, (M. Pollard, ed.), pp. 160-173. Burgess Press, Minneapolis, Minnesota.

Haguenau, Fr. (1960b). *Natn. Cancer Inst. Monogr.* **4**, 211-249.

Haguenau, Fr. (1966-67). *Rev. fr. Étud. clin. biol.* **11**, 969-986; **12**, 114-133.

Haguenau, Fr. and Beard, J. W. (1962). In *Ultrastructure in Biological Systems* (A. J. Dalton and Fr. Haguenau, eds), Vol. I, pp. 1-59. Academic Press, London.

Haguenau, Fr. and Bernhard, W. (1955). *Bull. du Cancer* **42**, 537-544.

Haguenau, Fr. and Hanafusa, H. (1968). *Virology* **34**, 275-281.

Haguenau, Fr. and Hollmann, K. H. (1963). *Bull. Ass. Fr. Étude Cancer* **50**, 29-48.

Haguenau, Fr. and Lacour, F. (1955). In *The Fine Structure of Cells*, pp. 316-321. P. Noordhoff, Ltd., Gröningen.

Haguenau, Fr., Rouiller, Ch. and Lacour, F. (1955). *Bull. du Cancer* **42**, 350-357.

Haguenau, Fr., Dalton, A. J. and Moloney, J. B. (1958). *J. natn. Cancer Inst.* **20**, 633-649.

Haguenau, Fr., Hollmann, K. H., Levy, J. P. and Boiron, M. (1963). *J. Microsc.* **2**, 529-538.

Haguenau, Fr., Hollmann, K. H. and Albot-Parturier, M. (1964). *Bull. Cancer* **51**, 55-72.

Haguenau, Fr., Hollmann, K. H., Mouriquand, J. and Mouriquand, C. (1965). *J. Microsc.* **4**, 253-264.

Halpern, B., Pessac, C. and Haguenau, F. (1968). *C.r. hebd. Séanc. Acad. Sci., Paris,* **267**, 1672-1675.

Hanafusa, H., Hanafusa, T. and Rubin, H. (1964). *Proc. natn. Acad. Sci. U.S.A.* **51**, 41-48.

Hartmann, H. A. (1965). *Archs Path.* **79**, 126-134.

Hay, E. D. and Revel, J. P. (1963). *J. Cell Biol.* **16**, 29-51.
Heine, U., De Thé, G., Ishiguro, H., Sommer, J. R., Beard, D. and Beard, J. W. (1962). *J. natn. Cancer Inst.* **29**, 41-105.
Herdson, P. B., Garvin, P. J. and Jennings, R. B. (1964). *Lab. Invest.* 1032-1037.
Hinglais-Guillaud, N., Moricard, R. and Bernhard, W. (1961). *Bull. du Cancer* **48**, 283-316.
Hollmann, K. H. (1962). *J. Microsc.* **1**, 159-162.
Hollmann, K. H. (1964). *Archs Mal. Appar. dig.* **53**, 975-994.
Hollmann, K. H. and Staubli, W. (1962). *J. Microsc.* **1**, 137-142.
Howatson, A. F. (1964). In *Advances in Cancer Research* (A. Haddow and S. Weinhouse, eds), Vol. 8, pp. 1-40. Academic Press, London.
Howatson, A. F. and Almeida, J. D. (1960). *J. biophys. biochem. Cytol.* **7**, 753-760.
Howatson, A. F. and Ham. A. W. (1955). *Cancer Res.* **15**, 62-69.
Hruban, Z., Swift, H. and Rechcigl, M. (1965). *J. natn. Cancer Inst.* **35**, 459-495.
Hruban, Z., Kirsten, W. H. and Slesers, A. (1966). *Lab. Invest.* **15**, 576-588.
Hsu, W. S. (1967). *Z. Zellforsch.* **82**, 376-380.
Hübner, G., Paulsson, F. and Kleinsasser, O. (1967). *Virchow's Arch. path. Anat. Physiol.* **343**, 34-50.
Imaï, H. and Stein, A. A. (1963). *Gastroenterology* **44**, 410-418.
Jezequel, A. M. (1959). *J. Ultrastruct. Res.* **3**, 210-215.
Joklik, W. K. (1966). *Bact. Rev.* **30**, 33-66.
Jones, A. L. and Fawcett, D. W. (1966). *J. Histochem. Cytochem.* **14**, 215-232.
Kalnins, V. I., Stich, H. F., Gregory, C. and Yohn, D. S. (1967). *Cancer Res.* **27**, 1874-1886.
Kepes, J. (1961). *Am. J. Path.* **39**, 499-510.
Kim, J. W. and Boatman, A. J. (1967). *J. Virology* **1**, 205-214.
Kleinfeld, R. G. and Von Haam, E. (1959). *Cancer Res.* **19**, 769-779.
Kobayashi, E. (1963). *Sapporo med. J.* **23**, 1-16.
Koinov, R. (1967). *Cancer* **20**, 1181-1185.
Krishan, A., Uzman, B. G. and Hedley-Whyte, E. T. (1967). *J. Ultrastruct. Res.* **19**, 563-572.
Lafontaine, J. G. and Allard, C. (1964). *J. Cell Biol.* **22**, 143-172.
Lardemer, F. and Haguenau, Fr. (1969). (In preparation.)
Lasfargues, E. Y. (1964). *Laval méd.* **35**, 901-908.
Lazarus, S. S. and Volk, B. W. (1962). *Lab. Invest.* **11**, 1279-1294.
Leak, L. V., Caulfield, J. B., Burke, J. F. and Mckhann, C. F. (1967). *Cancer Res.* **27**, 261-285.
Leduc, E. H. and Wilson, J. W. (1959). *J. biophys. biochem. Cytol.* **6**, 427-430.
Leduc, E. H., Bernhard, W. and Tournier, P. (1966). *Expl Cell Res.* **42**, 597-616.
Leplus, R., Debray, J., Pinet, J. and Bernhard, W. (1961). *C.r. hebd. Séanc. Acad. Sci., Paris* **253**, 2788-2790.
Lesseps, R. J. (1963). *J. exp. Zool.* **153**, 171-182.
Leuchtenberger, C. (1954). *Lab. Invest.* **3**, 132-142.
Levinthal, J. D., Cerottini, J. C., Ahmad-Zadeh, C. and Wicker, R. (1967). *Int. J. Cancer* **2**, 85-102.
Loewenstein, W. R. (1966). *Ann. N.Y. Acad. Sci.* **137**, 441-472.
Loewenstein, W. R. and Kanno, Y. (1967). *J. Cell Biol.* **33**, 225-234.
Lunger, P. D. (1964). *Virology* **24**, 138-145.
Lunger, P. D., Darlington, R. W. and Granoff, A. (1965). *Ann. N.Y. Acad. Sci.* **126**, 289-314.
Lupulescou, A. and Petrovici, A. T. (1963). *Acta biol. med. germ.* **11**, 409-416.
Luse, S. and Lacy, P. E. (1960). *Cancer* **13**, 334-346.

Lynn, J. A., Varon, H. H., Kingsly, W. B. and Martin, J. H. (1967). *Am. J. Path.* **51**, 639-661.
Maldonado, J. F., Brown, A. L., Bayrd, E. D. and Pease, G. L. (1966). *Cancer* **19**, 1613-1627.
Mao, P., Nakao, K. and Angust, A. (1966). *Cancer Res.* **26**, 955-973.
Mao, P. and Molnar, J. J. (1967). *Am. J. Path.* **50**, 571-603.
Martinez-Palomo, A. (1968). *Pathologia Microbiol.* **31**, 147-164.
Martinez-Palomo, A. and Brailowsky, C. (1968). *Virology* **34**, 379-382.
Martinez-Palomo, A., Brailowsky, C. and Bernhard, W. (1968). (In the press.)
McDuffie, N. G. (1967). *Nature, Lond.* **214**, 1341-1342.
McGavran, M. H. (1965). *Virchows Arch. path. Anat. Physiol.* **338**, 195-202.
Mengel, C. E. and Trier, J. J. (1961). *J. natn. Cancer Inst.* **27**, 1341-1360.
Mölbert, E., Hill, K. and Buchner, F. (1962). *Beitr. path. Anat.* **126**, 218-242.
Monneron, A. (1967). *J. Microsc.* **6**, No. 4, 71a-72a.
Moore, D. H. (1963). *Nature, Lond.* **198**, 429-433.
Morgan, H. R. (1968). *J. Virology* **2**, 1133-1146.
Mugnaini, E. (1964). *J. Ultrastruct. Res.* **11**, 525-544.
Mukherjee, T., Gustafsson, R. G., Afzelius, B. A. and Arrhenius, E. (1963). *Cancer Res.* **23**, 944-953.
Murad, T. M. and Scarpelli, D. G. (1967). *Am. J. Path.* **50**, 335-360.
Mutolo, V. and Abrignani, F. (1957). *Br. J. Cancer* **11**, 590-596.
Mylius, E. A. (1962). Reports from the 3rd Scandinavian Conference on Cell Research.
Nakai, T., Shubik, P. and Feldman, R. (1962). *Expl Cell Res.* **27**, 608-611.
Napolitano, L., Kyle, R. and Fisher, E. (1963). *Cancer* **17**, 233-241.
Nilsson, O. (1958). *J. Ultrastruct. Res.* **1**, 375-396.
Nilsson, O. (1962). *Cancer Res.* **22**, 492-494.
Novikoff, A. B. and Biempica, L. (1966). *Gann Monograph* **1**, 65-88.
Oberling, Ch. and Bernhard, W. (1961). In *The Cell* (J. Brachet and A. E. Mirsky, eds), Vol. 5, pp. 405-496. Academic Press, New York.
Oberling, Ch. and Rouiller, Ch. (1956). *Ann. Anat. Path.* **1**, 401-427.
Oberling, Ch., Rivière, M. and Haguenau, Fr. (1959). *Bull. Cancer* **46**, 356-381.
Oshiro, L. S., Rose, H. M., Morgan, C. and Hsu, K. C. (1967). *Virology* **31**, 183-186.
Ota, Z., Suzuki, S. and Higashi, S. (1963). *Gann* **54**, 481-486.
Pierce, G. B. Jr. (1966). *Cancer* **19**, 1963-1983.
Pillai, P. A. and Gautier, A. (1960). *Oncologia, Roma* **13**, 303-310.
Pinchouk, V. G., Zohkov, L. A. and Monastyrskaya, B. D. (1966). *Cytologia* **8**, 520-523.
Porter, K. R. and Bruni, C. (1959). *Cancer Res.* **19**, 997-1009.
Purdom, L. Ambrose, E. J. and Klein, G. (1958). *Nature, Lond.* **181**, 1586-1587.
Rabotti, G. F., Bucciarelli, E. and Dalton, A. J. (1966). *Virology* **29**, 684-686.
Raimondi, A. J., Mullan, S. and Evans, J. P. (1962). *J. Neurosurg.* **19**, 731-753.
Rappaport, H., Nakai, T. and Swift, H. (1963). *J. Cell Biol.* **16**, 171-186.
Remmer, H. and Merker, H. J. (1963a). *Klin. Wschr.* **41**, 276-283.
Remmer, H. and Merker, H. J. (1963b). *Science, N.Y.* **142**, 1657-1658.
Reynolds, R. C., Montgomery, P. O'B. and Karney, D. H. (1963). *Cancer Res.* **23**, 535-538.
Robertson, D. M. (1964). *Am. J. Path.* **45**, 835-848.
Robinson, H. L. (1967). *Proc. natn. Acad. Sci. U.S.A.* **57**, 1655-1662.
Ruiter, M. and Van Mullem, P. J. (1966). *J. invest. Derm.* **47**, 247-252.
Salomon, J. C. (1967). *Int. J. Cancer* **2**, 225-230.
Salomon, J. C., Salomon, A. and Bernhard, W. (1962). *Bull. du Cancer* **49**, 139-158.

Salomon, J. C., Betourné, C., Godeau, P. and Signier, F. (1963). *Path. Biol., Paris*, **11**, 718-728.
Salpeter, M. M. and Singer, M. (1960). *Anat. Rec.* **136**, 27-39.
Sankaranarayanan, K. and Hyde, B. B. (1965). *J. Ultrastruct. Res.* **12**, 748-761.
Scherrer, R. (1968). *Pathologia Microbiol.* **31**, 129-146.
Schrodt, G. R. and Foreman, C. D. (1965). *Cancer Res.* **25**, 802-811.
Schultz, H. (1961). In *Symposium über Krebsproblem*, pp. 13-35. Springer-Verlag, Berlin.
Schumacher, A. and Schultz, H. (1963). *Klin. Wschr.* **41**, 1188-1196.
Seljelid, R. and Ericsson, J. L. E. (1965a). *J. Microsc.* **4**, 759-770.
Seljelid, R. and Ericsson, J. L. E. (1965b). *Lab. Invest.* **14**, 435-447.
Seman, G. (1968). *Revue fr Étud. clin biol.* **13**, 763-772.
Setälä, K., Merenmies, L., Niskanen, E. E., Nyholm, M. and Stjernvall, L. (1960). *J. natn. Cancer Inst.* **25**, 1155-1189.
Setälä, K., Niskanen, E. E., Merenmies, L., Nyholm, M. and Stjernvall, L. (1961). *J. natn. Cancer Inst.* **26**, 985-1009.
Shipkey, F. H., Lieberman, P. H., Foote, F. W., Jr. and Stewart, F. W. (1964). *Cancer* **17**, 821-830.
Simard, R. and Bernhard, W. (1966). *Int. J. Cancer* **1**, 463-479.
Sjögren, H. O., Hellstrom, I. and Klein, G. (1961). *Cancer Res.* **21**, 329-337.
Smetana, K. and Busch, H. (1963). *Cancer Res.* **23**, 1600-1603.
Smetana, K., Steele, W. J. and Busch, H. (1963). *Expl Cell Res.* **31**, 198-202.
Smith, G. H. (1967). *Cancer Res.* **27**, 2179-2196.
Sorenson, G. D. (1964). *Lab. Invest.* **13**, 196-213.
Spjut, H. J. and Smith, N. M. (1967). *Exp. molec. Path.* **6**, 11-24.
Staley, N. A., Polesky, H. F. and Bensch, K. G. (1967). *J. Neuropath. exp. Neurol.* **26**, 634-653.
Stenger, R. J. (1963). *Am. J. Path.* **43**, 867-895.
Stewart, S. H., Landon, J., Lovelace, E. and McBride, J. (1963). *Lav. Ist Anat. Istol pathol. Univ. Perugia* **23**, 153-166.
Stone, S. R., Shope, R. E. and Moore, D. H. (1959). *J. exp. Med.* **110**, No. 4, 543-546.
Sugar, J. (1968). *Eur. J. Cancer* **4**, 33-88.
Suggestions for the Classification of Oncogenic RNA Viruses. (1966). *J. natn. Cancer Inst.* **37**, 395-397.
Svoboda, D. J. (1964). *J. natn. Cancer Inst.* **33**, 315-323.
Swift, H. (1959). In *Studies on Nuclear Fine Structure*. Brookhaven Symposia on Structure and Function of Genetic Elements. **12**, 134-151.
Swift, H. (1962). In *Interpretation of Ultrastructure* (R. J. C. Harris, ed.), Vol. 1, pp. 213-232. Academic Press, London.
Sykes, J. A., Recher, L., Jerstrom, P. H. and Whitescarver, J. (1968). *J. natn. Cancer Inst.* **40**, 195-224.
Takayasu, H. and Yamaguchi, Y. (1962). *J. Urol.* **87**, 935-940.
Tandler, B. and Shipkey, F. H. (1964a). *J. Ultrastruct. Res.* **11**, 292-305.
Tandler, B. and Shipkey, F. H. (1964b). *J. Ultrastruct. Res.* **11**, 306-314.
Tarin, D. (1967). *Int. J. Cancer* **2**, 195-211.
Tarin, D. (1968). *Int. J. Cancer.* (Submitted for publication.)
Tellem, M., Nedwich, A., Amenta, P. S. and Imbriglia, J. E. (1966). *Cancer* **19**, 573-584.
Theron, J. J., Pepler, W. J. and Liebenberg, N.v.d. W. (1962). *Nature, Lond.* **194**, 489-490.
Theron, J. J. and Meckel, R. C. (1964). *J. Gastroent.* **7**, 152-164.
Thiery, J. P. and Bader, J. P. (1962). *Arch. Mal. Appar. dig.* **51**, 301-322.
Thomas, A. J. (1965). *C.r. hebd Séanc. Acad. Sci., Paris* **261**, 267-270.
Toker, C. (1967). *J. Ultrastruct. Res.* **19**, 522-531.

Toker, C. (1968). *Cancer* **21**, 1164-1170.

Toker, C. and Trevino, N. (1966). *Cancer* **19**, 1594-1606.

Trujillo, J. M., Butler, J. J., Ahearn, M. J., Shullenberger, C. C., List-Young, B., Gott, C., Anstall, H. B. and Shively, J. A. (1967). *Cancer* **20**, 215-224.

Uzman, B. G., Foley, G. E., Farber, S. and Lazarus, H. (1966). *Cancer* **19**, 1725-1742.

Vasquez, C., Pavlovsky, A. and Bernhard, W. (1963). *C.r. hebd Séanc Acad. Sci., Paris* **256**, 2261-2264.

Verley, J. M. (1965). *Z. Krebsforsch.* **66**, 503-516.

Waggener, J. D. (1966). *Cancer* **19**, 699-709.

Watson, M. L. (1962). *J. Cell Biol.* **13**, 162-167.

Weber, A., Whipp, S., Usenik, E. and Frommes, S. (1964). *J. Ultrastruct. Res.* **11**, 564-576.

Wellings, S. R. and Roberts, P. (1963). *J. natn Cancer Inst.* **30**, 269-287.

Wildy, P., Russell, W. C. and Horne, R. W. (1960). *Virology* **12**, 204-222.

Yasutake, S., Nakao, K. and Matsunaga, Y. (1962). *Kurume med. J.* **9**, 193-204.

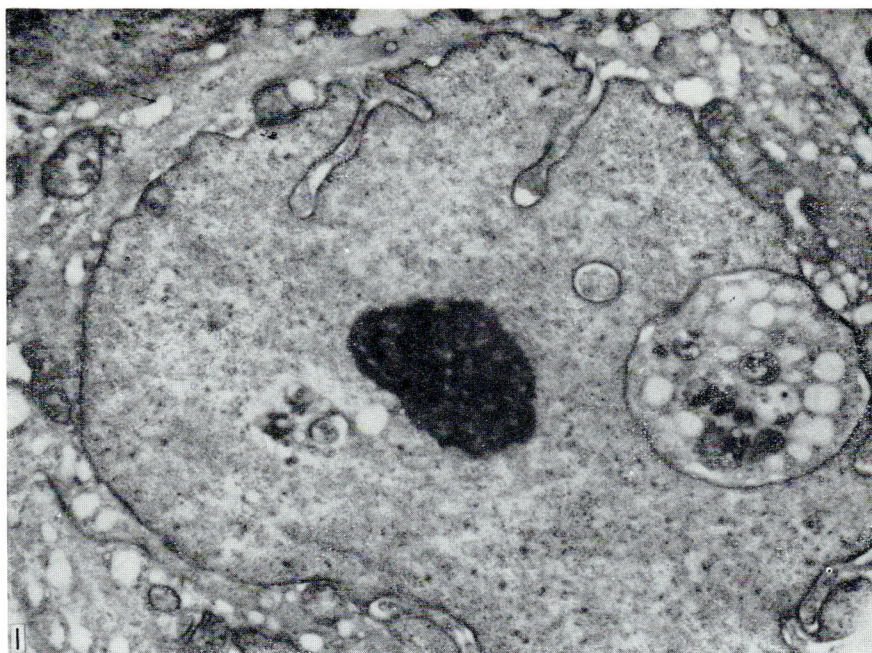

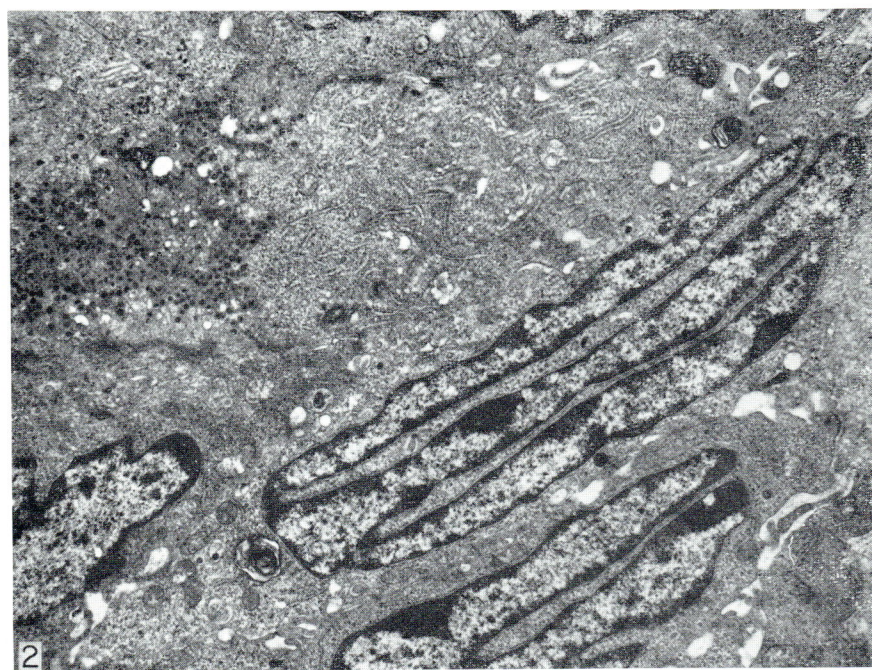

FIG. 1. Nucleus of a cell from a human mammary carcinoma showing "nuclear inclusions" and how they correspond to segregated invaginations of the cytoplasm (× 13 000).

FIG. 2. Hyperlobulated nucleus of a cell from a mouse mammary tumour. On the left-hand side viruses can be seen to have accumulated in the alveolar lumen (× 7200).

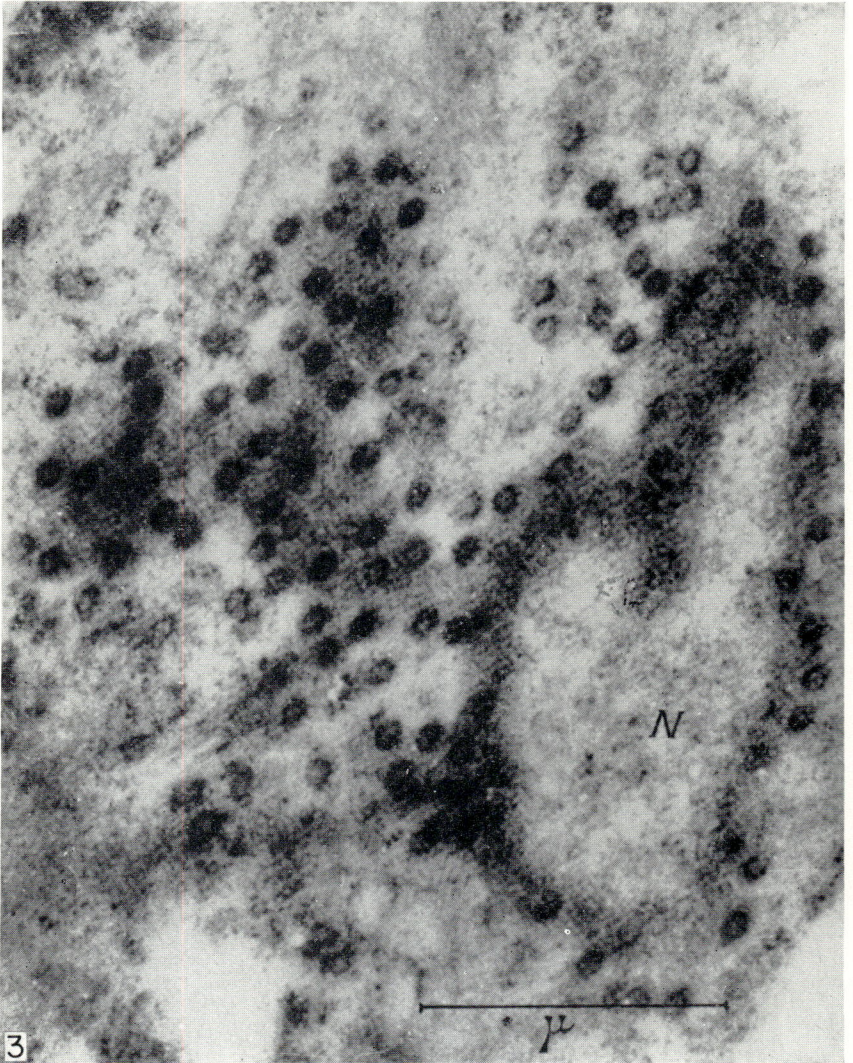

FIG. 3. Tangential section of a nucleus of a cell from a human hepatoma. The nuclear pores appear as annulate structures; their relationship to the nucleus is obvious but it is not difficult to understand why these structures have been mistaken for viruses when a nuclear cap is missing (× 40 000).

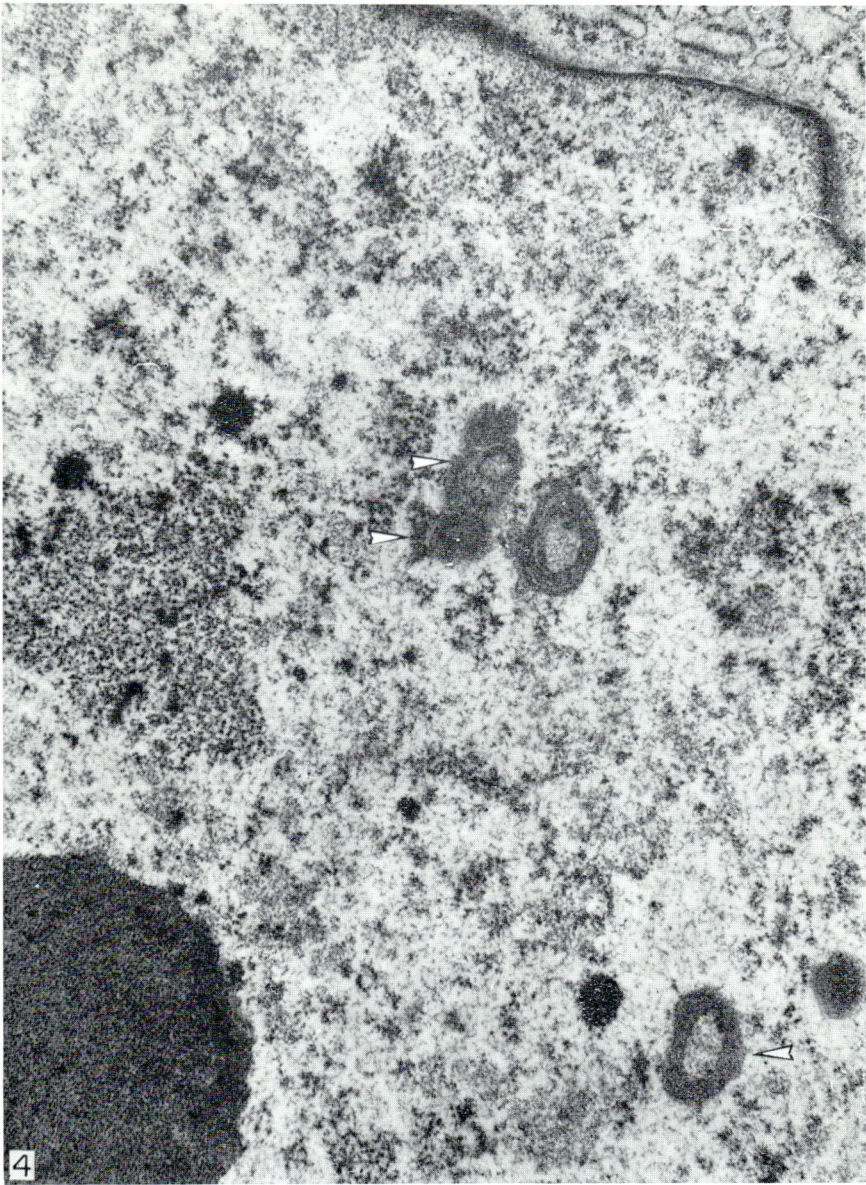

FIG. 4. Portion of a nucleus of a cell from a Rous sarcoma induced in a hamster, showing four of the nuclear components which may be hypertrophic in cancer: the nucleolus (low left), the interchromatinic granules forming patches above the nucleolus and close to which are two "dense bodies". The arrows indicate "nuclear bodies" (see text) (× 26 500).

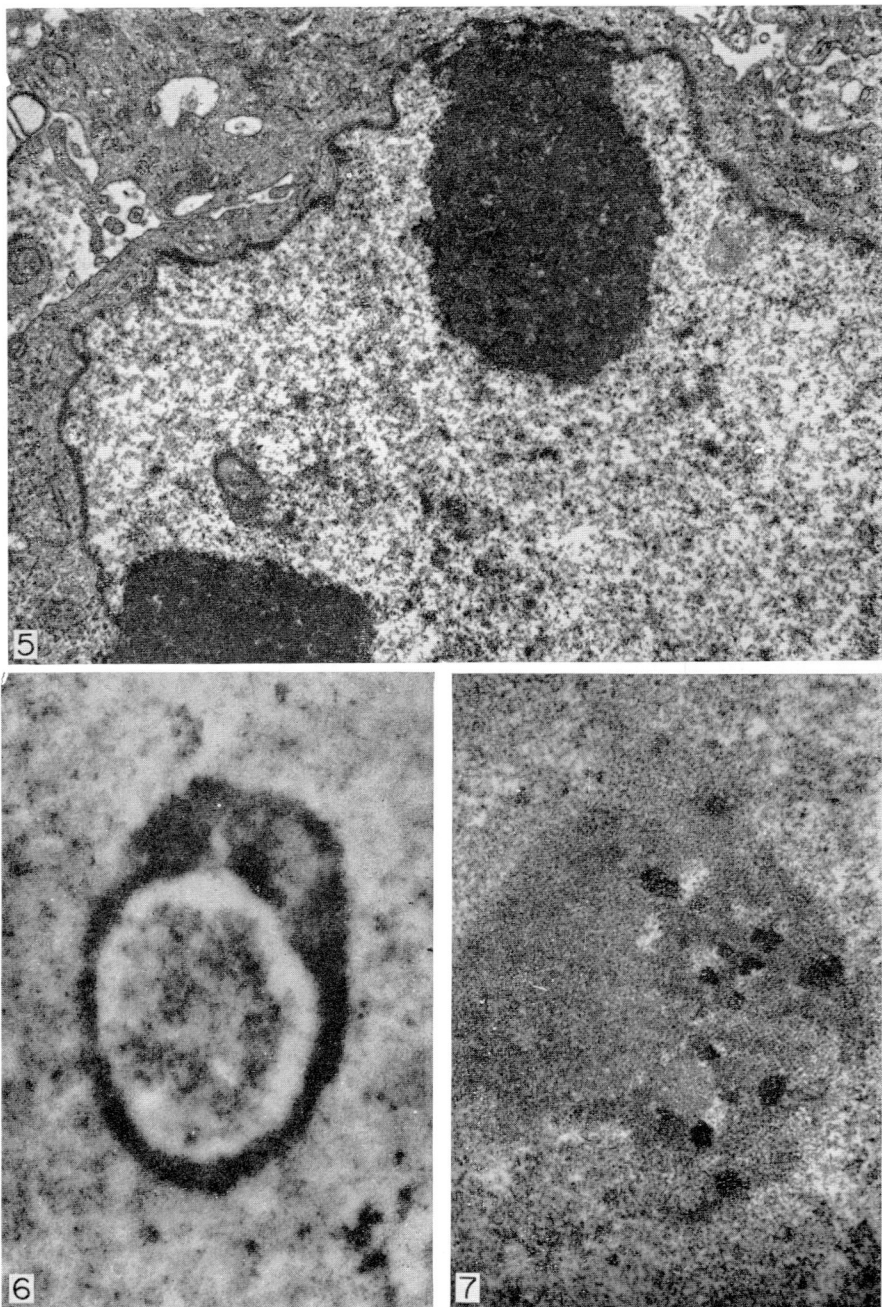

FIG. 5. Hypertrophic nucleoli apposed to the nuclear membrane in a hamster tumour induced by Rous sarcoma virus ($\times 15\ 000$). FIG. 6. Vacuolated nucleolus of a cell in human breast cancer ($\times 20\ 000$). FIG. 7. "Spotted" nucleolus in tissue culture from murine leukaemia—Rauscher infected cell leukaemia ($\times 21\ 500$).

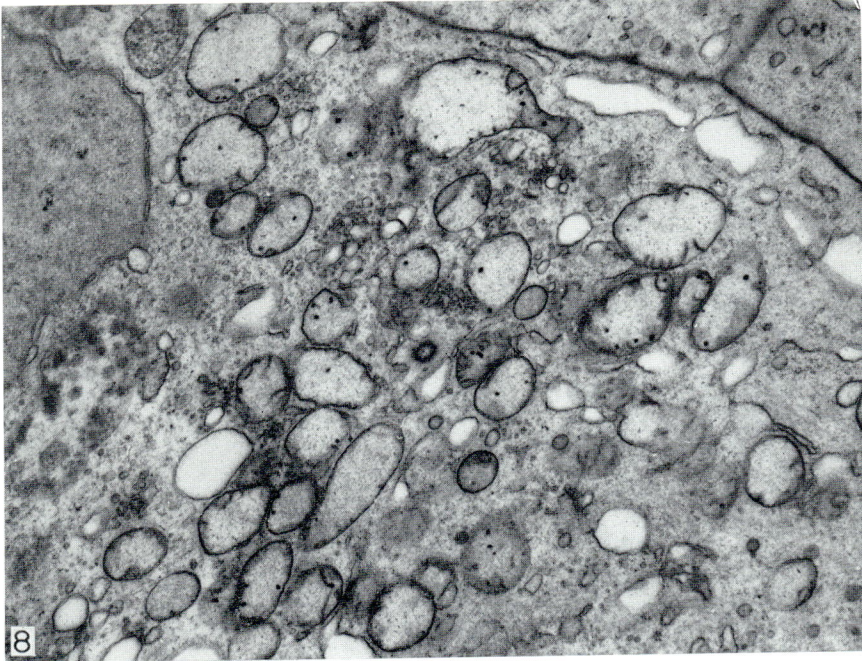

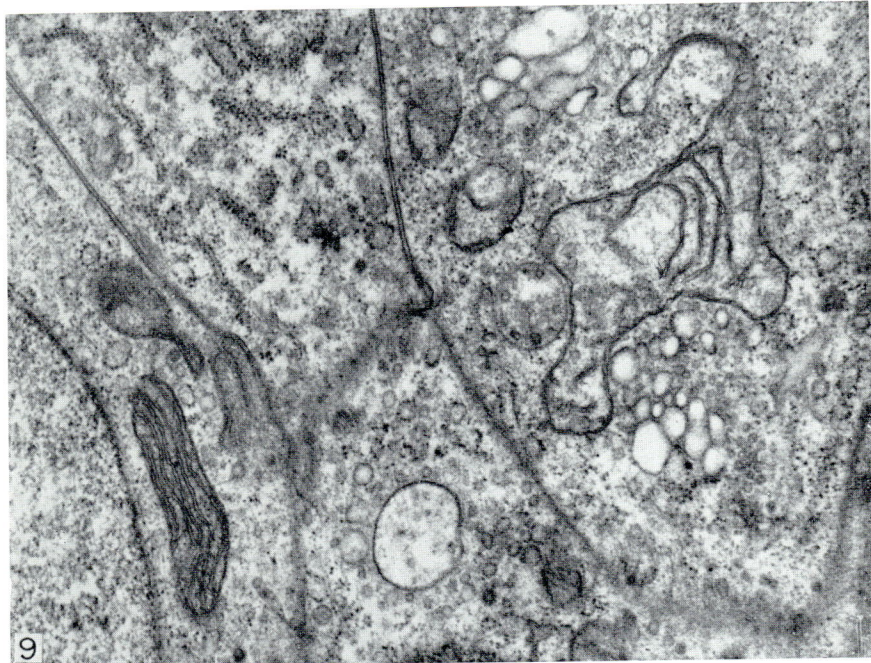

FIGS. 8 and 9. Diverse features of mitochondria in cells of human rectal cancer. Fig. 8 shows typical cloudy swelling while Fig. 9 includes on the right-hand side a gigantic bizarre-shaped mitochondrion (× 28 000 and × 18 000, respectively).

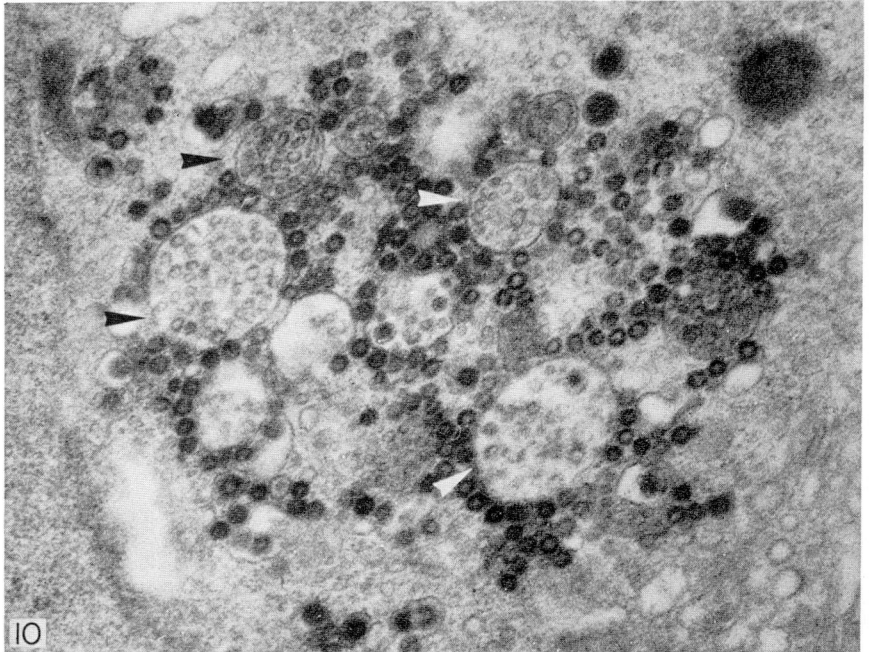

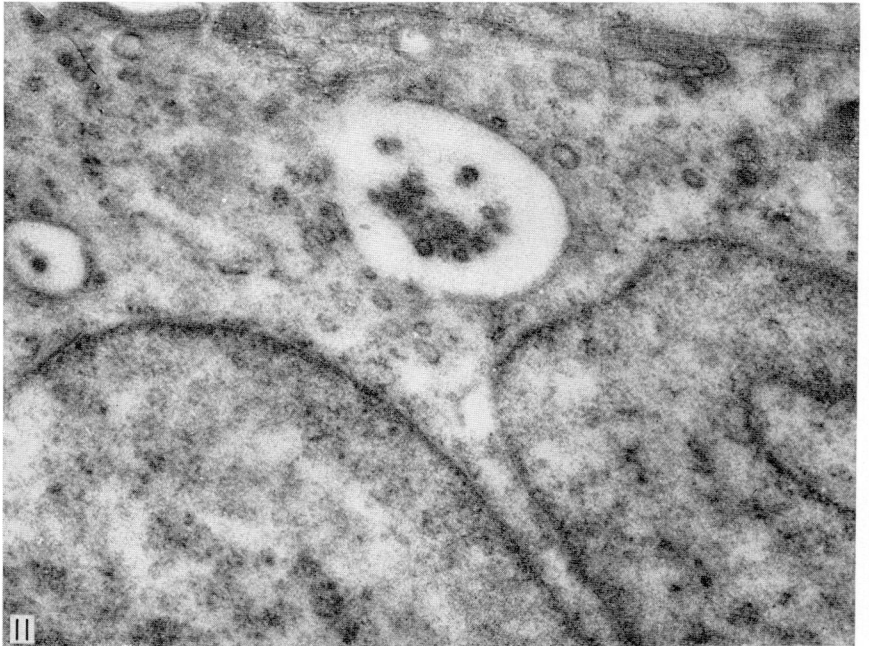

FIG. 10. Mammary cancer of the mouse. An inclusion body to illustrate the presence of typical multi-vesicular bodies (→) amidst the typical "A" particles (× 42 000). FIG. 11. A "multivesicular body" in a cancer of the breast (× 38 000).

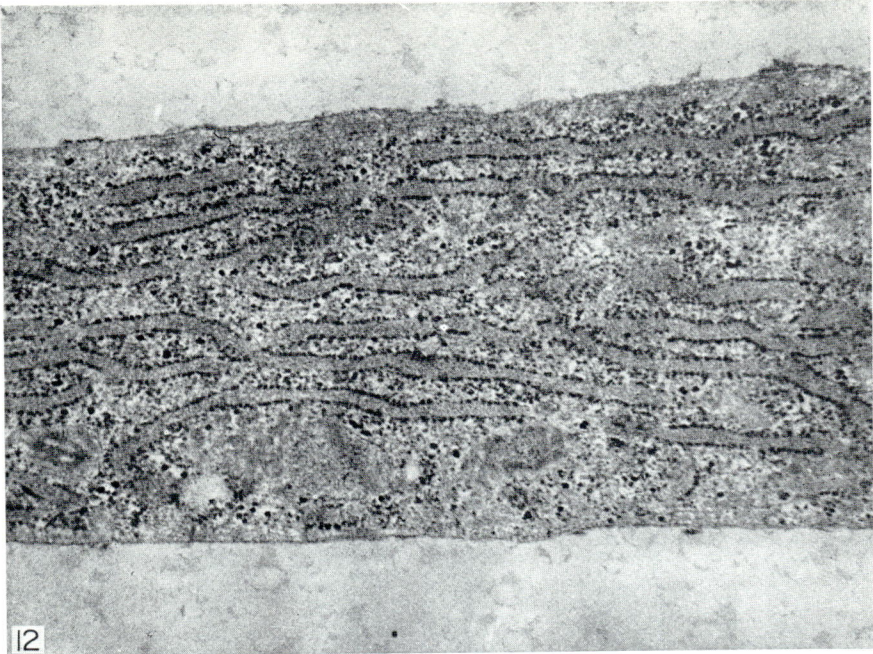

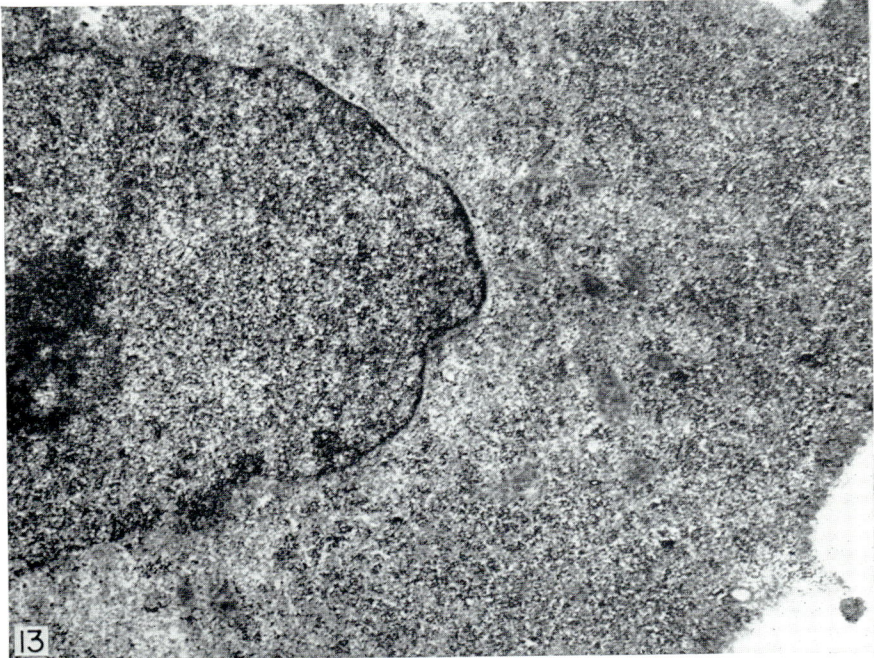

FIG. 12. Typical arrangement of the ergastoplasm in a normal chicken fibroblast. Note the array of ribosomes along the parallel cisternae ($\times$ 43 200).   FIG. 13. Lack of organization of the ergastoplasm in chicken fibroblast "transformed" by Rous sarcoma virus. Ribosomes are now randomly dispersed throughout the cytoplasm and are no longer disposed along membranes ($\times$ 24 000).

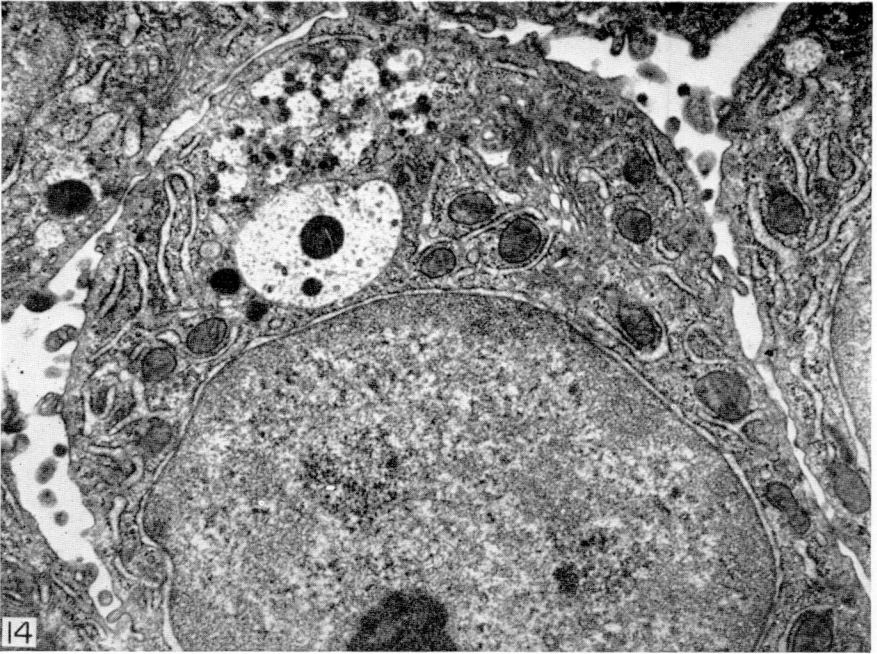

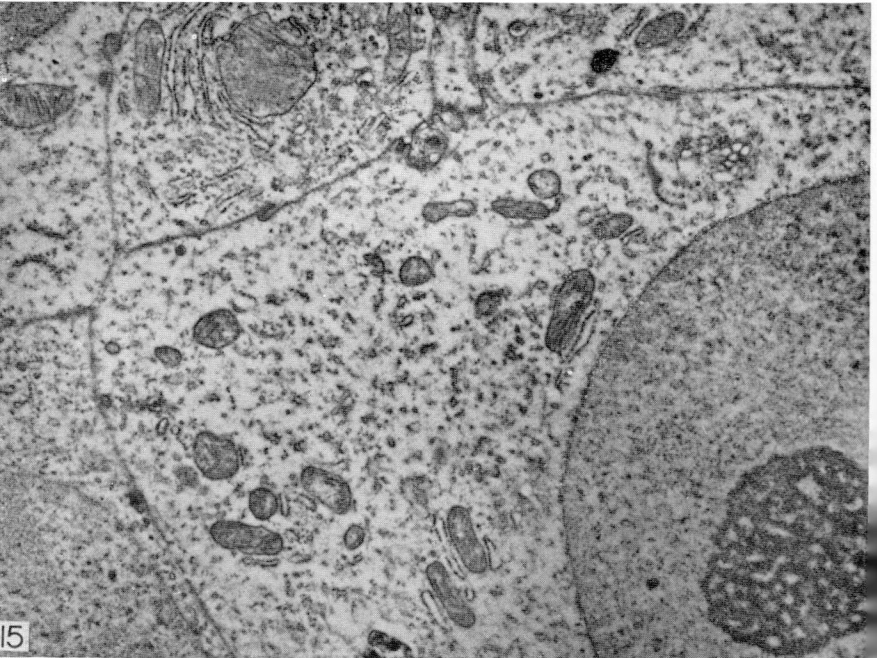

FIGS. 14 and 15 show two different features of cancer cells illustrating a highly differentiated condition and an anaplastic condition. Fig. 14. Note that milk elaboration taking place in hypertrophied and dilated Golgi vacuole as well as virus production are still proceeding in a mammary tumour of the mouse. Highly organized ergastoplasm is present ($\times$16 000). Fig. 15. Paucity of cytoplasmic organelles in a human breast carcinoma. Ergastoplasm is represented only by thin lamellae around mitochondria and the Golgi apparatus is reduced to a few vesicles. The nucleolus is hypertrophic ($\times$8500).

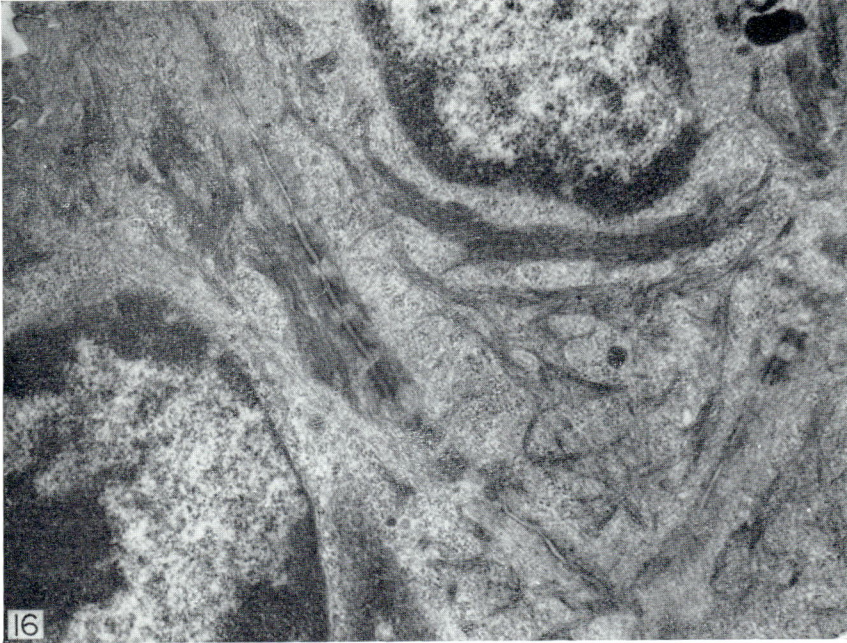

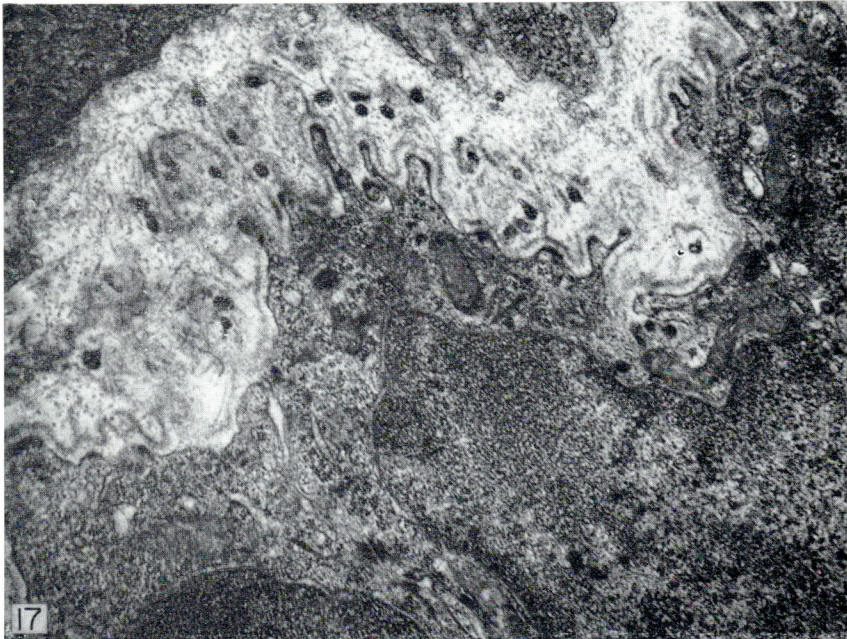

FIG. 16. Development of many tonofilaments and an increased number of desmosomes in mouse mammary tumour (× 19 000). FIG. 17. Hyperplasia and branching of basal membrane material in the same type of tumour (× 28 500).

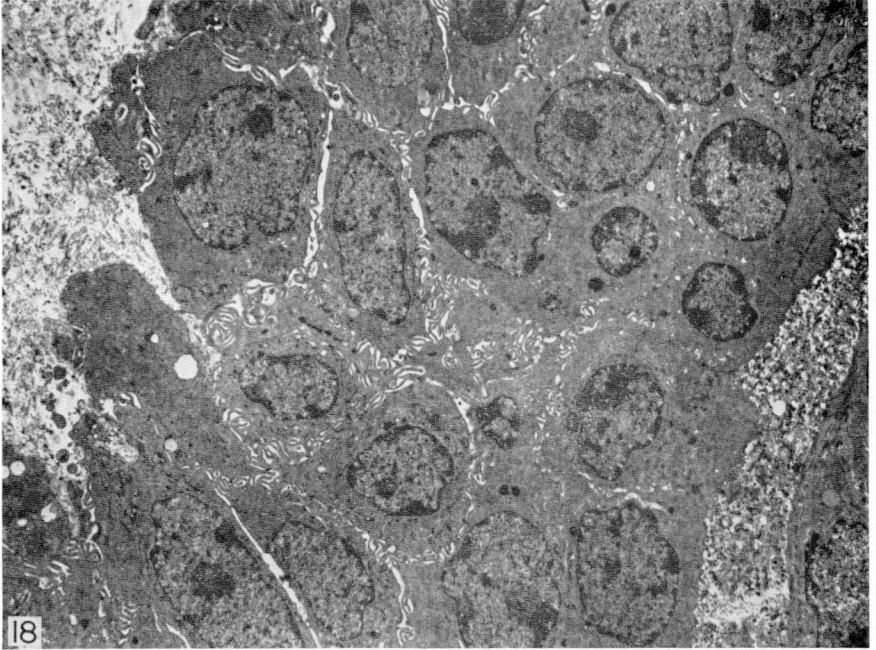

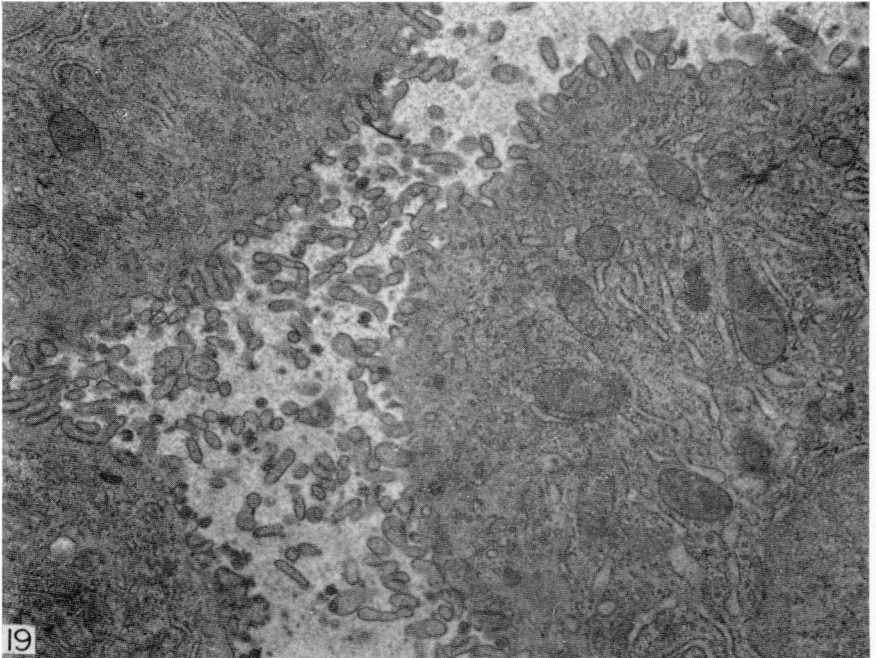

FIGS. 18 and 19. Two distinct features of mammary tumour in mice showing the "looseness" and widening of spaces in between cells, with the formation of inter-digitations (Fig. 18) and of hypervillosity (Fig. 19) ($\times$ 3200 and $\times$ 18 000, respectively).

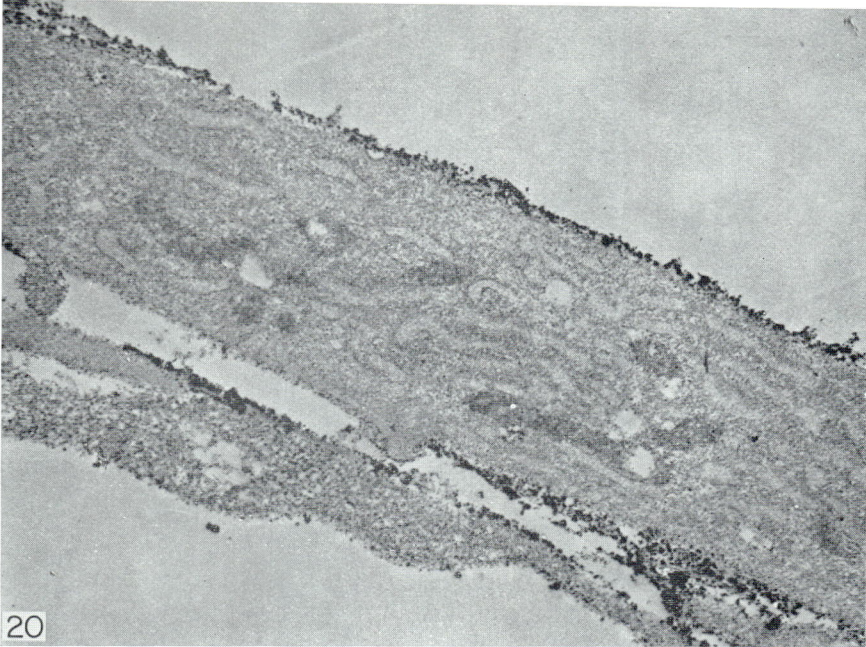

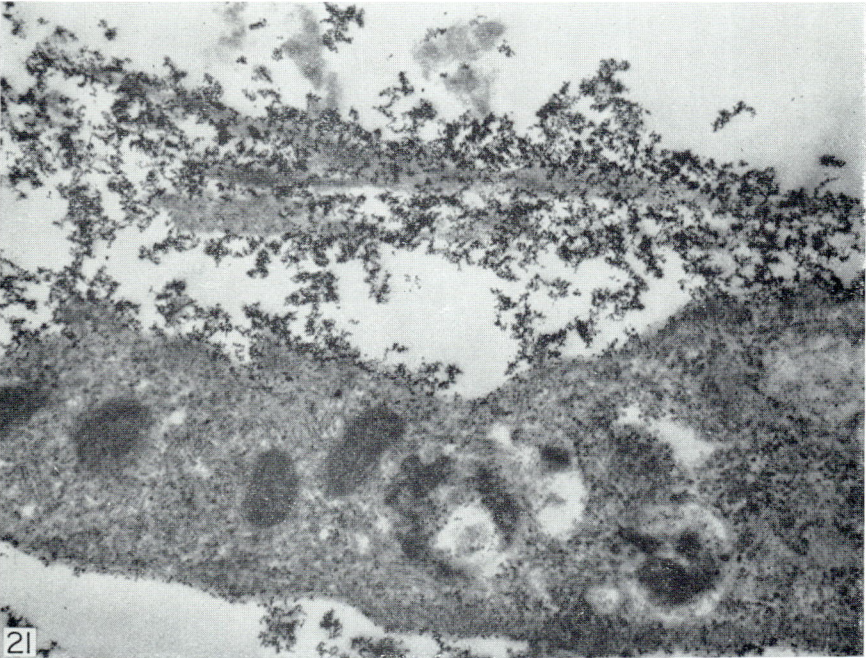

FIGS. 20 and 21. Surface of cells infected with leukosis (Fig. 20) and Rous (Fig. 21) virus showing accumulation of mucopolysaccharides (Hale's iron colloidal technique) (× 12 600 and 38 400 respectively).

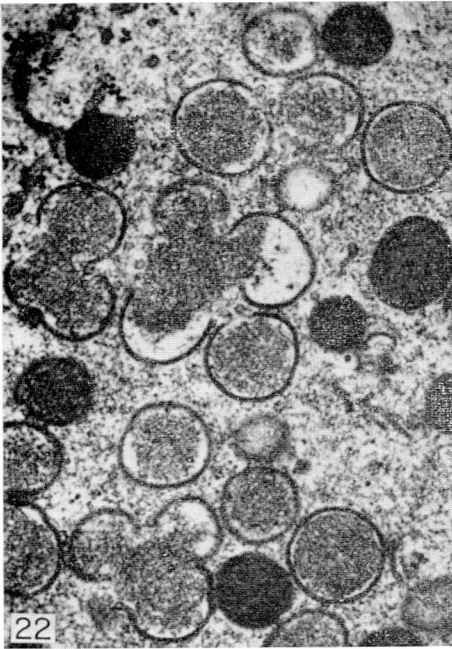

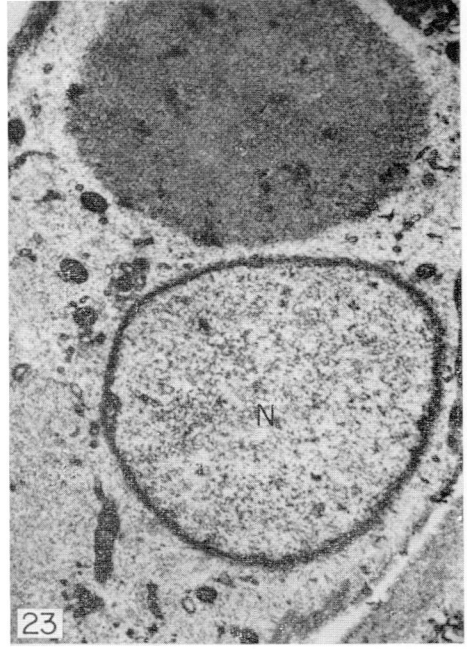

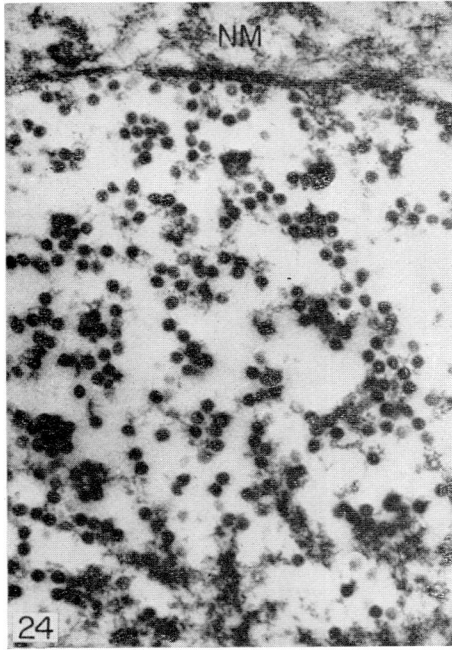

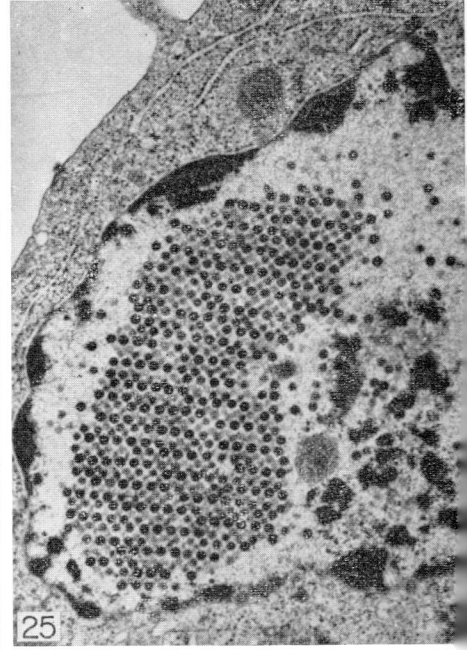

FIGS. 22 and 23. Two stages in the development of Shope fibroma in rabbit infected cells. Fig. 22 shows a portion of such a viroplasm at a stage where immature particles are being formed. Some of these particles are totally encircled, others possess only segments of envelope (× 7000 and × 30 000 respectively). (Courtesy of Dr R. Scherrer.) Fig. 23 shows a typical inclusion body ("viroplasm") in the cytoplasm at an earlier stage where no virus particle has yet appeared. FIG. 24. Portion of a nucleus of a polyoma infected cell. The nuclear sap has disappeared and the viruses fill the entire nucleus (× 52 000). (Courtesy of Dr W. Bernhard.) FIG. 25. An intra-nuclear "crystal" of Adeno-virus. Note the margination of chromatin (× 25 000). (Courtesy of Dr W. Bernhard.)

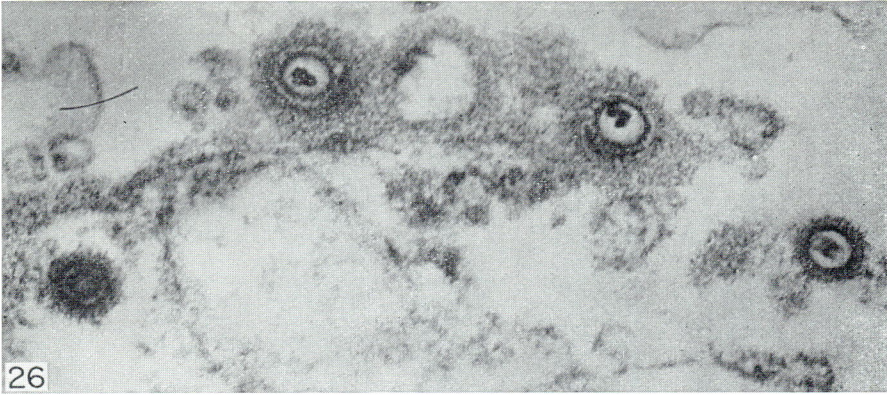

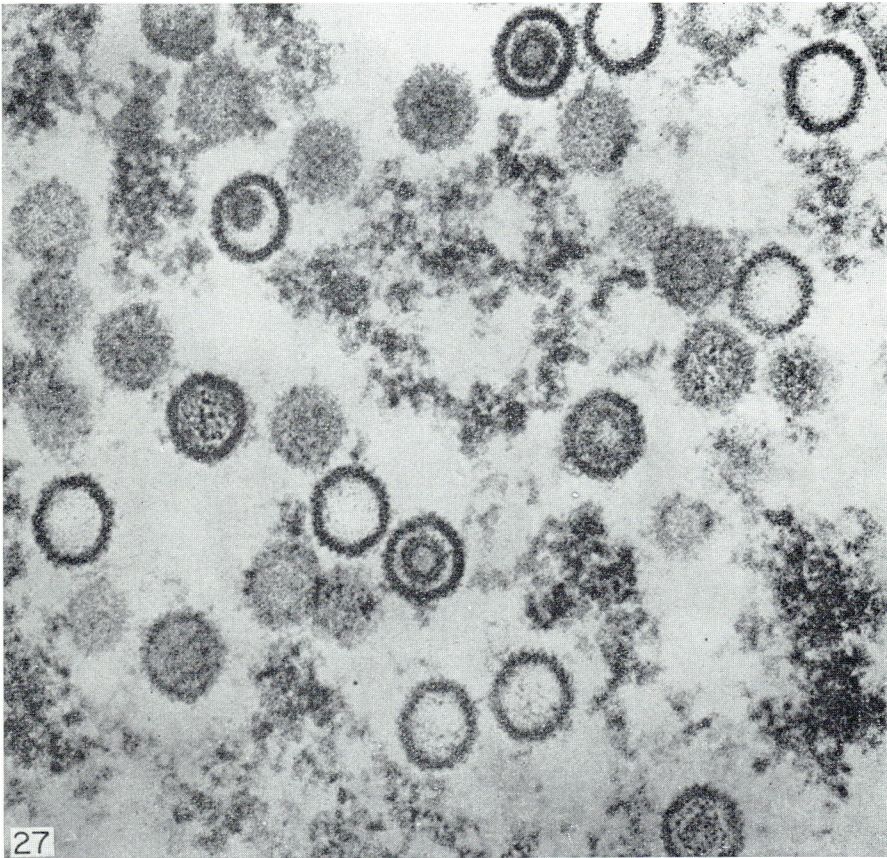

FIGS. 26 and 27. "Herpes-like" particles from tissue cultures of Burkitt lymphomas. Fig. 26 shows "mature" particles in the cytoplasm. Note their dense, coiled and retracted nucleoid and their outer envelope acquired by "budding" through the nuclear membrane (× 245 000). (Courtesy of Dr A. J. Dalton.) Fig. 27 shows immature particles in the nucleus. Note their ring-like appearance and their slightly polyhedral capsid with or without an inner core (× 100 000). (Courtesy of Dr E. De Harven.)

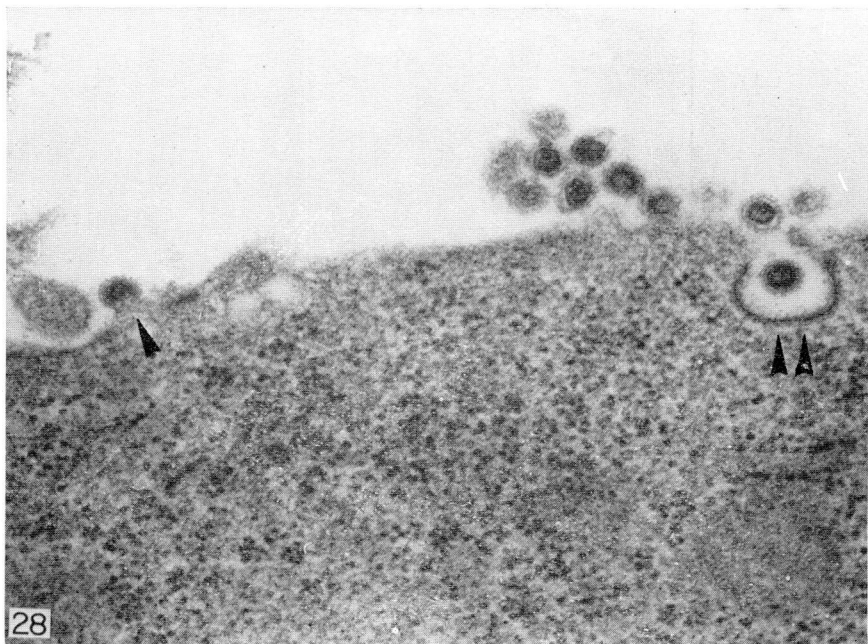

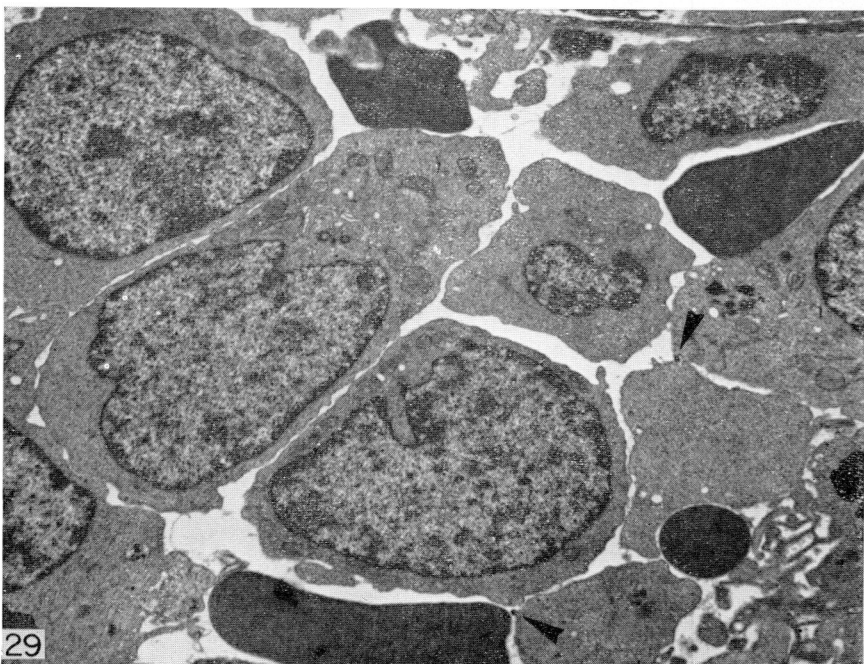

FIG. 28. Typical appearance of Mouse Leukaemia Virus (Rauscher) forming (→) or being

engulfed $\left(\begin{smallmatrix} \rightarrow \\ \rightarrow \end{smallmatrix}\right)$ at the surface of a cell grown *in vitro*. Note that some particles (immature) have three envelopes and one small electron-lucent nucleolus, while other particles (mature) show only one envelope and a denser and larger nucleolus (×51 000).

FIG. 29. A low magnification micrograph of cells from mouse leukaemic bone-marrow (Rauscher) showing that in spite of virus formation (→) cell morphology remains unchanged (×3800).

CHAPTER 13

Mechanisms of Carcinogenesis

FRANCIS J. C. ROE

Chester Beatty Research Institute,
London, England

I. Introduction and Definitions

The first need in any area of research is to define the problem. Lack of precise definition is hampering the elucidation of mechanisms of carcinogenesis both by epidemiological and by experimental means.

Most cancer research workers would agree that "carcinogenesis" refers to "the induction of cancer", but differences between their individual images of "cancer" are legion. Doubtless most share a similar picture of the usual course of the terminal stages of cancer in man – of a slowly killing, invasive and disseminating process, associated with the proliferation of abnormal body cells. But, of the earlier stages of the disease, either in the clinic or in the laboratory, views differ according to knowledge and particular experience. Lack of anything like a common image is currently making cancer research a much more confused subject than it need be.

Although numerous infective agents that cause a wide variety of disease states are recognized, it is still useful to be able to use the term "infectious disease". Undoubtedly an equally large number and even wider range of aetiological agents are involved in the genesis of the cancerous state. Nevertheless, even some of those who could be expected to know better still speak of "the cause" of cancer, as though cancer were a single disease entity.

Because cancer is in reality a group of diseases, and because multiple factors may contribute to its causation, it can only be defined in general terms which avoid any reference to aetiological mechanisms. Elsewhere (Roe, 1966*a*) we have suggested as a definition: "Cancer is a disease of multicellular organisms which is characterized by the seemingly uncontrolled multiplication and spread within the organism of apparently abnormal forms of the organism's own cells". Unfortunately neither this nor any other general definition meets the needs of all cancer researchers of all disciplines.

In some senses the morbid anatomist is in the best position to lay down the criteria that have to be fulfilled for a diagnosis of cancer to be made. He has the opportunity to examine the whole body macroscopically and microscopically and to establish the complete pattern of the disease state at one point in time – the time of death. Despite these advantages, even he is sometimes in doubt with regard to the diagnosis. If death is incidental to the disease state that is suspected of being cancerous (e.g. a possibly cancerous lesion is discovered at necropsy on a patient who died from some other cause), his findings may well be equivocal and subject to differences of opinion between himself and his colleagues. There are no hard and fast lines which separate the appearance of inflammatory, hyperplastic and neoplastic states. The classification of cancers into microscopically distinguishable types is the subject of even greater and more frequent differences of opinion between pathologists. For most experienced pathologists the areas of uncertainty are not wide, but they exist. When errors are made they are reproduced by the epidemiologist who bases his survey on necropsy findings – so that a distorted picture of mortality from a particular type of cancer may emerge. In the laboratory the cancerous nature of a lesion may be checked by seeing if it will grow as a tumour on transplantation into other genetically similar (syngeneic) animals of the same species. Growth of the transplant should certainly not be accepted as an absolute criterion of malignancy, but it is a procedure that may be helpful in some circumstances. Clearly this aid to precision is not available to the human pathologist.

In clinical practice the pathological diagnosis of biopsy specimens is more open to error than necropsy in so far as the information and amount of tissue available to the pathologist is much less. In many cases his report is in reality a prognostication based on previous experience of patients with lesions of similar macroscopic and microscopic appearance. The use of the word "malignant" in the pathological report is to be interpreted as "treat radically". But the "previous experience" on the basis of which such reports are made is sometimes ill-defined. Often it is not personal, but based mainly on the work of other observers. If radical treatment is recommended and followed, there is no means of knowing whether it was justified or not. Hence there is no feed-back of information that tells a pathologist that he is overdiagnosing malignancy. Under the most favourable conditions errors of judgement by pathologists are probably infrequent, but the potentiality for them increases sharply with distance from the necropsy department of the teaching hospital, and the margin of error in relation to epidemiological studies not based on pathological diagnosis is very wide.

Two aspects of cancer diagnosis are especially relevant to the present discussion, namely the concepts of the pre-invasive carcinoma and of latent carcinoma. The criteria for diagnosis of such lesions are far from generally agreed. Franks (1954), from a study of serial sections, has reported the presence of small foci of latent carcinoma in a considerable proportion of human prostates, the proportion increasing with age. He and others have described latent carcinomas in the lung and a number of other tissues. On the other hand, Whitwell (1955) and Cunningham *et al.* (1958) decided that the small neoplastic-like lesions or "tumourlets", often seen in association with bronchiectasis or chronic lung abscess are *not* true neoplasms. If an unknown proportion of such small and symptomless lesions were to be counted as examples of cancer, then it would become more or less impossible to arrive at a meaningful estimate of the human cancer burden.

In relation to this burden, ideally one would like to know the numbers and times of appearance of each type of cancerous lesion in every individual within a defined population. The study of correlations between genetic factors, environmental factors, and the incidence and progress of particular types of lesion would constitute the first logical step in the elucidation of the mechanisms of carcinogenesis involved.

The experimentalist is much better placed in the search for meaningful associations between the incidence of cancerous lesions and the operation of genetic and environmental factors. He can formulate, and rigidly adhere to, diagnostic criteria for malignancy and can, to a large extent, study the effects of single genetic or environmental factors whilst controlling the rest. Unfortunately, individual experimentalists often fail to take full advantage of these opportunities and the literature on experimental carcinogenesis is unnecessarily confused because of this.

As will be concluded below, it may well be that the value of many laboratory experiments in the field of carcinogenesis lies not in the fact that they reveal information of any basic relevance to the mechanism of induction of any form of cancer in man, but that they point to methods whereby the aetiology of particular forms of human cancer may be investigated. The study, however detailed in other respects, of pathologically and epidemiologically ill-defined lesions in genetically uncharacterized populations of laboratory animals is not very likely to be of much value in this latter connection.

II. Multi-factorial Causation of Cancer

If exposure to a particular agent is regularly associated with the subsequent development of cancer under a wide variety of circumstances and in a wide variety of species, it seems reasonable to regard the agent as "carcinogenic". Experiments with such agents are easy to perform and results that are both acceptable and quantifiable are more or less assured even if only scant attention is paid to the control of background genetic or environmental factors. More careful studies usually show that the effects of such agents may be modified by other agents operating simultaneously or sequentially. Depending on the direction of the modification, such agents have been regarded as exerting *co-carcinogenic* or *anti-carcinogenic* effects. In a recent review (Roe and Rowson, 1968) an attempt was made to list some of the ways in which modification may be brought about (see Table I).

Many examples are known in which the mechanism of modification is so obvious that one would hesitate to use the term co-carcinogenesis or anti-carcinogenesis to describe them. Thus in skin carcinogenesis experiments, lipophilic solvents which aid absorption, enhance carcinogenesis by polycyclic aromatic hydrocarbons in comparison with oily solvents which retard it (Riska, 1956). In germ-free mice the oral administration of cycasin gives rise to no neoplasms, whereas in conventionally maintained animals whose intestines contain bacteria which degradate cycasin to a potent carcinogen, intestinal tumours arise (Laqueur *et al.*, 1967). The elucidation of the reason why germ-free and conventional animals behave differently obviates the need to regard the bacterial flora as co-carcinogenic. What would have been the position if the mechanism was not apparent?

This question raises a more general problem. There are situations in which the distinction between carcinogens and factors which enhance the co-carcinogenicity of other agents is difficult. The induction of malignant lymphoma in mice may be taken as an example. A high proportion of mice of the AK strain develop the disease spontaneously. A peculiarity of the strain is the poor development of the adrenal cortex and low level of adrenocortical secretion. Administration of cortisone or corticosteroids reduces the incidence of the disease. Associated with the poor development of the adrenal cortex in AK strain mice there is a hypertrophy, or more correctly, a persistence, of the foetal state of the cortex of the thymus. A group of viruses (including Gross Passage A virus, Maloney virus, and Graffi virus), carried regularly by mice of several strains, may react with the primitive cells of the thymic cortex in such a way that lymphoma eventually develops. Any factor or agent which favours the persistence of a wide zone of foetal cortical cells in the thymus favours the development of malignant lymphoma. Adrenalectomy and the administration of oestrogens do this; in other words, these treatments make mice of various other strains similar to the AK strain in respect of thymic status. X-radiation causes first a partial destruction, and then a rebound and fairly persistent hyperplasia of the thymic cortex. It is unlikely that any of these procedures would predispose to lymphomagenesis in the absence of one of the lymphoma viruses. Genetic factors influence not only the extent of the thymic cortical overgrowth in response to stimuli, but also the susceptibility of mice to the carrying of the necessary viruses.

It is now known that viruses, such as the Gross Passage A virus, may act as helper viruses by providing the information necessary for the production of the protein coat for yet another virus, the mouse sarcoma virus (Harvey and Maloney strains), though there is no evidence that the mouse sarcoma virus is itself involved in lymphomagenesis. At present, therefore, the closest we can get to identifying the true basic cause of malignant

TABLE 1

Some mechanisms by which viruses and other agents may interact in carcinogenesis

True multifactorial carcinogenesis	Factors operating at the cellular level to modify		Factors operating at the tissue level to modify	
	Cell transformation	Tumour development	Cell transformation	Tumour development
Both agents act simultaneously or sequentially on the genetic apparatus of cells	1. Facilitation of entry of inducing agent into cell or its transport to the target site within the cell	1. Protection of the transformed cell against immunological defence systems	1. Facilitation of absorption of inducing agent into body or of its transport within the body to the target tissue, e.g., by suppression of circulating antibody levels or of cellular defence systems	1. Inhibition of immunological defence system
	2. Interference with mechanism whereby cell resists transformation, e.g., inhibition of the production of interferon, or of detoxification enzyme systems	2. Reduction of susceptibility of transformed cell to other homeostatic forces	2. Interference with excretion or detoxification of carcinogen	2. Alterations in hormonal or nutritional status
	3. An alteration in the physiological state of the cell such that it is more susceptible to transformation		3. Enhancement of exposure of target tissue to inducing agent by prior establishment of inflammatory state	3. Induction of hyperplasia (e.g., by an irritant) such that clones of cells of critical size (Berenblum, 1954a) develop from transformed cells
	4. Interference with balance between replication of cells and of the viruses they carry in favor of the latter		4. Increase in proportion of cells susceptible to inducing agent as a result of metaplasia or hormone activation	

lymphoma in mice is that it is one of a group of viruses. In the past, however, many other agents, including some of those mentioned above, have been regarded as causative.

Morton and Mider (1938) reported that certain carcinogenic polycyclic hydrocarbons predispose to malignant lymphoma in mice. Later Kawamoto *et al.* (1958) reported a similar response in respect of urethane. The administration of quite small doses of these agents to mice when they are newly born is especially evocative of lymphomas (Pietra *et al.*, 1959). The lymphomas that arise in response to these chemical agents are indistinguishable from "virus-induced" lesions which suggests that the chemicals do no more than enhance the lymphomagenic effect of viruses carried naturally by the mice. Thus, although there is abundant evidence from experimental studies in other systems that the polycyclic hydrocarbon and urethane referred to above may act as true carcinogens, it seems that in relation to the induction of lymphoma in mice their usual or sole role is one of co-carcinogenesis.

There are other examples of known carcinogens acting as co-carcinogens under certain circumstances. The administration of immuno-suppressive agents, such as X-radiation, prednisolone, cortisone, 6-mercaptopurine or methotrexate, change the response of rabbits to Shope fibroma virus from a trivial local reaction to one of generalized fibromatosis (see Roe and Rowson, 1968, for review). Coal tar, or carcinogens such as 3-methylcholanthrene (MC) or 3,4-benzopyrene (BP), may bring about the same type of enhancement (Ahlström and Andrewes, 1938). The evidence suggests that MC and BP bring about the enhancement not by reason of their carcinogenicity, but because they too suppress immune responsiveness (Stjernsward, 1965; Ball *et al.*, 1966; Weston, 1967).

There are, then, many examples both of multifactorial carcinogenesis and of known carcinogens modifying carcinogenesis by other agents. It follows that there is a real risk of confusing carcinogens and co-carcinogens, and that, in general, it is wrong indiscriminately to use as adjectives terms such as "carcinogenic" or "co-carcinogenic" in relation to individual agents without reference to the particular biological systems and conditions in which the adjective applies.

III. Investigation of Mechanisms

Because of the diversity of ways in which numerous factors may interact to bring about cancer, it would be presumptive for any worker to assume that a particular mechanism that he has unravelled in one biological system is directly, without modification, applicable to any other. If he is lucky he may discover a phenomenon of general application, but the onus is on him to demonstrate its wider significance and he should never assume it. This applies both to extrapolation between various laboratory species and extrapolation from the laboratory to man. History tells us that it is not always easy to demonstrate carcinogenesis by exposing laboratory animals to agents known to be potent carcinogens for man. Thus coal tar (soot) was recognized as carcinogenic for human skin 140 years before the first tumours were induced in animals by it. Investigators made many difficulties for themselves by failing to observe their animals for long enough, or by exposing them to doses of tar that were too small to elicit an effect. Even today there is one agent, arsenic, associated with the induction of cancer in man, which has not yet been shown to induce cancer in other species. It is possible that the apparently peculiar sensitivity of man to carcinogenesis in response to arsenic depends on the existence of another peculiarly human factor. If this is so the latter may be the true carcinogen, and arsenic merely a cocarcinogen, albeit an important one.

It is not always easy to arrange a laboratory model in which human exposure is satisfactorily mimicked. This is especially true in relation to the induction of lung cancer by tobacco smoke. Other animal species lack the higher faculties used by man in his voluntary inhalation of the smoke and it is difficult passively to introduce a comparable dose of smoke into the lungs of laboratory animals (see Roe and Walters, 1965, for review). Despite these difficulties, adenomas and adenocarcinomas of the lungs have been induced in mice by prolonged exposure to tobacco smoke (Essenberg, 1952; Mühlbock, 1955; Harris and Negroni, 1967). In man the types of cancer mostly associated with exposure to tobacco smoke are squamous carcinomas and undifferentiated (oat-cell) carcinomas. The difference in type of tumour induced may well be attributable to anatomical differences between mouse and man (Roe, 1966b).

The basic requirements of a laboratory model include comparable anatomy, the possibility of comparable exposure (dose, dose-schedule, route of administration), comparable transport to the target tissue and comparable observation time. In addition, if the agent administered is not the proximate carcinogen but only a precursor of it, there should be in the model relevant enzymic and metabolic pathways similar to those in man. These latter requirements frequently beg the question in the sense that neither the identity of the proximate carcinogen nor the need for metabolizing enzymes are known.

In practice, it is encouraging that, despite all the possible stumbling blocks, many potent carcinogens act similarly in a variety of species and under a variety of conditions. Differences in response that cannot be attributed to lack of comparability in anatomical structure, dose at the target site, or enzyme pathways should perhaps lead one to suspect that the agent concerned is not acting as a true carcinogen in any of the systems studied.

Smithers (1962) has attacked "cytologism", or the preoccupation with changes at the cellular level in relation to cancer. He points out that cancers often arise in pathologically changed tissues or organs, and that their appearance is frequently accompanied by evidence of hormonal derangement or immunological disturbance, etc. On the other hand, all cancers grow by the multiplication of cells, and there is abundant evidence that the cells of which tumours consist are themselves abnormal. If it is accepted that multiple factors may contribute to the genesis of cancer, then Smither's argument presents no conflict. What in effect he is recommending is a closer study of modifying (co-carcinogenic or anti-carcinogenic) factors which influence the risk that cancer will develop. From a practical point of view the distinction between carcinogen and modifier may be unimportant. If, as we know from animal experiments, it may be the modifier rather than the true carcinogen that determines whether cancer develops, then it is logical to conclude that the modifier deserves special study.

Several examples of what may be called "whole tissue carcinogenesis" are known. If the ovaries are transplanted into the spleen, the oestrogen it produces is destroyed in the liver and never reaches the general circulation (Li, 1948). Under these circumstances the normal feedback mechanism whereby circulating oestrogen inhibits the secretion of gonadotrophic hormones by the pituitary is interrupted. The latter are produced in excess and the ovaries become hyperplastic and eventually neoplastic. An exogenous agent may induce cancer indirectly by first producing an effect on a whole tissue, thus the administration of a sufficient dose of cadmium causes complete destruction of seminiferous tubules in the testes of rats, possibly through interference with the blood supply (Gunn et al., 1963). Later, probably because of interference with a feedback mechanism, Leydig-cell tumours arise in the atrophied testes (Roe et al., 1964). If the dose of cadmium is insufficient to cause testicular atrophy, then no Leydig-cell tumours are induced. There is no reason in this case to regard cadmium as a direct cause of the tumours since they also appear as a consequence of testicular atrophy from causes which involve no exposure to the metal.

IV. The Relationships Theory, Method between and Fact

Since the end of the last century there has been a succession of general theories of carcinogenesis, some of them based on facts gleaned from studies in only a small part of the wide field, and some of them based on no verifiable facts at all. A number of the more patently absurd theories are discussed in Oberling's excellent book, *The Riddle of Cancer* (Oberling, 1948).

That man should want to discover general patterns in relation to natural phenomena is one of his strengths. That he should imagine that he has done so when his only information stems from very limited experience is all too often a besetting weakness. At one time the microbiologists and proto-zoologists were the most productive of general theories of carcinogenesis, then the geneticists, embryologists and virologists came to the forefront. In recent years biochemical theories have predominated, but many of these already look outdated because of the emergence of molecular biology as a basic discipline. In fact, recent integrated observations in the fields of molecular biology, virology and immunology make virtually all the earlier general theories of carcinogenesis seem either wrong or irrelevant; not because they have led to the discovery of a new, generally applicable, mechanism, but because they have shown how complex and how numerous the possible aetiological mechanisms are.

Not only are multiple factors implicated in the aetiology of individual tumours, but the spectrum of factors, and the pattern of their interaction, is different for different tumours. It follows that *knowledge of aetiological mechanisms is intimately dependent on the methods that have been used to investigate them: fact is dependent on method.*

Theories that are too many steps ahead of facts and methods are usually too vague to be helpful. At the present time, therefore, the most stimulating theories of mechanisms of carcinogenesis are fairly closely related to observations made on specific tumour systems by the use of specific methods of investigation. The gap between this level of theory and the level of general theory of carcinogenesis is both wide and widening. In other words, it is becoming more difficult to conceive of a useful general theory that is likely to explain the increasing diversity of mechanisms which are being shown to operate in various test systems.

There are of course many repeating patterns in carcinogenesis. Certain chemical and viral agents freely cross inter-species barriers in relation to an ability to induce cancer. If this were not so, it would hardly be justifiable to hope that studies on laboratory animals may lead to knowledge of the aetiology of human cancer. Certain modifying stimuli such as "wound-healing" also operate in a variety of species. No doubt other bits of information will in time be pieced together to form patterns; but there is no reason to expect that the patterns so formed will necessarily ever fit together to make a single simple whole concept. The mechanism of carcinogenesis like nature itself is likely to prove an infinitely variable phenomenon.

V. Cancer as a Type of "Response"

Many writers have suggested the cancerous change should not be regarded so much as a positive response – an event which results from stimulation of a specific type – but rather as failure in response. The quality of the organic as opposed to the inorganic is that it has a capacity to reproduce itself. For most primitive form of life, reproduction is limited only by the exogenous environment – lack of nutriments, etc. In multicellular organisms different cells specialize in different functions, even though each cell has all the information necessary for performing all the functions of every cell in the body. The elegant proof of this comes from experiments in which the nuclei from differentiated cells derived from the blastula stage of the frog embryo were substituted for the nuclei of fertilized ova before the first cleavage had occurred. The ova with the substitute nuclei developed into normal frogs (Briggs and King, 1952).

It follows that, in the multicellular organism, the capacity of each cell to divide and to produce, either a replica of the whole organism or any part of it, or just more cells of the same differentiated variety as itself, must be inhibited, restrained or controlled.

At present little is known of the mechanisms of inhibition, restraint or control other than that they must be both multiple and of a variety of types. Some, no doubt, are built-in to cells in the course of embryogenesis and tissue differentiation. Others, possibly mediated by nervous impulses or local cell-contracts, act continuously throughout life, and yet others, such as hormones, act intermittently at one time permitting cellular proliferation, at other times inhibiting it. Every cell in the body, then, has the information necessary to enable it to divide, but it also has the structures necessary to enable it to respond to factors which normally restrain cell-division.

The cancer cell stands convicted of proliferating when it should not do so. Theoretically its failure to behave normally in this respect may stem from a failure in the generation of the restraining mechanism, or in its transport to the cell, a failure of the cellular apparatus responsible for receiving the restraining message, or a failure of the cell to act on the message even though it received it.

There is evidence that the process of carcinogenesis is sometimes associated with the escape of cells from the state of suppression of a large part of their genetic information which is normal in relation to the differentiated cell-status. It is now well established, for instance, that certain oat-cell carcinomas of the bronchus secrete hormones, e.g. ACTH and antidiuretic hormone, which it is normally the prerogative of the pituitary gland to produce (see Roe and Walters, 1965, for review).

However, it would be wrong to give the impression that most cancers could be explained simply in terms of failure of suppression of proliferation (i.e. failure of homeostatic mechanisms). It is possible that some of the cancers of early childhood represent developmental failures in the switching off of the capacity of particular cell types to divide, but the majority of cancers of adult life cannot be explained on this basis, first, because there is ample evidence that the cells are abnormal, and do not resemble cells seen at any time during the development of the organism; second, because individual cells within the same tumour may differ from each other. The significance of these observations, however, may be clearer if the phenomena of the latent interval and of tumour progression are first considered.

VI. The Latent Interval and Tumour Progression

A puzzling and complicating aspect of carcinogenesis is that a variable, and sometimes long, interval separates exposure to a causative agent and manifestation of its effect in the form of the development of a visible cancer. Part of this interval is taken up by the submacroscopic stage of tumour development, but in many cases calculations based on the observed rate of growth of a visible tumour indicate that, either its origin from a single cell occurred long after the time of exposure to the supposedly causative agent, or that the rate of growth must have got quicker during the course of the early growth of the tumour.

After a tumour has reached the visible stage, its rate of growth may suddenly increase. Microscopic examination of the tumour at this stage shows tissue of two types. Part of the lesion consists of less rapidly dividing cells and part, often to one side, of a mass of more rapidly dividing cells. The chemical history and the microscopic appearances both suggest that the more rapidly growing tumour has arisen by a sudden change in one (or possibly more) of the cells of the more slowly growing tumour. Perhaps in rather the same way the more slowly growing tumour arose in one of a mass of normal cells. The process by which a tumour undergoes successive changes towards greater and greater malignancy is referred to as "tumour-progression" (Foulds, 1954, 1957). Elsewhere (Roe, 1966a) we have suggested that the latent interval and tumour progression should be considered as related phenomena.

Unequivocal examples of tumour-progression, though not rare, are certainly not common. On the other hand, cellular pleomorphism is commonly encountered. Thus cells in any one neoplasm may differ in size, shape and chromosome number and indeed in every measurable parameter. This suggests a certain instability in the process involved in cellular reproduction.

The frequency of disorders of mitosis in some malignant tumours provides evidence of such instability. A consequence of this instability is that at any one time a neoplastic lesion consists of a mixed population of cells that compete, one with the other, for the available nutrients. Under these circumstances a process of natural selection is likely to operate, such that the most aggressive cells, i.e. those that can grow and divide most vigorously, tend to survive at the expense of the less aggressive. If this is an accurate representation of the situation, the predictable outcome would then be for tumours to become more and more malignant with the passage of time. By the same token, if one looks retrospectively into the history of a tumour one would expect the average growth rate of the constituent cells to be slower and slower the earlier in time after the inception of the neoplastic focus. The phenomenon of tumour-progression, therefore, may partly explain the length of the latent interval.

This biological concept of a tumour as a changing mixture of cell types has other important implications. For instance, it makes it unreasonable to expect that biochemical measurements made on homogenates of large pieces of tumour tissue, containing, perhaps, a wide variety of cell types, will necessarily lead to really meaningful results. The mixed cell-populations theory can also help to explain the difficulty of treating cancers with chemotherapeutic agents, particularly the fact that drug-resistant cell types appear sometimes relatively soon after the start of therapy. Cell variants that are less susceptible to a particular drug survive its initial onslaught and, without the competition of the cells that succumbed to the drug, flourish more than they might otherwise have done.

S

So far, it has been suggested that during the latent interval the rate
of cellular proliferation increases because less and less "restrainable" cell
lines emerge within the tumour focus. However, it is also possible that
one or more of the restraining mechanisms becomes less and less effective.
Berenblum (1954) postulated, for example, that it was necessary for a
"cancer" cell to have given rise to a cellular mass or colony of "critical
size" before it was assured of giving rise to cancer. He suggested that
certain agents which cause hyperplasia could, by enabling proliferation
beyond the critical colony size to be achieved, act co-carcinogenically in
the induction of cancers.

It is natural to think of immune mechanisms at this point since it is conceivable that this is a type of restraining mechanism which may suddenly
fail if the antigenic stimulus rises above a certain critical level, or if the
capacity for immune response is reduced.

VII. Immune Mechanisms in Carcinogenesis

It is no part of the object of the present discourse to review the present
state of knowledge with regard to immune mechanisms. However, a brief
survey of what is known and not known may help to dispel premature belief
in certain naively simple theories.

By the use of modern techniques it has been shown that abnormal
antigens are associated with most, possibly all, neoplasms. In the case of
some cancers there is also evidence of loss of antigens. The use of the term
"antigens" in this context stems from the methods used for detecting their
presence, and offers the advantage that no one expects the precise chemical
structures to be known. All antigens are in fact proteins or polypeptides,
and the possible variety of abnormal proteins that may occur in cells is
legion. The presence of abnormal proteins in cells is by no means unique
for cancer. There is, however, comparatively little information concerning
the presence of new proteins or lack of normal proteins in non-cancerous
diseases.

The most readily interpretable information on new antigens comes from
studies in viral oncogenesis. Specific proteins are produced in the course of
virus replication within the cells of the host. The proteins are of two types,
those that form the protein envelope of the virus itself, and those (probably
enzymes) that are involved in the replicating process itself. Both are coded
for in the nucleic acids of the virus.

Cells that undergo malignant transformation as a result of infection with
an oncogenic virus show surface changes including the appearance of new
proteins. New proteins that appear in cells transformed by a particular
virus are specific in the sense that they are identical irrespective of the
species, strain or tissue from which the transformed cell originated. The
specificity of the new proteins enables the virus concerned to be identified.
It is broadly assumed that "transformation" which refers to a morphological and behavioural change of cells grown *in vitro* corresponds to an

in vivo change from normal to cancerous. There is much evidence that there is some truth in this, but not enough information, particularly with regard to states intermediate between normal and full transformation, for one to be completely committed to this assumption at the present time.

Much less is known concerning the presence of new proteins in cells transformed by chemical or physical agents. It is not yet fully established that exposure of cells *in vitro* to chemical agents or to X-irradiation can bring about malignant transformation. The success claimed in various published papers by some (e.g. Berwald and Sachs, 1963, 1965; Borek and Sachs, 1966; Heidelberger and Iype, 1967; Sanders and Burford, 1967) is offset by an unknown large number of unpublished negative observations. It is possible that success has only been achieved where a potentially oncogenic virus, capable of being activated by the test chemical, was also in the flask with the cells at the time of exposure to X-rays or to the "carcinogenic" chemical agent. However, if this were so, one could expect that the transformed cells would possess common virus-determined new antigens. According to Sachs (1966, personal communication), however, this is not the case. Cells of the same type and in the same flask, transformed as a result of exposure to the same chemical agent, produce different arrays of new antigens. The variety of new antigens is probably large, but it is not yet certain whether it is finite or infinite, nor whether different chemicals ever give rise to the same new antigens as each other. More recent studies of Reiner and Southam (1967) suggest that different sarcomas induced by 3-methylcholanthrene may possess some common antigens though the margin of antigenic overlap indicated by their findings is not very wide. Precise knowledge concerning *in vitro* transformation by chemical agents is urgently awaited.

There is no evidence at the present time of the presence of particular new proteins especially correlated with cancer nor is there evidence of a correlation between the number or concentration of new proteins in transformed cells or in cancer cells and their malignancy: it is probable that most of the new proteins, especially those that appear as a result of the induction of cancer by X-rays or chemical agents are non-functional and quite incidental by-products of the cancerous change.

So far in this section the assumption has been made that proteins that appear during the course of carcinogenesis are not only "new" but also "abnormal". This assumption is usually unwarranted in the light of the information available. During the course of embryogenesis and differentiation of tissues it is likely that a wide variety of proteins are produced transiently. The information for their production thereafter normally remains unexpressed in the "adult" differentiated cell. It would not be surprising if, in future, some of the proteins that appear in association with carcinogenesis are shown to be identical with proteins produced transiently during early embryonic life.

This possibility has important implications, because if true, it then follows that some of the so-called "cancer antigens" are not foreign to the cancer-bearing host, and no immunological reaction against them is to be expected.

Where the new proteins are foreign to the host, the immunological response to them is likely to vary. However, no sure method for predicting the extent of the response to particular antigens is at present available. These remarks apply both to soluble antigens that can escape from cells and to cell-surface, "transplantation", antigens.

There is plenty of evidence that experimental animals may mount an immunological attack against induced cancers (Klein *et al.*, 1960), but no evidence, in terms of spontaneous regression, that chemically-induced tumours ever succumb to this attack. However, perhaps success is really the rule at the submacroscopic level, and perhaps the appearance of a visible tumour is a relatively rare expression of failure. Alternatively, as suggested by Old and Boyse (1964) and others, perhaps the problem is that the growth of malignant cells outpaces the immune responses of the host: inocula as small as 40 malignant cells that are capable of rapid multiplication can produce a tumour in a isologous host (Old *et al.*, 1962).

Both in man and in experimental animals there are examples of regression of cancer, occasionally entirely spontaneously, but more usually following large-scale, though incomplete, destruction or removal of the tumour (Everson and Cole, 1966; Boyd, 1966). It is interesting that chorio-carcinoma, a rare malignant tumour arising because trophoblastic cells derived from a foetus invade the mother, comes high in the list of types of tumour that exhibit spontaneous regression. It is presumed that anti-genic differences between the cancer and the maternal host eventually stimulate a successful immunological response (though hormonal factors may also be important in this case). Long-term survival of patients with Burkitt's lymphoma following treatment with cytotoxic drugs has also been attributed to immunological rejection of the small residue of tumour cells left after drug treatment. But these examples are the exception and not the rule.

Some potent chemical carcinogens, most cytotoxic drugs, corticosteroids, and a variety of other agents and procedures such as neonatal thymectomy suppress immunological responsiveness. This may influence the process of carcinogenesis by other agents in a number of different ways (see Roe and Rowson, 1968, for review). However, there is no indication that any of these agents, or procedures induce cancer. By the same token, there is no good evidence that the natural immunological response of an animal against its tumour can ordinarily be so boosted that the tumour is rejected (Old *et al.*, 1961). If, however, newer approaches to the treatment of cancer by the introduction into the tumour-bearing host of large numbers of lympho-cytes (Alexander, 1965) that have been exposed to tumour-specific anti-gens prove successful, then it may be necessary to reconsider the role of immunological factors in carcinogenesis. At present it seems unlikely that they play more than a secondary, and often comparatively minor, role.

VIII. Possible Modes of Action of Potent Chemical Carcinogens

Cancer and carcinogenesis are four-dimensional: the finished article, the tumour, is the result of a series of changes taking place over many cellular generations and subject to many influences. Many of the measurable consequences of first exposure to a potent carcinogen are probably incidental and irrelevant to the carcinogenic process. Others may influence the rate at which tumours grow or appear, or the likelihood that they will appear and yet not be responsible for the primary change. We do not yet know for certain that the cancerous change necessarily involves an alteration (mutation) in the genetic information coded in the nucleic acids of cells. It is possible, as suggested by the work of Brookes and Lawley (1964 – review), that carcinogenic alkylating agents react principally with the N-7 position of the guanine moiety of both DNA and RNA and that, in the case of bifunctional alkylating agents, two such reactions could link the two strands of DNA in such a way that the genetic code is altered. But such a theory cannot easily explain carcinogenesis by mono-functional alkylating agents such as ethyl methane sulphonate (Walters *et al.*, 1967). Indeed it may be that such observations amount more to a definition of the reactivity of different parts of the guanine molecule rather than to a meaningful theory of carcinogenesis. By the same token, the elaborate calculations of the theoretical chemists with regard to the relation between chemical structure and carcinogenic activity (e.g. Pullman and Pullman, 1955) never seem capable of supporting a theory of carcinogenesis which applies to more than a very narrow range of chemical structures.

A priori it seems unlikely that the important reactions which lead to cancer induction will be learned from studies on highly reactive carcinogenic agents capable of combining with many cellular components. The perfect chemical carcinogen for study purposes would be one that was capable only of one reaction, namely that basic to the induction of cancer. Perhaps no such substance exists. But while we are waiting to find out if it does, we might stand a better chance of discovering the essential alterations in cells that lead to carcinogenesis by careful studies of the effects of single low doses. Under these circumstances some of the irrelevant effects will not be produced and can therefore be ruled out for the purposes of further consideration.

IX. Résumé and Conclusions

Cancer is a general term that refers to a large number of diseases. Many factors in many and various combinations contribute to the causation of different types of the disease. In some cases a single factor seems to be of such predominant importance that it is justifiable to regard its activity as being carcinogenic. However, it is not justifiable to assume that carcinogenicity in one biological system implies carcinogenic potential for others. Even when an agent that is known to be carcinogenic in other systems appears to contribute to the induction of cancers in a new system, it cannot be assumed that its contribution relates to its carcinogenic potential.

It is difficult to distinguish between carcinogenic and co-carcinogenic activity. Only when information from a variety of test systems is available may it become justifiable to regard a particular agent as "carcinogenic". In any event, the use of such a term should normally relate only to the findings under the actual conditions of testing. In this connection there is a serious need, especially in relation to biochemical and molecular biological studies, constantly to define the "cancers" that are the objects of investigation. Lack of precision in this is both a constant handicap to the detection of aetiological mechanisms and a source of increasing confusion in experimental cancer research. Oversimplification is a continuing danger in relation to the elucidation of mechanisms of carcinogenesis. This is particularly obvious in the search for carcinogenic metabolites from apparently non-carcinogenic precursors. Examples of conclusions having been based on inadequate experimental data, and of the over-ready extrapolation from one biological test system to another are all too numerous. Theories of carcinogenesis in which an attempt is made to explain the causation of all forms of cancer in terms of a single mechanism are either too broad to be of much value, or simply ridiculous in the extent to which pertinent facts about cancer are overlooked. The latter include the width of the array of cancer types that may be derived from a single tissue, the fact that relatively similar cancers may arise after exposure to quite different aetiological agents, the extent of the variation between tumours in every measurable property, the latent interval that often separates cause and effect, and the phenomenon known as tumour progression.

Some of the variation between induced tumours in structure and behaviour is attributable to structural, physiological or pathological differences between target cells and some to differences in exposure to the relevant agent. Variation in response may also arise because of genetically or experimentally determined host factors such as hormonal or general immunological status. It is because of the multiplicity of these possibilities for variation that the theories of mechanisms of carcinogenesis must be tailored to each individual situation.

Detailed research on mechanism of action of potent carcinogens is still a fully justified pursuit, though the study of the effects of doses small enough not to cause general effects outside the target area is to be recommended. Investigators should be quite clear as to whether they are studying the immediate interaction between the carcinogenic agent and its biological target or the consequences, immediate or remote, of this interaction. The biochemical complexity of living matter is such that the longer the interval after exposure to an agent, the harder it will be to deduce the nature of the initial event from the changes found. In experiments that involve repeated exposure to an agent, it may well be impossible to discover the nature of the initial interaction amid the background of secondary effects in the cells concerned and of general effects on the tissue or organism as a whole.

The full examination of the mechanisms of induction of any single form of cancer includes investigations at the whole organism level, of tissues, of cells, and of subcellular constituents. Many disciplines are needed and the protagonist of one discipline ignores the rest at his peril. Elucidation is unlikely ever to be complete in so far as mystery is an intrinsic component of biology. However complete the knowledge of the mechanisms involved in the genesis of one particular form of cancer, the details may be largely irrelevant to the causation of any other form of cancer. But, with luck, the *methods* developed for tackling the problem will be applicable to other situations.

Acknowledgements

I am most grateful to Dr K. E. K. Rowson, Institute of Laryngology and Otology, London, for his expert advice, and to Mrs A. Englefield and Miss L. Barlow for their assistance in the preparation of the manuscript.

References

Ahlström, C. G. and Andrewes, C. H. (1938). *J. Path. Bact.* **47**, 65-86.
Alexander, P. (1965). In *The Biology of Cancer* (E. J. Ambrose and F. J. C. Roe, eds), pp. 91-123. Van Nostrand, London.
Ball, J. K., Sinclair, N. R. and McCarter, J. A. (1966). *Science, N.Y.* **152**, 650-651.
Berenblum, I. (1954). *Cancer Res.* **14**, 471-477.
Berwald, Y. and Sachs, L. (1963). *Nature, Lond.* **200**, 1182-1184.
Berwald, Y. and Sachs, L. (1965). *J. natn. Cancer Inst.* **35**, 641-662.
Borek, C. and Sachs, L. (1966). *Nature, Lond.* **210**, 276-278.
Boyd, W. (1966). *The Spontaneous Regression of Cancer.* Charles C Thomas, Springfield, Illinois.
Briggs, R. and King, T. J. (1952). *Proc. natn. Acad. Sci. U.S.A.* **38**, 455-463.
Brookes, P. and Lawley, P. D. (1964). *Br. med. Bull.* **20**, 91-95.
Cunningham, G. J., Nassau, E. and Walter, J. B. (1958). *Thorax* **13**, 64-68.
Essenberg, J. M. (1952). *Science, N.Y.* **116**, 561-562.
Everson, T. C. and Cole, W. H. (1966). *Spontaneous Regression of Cancer.* W. B. Saunders, Philadelphia.
Foulds, L. (1954). *Cancer Res.* **14**, 327-339.
Foulds, L. (1957). *Cancer Res.* **17**, 355-356.
Franks, L. M. (1954). *Ann. R. Coll. Surg.* **15**, 236-249.
Gunn, S. A., Gould, T. C. and Anderson, W. A. D. (1963). *Am. J. Path.* **42**, 685-702.
Harris, R. J. C. and Negroni, G. (1967). *Br. med. J.* **4**, 637-641.
Heidelberger, C. and Iype, P. T. (1967). *Science, N.Y.* **155**, 214-217.
Kawamoto, S., Ida, N., Kirschbaum, A. and Taylor, G. (1958). *Cancer Res.* **18**, 725-729.
Klein, G., Sjögren, H. O., Klein, E. and Hellström, K. E. (1960). *Cancer Res.* **20**, 1561-1572.
Laqueur, G. L., McDaniel, E. G. and Matsumoto, H. (1967). *J. natn. Cancer Inst.* **39**, 355-371.
Li, M. H. (1948). *Am. J. Obstet. Gynec.* **55**, 316-320.
Morton, J. J. and Mider, G. B. (1938). *Science, N.Y.* **87**, 327-328.
Mühlbock, O. (1955). *Tijdschr. Diergeneesk.* **99**, 2276-2278.
Oberling. C. (1948). *The Riddle of Cancer.* Oxford University Press, Oxford.
Old, L. J. and Boyse, E. A. (1964). *A. Rev. Med.* **15**, 167-186.

Old, L. J., Benacerraf, B., Clarke, D. A., Carswell, E. A. and Stockert, E. (1961). *Cancer Res.* **21**, 1281-1300.

Old, L. J., Boyse, E. A., Clarke, D. A. and Carswell, E. A. (1962). *Ann. N.Y. Acad. Sci.* **101**, 80-106.

Pietra, G., Spencer, K. and Shubik, P. (1959). *Nature, Lond.* **183**, 1689.

Pullman, A. and Pullman, B. (1955). *Adv. Cancer Res.* **3**, 117-169.

Reiner, J. and Southam, C. M. (1967). *Cancer Res.* **27**, 1243-1247.

Riska, E. B. (1956). *Acta path. microbiol. scand.* Suppl. **114**, 1-110.

Roe, F. J. C. (1966*a*). In *The Biology of Cancer* (E. J. Ambrose and F. J. C. Roe, eds), pp. 1-32. Van Nostrand, London.

Roe, F. J. C. (1966*b*). In *Lung Tumours in Animals* (L. Severi, ed.), pp. 101-126. University of Perugia, Perugia.

Roe, F. J. C. (1968). *Fd. Cosmet. Toxicol.* (In the press.)

Roe, F. J. C. and Rowson, K. E. K. (1968). *Int. Rev. exp. Path.*, **6**, 181-227.

Roe, F. J. C. and Walters, M. A. (1965). *Prog. exp. Tumor Res.* **6**, 126-227.

Roe, F. J. C., Dukes, C. E., Cameron, K. M., Pugh, R. C. B. and Mitchley, B. C. V. (1964). *Br. J. Cancer* **18**, 674-681.

Sanders, F. K. and Burford, B. O. (1967). *Nature, Lond.* **213**, 1171-1173.

Smithers, D. W. (1962). *Lancet i*, 493-499.

Stjernsward, J. (1965). *J. natn. Cancer Inst.* **35**, 885-892.

Walters, M. A., Roe, F. J. C., Mitchley, B. C. V. and Walsh, A. (1967). *Br. J. Cancer* **21**, 367-372.

Weston, B. J. (1967). *Nature, Lond.* **215**, 1497-1498.

Whitwell, F. (1955). *J. Path. Bact.* **70**, 529-541.

Author Index

The numbers in *italics* indicate the pages on which names are mentioned
in the reference lists

A

Attardi, G., 94, 97, *106, 107*
Attardi Gandini, D., 96, *109*
August, A., 438, 462, *470*
Auricchio, S., 396, 422, *424, 426, 427,*
429
Austad, W. J., 416, 420, *425, 428*
Austin, L., 43, 66, 67, *71, 74,* 85, 86, *106*
Avery, O. T., 103, *106*
Avigan, J., 297, *309, 312*
Axelrod, J., 59, 61, *72, 73, 74,* 265, *273,*
276
Azcurra, J. M. 54, *72*

B

Baastrup, P. C., 124, *137*
Babich, F. R., 104, *106*
Bachelard, H. S., 17, 26, 27, 28, *32,* 65,
67, *72*
Backer, H. van, 5, *36*
Badenoch, J., 424, *425*
Bader, J. P. 443, *472*
Baer, S., 53, *72*
Baggenstoss, A. H., 271, *273*
Baird, J. M., 413, *425*
Baker, G. D., 295, *309*
Baker, R. D., 291, *309*
Balakrishnan, S., 53, *72*
Balázs, R., 23, *34,* 63, 64, 67, *72,* 79, 86,
94, *106,* 122, *137*
Balfour, Y. M., 53, *72*
Baliah, T., 270, *276*
Balint, J. A., 409, *425*
Balir, P. V., 157, *179*
Ball, E. G., 157, *178*
Ball, J. K., 492, *503*
Bandow, F., 290, 312
Bane, R., 321, *342*
Bang, H. O., 415, 423, *425, 430*
Bang, Nils, U., 329, *340*
Baranov, M. N., 101, *106*
Baraona, E., 323, 336, *340,* 416, *428*
Barbato, I. W. M., 98, *106*
Barbato, L., 98, *106*
Barboriak, Joseph J., 327, *340*
Barka, T., 324, 328, *343*
Barker, L. A., 59, *72*
Barlett, G. R., 318, *340*
Barnet, H. N., 318, *340*
Barondes, S. H., 43, 66, *72,* 85, 93, 101,
104, *106, 107*
Barrnett, R. J., 144, *181*
Barrowman, J., 390, 400, 401, 402, *424,*
428
Barry, B. A., 379, *380*

Barry, R. J. C., 373, 374, 375, 379, *380*
Bartsch, G. E., 225, *243*
Basford, R. E., 65, *72*
Bashore, R. A., 259, *276*
Bass, P., 406, *425*
Bässler, R., 443, *465*
Baudhuin, P., 144, 157, 158, 168, 171,
172, 174, *178,* 239, *242*
Bauer, A., 452, *465*
Bauer, K. F., 5, *32*
Baumslag, N., 339, *343*
Baxter, C. F., 5, *36*
Bayliss, L. E., 357, *380*
Bayrd, E. D., 434, 438, 440, 441, 459,
470
Beams, H. W., 144, *178*
Bear, E. S., 321, *341*
Beard, D., 457, *466, 469*
Beard, J. W., 440, 457, *465, 466, 467,*
468, 469
Bearn, A. G., 224, *242*
Beattie, D. S., 65, *72*
Beaudreau, G. S., 457, *466*
Beaufay, H., 144, 168, *178,* 239, *242*
Becker, C., 457, *466, 467*
Becker, I. M., 412, *429*
Becker, M., 438, *465*
Beckett, P. G. S., 134, *137*
Beer, C. T., 16, *32*
Begley, M. D., 414, *426*
Behar, M., 414, *430*
Beher, M. E., 301, *309*
Beher, W. T., 295, 301, *309*
Behki, R. M., 447, 448, 449, 463, *468*
Behnke, O., 439, *465*
Behrman, R. E., 259, 268, *274, 275*
Bell, T. M., 459, *468*
Bellet, S., 26, *32*
Benacerraf, B., 143, *178,* 500, *504*
Bencosme, S. A., 440, 443, *465*
Bendi, K. G., 67, *73*
Benedetti, E. L., 144, 155, 156, 174, *178,*
444, 445, 447, 448, *465, 467*
Ben-Ezzer, J., 277, *277*
Benjamin, B. J., 409, *425*
Bennett, E. L., 31, *32,* 104, *106*
Bennett, H. S., 40, *72*
Bensadoun, M. 264, *274*
Bensch, K., 144, *181*
Bensch, K. G., 464, *471*
Bentley, P. H., 415, *427*
Berenblum, I., 498, 503
Berg, C. J. van den, 21, *32,* 63, 64, *75*
Berg, J. M., 113, 115, *137*
Berger, B. D., 104, *106*

520 AUTHOR INDEX

Lupulescou, A., 440, 441, *470*
Lurbel, F. J., 444, *465*
Luse, S., 443, *470*
Lynen, F., 296, *309*
Lynn, J. A., 438, 462, *470*

M

Maanen, E. F., van 54, *75*
Maas, J. W., 60, *72*
McAllan, A. B., 408, *429*
McBride, J., 460, *471*
McCaman, E. R., 57, *74*
McCance, C., 134, *137*
McCandless, D. W., 256, 260, *276*
McCarter, J. A., 492, *503*
McCarthy, B., 94, *107, 109*
McCarthy, C. F., 420, *428*
McCarthy, E. A., 257, *274*
McCarty, M., 103, *106*
McClary, B. G., Jr. 406, *425*
McConnell, J. V., 104, *108*
McDaniel, E. G., 490, *503*
MacDonald, R. A., 339, *343*
MacDonald, W. C., 419, *428*
McDuffie, N. G., 459, *470*
McEwen, J., 277, *277*
McGavran, M. H., 438, *470*
McGuigan, J. E., 392, *428*
McGuire, M. T., 329, *343*
McHardy, G. J. R., 374, *382*
McHenry, E. W., 329, *343*
Machiyama, Y., 23, *34*, 68, *73*
McIlwain, H., 14, 16, 17, 18, 20, 21, 22, 24, 26, 27, 28, 29, 30, 31, *32, 33, 34, 35, 36, 37*, 53, *72*
MacIntosh, F. C., 56, *74*
MacIntyre, D. R., 387, 404, *428*
MacIntyre, I., 409, *428*
McIntyre, J., 408, *424, 428*
McKay, R. J., 269, *273*
McKhann, C. F., 440, 442, 443, 464, *469*
MacLeod, C. M., 103, *106*
McManus, J. P. A., 392, *428*
McMaster, P. D., 262, *275*
McMillan, W. O., 323, *343*
Maddock, L. K., 307, *314*
Madison, L., 326, *343*
Madsen, S., 329, *340*
Maenpaa, P., 324, *341*
Magasanik, B., 90, *108*
Maggs, R., 126, *137*
Magnes, J., 12, *33*
Mahanand, D., 119, *139*

Mahler, H. R., 54, 67, *72, 75*, 87, 88, 90, *108*
Mahowald, T. A., 293, 294, *311, 312*
Maickel, R. P., 336, 337, *340*
Majchrowicz, E., 16, *34*, 321, *342*
Majee, W. L., 95, *107*
Makhlouf, G. M., 392, *428*
Maldonado, J. F., 434, 438, 440, 441, 459, *470*
Malhotra, S. K., 7, *36*
Malik, G. B., 420, *428*
Maling, H. M., 336, 337, *340, 341*
Malis, G. Y., 132, *138*
Malleson, A., 124, 127, *137*
Mallory, T. B., 332, *344*
Mallov, S., 330, 333, 336, 337, *343*
Malloy, H. T., 247, *275*
Malm, V., 126, *137*
Manuel, D., 104, *106*
Manaker, R. A., 455, 456, *467*
Mandel, P., 80, 81, 88, 94, *108*
Manfield, P., 267, *273*
Mangan, J. L., 25, *34*, 63, *74*
Mangoni, A., 127, *137*
Manis, J., 409, *428*
Mann, J. D., 135, *138*
Manning, R. T., 328, *344*
Mao, P., 438, 443, 462, *470*
Marcand, L., 94, *108*
Marchbanks, R. M., 51, 52, 56, 57, 59, 69, *74*
Mardell, R., 80, 81, *108*
Margules, D. L., 104, *106*
Markowitz, H., 420, *427*
Marks, N., 97, *108*
Marks, V., 125, *138*
Marsh, C. L., 369, *382*
Marthaler, T., 422, *427*
Martin, J. H., 438, 462, *470*
Martinez-Palomo, A., 445, 446, 454, *470*
Marver, H. S., 255, 277, *276, 277*
Mascherpa, G., 127, *137*
Mason, H. L., 266, 267, *274*
Masui, T., 284, *312*
Masuoka, D., 59, *74*
Mate, H. O., 416, *428*
Matkovics, B., 288, *312*
Matschiner, J. T., 290, 293, 294, *311, 312, 314*
Matsumoto, H., 490, *503*
Matsunaga, Y., 463, *472*
Matsutani, T., 22, 27, *36*
Matsuzawa, T., 270, *276*
Matthews, D. M., 363, *382*, 398, 399, 400, *428*

Subject Index